A SHORT HISTORY OF

TECHNOLOGY

FROM THE EARLIEST TIMES
TO A.D. 1900

BY

T. K. DERRY

AND

TREVOR I. WILLIAMS

OXFORD   NEW YORK   TORONTO   MELBOURNE

OXFORD UNIVERSITY PRESS

Oxford University Press, Walton Street, Oxford OX2 6DP

OXFORD LONDON GLASGOW
NEW YORK TORONTO MELBOURNE WELLINGTON
IBADAN NAIROBI DAR ES SALAAM CAPE TOWN
KUALA LUMPUR SINGAPORE JAKARTA HONG KONG TOKYO
DELHI BOMBAY CALCUTTA MADRAS KARACHI

ISBN 0 19 881231 0

© *Oxford University Press 1960*

First published by the Clarendon Press 1960
First issued as an Oxford University Press paperback 1970
Fourth impression 1979

Printed in Great Britain by
Fletcher & Son Ltd, Norwich

PREFACE

THIS book is the sequel to a very much larger work, a five-volume *History of Technology*, endowed by Imperial Chemical Industries Limited and published by the Clarendon Press, Oxford. When the compilation of this large work was approved in 1949 it was expected that there might in due course be a demand for a smaller book covering much the same ground. This expectation has been fulfilled: many reviewers of the earlier volumes specifically urged the publication of a shorter version that would introduce the subject to a much wider body of readers. In view of this, I.C.I. agreed to make available the further endowment that was necessary and the Clarendon Press undertook publication: the present book is the result.

In planning this work much thought has been given to how the needs of both the general reader and students interested in the technical aspects could best be met. From the outset it was evident that any attempt merely to summarize the five-volume *History* was quite impracticable, not only because of the enormous compression that would be necessary, but because the plan of the original did not lend itself to such treatment. A different book was clearly necessary, and although this made the task much more exacting it provided a welcome opportunity of approaching the subject in a new way. With this freedom of action, it was decided to attempt a book in which the story of technological development was at every epoch closely related to the historical background. This book aims at being as much a technological history as a history of technology, and in pursuing this course we believe ourselves to be following an important modern trend. Notwithstanding the achievements of Lecky and Buckle and such brilliant interludes as Macaulay's Third Chapter—to quote only English examples—historians in the nineteenth century largely restricted themselves to political and constitutional history. In the twentieth century a more liberal interpretation of the meaning of history reappeared, and economic and social factors began to receive due attention from the historiographer. The importance of technological factors, however, is still far too little recognized, and it is hoped that this present book will help to direct greater attention to these.

The decision to write a book of a different kind conferred other advantages. Although the range of technological subjects discussed naturally falls mainly within the confines of the major work, some extensions of interest have been made and many fresh sources have been consulted: for the reasons given in the previous paragraph, a great deal of entirely new historical material has been introduced. While many of the illustrations are taken from the earlier work, here, too, the opportunity has been taken of introducing much that is new. At the same time, we must put on record our very great indebtedness to the original work, and to those who contributed to it, as an authoritative conspectus of the subject as a whole and as a source of factual information. The present book has benefited in many ways from the experience gained by one of us (T. I. W.) as managing editor for the later volumes of the original *History of Technology*, and it is a pleasure to recall the years of stimulating collaboration on that project with the late Dr Charles Singer—who initiated it—the late Dr E. J. Holmyard, and Dr A. R. Hall. In the original work, and through its extensive lists of references and bibliographies, those who wish to delve more deeply into particular aspects of the history of technology will find much additional information.

A brief account of the way in which the text is arranged may perhaps assist the reader to use this book to the fullest advantage. There are obvious difficulties in marshalling the salient features of so vast a subject over the whole period of civilization and without restriction to a single country or people. Neither a chronological, geographical, nor technological arrangement of the material is alone appropriate to our object of providing a readable and connected account of the evolution of modern industry: of necessity we have had to seek a compromise. Chronologically, the text is divided into two parts, the first telling the story up to 1750—the beginning of the industrial revolution in Britain—and the second continuing it up to 1900. In the belief that it is events during and since the industrial revolution that are of the greatest interest to most readers we give the greater space to this later period. The decision to end our story at 1900 was prompted by two principal considerations: the first, that the true historical significance of more recent developments is difficult to assess, and the second, that the great technical complexity of modern scientific industry makes it virtually impossible adequately to tell its story in the non-technical terms of the present text.

To some, our division at 1750 may seem artificial, for there is today a tendency to discount the importance, or even the reality, of what has long been called the industrial revolution. While it is true that changes that were spread over a period of two or three generations can scarcely be termed revolutionary—especially as they were clearly continuous with events before and after that period—it is nevertheless indisputable that the period 1750–1830 was one in which technological progress showed a marked and sustained upward trend that proved of fundamental importance to modern civilization.

Geographically, our story is largely confined to the ancient Near East, western Europe, and north America. In respect of the Far East this limitation is a reflection of the lack of suitable sources for western scholars: Dr Joseph Needham's *Science and Civilization in China* will greatly relieve this deficiency, but it will be several years before that work is completed. Our debt to the Far East may well prove much greater than is now generally supposed. Eastern Europe, too, figures relatively little: although lack of readily accessible sources is also a problem here, a further consideration is that during the period of our main study changes there were generally speaking parallel with, and consequential to, those of western Europe.

The choice of what to include in such a work and what to omit must necessarily be very subjective: our hope is that our choice will be found to be an acceptable blend of those branches of technology that have decisively changed the course of history with homelier crafts of greater human interest but lesser consequence. The select bibliography is designed to help the reader to carry the study farther along lines of his own choosing. Our underlying intention, as we have stated, is to relate the history of a technology to the history of its age: each section is therefore preceded by an historical introduction and the book concludes with a series of tables designed to show the interrelation of events named in the text.

We have been fortunate indeed in the help we have had in connexion with this work, and we are happy to take this opportunity of thanking those who have assisted us. In the absence of any earlier synthesis of this particular kind we had little to guide us in seeking to contrive a text acceptable to the historian and the technologist as well as to the general reader. We therefore count ourselves very fortunate in having had the whole of the text read before it went to press by Professor R. R. Betts, Masaryk Professor of Central European History in the University of London. His wide knowledge enabled us to correct numerous points of historical detail and emphasis; at the same time he drew our attention to passages where our account of technical matters seemed likely to present difficulties for the non-technical reader. For such errors and obscurities as remain we ourselves are, of course, responsible.

In the course of our search for material for the book we visited—among other collections relating to the history of technology—the Museum for the History of Science and Technology in Stockholm, and we would like to record our thanks to the Director, Dr Torsten K. W. Althin, both for showing us his splendid collection and for a stimulating discussion of various problems connected with the work. We would like also to acknowledge the help and advice of Mr A. Stowers of the Science Museum, London, in determining the design of the earliest Watt steam-engine.

There are great difficulties in clearly and briefly describing processes and machines unfamiliar to the general reader. The better to clarify our own ideas we visited a number of works in order to observe the modern counterparts of some traditional crafts, such as those of the potter, blacksmith, boiler-maker, spinner, miner, and glass-worker. In this connexion we are particularly indebted to British Railways (Derby Locomotive Works); Mintons Limited, Stoke-on-Trent; Combined English Mills (Spinners) Limited, Manchester; the Salt Division of Imperial Chemical Industries Limited; and Pilkington Brothers Limited, St Helens.

The majority of the drawings required for the *History of Technology* were prepared by Mr D. E. Woodall. In view of this, we were very glad that he was able to undertake all the new drawings required for the present work; the three maps required for Chapter I were drawn by Mr T. Hilditch.

Our special thanks are extended to Miss M. Reeve who, assisted by Miss Y. Pyke, has been responsible for all the exacting administrative work connected with the preparation of the text and illustrations and seeing them through the press. The book owes a great deal to her care and patience.

As we have noted, this book would not have been possible without its financial endowment by Imperial Chemical Industries Limited. We must in particular acknowledge the active support and encouragement the project received from Sir Walter Worboys, a director of the Company, until his retirement in October 1959.

T. K. DERRY
TREVOR I. WILLIAMS

July 1960

CONTENTS

PART I

FROM THE EARLIEST TIMES TO A.D. 1750

ACKNOWLEDGEMENTS

MUCH thought was given to the choice of illustrations for this work, but the reproduction of many that seemed most appropriate would have been impossible without the permission of the owners of the copyright. Our thanks are due to all who have helped us in this respect, and we are glad to take this opportunity of making the following acknowledgements.

Institut de Paléontologie Humaine (Paris), Monaco, for Fig. 1 (from E. Cartailhac and H. Breuil, *La Caverne d'Altamira*); Director-General of Antiquities, Iraq Government, for Fig. 3 (from M. E. L. Mallowan, *Iraq*, 3, 1936); Propyläen Verlag, Berlin, for Figs. 6, 8, 15, 70, 71, 84, 87, 134, 137A and B, 174, 203, 243, 254, 347 (from *Propyläen Weltgeschichte*, Vols. III, IV, VI, and VIII; H. Schäfer and W. Andrae, *Propyläen Kunstgeschichte*, Vol. II); The Bodley Head, London, for Figs. 9, 136, 138, 194, 231 (from Jean Amsler and others, *Europe—A Visual History*); Metropolitan Museum of Art, New York, for Figs. 11, 12, 26, 31, 62, 123, 125 (from N. de G. Davies, *Robb de Peyster Tytus Memorial Series I, The Tomb of Nakht at Thebes*; ibid., *The Tomb of Nefer-Hotep at Thebes*, Vol. I; ibid., *The tomb of Rekh-mi-ré at Thebes*, Vol. II; H. E. Winlock, *Materials used at the embalming of Tut-ankh-amun*, Metr. Mus. Occas. Pap. no. 10, 1941; also photographs); Kröner of Leipzig for Figs. 13, 42 (from P. Brandt, *Schaffende Arbeit und bildende Kunst im Altertum und Mittelalter*); Courtauld Institute of Art, University of London, for Fig. 14 (from London, British Museum, Add. MS. 47682, fol. 6); Hachette of Paris for Fig. 16 (from C. Daremberg and E. Saglio, *Dictionnaire des antiquités grecques et romaines*, Vol. IV); Trustees, British Museum, for Figs. 17, 27, 33, 61, 81, 82, 85, 120, 126; University of Minnesota, Minneapolis, for Fig. 19 (from J. Storck and W. D. Teague, *Flour for Man's Bread: A History of Milling*, Copyright 1952); Museum of English Rural Life, University of Reading, for Figs. 20, 21 (Photographs); Agricultural History Society, Washington, D.C., for Fig. 22 (from *Agricultural History*, 10, 4, 1936); Service des Antiquités Egyptiennes, Cairo, for Fig. 23 (from J. E. Quibell, *Excavations at Saqqara 1907–08*); British School of Egyptian Archaeology, London, for Fig. 24 (from W. M. F. Petrie, *Tools and Weapons*); Bruckmann, Munich, for Figs. 28, 29 (from A. Furtwängler and C. Reichhold, *Griechische Vasenmalerei*, Vol. I); Harvard University Press for the American Council of Learned Societies, Cambridge, Mass., for Fig. 30 (from C. Alexander, *Arretine Relief Ware*); Insel-Verlag, Leipzig, for Figs. 34, 49 (from F. Bock (Ed.), *Deutsches Handwerk im Mittelalter*); Labatorio Fotografico della Biblioteca Ambrosiana, Milan, for Fig. 35 (from Photograph: Cod. G. 301, fol. 4ᵛ); Collection, Dr. Stent, Shere, Surrey, for Fig. 37; *Illustrated London News & Sketch Ltd.* for Figs. 41, 200 (20 Feb. 1937; 31 July 1909); Clarendon Press, Oxford, for Figs. 43, 104 (from O. Davies, *Roman Mines in Europe*; C. Singer, *A Short History of Science*); I.C.I. Ltd. for Figs. 47, 274 (from H. B. Pereira, *The Colour of Chivalry*); Staatsbibliothek, Vienna, for Fig. 48 (from A. Schultz, *Jb. Kunsthist.* 6, 109, 1887); Victoria and Albert Museum, London, for Fig. 50*; Cassel, London, for Fig. 52 (from R. Held, *The Age of Firearms*); Francke, Bern, for Fig. 55 (from U. E. Paoli, *Das Leben im alten Rom*); Oxford University Press, New York, for Figs. 56–58, 164 (from S. Giedion, *Mechanization Takes*

Command); Oxford University Press, London, for Figs. 59, 235, 326-31 (from R. T. Gunther, *Early Science in Oxford*, Pt. II, 'Mathematics'; D. A. Stevenson, *The World's Lighthouses before 1820*; H. and Alison Gernsheim, *The History of Photography*); Whipple Museum of the History of Science, University of Cambridge,for Figs. 60, 99C (Photographs); Penguin Books, Harmondsworth, for Fig. 63 (from I. E. S. Edwards, *The Pyramids of Egypt*); Hinrichs, Leipzig, for Figs. 64, 77 (from R. Koldewey, *Das Ischtar-Tor in Babylon*; G. Steindorff, *Das Grab des Ti*); McGraw-Hill Book Publishing Co., Inc., New York, for Figs. 166, 167, 170 (from D. S. Kimball, *Amer. Mach., London*, 60, 726; G. Hubbard, *Amer. Mach., N.Y.* 60, 255, Copyright 1924); Martin S. Briggs for Fig. 68 (Drawing); Royal Archaeological Institute of Great Britain and Ireland, London, for Fig. 69 (from R. E. M. Wheeler, *Archaeol. J.* 36, 38, 1929); Vromant, Brussels, for Fig. 72 (from J. van den Gheyn, *Cronicques et conquestes de Charlemaine*); Williams & Wilkins, Baltimore, for Fig. 75 (from W. B. Parsons, *Engineers and Engineering in the Renaissance*); Foreningen til Skiidraettens Framme, Norway, for Fig. 76 (from Nils Lid, *The History of Norwegian Skis*); The Syndics of the Fitzwilliam Museum, Cambridge, for Fig. 78; Egypt Exploration Society, London, for Figs. 79, 98 (from Norman and Nina de G. Davies, *The Tombs of Menkeperrasonb, Amenmose*, etc. The Theban Tomb series mem. 5; R. W. Sloley, *J. Egypt. Archaeol.* 17, 1931); Society for the Promotion of Hellenic Studies, London, for Fig. 80 (from H. L. Lorimer, *J. Hell. Stud.* 23, 137, 1903); Dreyer, Oslo, for Fig. 83 (from A. W. Brøgger and H. Shetelig, *The Viking Ships*, 1951); Hiersemann, Leipzig, for Fig. 86 (from M. Lehrs, *Der Meister W.A.*); The Master and Fellows of Magdalene College, Cambridge, for Fig. 88 (from Mathew Baker, *Fragments of Ancient English Shipwrightry*, fol. 8ᵛ); *The Railway Gazette*, London, for Figs. 90, 176, 236 (from C. E. Lee, *The Evolution of Railways*); Benn, London, for Figs. 91, 94, 185, 318 (from A. H. Brodrick, *Lascaux*; H. Degering, *Lettering*; R. Jenkins, *Motor Cars*; M. E. and K. R. S. Swan, *Sir Joseph Wilson Swan, F.R.S., A Memoir*); Edwards, Newbury, for Figs. 92, 93 (from S. H. Hooke, *Antiquity*, II); Nina de G. Davies for Fig. 95 (Restored drawing); The Director, Science Museum, London, for Figs. 96, 97, 143, 146, 147, 148*, 150*, 153*, 154*, 163, 178, 191*, 227*, 255, 309*, 311*, 312*, 332, 335; Oxford Historical Society for Publications, for Fig. 99A (from R. T. Gunther, *Early Science in Oxford*, Vol. 2); The Director, Deutsches Museum, Munich, for Fig. 99B (Photograph); The Director, Germanisches Museum, Nuremberg, for Fig. 100 (Photograph); Mr. P. P. Howgrave-Graham for Fig. 101 (Photograph); Hoepli, Milan, for Fig. 102 (from *Il Codice Atlantico di Leonardo da Vinci*, facs. ed. by G. Piumati); Himmer, Augsburg, for Fig. 103 (from *Ars memorativa*, fac. ed. by Dr. Bennofilser, No. 28); Librairie Ancienne Honoré Champion, Paris, for Fig. 105 (from H. Omont, *Miniatures des plus anciens manuscrits grecs de la Bibliothèque National du VIᵉ au XIVᵉ siècle*); The Paper Publications Society, Hilversum, for Fig. 106 (from Henk Voorn, *The Paper Mills of Denmark and Norway and their Watermarks*); Karl Alber, Freiburg, for Figs. 111, 122, 141, 155 (from F. Klemm, *Technik, eine Geschichte ihrer Probleme*); Alinari, Florence, for Fig. 112 (Photograph); The Director, Bayerische Staatsbibliothek, Munich, for Fig. 113 (Photograph: Cod. lat. 23638, fol. IIᵛ); Orkney and Shetland Folk-Lore Society for Fig. 117 (copyright photograph J. D. Rattar, Lerwick), (from M. M. Banks, *British Calendar Customs*); Taylor & Francis, London, for Fig. 124 (from F. Sherwood Taylor, *Annals of Science*, 5, 3, 1945); The Master and Fellows, Trinity College, Cambridge, for Fig. 127 (MS. O. 9. 34, fol. 32ᵇ); Archives Photographiques, Paris, for Fig. 128 (Copyright photograph); *Year*—the Annual Picture History, Los Angeles, for Figs. 139, 199 (from B. H.

Ward (Ed.), *Flight—a Pictorial History of Aviation*); City Museum and Art Gallery, Birmingham, for Fig. 144 (Engineer's drawing); University Press, Cambridge, for Fig. 145 (from H. W. Dickinson and A. Titley, *Richard Trevithick*); Batsford, London, for Figs. 151, 179, 195, 197, 212 (from O. S. Nock, *The Railway Engineer*; C. H. Gibbs-Smith, *A History of Flying*; Marjorie and C. H. B. Quennell, *A History of Everyday Things in England*, Vol. 3); Cyril Aldred for Fig. 156 (Reconstructed drawing); Friederichsen und de Gruyter, Hamburg, for Fig. 157 (from B. Martens, *Meister Francke*, Tefelband); *The Woodworker*, London, for Fig. 158 (from R. A. Salaman, *Woodworker*, **59**, 165, 1955); The Director, Museum of Science and Industry, Birmingham, for Fig. 161 (from *Illustrated Exhibitor and Magazine of Art*, 1851); *Engineer*, London, for Fig. 165 (from Centenary No., 1856-1956); W. & T. Avery Ltd., Birmingham, for Fig. 169 (from *Soho Foundry*); The Trustees, National Maritime Museum, Greenwich, for Fig. 172 (Photograph of lithograph by T. G. Dutton, 1866); Royle Publications, London, for Fig. 180 (from F. D. Klingender, *Art and the Industrial Revolution*); Modern Transport Publishing Company, London, for Fig. 182 (from C. Hamilton Ellis, *Nineteenth-century Railway Carriages*); Methuen, London, for Fig. 184 (from A. B. Filson Young, *The Complete Motorist*); Longmans, Green, London, for Fig. 186 (from A. C. Harmsworth, *Motors and Motor Driving*); H. O. Duncan, Paris, for Figs. 187, 189, 190, 299 (from H. O. Duncan, *The World on Wheels*, Vol. II); Francis Edwards, London, for Fig. 188 (from [F. J. Bottomley], *The Velocipede*); Lanchester Motor Company Ltd., Coventry, for Figs. 192, 302 (Photographs); Director, Technical and Science Museum, Stockholm, for Fig. 193 (Photograph); Libraire Vuibert, Paris, for Figs. 196, 198 (from J. Lecornu, *La navigation aérienne*); H.M.S.O., London, for Fig. 202 (from C. H. Gibbs-Smith, *The Great Exhibition of 1851*); International Correspondence Schools Ltd., London, for Fig. 204 (from *Instruction Paper: Carpentry*, Pt. 3); *Engineering News* for Fig. 205 (from Supplement, 8 June 1889); American Iron and Steel Institute, New York, for Fig. 206 (from *Steelways*, **9**, No. 5); Yale University Press, New Haven, for Figs. 209 and 213 (from R. S. Kirby and P. G. Laurson, *The Early Years of Modern Civil Engineering*); Corporation of Liverpool for Fig. 211 (Copyright photograph); Staples Press, London, for Fig. 214 (from London County Council, *Centenary of London's Main Drainage, 1855-1955*); Chapman & Hall, London, for Fig. 215 (from A. T. Byrne, *A Treatise on Highway Construction*); Aveling-Barford Ltd., Grantham, for Fig. 217 (Photograph); C. Hadfield and J. F. Horrobin for Fig. 218 (Map); CIBA Ltd., Basle, for Fig. 220 (*CIBA*, No. 11, Autumn 1959); *Scientific American*, New York, for Figs. 221, 310, 345, 353 (*Supplement*, **15**, 1883, and *Supplement*, **16**, 1883); British Railways for Fig. 223 (Photograph); Institution of Civil Engineers, London, for Fig. 226 (Engraving); Mr. H. Shirley Smith for Fig. 228 (Photograph); Grant, Edinburgh, for Fig. 229 (from P. Phillips, *The Forth Bridge*); Institution of Mining Engineers, London, for Fig. 240 (from F. W. Hardwick and L. T. O'Shea, *Trans. Instn. Min. Engrs.* **51**, 584, 1915-16); Fachberichte des Vereins Deutscher Eisenhüttenleute und des Max-Plank Instituts für Eisenforschung, Düsseldorf, for Fig. 241 (from E. H. Schulz, 'Über den Werkstoff des Schweisseisen-Zeitalters', *Arch. Eizenhüttenw.* **26**, no. 7, 1955); Thomas Firth & John Brown Ltd., Sheffield, for Fig. 252 (from *100 Years in Steel*, 1937); Dutton, New York, for Fig. 253 (from W. C. and Ruth White, *Tin can on a shingle*); Shakespeare Memorial Library, Birmingham, for Fig. 256 (from Newsbill, 15 June 1814); Princeton University Press, Princeton, N.J., for Figs. 260-2 (from P. H. Giddens, *The Early Days of Oil*); Henley Publishing

Co., New York, for Fig. 264 (from T. O'Conor Sloane, *Rubber Hand Stamps and the Manipulation of Rubber*); Director, Royal Botanic Gardens, Kew, for Fig. 265 (Photograph); Williamson, London, for Fig. 284 (from L. Lyons and others, *The Sewing Machine*); Gresham Publishing Company, London, for Fig. 287 (A–E), (from W. S. Murphy, *The Textile Industries*, Vols. 6, 7); Pitman, London, for Fig. 287 (F) (from R. S. Brinton, *Carpets*); Madgwick Houlston, London, for Fig. 292 (from M. Graham, *Cup and Saucer Land*); Caxton Publishing Company, London, for Fig. 301 (from R. Kennedy, *The Book of the Motor Car*, Vol. I); Marconi's Wireless Telegraph Co. Ltd., Chelmsford, for Fig. 315 (from *Marconi Jubilee 1897–1947*); Linotype GMBH, Berlin, for Fig. 321 (from W. Mengel, *Die Linotype erreichte das Ziel*); R. Hoe, New York, for Fig. 325 (from R. Hoe, *A Short History of the Printing Press*); Dr. A. R. Michaelis for Fig. 333 (Model); Liesegang, Düsseldorf, for Fig. 334 (from F. P. Liesegang and others, *Wissenschaftliche Kinematographie*); Hatton Press, London, for Fig. 336 (from H. V. Hopwood, *Living Pictures: their History, Photo-Production and Practical Working*); Prisma, Paris, for Figs. 337, 338 (from M. Bessy and J. M. Lo Duca, *Georges Méliès, Mage*); Cappelens Forlag, Oslo, for Fig. 350 (from S. Risting, *Av Hvalfangstens Historie*).

PART I

FROM THE EARLIEST TIMES
TO A.D. 1750

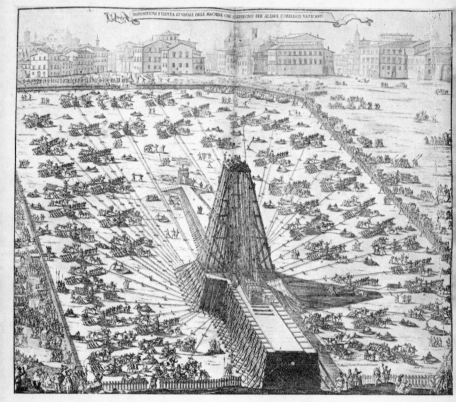

Removal of a 327-ton obelisk in Rome, 1586, by massed and skilfully organized manpower (*see* p. 180). The method differs little from that used for similar tasks in Early Dynastic Egypt (Fig. 111) more than three millennia earlier, and even in the nineteenth century A.D. great civil engineering projects still depended upon massed manpower using only very simple equipment (Fig. 223)

I

GENERAL HISTORICAL SURVEY

MAN BEFORE CIVILIZATION

SINCE technology comprises all that bewilderingly varied body of knowledge and devices by which man progressively masters his natural environment, its history is a subject with wide and ill-defined ramifications. The study is complicated by the fact that, until we reach modern times, the emphasis in technological history is different from that made familiar by the story of political or intellectual development. By restricting our attention to the growth of western technology, we shall escape one such difficulty, namely, the great part played by the inventiveness of the Far East in former ages: this is a subject that would certainly require much space in any properly balanced global account but which is only now beginning to be properly explored in the West. Even with our more limited scope, however, the deviation of technological from conventional history is such that a preliminary historical outline, to place in a chronological framework the peoples and eras of most significance for our purpose, may make it easier to see the growth of each main branch of technology in due perspective. The present chapter and Chapter 10 will therefore lay before the reader some facts of general history that seem relevant to our study.

At least nineteen-twentieths of the human story, a gigantic span of time, must here be passed over very briefly. The men of the Old Stone (or Palaeolithic) Age, few and scattered, developed little to enable them to conquer their environment; the four Ice Ages by which their history was punctuated were in any case environmental changes, affecting huge regions, which even the technology of twentieth-century man would find it hard to conquer. As food-gatherers, they must have dimly studied the phenomena of climate, soil, and season, which determined whether their stomachs were to be full or empty. More susceptible than most animals to cold, they improvised shelters, frequented caves, and made use of fire. To tame it by restricting the fuel on which the flame was seen to feed; to spread it by improvised torch or draught; to quench it with water, were arts which could be learnt from nature. Even the lighting of fire by wood-friction may possibly have been derived from seeing the effect of dry boughs being rubbed together by the wind.

Among the many uses of fire was the hardening of wood for weapons or tools. Lacking the strong canine teeth of true carnivores, men had at a very early stage learnt the handiness of sticks and stones for tearing up carcases they scented, and later for hunting. From the finding and collection of ready-made implements they graduated to their manufacture—using a hammer-stone to chip and flake flint and other of the finer-grained stones so as to produce a cutting-edge and other desired shapes. After many generations of careful imitation and sporadic improvement, there emerged a recognizable ancestor of the stone axe which, transmuted into metal, still rings through the forest. The hand-axe, made of sandstone, quartz, or lava as well as of flint, served mankind for at least a thousand centuries and spread over nearly one-fifth of the land-surface of the globe. It is well known to us because of its durability; objects made of less durable materials like wood or horn, though sometimes preserved in sand, peat, or even ice, are usually known only indirectly. With the development of the spear-thrower and the bow, man the technologist began to win his long struggle for human supremacy by matching skill against animal strength. Moreover, his aesthetic achievement, as represented by the astonishingly high quality of the paintings and engravings (Fig. 1) which Palaeolithic man left behind him in caves and remote rock-faces, not only serves to call back a very distant past to our eyes, but is a challenging reminder that the unevenness of technical development runs right through human history.

The Middle Stone (or Mesolithic) Age is the name given to the period of transition between the end of the last Ice Age and the beginning of the era of human settlement and cultivation. It might be termed more accurately a stage, since its dating must vary with proximity to the shrinking polar ice-cap. For Europe it may be defined as stretching from the ninth or the eighth to the close of the fourth millennium B.C.; it witnessed the rise of sea-level, which ultimately separated Sweden from Denmark and Britain from France, and the growth of the northern forests. Even more important in its effects on man's habitat was the increase of the desert areas in the Near East, which resulted from the same tremendous changes of climate.

Neolithic man is man emerging from savagery, having solved the basic problem of his food-supply by an increasing, though incomplete, reliance upon stock-keeping or tillage or a combination of the two. He could grind and polish, and even drill, his implements of hard stone; he needed only to gain a knowledge of metal-working to make a much more effective conquest of his physical environment. The immediate result seems to have been a rapid growth of

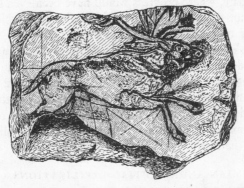

FIG. 1. Stone Age engraving of galloping reindeer

population without earlier parallel—the so-called Neolithic revolution. The long-term result, roughly coincident with the first use of metals, was the dawn of civilization as we know it. On its material side the history of civilization is the history of technology, so that the main interest of the Neolithic stage, even for west Europeans, lies in lands south-east of Europe, where this stage seems to have been reached earliest, where it led most rapidly to the growth of civilized life—and where climatic conditions have enabled the distant past to leave the clearest traces.

Cattle-herding would arise most naturally in the great river valleys of the east, which must have become crowded with animal life as the desert expanded. Such were the lower valleys of the Nile, the Tigris and Euphrates, and the Indus. Moreover, the rich mud of their deltas provided an ideal medium for the discovery that the self-sown plants so laboriously searched for might be replaced by crops of man's own planting. Stock-keeping no doubt came first, since it could be practised by nomads. Agriculture, even if a new site was picked every season, implied at least a temporary settlement, and the very fact of settlement made men conscious of new wants, which the new ease of food production made it possible to satisfy. Time and skill were no longer monopolized by the needs of the stomach, for the agriculturist, unlike the hunter, has seasons of comparative leisure and makes a permanent home. Society could now find scope for handicrafts and trade.

This Neolithic culture spread by slow degrees from these eastern lands to Europe. North of the Mediterranean it reached a region of harsher climate, where progress would have been even slower than it was had not the practice of extensive agriculture, which required the selection of a fresh site for tillage every few years, by its very wastefulness encouraged the gradual penetration of new areas. Hence the unrecorded millennia of Neolithic Europe, lasting in the case of Britain as late as 2000 B.C. Among its few memorials are the numerous flint-mines and the Megalithic tombs, which by their aura of mystery and their uncertain origins suggest to us in retrospect a darkness in marked contrast with the splendours of civilization then dawning in the east.

MESOPOTAMIAN AND EGYPTIAN CIVILIZATIONS

The middle of the fourth millennium B.C. is the period at which Neolithic society in the great eastern river valleys developed the first forms of civilization. If the invention of writing be taken to mark the transition from barbarism, then civilized man almost certainly makes his appearance first in Mesopotamia, though the earliest civilized state of important size and long-continued history was that which arose soon after in the valley of the Nile, where it was easier to keep out barbarian intruders; the course of events by the Indus is as yet little known.

The existence of pottery and textiles in the Neolithic period presupposes some degree of specialization. But the specialist craftsman can be maintained only if food-producers are organized to produce a regular surplus, a result which could not be achieved on a significant scale except by the banks of the great rivers, where the crop-yield was most prolific and the collection of the surplus easiest. The profitability of irrigation was taught by natural floodings; the chief obstacle to its systematic and disciplined practice was man's natural laziness and indifference to distant ends. Archaeological evidence points to the growth of the Sumerian city round the temple: the surplus was brought to propitiate the god; the land became his land;

his priests were the first leisured class; and the crafts which did honour to the god marked the beginning of civilization—and of technical progress. In Egypt, on the other hand, the original impetus seems to have been given not by man's fear and awe of the divine but by his enforced submission to a human conqueror and the natural appetite for power. The difference, however, is apparent rather than real. The war chief of the Falcon clan, who first unified the valley of the Nile, became a god, the source of the river's gift of fertility, and as such entitled to tribute from every dweller on its banks. Lacking the temple nucleus, cities grew at first more slowly, but the function of the Pharaoh's civil servants in collecting and administering the surplus produce of the land was essentially the same as that of the Sumerian priesthood.

For understanding how the impressive technological achievements of the early civilizations were brought about, it is important to notice that, even when the tiller of the soil was regarded as a free man rather than as a serf, forced labour on public works was commonly exacted: in Egypt it was still customary when de Lesseps began to dig the Suez Canal (p. 445). In addition, we may trace from this period the growth of slavery, which had its origin at the stage when it first paid to keep captives alive because their work was worth more than their keep. Every war produced its quota of human plunder; traders, too, dealt readily in a commodity that could carry itself to market; and within the community enslavement was commonly the fate of the criminal and the debtor. Slaves of the god or of his temple and of the king or of his state provided a numerous body of workers, sometimes well trained and often cruelly exploited, while throughout ancient history almost every reference to agriculture or industry in civilized countries must be taken to imply the employment of slaves, usually in small numbers, alongside farmers and craftsmen enjoying different degrees of personal freedom.

It is claimed that copper was the first luxury to become a necessity. Accordingly, the growth of civilization during the third millennium B.C. accompanies a slowly increasing use of copper and bronze, its alloy with tin. The ox-drawn plough and the irrigated field having been already known among the Neolithic food-producers, as was the oar-driven boat, the first major labour-saving devices invented by civilized man were probably the wheeled cart and the sail (p. 191). As for the artistry of the craftsman working in delicate detail, Egypt even before its unification produced astonishing ivory-carvings, while

FIG. 2. The Ancient Empires and classical Gre

...how the location of places mentioned in the text

the royal tombs of Sumerian Ur (Fig. 2) show that most of the techniques employed in the whole history of fine metal-work were already in use before 2500 B.C. In building, too, the Sumerians had by then erected brick temples only a little smaller than the famous ziggurats, of which ruins survive from the following age. The early dynasties of Egypt, however, having stone to work with, left a memorial that does not require the help of the archaeologist to interpret its splendours: nearly fifty centuries have passed since the Great Pyramid of Gizeh was raised over the mummified body of Cheops, yet it is still the most magnificent tomb in the world.

Both in Mesopotamia and in Egypt the third millennium, which had opened up such brilliant prospects for mankind, ended in political upheaval and technological stagnation. The earliest of the great Semite leaders, Sargon the Great of Akkad (Fig. 3), brought the first of a series of conquering peoples (Akkadians, Amorites, Kassites) down from the hinterland of the Tigris and Euphrates delta. All alike built their civilization upon Sumerian foundations, though Hammurabi, the great Amorite lawgiver and administrator, made the city of Babylon supreme over

FIG. 3. Bronze head of Sargon

the whole region. An 8-ft shaft of closely inscribed stone preserves his legal code; his letters preserve the man himself. But Hittite raiders from the north-west and Kassites from the north-east overthrew his successors, after which Babylonia under Kassite rule relapsed into many centuries of barbarism. Meanwhile in Egypt the highly centralized autocracy of the Pharaohs who reared the first pyramids gave place to a feudal age, characterized for us by the fine rock tombs of the nobles. The Pharaohs of this Middle Kingdom led their feudal hosts up the Nile to conquer Nubia, and nearer home provided new lands by vast irrigation works based on Lake Moeris in the Fayum. About 1700 B.C. the kingdom fell to the Hyksos or shepherd kings, horsed nomads from western Asia; it is with their expulsion, about the year 1580 B.C., that the New Empire begins.

This was an empire over many nations, extending from the Fourth Cataract of the Nile to the banks of the Euphrates. It was an empire also in the sense that it depended upon military power, the power of the horsed chariot, asserted with varying success against such strong enemies as the Hittites. For us, however, its interest lies mainly in its aesthetic triumphs. Among the temples at Thebes, which had now become the Egyptian capital, there stands, for instance, the Great Hall of Karnak, a single room of 329 × 170 ft, covering as much space as the cathedral of Notre Dame, and still the largest colonnaded room in existence. Close by, the tomb of Tutankhamen marks the climax of Bronze Age achievement in the fine arts, not only in the working of gold and silver, semi-precious metals, and ivory, but in the marvellous curved furniture revealed there, which is unrivalled by European technique until the Renaissance. At the same time, a newly realistic portraiture sets the Pharaoh before our eyes—not merely the godlike ruler but the man and lover, with fortunes as frail as our own. Thus we can share for a moment in the pathos of a civilization which had reached such perfections before Moses lay in his cradle, and which, though its thirty dynasties continued until the time of Alexander the Great, passed its zenith more than 3,000 years ago.

Since progress is the rare exception, and not the rule, among the communities of mankind, it is less important to speculate about the reasons for its cessation among the ancient Egyptians than to observe how the technological advances made in the Near East became by degrees more widely diffused until they penetrated Europe. Neither Mesopotamia nor Egypt had the resources which would have enabled it to develop its civilization on a basis of autarky. They had never been self-contained as regards timber or metals or even ivory: in the second millennium B.C. the development of larger ships and better-organized land transport encouraged greater efforts to satisfy their needs by importations. In exchanging the products of their superior technology for raw materials they stimulated imitation. Moreover, in ancient as in modern times the needs of trade often stimulated the desire for conquest, which likewise left its mark upon the life of neighbouring peoples long after the tide of conquest had receded. Aggression then provoked counter-aggression: some barbarian intruders were eventually absorbed into the life of the two empires (pp. 10, 217), others clashed with them, learnt from them, and kept their independence.

Of the latter group, the most important for our purposes are the Hittites of Asia Minor, the first Indo-European people to emerge into the full light of history. Matching weapons of iron against bronze, they wrenched away provinces from both empires, and for a few centuries in the middle of the second millennium established a third civilized state, stretching southwards to Palestine and eastwards to the Euphrates. Its centre was Bogazköy in the mountains of Anatolia, which was in its prime a far bigger city than Babylon, built where both wood and stone were abundant. Having a plentiful supply of silver, which had long replaced grain as a medium of exchange, the Hittites apparently struck the first coins, and passed the technique westwards. Thus civilization had been brought very close to Europe overland, though, as we shall see, its diffusion there was destined to be mainly by sea.

Fig. 4. Battering-ram on wheels, Nineveh, seventh century B.C.

But it will be convenient to continue with the history of the eastern empires as far as the first great reverse they suffered at the hands of the West. About 1200 B.C. the collapse of the Hittite realm was roughly coincident with, and partly occasioned by, the rise of Assyrian power. For a time the rise was checked, but eventually the Assyrians captured Babylon, obliterated the ten tribes of Israel, and held little Judah and Benjamin in subjection. In the days of the so-called Sargon II (722–c. 670 B.C.)—his choice of name is significant —they based on Nineveh the most extensive empire that had yet arisen in western Asia. The Assyrians were great users of stone, both in facings of masonry for their colossal brick buildings and for sculptures in relief. The figures of animals which they devised still fascinate the western mind, though it was their iron-equipped army and battering-rams (Fig. 4) which most impressed contemporaries. They conducted an immense trade to east and west, using the tongue of a conquered people, the Arameans of Syria, as their language of commerce. From India they brought the cotton plant to adorn Sennacherib's park; from their trade with Asia Minor came Cilician silver, employed by them as a medium of exchange. When Nineveh fell to the Medes and Chaldeans in 612 B.C., it left a tradition of world empire which was not without effect as late as the rise of Rome.

The neo-Babylonian or Chaldean empire which followed was the empire of Nebuchadnezzar, who led the Jews captive to Babylon— into a city adorned with the Hanging Gardens, with the temple which suggested the Tower of Babel, and with the still-visible Ishtar gate (see Fig. 64). A more lasting memorial, however, was the remarkably accurate astronomical data, accumulated there over many centuries without the telescope or any form of chronometer, upon which Greek astronomy was largely to be based. For the final decline of Babylon set in with its conquest in 539 B.C. by Cyrus the Great, the founder of the Persian empire, which already stretched as far as the rich kingdom of Lydia in western Asia Minor. The second of his line overthrew Egypt, the third spread Persian rule to the Danube. Their power was consolidated by the institution of a famous network of postal routes and stations. The Persians were also at home upon the sea, launching their ships in the Indian Ocean, labouring to restore an ancient Egyptian canal to link the Red Sea with the Mediterranean, and organizing that great seaborne invasion of Europe which is described by Herodotus. This Persian empire, which eclipsed all its predecessors in size and strength and in the glories of its great architectural complexes at Persepolis and Susa, gave the Orient nearly two centuries of peace. It was awakened again by the tramp of the armies of Alexander the Great, who, when Greece itself had passed its zenith, pitted the strength of his youth against civilizations which were already old when Greece was young.

THE RISE OF GREECE AND ROME

As we turn back to trace the first beginnings of civilization in Europe in the second millennium B.C., we may perhaps pause to emphasize this last point. The best-known portion of ancient history, which may here be passed over with corresponding brevity, is the story of the rise of Greece and Rome. In the domains of politics and literature, indeed, there are obvious reasons for according it this traditional pre-eminence; but from the technological standpoint the glories of Greece and Rome can easily be overestimated. When the Greeks and Romans in succession overthrew the ancient civilizations of the Near East, they appropriated and inherited much; but there was also much that they destroyed, and what they devised in its place was rarely superior, and often inferior, to the technical achievements of earlier ages.

Those techniques had included, since a remote period in Egyptian history, the construction of seagoing ships, which traded pottery and other wares along the Syrian coast in exchange for the cedars of Lebanon and many other raw materials in which the Nile valley was deficient. Thence a short but momentous step took them to the wooded island of Crete, where Egyptian imports—possibly also the teachings of refugees from Egypt at the time of its first unification—first enabled a European people to attempt a civilized way of life. By the beginning of the second millennium B.C. the Cretans were already exporting pots and vases to Egypt, often in their own ships. But the zenith of this Minoan civilization was the period 1600–1400 B.C., when Knossos was a metropolis of brick, housing a population of perhaps 80,000. The palace of Minos, famous in Greek legend, was the first great architectural achievement of the northern Mediterranean, important as a centre of industry as well as of the royal administration. Highly skilled potters, workers in metal and ivory, painters, and glaziers provided the basis of an overseas trade which reached across the eastern Mediterranean in all directions. From the gold of Spain to British tin, from Baltic amber to the furs of Russia, the outer barbarians all had something to offer; what they received in return were the goods that stimulated the slow passage of the western lands into the Bronze Age. We have no direct knowledge of the bronzesmiths, who may well have travelled long distances to find customers; but the design of a carving of a dagger at Stonehenge (p. 162) finds its nearest parallel in the bronze daggers of Mycenean Greece, the mainland outpost of Minoan culture.

The fall of the Hittite empire in Asia Minor, the sack of Knossos, which seems to have had Greek rulers at the last, the ending of the Minoan/Mycenean culture in Tiryns and Mycenae itself, and the decline of the Egyptian New Empire, are events in the closing centuries of the second millennium which mark the onrush to the Mediterranean world of Indo-European invaders from the north. Among them were the main body of the Greeks, the Dorians, who for several centuries after their arrival in the land which they were to make famous lived at a cultural level below rather than above that of their heroic age as depicted by Homer. Meanwhile, with the decline of Crete, the Semitic Phoenicians of Tyre and Sidon rose to be the chief sea-power in Mediterranean waters, and the founders of great colonies such as Carthage and Cadiz. Then in the same period the people which we call Etruscan was driven overseas from its home in Asia Minor, and ultimately transplanted a rich Oriental culture to the soil of north Italy. So, when the Greeks in turn began to develop their civilization and to unite commerce with colonization, to which a barren hinterland impelled them, the western Mediterranean was already occupied by two great rivals. The momentous consequence was that, in spite of the great importance of Syracuse, which rose to be the second-largest Greek city, and of the many other Greek colonies in Sicily and south Italy, classical Greece left its more direct and immediate imprint upon the world of the east.

By 600 B.C. Greek technicians had in some respects reached, and in matters of taste surpassed, the level of their Oriental teachers. Iron is described in the Homeric poems, though not as a material for weapons. In classical times the Greeks were expert in many forms of metal-work and conducted their trade with the help of coined money —an enormous stimulus to small-scale trade—imitated from the Lydians, who had been neighbours of the Hittites. Their most essential imports were grain and fish from the Black Sea colonies and their hinterlands; they also imported slaves and many luxuries, ranging from Etruscan art treasures to the carpets and rich silver vessels of the East. A huge industrial development was required to produce the metals, cloth, pottery, oil, and wine, which Greece, and especially Attica, exported in exchange. Fifth-century Attic vases have been found in the Rhineland and on the banks of the Marne, though it was the Greek wine, sold mainly in skins which leave no trace, that had the biggest success among the barbarian Celts.

The final defeat of the Persian invaders in 479 under Athenian leadership marked the ascendancy of the Greeks among the nations and of Athens among Greek states. For two generations she was the mistress of a tributary empire: the Athenians seized their golden hour, and Phidias's chryselephantine statue of Pallas Athene presided over a capital embellished as was no other. But for the history of technology it is perhaps more important to notice that the position of Athens as the chief business centre and virtual metropolis of the Mediterranean world long survived its political downfall. Industrialized to an extent which was then a novelty, and which was facilitated by the fact that the mother-city of democracy had a population that was about one-half slave, Athens would have starved but for the continuing reputation of its pottery, bronzes and other metal-work, and furniture, which brought the corn-ships to the Piraeus.

Unable to reconcile their quarrels, the Greeks were soon to be laid under the heel of the Macedonian highlanders of their own hinterland. The immediate sequel was the decade of Alexander's conquests (333-323), in which the civilization of the conquered Greeks marched across Asia with the conqueror. Although the military advance was halted at the Indus, Greek art penetrated the whole of India and even to China, while the string of Alexandrias, founded as far afield as Afghan Kandahar, gave the Greek way of life a whole series of new *points d'appui*. Alexander had in fact made world commerce supreme over national barriers: if the £40 million of state treasure, which he captured in Persia and put into circulation, gave only a temporary stimulus, the spread of the Greek language throughout his vast dominions proved more lasting than most political successes. When on his untimely death the inheritance was divided among three successor states, none of them repudiated the Greek tradition and one, the Egypt of the Ptolemies, entered upon a new lease of life with the greatest of the Alexandrias as its capital.

The Hellenistic age that followed was one of great industrial activity, helped by the existence of trade routes stretching all across Asia. It was an age distinguished for its town-planning, good water-supply, and drainage systems. Fine government buildings arose, with the clerestory and arch introduced from the East; houses were increasing in comfort and furnishings were often luxurious. Important advances in mathematics, astronomy, and medicine were accompanied by practical labour-saving inventions. At Alexandria a great library brought together all the learning of the known world, while its huge lighthouse looked out over a mass of shipping which gave the city something of the character of a great modern port. Alexandria also had its Museum, which exercised the characteristic-ally Greek functions of a University. But we must not exaggerate the degree of hellenization. Although Alexander had obliterated the military power of the Near Eastern empires, the imprint of their older civilizations upon many generations of men could not vanish so easily. Religion was only one of the great indigenous forces that continued to travel chiefly from east to west.

If Alexander had lived longer he would probably have pursued his career of conquest westward, so that the whole of the Mediterranean world, west and east, might have been knit together some three centuries earlier than it was. The time was ripe, for the impulse of civilizations that waxed and waned elsewhere had by now penetrated far into barbarous Europe, up the Danube valley as well as across the inland sea. In most areas tools of stone had been at least supplemented by those of bronze, and since the beginning of the last millennium B.C. iron-working, with its centre in the eastern Alps, had started to spread among the German and Celtic tribes. The latter were much on the move, and by their penetration into Italy broke the power of the Etruscans. But in the lifetime of Alexander the Great it was the obscure state of Rome, long under Etruscan tutelage, which was coming to the fore as leader of the Latin tribes of its immediate neighbourhood and unconsciously preparing itself for the destiny which the Macedonian was not spared to fulfil. By the middle of the third century B.C. the Romans had mastered the Greek cities of south Italy, whose shipping had laid the foundations of Rome's commerce, and had expelled the Carthaginians from Sicily. Within the next century they had won a titanic struggle for control of the western Mediterranean by the subjugation of Carthage, a city three times the size of Rome and one that had risen through the carrying trade to be the wealthiest port in the known world, but handicapped, as republican Rome was not, by dependence upon a system of slave estates. When they razed Carthage to the ground in 146 B.C., their power already ranged from southern Spain to Macedonia and Syria; and the burning of Corinth in the same year showed their ability further to impose a ruthless will upon the squabbling rulers of the east Mediterranean world.

Like Alexander, who had been made irresistible by his combination of the well-drilled infantry phalanx with flanking forces of heavy cavalry, the Romans excelled in the techniques of war. They took over from the Greeks of south Italy two elaborations of the principle of the bow—the arrow-discharging catapult and the heavy ballista. But the conquests of the republic depended primarily upon the carefully trained legionaries, who marched to the Euphrates and the Caspian Sea, subdued the Celts of Gaul, bridged the Rhine, and crossed the tempestuous Channel to Britain. Finally, with the absorption of the Egypt of Cleopatra, Roman military technology completed the union of east and west.

The age of foreign conquest was also an age of domestic strife, in which the republic perished. Its political leaders were enriched and demoralized by the plunder of provinces that had long been the centre of western civilization: Rome now attracted the trade of the world and paid in money more than in goods. The traditional agriculture of Italy largely collapsed, small farms giving place to vast estates, where stock was raised and the vine and olive were cultivated by gangs of imported slaves. Rome itself, the workshops owned by Romans, and the country residences of the great were all crowded with slaves: we hear of 150,000 prisoners from a single campaign, and the island of Delos, which the Romans made into a general entrepôt market, is said by Strabo to have auctioned as many as 10,000 slaves in a day at prices of £20–60 a head. In the century of violence and confusion with which the history of the Roman republic closes, the slave revolts, put down with great severity, may claim our sympathy more readily perhaps than the bitter struggle for power between rival groups of politicians. Its upshot, however, was the victory of a great statesman, Augustus, the founder of the Roman empire, who in 30 B.C. completed the overthrow of his last enemy, Mark Antony, in the same campaign that won him Egypt.

THE ROMAN EMPIRE

Thus it was given to the Mediterranean world to enjoy a unique two centuries of peace (Fig. 5). Although it proved impossible to hold the ancient Mesopotamian lands beyond Euphrates, and there was no lasting conquest of Germany east of the Rhine or of modern Romania north of the lower Danube, the all-important fact is the security of the inner region, an economic unit of a size that has never been based on Europe since, throughout a period as long as separates ourselves from the elder Pitt and George Washington. The shadows began to close in again during the reign of the philosopher emperor, Marcus Aurelius Antoninus, but the golden age did not terminate definitively until the death of his son, the emperor Commodus, in A.D. 192.

Meanwhile Rome had replaced Alexandria as the most splendid city of the western world, crowned by Augustus's sumptuous residence on the Palatine Hill, from which our word 'palace' derives. Two generations later the great fire of Nero's reign provided the occasion for a more general rebuilding of the city. Much of it was now made of brick-faced concrete, and the brick-yards which arose to meet this need led to the creation of a brick-making monopoly in Italy on modern lines, the wealth of which helped to raise the Antonine dynasty to power. Of other building materials we may notice that lead became very cheap (partly as a by-product of the silver mines) so that plumbing reached a high standard of efficiency. A barge canal planned by Julius Caesar linked the capital with Ostia and was intended to join up with Puteoli, its main out-port, for some five million bushels of wheat, about one-third of Rome's annual bread supply, was of Egyptian origin.

Politically, Rome and Italy were favourably placed to conduct a world-wide trade: not only did all roads lead to Rome but the Mediterranean seaways were, for the only time in their long history, subject to a single efficient police authority. Thus the potteries of Puteoli, Arretium, and the Po valley provided tableware for all except the south-eastern provinces of the vast empire, while south Italy had a large-scale woollen industry. Economic historians maintain that the Mediterranean world as a whole has never recovered the prosperity it enjoyed in the late first and early second century, at the time when the Emperors Domitian and Hadrian consolidated its natural frontiers on Danube, Rhine, and Tyne. But from the point of view of the historian of technology this is, above all, a period marked by the wide diffusion of skilled handicrafts, for the trade of the Roman empire did not develop along the lines of a single Italian 'workshop of the world'.

If we look towards the Near East, one important factor was the steady development of the trade route across the Mediterranean; numerous docks and lighthouses were installed primarily for the benefit of the government grain ships, which carried a thousand tons at a time between Egypt and Rome. It was therefore natural that the attempt should be made also to increase the traffic farther east. The existence of seasonal winds in the Indian Ocean was known, and at one time a fleet of 120 vessels plied between the Red Sea and India. Nevertheless, what the close contact with the Near East chiefly implied was an economic revival there, against which Italy could not in the long run contend, even though the ranks of her own craftsmen were largely reinforced by technicians from the east.

If we look instead to the formerly less civilized areas of the west and north of the empire, we find a different sequence of events. They were penetrated first by the Roman army, which often brought with it its own potteries and other manufacturing equipment. In the wake of the army there soon followed Italian traders, to serve both military and civilian needs. But the heavy cost of transport in all areas remote from navigable rivers quickly stimulated an outward shift of industry:

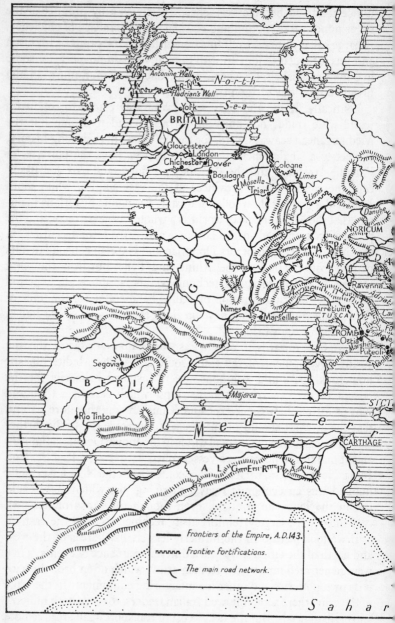

FIG. 5. The Roman empire, with nam

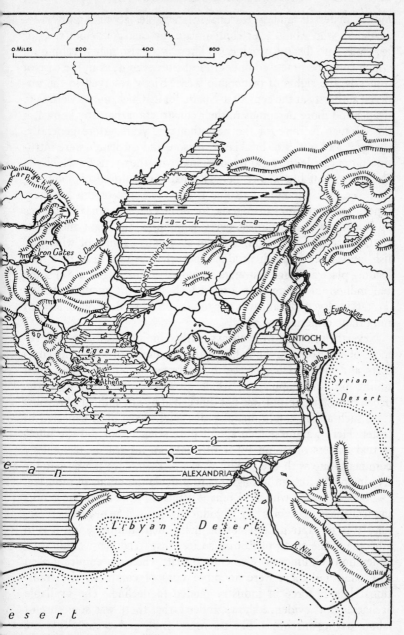

places mentioned in the text

for, if materials and a reasonably tractable labour supply were available, who would ever contemplate the carriage of pottery, for example, into distant provinces? There were also many techniques which could be practised only at local sites even if, as in the case of minerals, the rights of ownership were strictly reserved to the imperial authority at the centre: in Spain, for instance, mines were dug, deeper and more ingenious in their construction than any known in post-Roman Europe for the next thousand years. More generally, the tools and trades of bricklayer, mason, and carpenter were introduced to provide the conquered regions with the towns by which the Roman way of life was to be sustained. Agricultural exploitation, however, was paramount. Rome laid every shore of the Mediterranean under tribute: in Algeria, for instance, there are still vestiges of Roman works in almost every commune. In Spain there was state-supervised irrigation, and the enormous exports of wine, oil, fish, and other Spanish products have left behind near their unloading place at Rome a strange memorial, in the fragments of some ten million 11-gallon amphorae which form the modern Monte Testaccio. Even Britain was not too far off to be developed into an important imperial granary.

Nevertheless there were always marked limitations to the achievement of the Romans. They had made an empire in which the comforts and civilized life of the towns rested upon the backs of a toiling peasant population which produced the food; yet the urban industrial output was not quickened by any industrial revolution, such as the conditions of peace might have been expected to foster. Here was no golden age of pure science, nor did the intellectual leaders of Rome apparently take an interest in technology commensurate with the public works of their day: it was left for freedmen and foreign immigrants to provide the brains of industry.

The true reason why the Romans displayed little inventive genius in mechanical matters is largely hidden from us. The need was there, for slaves in captivity did not maintain their numbers, and it is in any case to the credit of Roman society that freedmen were in each generation a numerous element, so that, when the empire ceased to expand and there were no more wars of conquest, the traditional labour force in industry tended to decline. The available archaeological evidence shows, indeed, that there was some use of labour-saving machines, like the water-mill, and eventually some concentration of industry in imperial factories for arms and cloth.

But no revolutionary impetus was imparted to Roman technology, such as might have helped to save an empire in decline.

As regards agriculture, interest centres upon those outer provinces into which the empire had begun to expand in the time of Julius Caesar. The Mediterranean lands had their own long-standing problems of seasonal rainfall and lightness of soil; they were often under-manured, the sheep being sent to graze the hills; and there was a general scarcity of land for stock-raising. It has even been suggested that exhaustion of the soil was one cause of the empire's eventual downfall, though the prices of corn in the Republican and Late Empire periods when compared show little change. In any case, the Roman economy had much to gain by bringing a wider area into cultivation, and the stimulus given to tillage outside the Mediterranean lands is one of the important developments of this period. But the regions affected, such as northern Gaul and Britain, were mainly places of damper climate and predominantly heavier soil, for which the agricultural techniques practised by the Romans had little to offer, except as regards viticulture, where they were the heirs of the Greeks.

After the death of Commodus the empire was for three generations on the verge of collapse, being rescued from complete disintegration by two great rulers, Diocletian (284–305) and Constantine the Great, who obtained complete power in 312 and died in 337. The restored empire, however, was a bureaucratically administered autocracy, whose head wore the costume and imitated the traits of an eastern despot on the pattern of its oriental rival, the new Persian empire of the Sassanian kings. Although Constantine made Christianity the official religion, neither this momentous change nor the division of the empire into two halves, which was first practised by Diocletian and made permanent in 395, could restore the spirit that had left it.

The reasons why the empire in the west declined and fell are still uncertain. On the technological side, if we find inadequate the theory of the impoverishment of the soil, there is a well-attested decline in the output of metals, though it is hard to tell whether this was cause or effect. Having less gold to pay for imports, Rome lost, for instance, the stimulus of her trade with the East. It is also suggested that the failure to cope with the sanitary problems of life in large towns supplies a reason for the fall in the population of Greece and Italy at this period; neglect of existing drainage works, particularly in the Roman Campagna, may well have contributed to a grave increase in malaria. More generally, it would seem that the attempted concentration of industry, referred to above, did little to check the impoverishment of town life, which, when coupled with the excessive burden of imperial taxation, fatally disheartened the middle classes. In their dealings with the barbarians, the Romans seem to have lost confidence in their civilizing mission long before the barbarians themselves lost their awe of the grandeur that was Rome. Indeed, the empire, as viewed from such a province as Gaul or Britain, which in the fourth century enjoyed exceptional prosperity, was long in dying. Rome itself had been twice sacked by barbarians; Attila the Hun had stood on Italian soil; and barbarian kingdoms were springing up from North Africa to Britain, before the Herulian Odoacer intervened in 476 to depose the last fugitive Roman emperor in the west.

What did this Roman empire in its death throes transmit to its heirs? The answer is, more than might be expected. Every one of the barbarian peoples, except perhaps the Huns, had long been in contact with the empire through trade; the finds of Roman coins as far away as northern Scandinavia and central Russia bear silent witness to this. Moreover, the barbarians had for centuries entered the empire and sampled its economy as mercenary soldiers and pioneer settlers. Further, there was the influence of the Christian state church, its bishops, and its monasteries. In spite of the teachings of Augustine's *De Civitate Dei*, churchmen cherished the memories of the material splendours of the earthly Rome. When what were once Roman cities became the centres of episcopal administration among converted barbarians, it was natural for the bishop to preserve what he could of the Roman way of life—if it was only the keeping of an aqueduct in repair or a fashion in the building of a basilica (Fig. 6). Thus it came about that the western world never wholly lost the technological traditions that Rome had received from the Near East. There was a teasing memory of vanished comforts and luxury, useful skills in Mediterranean agriculture, and, even while the Roman roads fell slowly into decay, a continued employment of fine techniques of metal-work for ornaments and weapons.

Nevertheless, from the point of view of technology and much else, the key event of these centuries was not the destruction of Rome in the west but the transfer of Roman ideas to the east. In the four years 326–30 Constantine the Great had built his new capital of Constantinople: in Gibbon's memorable phrase, 'the eastern city rose like an exhalation'—and changed the course of history. Here, in a Greek setting, the eastern half of the empire continued its independent existence for twice as long as the lifespan of that empire which we loosely think of as the only Roman empire. At the time when the western empire disappeared, that of the east included the only two provinces that were economically sound, namely, Asia Minor and Egypt. While the flow of trade elsewhere slackened, Constantine's gold *aureus* was beginning a circulation which lasted for 700 years. In an age when many western cities were left deserted ruins, Constantinople boasted a population of a million.

THE EARLIER MIDDLE AGES

A ruined Roman forum and an unfrequented Roman road are, perhaps, fair symbols of the life which prevailed in western Europe at the end of the great migrations. Few records survive from the

FIG. 6. Church building, from a ninth-century Psalter

period of the settlement, which was in a sense completed with the arrival in north Italy of the Lombards in 568. But the birth of Islam in Arabia in 622 followed so quickly that it is perhaps more realistic to include the swift extension of Muslim power east to the Indus and west to Spain as part of a single great upheaval, which lasted until Charles Martel repelled the Muslim advance into France (732) and prepared the way for his grandson Charlemagne briefly to revive a Christian empire of the west. If we take our stand, however, at the day when Charlemagne was crowned 'Emperor of the Romans', Christmas Day 800, it is possible already to discern several factors which suggested for western Europe a future less dark than the four centuries which were past.

The coronation of Charlemagne bore witness to the increasing ascendancy of the Christian church in secular as well as spiritual affairs. Since 529 monks of the Benedictine Order had improved tillage and reclaimed waste land in many parts of the west. In the time of Charlemagne great abbeys were growing up in north Gaul and Germany. Town-life being still at a low ebb, they served an important purpose in preserving skilled handicrafts and in the organization of trade, without which the monastic brethren, who needed much they did not themselves produce, could not exist, much less flourish. They had a direct interest in the techniques of agriculture, and it seems likely that the monks of the great abbeys were among the first landowners to adopt what was the central agricultural improvement of the Middle Ages, namely, the substitution of the three-field for the Roman two-field rotation of crops. This more intensive use of the tilled area developed side by side with the increase in its size as the forests fell before the axe. Here, too, the Church played its part by setting its face, though with varying determination, against the enslaving of fellow-Christians: on the medieval manor the institution of serfdom did not usually prevent the winner of new soil from profiting by his enterprise. On a larger scale, the colonization of Charlemagne's Eastern March (Austria) by the Germans was likewise a significant advance.

The stimulus of large-scale commerce, however, was still lacking, and when Charlemagne died the sea and river routes were being bloodily transformed into the highways of Viking raid and conquest. A large proportion of the valuables of western Europe, which might have been the objects of trade, went to adorn the homes of barbarians beside the fiords of Norway and elsewhere, while farther east the frontier-lands of Charlemagne's empire were laid waste by the Magyars, who came by way of south Russia to make their permanent home on the plains of Hungary, and who were with great difficulty driven back from the heart of Europe. The tenth and eleventh centuries likewise saw men of Norse, Danish, and Swedish blood firmly settled in new homes from Limerick to Kiev and from Iceland to Sicily, where they became zealous Christians, like those liegemen of William the Conqueror who reared the great Norman abbeys at Durham and St Albans. As Europe became more nearly co-terminous with Christendom, the stage was set for the Crusades.

The glamour of the crusading movement has often tended to con-ceal its true position as only the most dramatic episode in a long-continued interaction between east and west. Ever since the fall of Rome, the recovery of material civilization in the west had depended primarily upon the Byzantine and other technologically more ad-vanced societies farther east; their influence upon the petty warring states which emerged from the barbarian invasions of Europe was more gradual and less obvious, but scarcely less profound, than that which western Europe in its turn exercised upon the American continent. How much came, for instance, through the peoples of the steppes, and by what routes, is still a mystery. The open land frontier in Asia certainly provided a means of contact with the tech-nically fertile civilization of China: it seems likely that the horse-collar, the breast-strap, the cross-bow, the stirrup, and even the wheelbarrow made their unrecorded entry into western Europe by this route. The respective debts to the Byzantine and Islamic worlds can, however, be stated less tentatively.

Constantinople, the terminus of a long-established silk-route from China, was naturally a centre for the diffusion of Far Eastern tech-nologies, including the most sedulously guarded ones, such as the culture of the silkworm, whose eggs were successfully smuggled in during the reign of Justinian I. Constantinople was also the inter-mediary for the skills of the Middle East, both in the time of Sassanian Persia (p. 23) and throughout the ascendancy of Islam down to the final overthrow of the eastern empire in 1453. Last but not least, there was a whole range of handicrafts which Rome had inherited from the Near East and which retreated again eastwards, to sur-vive throughout the Dark Ages in the haven of New Rome beside the Bosphorus.

Byzantine influence upon the west took various forms. On the mainland of southern Italy direct Byzantine control, which the armies of Justinian established in 536, lasted five centuries. For about the same period, Constantinople was the great trade centre of the Medi-terranean, having control of a network of Roman roads, of the Black Sea, and of the Levant. Moreover, being by far the most impos-ing city of the Christian world, it was a natural centre of attraction. From the eastern empire the peoples of the west received mosaics, silks, ivories, and Egyptian and Syrian glass and metal-work superior to anything they could devise for themselves. Even its weaknesses contributed to spread Byzantine influence westwards—when craftsmen emigrated as a result of religious schism or unsuccessful war, and when, as we shall see, the north Italian states found in the Crusades their chance to plunder the treasures of the east.

In relation to the Byzantine empire the power of Islam was a destructive force. Seven centuries lie between the first siege of Constantinople by the infidel and his eventual triumph in 1453, during which survival was partly due to technological advantages—superb fortification of a strategically placed capital, excellently equipped armies, with engineers and even ambulances, and the terror inspired by the mysterious 'Greek fire' (p. 268)—until the Muslims learnt flame-throwing from the Christians. But in relation to the west, Islam must be considered mainly as a constructive influence. Although it was not until the ninth and tenth centuries, when Baghdad and Bokhara rose in the east and Cordova and Seville in the west, that Islamic civilization reached its height and made its full impact upon the west, from much earlier days the huge size of the area the Muslims dominated made naturally for an increase in trade. They were glad to import slaves (usually Slavs whom it was held no sin for Christians to buy or kidnap from beyond the Elbe), metal goods, and timber from western Europe. West Europeans received in exchange goods of superior workmanship in familiar materials, such as glass and leather, and in completely new materials supplied by a society which was economically far in advance of their own. The west also acquired a much-desired supply of gold, which was mined chiefly under the Crescent: the Islamic *dinar*, like the Byzantine *aureus*, was used in western Europe as money of account, and hoards of the coins are to be found as far north as Sweden. In the long run, however, Islamic civilization, as we shall see, had more to offer than to receive; and a balance of bullion resumed its passage eastwards, as under the early Roman empire.

Islamic civilization combined three advantages. It was in direct contact with the Far East, from which came materials, such as high-quality steel, silk, paper, and porcelain, and valuable techniques, like the Indian system of notation which we still call Arabic numerals. It was also a secondary heir of Greece, having overrun Syria, Egypt, and other areas of the Near East where, for example, the works of Aristotle were still available to stimulate inquiry. Thirdly, the

Islamic religion, unlike medieval Catholicism, did nothing to stifle the spirit of scientific inquiry: hence came remarkable achievements in chemistry, which passed on to the west under the Arabic name of alchemy. From Basra to Cordova great universities arose centuries before the earliest *studium generale* in Christendom: by A.D. 1000 Cordova had a catalogued library of 600,000 books. The craftsmanship of the Arab world was on a par with its scholarship: for example, when the Normans built the great cathedral at Durham over the relics of Cuthbert, the highest honour they could pay the saint was to inter his bones in a silk wrapping of Mesopotamian manufacture, inscribed—though the devotees of the saint were happily unaware of this—with a sacred text from the Koran.

Geography, tradition, and the fortunes of war combined to give Italy the role of middleman between east and west (Fig. 7). Amalfi was almost an outpost of Constantinople; Genoa and other cities of the north as well as of the south kept some part of their economic activity from classical times; in the sixth century they were joined by Venice, a new town admirably located for an entrepôt between the east Mediterranean coastline and the hinterland of central and northern Europe. In the early Middle Ages Italy took the lead among western countries in agriculture, in the cloth industry, and in most of the arts of urban life. After the fall of Rome, easterners (known collectively as 'Syrians') had continued to conduct such fragmentary east–west trade as survived, but the Italians replaced them in the slowly advancing distribution in western Europe of the superior products of the east. In quantity, no doubt, the chief trades of western Europe were in food—corn, fish, wine, and dairy produce—without which the populations of many regions would have fared most miserably; but it was through the Italians that access was obtained to goods of high quality. When trade fairs grew up, such as that of St Denis in Paris which existed by 629, or at Troyes in the county of Champagne, whence the overland route led across eastern France to Genoa and Florence, it was chiefly Italian merchants who came to buy the raw or half-finished materials of the north. Such fairs, of exceptional commercial importance in a generally primitive economy, were becoming numerous about the time when Europe, recovering from the Norse invasions, gathered its strength for the Crusades.

What has been said may make it possible to see in better perspective the effects that the four main crusades of 1097–1204 had upon the material development of the west European society which

FIG. 7. Medieval trade routes

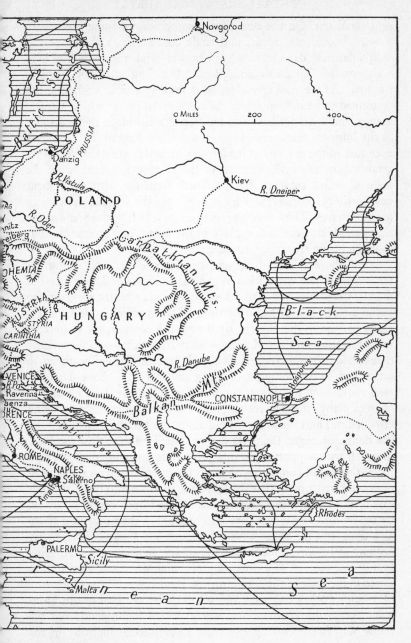

● places named in the text

sent them out. On the one hand, they produced some immediate flow of booty, new ideas, and trade contacts with the east—the words damask, damascening, and muslin recall the industrial pre-eminence of Damascus and Mosul. But long after the French, English, and German crusaders slept in their tombs, economic life continued to be influenced by the commercial power which Venice, Genoa, and other Italian cities built up at this time in their capacity as the business managers of the crusading movement. In 1204 they even turned the movement itself into a business, when the Venetians arranged for the dethronement of the Eastern Emperor to be the main objective achieved by the fourth Crusade, with consequent new territory, plunder, and trade privileges throughout the empire for themselves. They were no less ready to take full advantage of the changes which were taking place in the north, less spectacular but more enduring than the Crusades.

While the arable lands of northern Europe were still being ex-tended piecemeal, generation by generation, from hard-won forest or marsh, Christians had made the discovery that heathen were to be found nearer home than Palestine, in lands which would yield a ready harvest to the plough. By the twelfth century, the Cistercian monks, setting up their Houses—328 in forty years—'in the wilder-ness', had no apparent difficulty in recruiting lay-brothers to serve them in the conquest of forest and marsh. The secular Ger-man movement was being supported, too, by the Dutch who, in spite of many efforts to reclaim inundated coastal lands, were being crowded out and therefore spread along the marshy south shore of the Baltic. So began the great drive of the Teuton against the Slav, in which arms supported the interests of religion, and migration pre-pared the way of commerce. Perhaps the heavy plough was the most important instrument that the Germans brought into the Slav lands east of the Elbe, where hitherto the soil had been barely scratched by the hooked *uncus*: but they also brought in the heavy axe, sheep and vines, and the water-wheel. In Silesia and Prussia alone, to say nothing of Poland, Bohemia, and Hungary, new villages were being founded at the rate of a dozen a year; miners and salt workers fol-lowed in the wake of the agriculturists. By 1250—while less fortunate Slav lands farther east were being laid under the heel of the Mon-gols—corn from Brandenburg was exported to England, and the Baltic was fast becoming the second commercial highway of the medieval world.

THE LATER MIDDLE AGES

It has been claimed that the High Middle Ages are probably the greatest turning-point in the history of civilization in western Europe. During the 200 years preceding the outbreak of the Black Death in 1348, there was a commercial expansion comparable in its pervasive effects to the industrial revolution at the end of the eighteenth century. The part which England played in the later revolution was played in the former by the Italian states; it will therefore be convenient to take their dominant position as the last feature in a brief survey.

Perhaps the most striking aspect of the age is the growth of population, which rapidly rose towards its saturation point under existing conditions in both England and the Continent, at least west of the Elbe. Paris was the undisputed metropolis of the north and rivalled in size the cities of north Italy; half of the inhabitants of Flanders and Brabant lived in towns. By 1300, pressure on food-growing resources had caused the disappearance of fallow from many parts of Flanders and the completion of the dyke system in Holland. Large areas, including substantially the whole of France, were now supporting the maximum population, about 100 to the square mile, of which medieval agriculture was capable. It must be remembered that the average yield of rye and wheat was then only about five-fold, that of oats and barley rather less than fourfold; stock-raising was still limited by the shortage of high-quality grasses; and not until the fifteenth century did progress in iron-working bring into use an additional farm tool as simple as the three-pronged fork.

As regards industrial techniques, there is a marked contrast with the primitive agrarian society of the Dark Ages. The great Gothic churches (Fig. 8) were being built, in which sculpted figures gazed down from the heights or loomed through the shadows, and the sunlight streaming through stained glass seemed to shed a spiritual as well as a physical radiance. In secular architecture, too, although Hungarian nobles in the twelfth century still lived in huts of reed and the wooden castle did not disappear from Scotland until the fifteenth century, the skill of the masons was filling the landscape with stone castles. Second to the masons were the millwrights. The England of Domesday Book (1086) already ground its corn at nearly 6,000 water-mills; by the middle of the twelfth century windmills also had reached Europe, and water-power was being applied to new purposes, especially the fulling of cloth. But what was probably the

FIG. 8. Ecclesiastical building work, from a miniature of 1460

most important development, at least as regards Europe, was a new
prowess in the mining, extraction, and working of metals. A great
development of silver-mines took place in Hungary, Bohemia,
Saxony, and the Harz, and widespread communities of free miners
also worked the baser metals: Cologne and Dinant, for instance,

became famous for bells and other ware of copper and bronze and the Meuse valley for its cutlery, hardware, and weapons.

In the Middle Ages commerce dominated industry, and, as we have seen, the Italians dominated commerce. The six fairs of Champagne, which by the twelfth century ran through the year from January to October, and then the three great cloth towns of the Netherlands, were the first centres to which the Italian merchants came. The route southwards across France was therefore of prime importance, though other traffic reached Italy through Alpine passes from regions east of the Rhine. Towards the end of the thirteenth century, however, the county of Champagne was annexed by the French monarchy, whose policy so hampered trade that much of it was transferred to the sea: thus the great galleys of the Genoese and Venetians began to undertake an annual voyage from the Mediterranean to the ports of the Low Countries and England, where their length made them conspicuous among the ships of the north. Their imitators were the merchants of the Hanseatic league, who, in the next century, linked up the ports of the Baltic and the west coast of Scandinavia with the markets of Germany and the Low Countries and England: their London depot, the Steelyard, was not finally closed until 1597. But it is significant that the Hansa did not attempt to sail farther west than Bruges, where the Italian galleys lay.

Perhaps the two best-known facts about Italy in this period are its financial hold upon England, to which the names of the florin and of Lombard Street still bear witness, and its link with China, initiated by the travels of the Polos: the one is a reminder of the bourgeois society which first emerged in Italy and has influenced Europe to this day, the other of the tremendous reach of the Italian trade interests (Fig. 9). But there were many other ways in which the Italians already anticipated the modern world. The medicine taught at the university of Salerno was one of the principal roots of Renaissance science, and the earliest of all surviving naval charts comes from Pisa. They were great improvers of land: the Grand Canal of Lombardy, for instance, irrigated some 80,000 acres. The cloth-making, the dyeing and finishing of coarser cloths from northern Europe, and the cloth merchandising, by which they paid for food imports for an ever-increasing population, were conducted by modern business methods; as late as the sixteenth century the Fuggers of Augsburg went to Italy to serve their financial apprenticeship. As papermakers, as armourers, as glass-blowers, and as silk-throwers, the

Italians were famous for their advanced techniques. Venice anticipated some of the reforms of a later age by a ban on child labour in dangerous trades and by the institution of a 'Plimsoll' line for its shipping. Milan and Venice were able to sustain populations of about 200,000 each, and Florence, Genoa, and perhaps Palermo and Naples of about 100,000 each, at a time when not a single big town except Paris had arisen in the north—these estimates relate to a period just before the Black Death. Moreover, it is fairly safe to say that the average standard of life in these great urban aggregations of

FIG. 9. Caravan from the East, as depicted in the Catalan Atlas of 1375

population was higher than in the mainly agricultural north. As for other standards, this was the Italy which had already known the lives and writings of Aquinas and Dante.

Towards the middle of the fourteenth century, however, the High Middle Age of Western Europe gave place to a period of decline. The Black Death of 1348 was a social catastrophe to which only the world wars of our time provide a parallel—and they, it must be remembered, came in an age when material losses can be made good at a rate which was unthinkable for medieval man. If a third of the population perished in two years, which seems to be the likeliest approximate figure, it is easy to understand that agriculture, the basis of all other industries, must have suffered a tremendous blow. By 1348 the cultivated area had reached limits which were not appreciably extended before the period of the industrial revolution, except in such minor respects as the substitution of cultivated meadow for much of the old forest pasture in Germany; but the ground lost to agriculture through the Black Death took at least a century to restore. That century, too, virtually coincides with the Hundred Years War (1337–1453), in which England, and still more France, wasted and exhausted their resources. Thus the English customs accounts for 1350–1450, which provide our best statistical check, show that the increase in cloth exports, which was a by-product of the war, did not compensate for the decline in the English export of wool. A similar decline can be traced in other great European industries, such as fishing, mining, and the metal trades, with the significant exception of iron and armaments.

If we look farther south, at the Mediterranean area, we find that this was entering upon the sunset of its long golden age. The eastern empire had never recovered from the period of Latin rule that followed the sack of Constantinople in 1204, and which left the restored eastern dynasty intensely resentful of the outrages it had suffered at the hands of the west. As its power waned, Venetians, Genoese, and others fought to establish themselves as its western heirs, without regard to the advance of the Ottoman Turks, whose conquest of Asia Minor and much of the Balkans foreshadowed the final downfall of Constantinople as a Christian capital long before 1453. The towns of southern Italy, like those of southern France, had long been in decline. Those of northern Italy, Florence, Milan, and others, as well as the great sea-traders, Venice and Genoa, still indeed retained their pre-eminence in industry, commerce, and the arts. Financially, too, they were immensely strong, but, like Britain in the last quarter of the nineteenth century, they were carried forward by the impetus of their past successes rather than by new economic achievements. Meanwhile, the rise of Barcelona as a commercial competitor foreshadowed the growth of Spanish power. Still more significant were the voyages of the new Portuguese caravels, which by 1450 had reached the mouth of the Gambia, heading for the Indian Ocean and the interception of that eastern trade which, carried overland, had confirmed the Mediterranean and its cities in their long ascendancy.

THE RENAISSANCE

The opening-up of the ocean routes to trade and conquest by Europeans, which begins with the rounding of the Cape of Good Hope by the Portuguese Bartholomew Diaz in 1487, is only the last and perhaps the most dramatic of a cumulative series of changes. Of these, the introduction of printing to Europe about 1450 is by far the most significant; the rapid spread of what was known as the 'German art'—by 1500 there were a hundred German presses in Italy and thirty in Spain—shows us a Europe which was now ripe for an immense new development. Both the artistic achievements of the Renaissance and, still more, the technology and craftsmanship on which the architect, the sculptor, and the painter depended, could be described in print. Interest in the work and viewpoint of the ancients, from which the Renaissance derived its first inspiration, had been slowly growing through the later medieval centuries. The mind of the age was now ready to turn from imitation to creation and from humanist studies to independent scientific inquiry.

The enormous and enduring impact that all this had upon western Europe as a whole was largely the result of the new means of diffusing knowledge. This is important above all for the history of technology, because the Italian geniuses of the Renaissance rose superior to the ancient snobbery which had despised the base mechanic arts. It must suffice to mention the names of Verrocchio, sculptor and anatomist, silversmith, engineer, and lapidary; of Alberti, with his interest in the whole of applied science; of Michelangelo, defending Florence by his skill in the art of fortification; and, above all, of Leonardo da Vinci, who investigated the ultimate truths of mechanics while condescending to such inventions as a practical marble saw and a machine for making ropes. At the same time, printing enhanced the need for a system of patents, which was first introduced at Venice in 1474. From there it spread to Florence and other Italian states, and it was for the most part Italian glass-makers (p. 109) who in the following century carried the practice into other parts of Europe. In England, where the first patent dates from 1552, their abuse by the Crown for the issue of money-raising grants of monopoly led to the important Act of 1624, which swept away the abuses but left the Crown free to grant exclusive rights under letters patent for not more than twenty-one years to 'the first and true inventor or inventors of manufactures'. Thus England, and after 1707 Scotland, began to give a clear legal incentive to inventors, while other states, including those of Italy in her decline, often awarded exclusive rights on a basis of princely favour rather than for technical innovations.

A decline, from which the homeland of the Renaissance has never wholly recovered, dates from the Italian wars of France and Spain, which lasted for two-thirds of a century. The fact that Charles VIII of France in 1494 launched the earliest of these successive invasions of Italy with what has been called the first modern army, excellently equipped with artillery, is a reminder that the introduction of explosives in warfare is a second technological change characteristic of this period (Fig. 10). But the gun, unlike the printing-press, was slow to develop its full efficiency: cannon were fired at the battle of Crecy in 1346, yet the bow was not finally and officially discarded as an English weapon until 1595. The development of the new arm was closely related to the growth of mining and the metallurgical industries, progress in which gave to central Europe, and south Germany in particular, a counterweight to the achievements of the Renaissance Italians farther south. It was the more intense exploitation of silver-mining, by which the German supply was approximately quintupled between 1460 and 1530, that made the Fuggers of Augsburg the richest family in the western world. Similarly, the metallurgical works described at this time by the German Agricola (p. 140) represented record concentrations of capital and labour in single plants.

FIG. 10. Laying siege guns. Ramelli, 1588

Agricola (Georg Bauer) was born two years after Columbus's discovery of America had opened up vast new fields for European exploitation, of which the instruments were not only the ocean-going ship and new navigational equipment, but the cannon, the flintlock, and the improved cutting-edge of western steel. In two generations navigators under Spanish and Portuguese auspices circled the world, organized the rich trade routes from the Far East, and overthrew the empires of the Aztecs and the Incas. The immediate consequences were impressive. New foodstuffs and new raw materials poured into Europe, while an awareness of far horizons also gave an incalculable stimulus to the life of the intellect and the imagination. In addition, there was the tremendous impact of the treasure seized in the conquest or won later from Peruvian and Mexican mines.

Between 1521 and 1660 the official imports to Spain were 200 tons of gold and 18,000 tons of silver: this completely swamped both the European output, which declined after 1550, and the supply from Africa. With some help from debasement of currency, such as was practised in England by Henry VIII and Protector Somerset, the spread of Spanish treasure across Europe occasioned a price revolution lasting until about 1650. In the second quarter of the seventeenth century, wheat prices in western and central Europe were more than four times what they had averaged a hundred years before. The steep, persistent rise in prices caused much distress to individuals, but the tendency for wages to lag behind offered a great incentive to industrial expansion, such as was experienced, for example, by Elizabethan England. In Spain itself the lag was smaller than elsewhere and the expansion correspondingly slower, yet typical industrial cities there are known to have doubled their population between 1530 and 1594, while the Spanish-ruled port of Antwerp soared to its zenith as a world market before the outbreak of the religious struggle in the Netherlands in 1566.

However, the states of the Iberian peninsula did not retain their leadership for long. Portugal, with a smaller home-base and population than Spain, fell rapidly from the position she had held in 1493, when the Pope purported to divide the world of the new discoveries east and west between them. By 1540 her blockade of the Red Sea, which secured the monopoly of the spice trade for the route round the Cape of Good Hope, was proving ineffective, and pepper and other eastern goods were again entering Europe from the eastern shores of the Mediterranean, to the profit of Venice and other Italian and French ports. Forty years later, Portugal and her empire of the east became absorbed (until 1640) among the possessions of the Spanish Crown. As for Spain, her Golden Century was directly followed by a century of decline, marked by shrinkage of population, waning industries, and financial instability, while the voyages of Columbus and Magellan, the campaigns of Cortés and Pizarro, served the rise of other, mainly heretical powers.

THE EMERGENCE OF THE MODERN WORLD

Spain had been in the forefront of the religious wars, which began when the Renaissance helped to kindle the spark of the Lutheran Reformation in the Germany of Charles V and were seen at their fiercest in the Spanish Netherlands, which became irremediably split between a largely Calvinist Holland and a Catholic Spanish province, the future Belgium, with its port of Antwerp now declining. By 1600 the Dutch had virtually won their independence; at about the same time, their fellow-Calvinists, the Huguenots of

France, at the end of nine hard-fought campaigns had become the beneficiaries of a religious truce. The struggle was beginning to lose its religious character, though the fate of the Reformation in Germany remained to be determined in the Thirty Years War of 1618–48.

In technology, these wars produced no important advance, though the intervention of the Swedes in Germany under Gustavus Adolphus, with mobile field artillery and superior muskets, is a reminder that the little-known land these Protestant champions came from was rich in iron and copper, if in little else. But a striking fact about these wars and the bitter struggle of ideas of which they were the outcome is that they did not prove incompatible with a simultaneous growth in population and wealth. After the great setback of the Black Death, the population of Europe had begun to rise again near the end of the fifteenth century; by 1600 it is believed to have totalled 95 millions and by 1700, 130 millions, the rate of growth having slowed down at about mid-century. In the history of individual countries the evidence of economic progress, which does not necessarily accompany the rise of population, is likewise considerable. In England, for example, Henry VIII's dissolution of the monasteries, which made land readily available to the entrepreneur, coinciding with the start of the steepest phase in the rise of prices, marked the beginning of a period of rapid development in mining, glass-making, soap-boiling, and other industries. The civil wars interposed a serious check, yet by the time of the Revolution of 1688 the annual coal output —a most significant item—was approaching 3 million tons, a fourteen-fold increase in 140 years. In France the religious truce of 1598 was followed immediately by the great improvements in agriculture, communications, and commerce associated with the names of Henry IV and his minister Sully. In the Netherlands a population of less than $2\frac{1}{2}$ millions established the one new state of the period on a basis of commercial wealth, accumulated during their struggle for independence. In shipbuilding, the carrying trade, the organization of entrepôt markets, and the adaptation of new ideas to industry, the Dutch now led the world. Even Germany, which was fought over so fiercely and so frequently, seems to have suffered its worst losses from the shifting of the European trade routes, and retained sufficient energy and resources for the port of Hamburg to rise immediately after the Thirty Years War.

The second half of the seventeenth century bears the stamp of the monarchy of Louis XIV, with his palace of Versailles as the cynosure of kings and courtiers in every land, and his minister Colbert, striving to harness all industry and commerce to the service of the state, as the exemplar of political wisdom. But the excellence of Gobelins tapestries and all the skills which spread from France with the expelled Huguenots in 1685 must not blind us to the solid, if sometimes more humdrum, accomplishments of the tenacious bourgeois societies of England and the Netherlands: three Anglo-Dutch wars produced no decisive result, but as allies the two countries proved able at length (1713) to impose their will even upon the king of France. This was the age of Russia's first effective contacts with the more advanced technology of the west, when Peter the Great paid his famous visits to the merchants of Amsterdam and the shipwrights of Deptford. It was also the age in which a more advanced technology was making some tentative contact with science, and if the Royal Society in London had its counterpart in the French Academy of Sciences, founded by Colbert, and some older continental institutions, such as the Accademia dei Lincei in Italy (1603), there was no equal to Isaac Newton, 'voyaging through strange seas of thought alone'.

We must, however, beware of the temptation to overstress the beginnings of the rapprochement between science and technology because of the immense importance of its consequences in our own day. The rise of the scientific spirit was a notable feature of the Renaissance: men no longer accepted without question the opinions of the ancients about the universe and the laws governing the natural world; dogma was subjected to experiment, and when it failed to survive the test it was rejected and new theories were formulated. Thus science in the modern sense was born, and rapid progress was made in mathematics, physics, chemistry, and biology. But the immediate consequences for technology were confined to a few specialized fields; in the main, technological progress still depended upon the use of empirical methods by practical men. On the whole, up to 1750 science probably gained more from technology than vice versa. Among the notable exceptions, which we shall consider in later chapters, were the navigational instruments that played so important a part in the great voyages of exploration and in surveying and cartography; the application of the principle of the pendulum to time-measurement; and, particularly, the growing exploitation of chemistry.

However, the new outlook on natural phenomena was only one manifestation of a healthy scepticism: technological processes which often had changed very little for centuries were carefully scrutinized to see what improvements could usefully be made. The Royal Society, founded in 1660 to further the investigation of natural phenomena by observation and experiment, in its early days directed at least as much of its attention to the improvement of existing arts and industries as to the advancement of fundamental scientific knowledge. Among the Society's early activities was the founding of Greenwich Observatory in 1675 for the strictly practical purpose of 'finding out the longitude for perfecting navigation'.

Only two generations separate the Newcomen 'fire-engine', which, as we shall see (p. 313), owes something at least to the experimental study of atmospheric pressure by the members of the Royal Society and their confrères on the Continent, from the much more effective steam-engine of Watt. Meanwhile, the political scene had changed from the demolition of French ambitions by the Grand Alliance of Britain, Holland, and Austria at the Peace of Utrecht (1713) to the consummation of those of Britain at the Peace of Paris (1763). The Britain which conquered Canada and Bengal was drawing rapidly ahead of a stationary Holland, handicapped in raw materials and population; Austria, to which the Spanish Netherlands had passed, was never a serious commercial rival; and France was the enemy Britain had just defeated in both hemispheres.

Nevertheless, it is a mistake to regard the reigns of the first two Georges as a period in which Britain was staking out a kind of advance claim to the benefits of the more rapid technological progress of the following era. Indeed, if a contemporary could have grasped our concept of an impending industrial revolution, he would have seen some good reasons for anticipating its first location elsewhere than on British soil. France, with a population three or four times as great as Britain, continued to have a bigger output in cotton goods and iron; in the building of men-of-war, where interest was equal, French technique was so far superior that a fifty-two-gun French ship was reckoned as practically equal to a British ship of seventy guns. Russia was smelting more iron than Britain, to say nothing of Sweden, then the leading European iron-maker as regards both quantity and quality. Holland was still the main creditor nation and was a great source of British agricultural improvements; and it was, again, from Dutch sources that the Scottish universities mainly derived their progress in medicine and chemistry. Societies for industrial improvement, which had sprung up in London, Birmingham, and Manchester by the middle of the century, had their counterparts in Paris and Hamburg. France vied with Britain in the development of lighter textiles, intended to please sophisticated urban and distant tropical markets, such as those of the Far East. As for total exports, while those of Britain rose from £8 million to £15 million a year between 1720 and 1763, over the longer period 1716–87 the total of French foreign trade increased almost as rapidly as our own.

What were the factors that already marked Britain, rather than any other European country, as the destined first home of the industrial revolution? The answer lies partly in things remote from technology, such as the religious freedom which brought in the Huguenots and other refugees with their numerous arts and encouraged the native Puritan capitalist. There was the confident attitude natural to an island people that had ceased—except for a few breathless weeks in 1745—to reckon seriously with the prospect of invasion. The island possessed a valuable stimulus to trade in its long coastline and frequent navigable rivers: how important the latter were in all questions of inland transportation can be judged by the fact that an army of this period on the Continent was not expected to operate more than fifteen miles from a river bank. Moreover, the Act of Union in 1707 had made Britain into a single economic unit long before any other area of comparable wealth and resources had ceased to be divided by numerous customs barriers. But even with the addition of the Scots, the smallness of the population as compared with the French gave at the same time an important incentive to the use of labour-saving devices.

Lastly, there was the plentifulness and accessibility of coal in the island, where it was used increasingly, as the supply of native timber diminished, for both domestic and industrial purposes; only in the case of iron had the difficulty of applying the new fuel in general restricted output, and that restriction was beginning to disappear. Since 1660 the mines of Britain had been producing five times as much coal as all the rest of the world. What country, then, could hope to rival her in the development of a new form of power which, unlike the water-mill or even the windmill, could be made ubiquitously and unfailingly available, but only to the owner—or purchaser—of coal? The Age of Steam began slowly, but for a century or more its various applications to manufactures, transport, and even agriculture served to enhance a British industrial ascendancy without parallel in the earlier history of the west.

THE PRODUCTION OF FOOD

DOMESTICATION OF ANIMALS

THE transition from food collection to food production, which is characteristic of the Neolithic stage in human history (p. 5), was the result of a fundamental advance—it might almost be said, the fundamental advance—in technology. Every other use which we have learned to make of the material universe depends upon our ability to produce food for a given population by means which do not of themselves entirely exhaust the energy and time of that population. Man as a hunter had no such surplus; it was man the keeper of flocks and herds and cultivator of the soil who first accumulated the surplus that has always been the basis of all civilization. In ancient and modern times alike, the dietary of man the producer has derived both directly from his crops and from the flesh or milk of animals to which, in most cases, he feeds a part of the crops he grows: the proportion of food taken from these two sources varies greatly both between and within different communities. Although this inter-action of crops and herds dates from the Neolithic stage, it will be convenient to consider the domestication of animals first, both because it began a little earlier than agriculture, and, more important, because its main technological history was much earlier completed.

Since domestic animals are a source not merely of food but of industrial materials, means of transport, power resources, and protection for man, it is easy to exaggerate the purposefulness of early contacts. In the eyes of the primitive savage the only valuable animal was a dead one: nevertheless, the taming of some animals by man was a natural result of coexistence. There lived in the same regions of the earth as primitive man animals that were unlikely either to exterminate him or to be exterminated by him. In certain cases, notably the dog and the pig, animals had an interest in attaching themselves to primitive man as scavengers: they found a ready food supply in rejected offal and scraps from carcasses, husks, and fruit skins, and whatever was lost or discarded when man moved on. Conversely, man as a hunter might learn the usefulness of an animal through its unintentional co-operation—the pack of wild dogs driving game within reach or the hind near the camp attracting stags. As for how experiments in domestication are likely to have arisen, the dog is only one particularly good example of the many animals whose young, in the absence of their mother, are easily caught, fairly easily reared, and—to begin with at least—harmless, entertaining, and docile. In the case of the reindeer, where the distinction between wild and tame remains in modern times comparatively small, its early domestication can be attributed to yet another factor: man's natural functions made him a provider of the salt which was lacking in snow-water but available around human settlements.

Whatever tentative steps towards domestication had been taken earlier, particularly as regards the dog, which could be used in the chase, Neolithic agriculture provided the first big inducements to experiment with the taming of other animals on a larger scale. The new settled abodes of mankind made it easier to protect stock and so to derive full benefit from its multiplication. Fallow ground and stubble were good for grazing, and it was not a big step for man to take from the growing of grain for himself to the growing of easy fodder crops for his cattle. In addition to their milk and their flesh, the sheep, the goat, and the ox provided material for clothing, shelter, and containers. From the use of the dog to assist man's legs as a hunter, it was not a very big transition to the use of larger animals to save man's back as a burden-bearer. From general burden-carrying there follows both burden-pulling and the carrying of a special burden—man the rider. All these uses of the domestic animal belong to a remote antiquity; and the same is true indeed of his less work-a-day uses as an object of worship and as a pet, in both of which capacities the cat figured prominently in ancient Egypt, promoted thereto from his original task as a guardian of corn-bins. It is therefore possible to make a single general survey both of the processes of domestication and of the field of animal life which it covers.

The domestication of any particular species of animal must have begun with a phase in which the taming was so casual and partial that interbreeding with the wild form remained common. When the domestic stock became fully separated from the wild and bred within itself, its appearance underwent modification and gave rise to a distinct domestic breed. Hence the distinctive breeds of sheep, cattle, and pigs which Neolithic migrants brought with them into Europe.

Then began the still-continuing phase of conscious control of breeding in the hope, not always fulfilled, of developing the most useful characteristics: the enormous variety of dogs that has been evolved is a striking example of the results of interbreeding within a species. For a time, the object of producing more productive cattle and fiercer watchdogs may have been sought by allowing interbreeding with wild specimens; but it was soon found that dependable qualities of colour and shape, strength and speed, and superior yields of milk, wool, and meat, were mainly to be achieved by the establishment of standard breeds. In the Near East this stage had already been reached 5,000 years ago, and as the differentiation from the wild species of the same animal became more marked, any interbreeding with the latter came to be regarded as a serious disadvantage.

In the final stage, the wild species might dwindle or even disappear. This might be partly the result of changes in environment and food supply, produced naturally or by the works of man, against which the domestic species was protected artificially. Partly also it could be the unplanned consequence of indiscriminate hunting, such as destroyed the millions of bison on the great American plains less than a hundred years ago. There are also a few known instances of deliberate extermination in the interests of the domestic breed, particularly in the case of the highly mobile, and therefore troublesome, wild horse: thus the tarpan was exterminated by the peasants of south-eastern Europe because their mares eloped with the wild stallions. Farther north, the last wild horses in Poland were caught and handed over to the peasants in 1812, while the nomads of Mongolia are said to have absorbed within quite recent years the last tiny herds of wild horse, each only ten or fifteen strong. In our own times the elephant appears to be the only animal which man still uses—though no longer in Europe—as an important beast of burden without the domestic herds having become altogether more important than the wild. In this case, however, the domestic stock is still directly dependent on the wild for replenishment, since the elephant generally fails to breed in captivity.

Cave-remains provide some confirmation for an order of domestication that would seem likely on theoretical grounds. Scavengers came first, for reasons which have already been indicated, and this gives pride of place to the dog, and, in the earliest period, the jackal. Next there is the group of animals which in their wild state carry out a seasonal migration, and which may, therefore, have been brought in some degree into relationship with man while he himself was still a nomad. This group includes the reindeer, the goat, and the sheep. The domestication of cattle, however—which requires, in its initial stages at least, a settled life—belongs certainly to the period of agriculture, when domestication of the earlier species would also have become much more common. This was, too, the period when the honey-bee, which down to modern times provided the main sweetening-agent in man's diet, was first induced to take up its residence in skeps made from the straw of the harvest. The last group is made up of the animals domesticated primarily for transport, including the ass, the horse, and the camel; the horse and the camel seem to have entered man's service last, their use being virtually unrecorded before the second millennium B.C.

But from that time to this the development in this technological instrument has been, in most respects, extraordinarily small. On the one hand, it is difficult to find any big new use of domesticated animals—unless we count as such their ever-increasing importance to modern science for experimental purposes. On the other hand, the range of species chosen for regular domestication seems to have contracted rather than expanded. The rabbit warren on the medieval manor, like the fur-farm of the present day, has not effectively added to the list. On the other hand, in 2500 B.C. the Egyptians apparently made domestic use of such animals as gazelles, ibexes, and antelopes; tamed monkeys; and fed hyenas for the table, like Strasbourg geese. Great progress has, however, been made in modern times in breeding for required purposes, such as the provision of meat, milk, pelts, or tractive power. To this aspect we shall return later (Ch. 24).

ORIGINS OF AGRICULTURE

The cultivation of plants, like the domestication of animals, must undoubtedly have had some accidental beginnings in the camping places of primitive man. Seeds and roots from vegetable spoil which he had gathered and brought home must often, under favourable conditions, have been seen to germinate and sprout; there may sometimes have been a return to see what might have sprung up, as if by magic, at some former camping site. But the systematic cultivation of the soil depended upon an awareness of the processes of nature and their seasons and the choice of a suitable area, such as nature provided in the great river valleys of the Near East, for a more or less deliberate act of social experiment. The result was the securing, save in bad seasons, of a far bigger surplus food-supply than man the food-gatherer or tentative domesticator of animals could have dreamed of—the food-supply which launched the Neolithic revolution.

Agriculture in its simplest forms involves the clearing and breaking-up of not too arid surface soil; the sowing and covering of the seed; destruction of weeds and the conservation or application of water during the growth of the crop; and, after harvesting, the safe storage of the crop and the setting aside of seed for the next season. Virgin soil might be found and used for each crop—the practice known as 'extensive' agriculture—but as soon as it became necessary, or convenient, to till the same ground year after year, deeper cultivation was required to delay exhaustion. Hence the fundamental invention of the plough, though its full development came when men had to wrestle with the heavy soils of northern Europe. In Mesopotamia and Egypt the most important problem was that of supplying the soil with water.

Though tillage and irrigation were arts in which man developed his new technical skill, what had to come first was the choice of plants on which to practise them. A list of those used in prehistoric Europe is astonishingly varied, including industrial as well as food plants, and among the latter are a good many varieties that are nowadays ignored. Green and root vegetables are too perishable to leave many traces in the archaeological record, but their quick growth makes it tolerably certain that they were cultivated early. Fruit, which takes several seasons to become established, is likely to have been cultivated rather late, but evidence of figs, apples, pears, and small plums is to be found at late-Neolithic sites in Europe. Nuts had certainly been important as a gathered food from the very earliest days: the walnut was brought into northern Europe from southern climates such as that of Greece, where it was first cultivated on a large scale. In the hazel-nut we have an example of a tree of which the fruit has been eaten since Mesolithic times at latest, but which has even now barely entered the stage of cultivation. With nuts may be grouped the oil-bearing seeds, ranging from those of flax and the opium poppy and the sesame of ancient Mesopotamia to the olive-tree, which spread from the eastern shores of the Mediterranean to make its home also in Greece, Italy, the south of France, and Spain. The cultivation of oil-producing plants became especially important because it provided mankind with a far larger supply of oils and fats —indispensable as a foodstuff and highly valuable also for certain industries and as an illuminant—than could possibly be produced through the domestication of animals.

There remain the two great stand-bys of man's larder, the pulses and the cereals. Both crops are easy to cultivate and easy to store; if the spread of the pulses may be connected with the fact that this is of all the crop-plants the one with the largest number of species, the cereals present a picture of few species very widely distributed. Beans, peas, and lentils have all been cultivated in Europe from Neolithic times, and pulses, particularly in the form of the soya bean, continue to provide the main protein food for whole populations in the East today. But cereals have become the most important crop of all, and it is therefore of interest that a primitive type of wheat and two-row barley are both found at one of the earliest agricultural sites—Jarmo, in north-eastern Iraq—in a Neolithic deposit dated at about 5000 B.C. The six-row type of barley came later, from the Far East, but both forms of barley entered Europe together, along with primitive types of wheat. Rye, a common weed of the wheat field, largely took the place of wheat in the north when a worsening of the climate at the end of the Bronze Age drove the wheat southwards. Weed is a relative term, however: the stomach-contents of an Iron Age man, whose body was preserved in a Danish bog for 2,000 years, show that he had eaten at least a dozen of our commoner weeds, some of which were once cultivated and all of which may well have served to make his cereal porridge less monotonous in taste and more nourishing in content. Oats are native to Europe, and in northern regions climatic conditions render them the most dependable cereal crop. This is a fundamental factor determining local patterns of agriculture, since farmers grew what experience had shown to be best suited to their particular soil and climate: other requirements were imported, as trade routes permitted, from regions more favourable to their production.

There is the same uncertain dividing-line between weeds and useful plants in the case of industrial crops. Flax, cultivated originally for its linseed oil, was being grown for textile use in both Mesopotamia and the Nile valley by about 3000 B.C. We think less readily of the part which the nettle played as a fibre plant, though in fact nettle-cloth was still being made in Europe at the time of the First World War.

Cultivation proceeded for a long time by trial and error, many kinds of crop and different methods of growing it being tried until the few best came very slowly to predominate. The establishment of regular crops produced the first big surplus; the surplus in turn gave rise to the specialist (p. 6); the existence of the specialist to the specialization of agricultural tools.

There is a sense in which agricultural implements precede agriculture. Thus the reaping knife or sickle was developed originally for the cutting of wild grasses. In Mesopotamia it was made of baked clay; in Europe the most primitive form had handles made of antlers, grooved to take overlapping flint flakes; but the commonest

FIG. 11. Egyptian land reclamation, from a tomb at Thebes, *c.* 1420 B.C.

form, as we might expect, had a short wooden handle holding either flint teeth or a single sharp piece of flint. Moreover, the ground and polished stone celts—the axes and adzes of flint and other stones that are characteristic of the Neolithic stage—had their place in a hunting economy as well as in an agricultural one. The improved axe, with which the farmer began his long task of clearing the European forests, must also have helped in the chase. The adze, which we think of as a wood-working tool, was used by early cultivators also as a hoe.

The course of development can be traced most clearly in Egypt (Fig. 11). In the earliest times the ground was roughly tilled with a hooked branch of wood, but a two-man hoe became a plough, with one man pulling on a rope or thong in front, while the other pressed the point of the hoe into the ground behind. The deeper the ploughing, the slower the exhaustion of the soil. When the pull came to be provided by oxen, handles were introduced so as to drive the point properly into the ground, though it still had to be broken up in advance by hoe or mallet. In the second millennium B.C., however, a stronger ploughshare of wood or stone came into use, and a double yoke passing over the horns of the oxen was bound firmly to the shaft; this gave a very much more powerful tool. Seed was often sown broadcast in front of the plough, which covered it, or was trodden into the newly made furrows by sheep or goats driven over the field; flax, however, was sown carefully along the furrows to make the pulling easier at harvest-time. As for the harvesting implement, the straight reaping-stick developed into a rounder and sharper sickle of copper or bronze.

IRRIGATION

The methods of early agriculture might be dismissed as being mainly of archaeological interest, were it not for the advanced techniques that were developed in the great river valleys to feed water to

the crops. It is possible that man as a food-gatherer early learned to encourage the growth of wild plants by splashing water on to the banks of a spring or stream; it is certain that the shaduf, still widely used, was being employed to water the date palms and vines, the vegetable plots and flower beds of the Egyptians in the second millennium B.C.

FIG. 12. Irrigation by shaduf in Egypt, from a tomb at Thebes, c. 1500 B.C.

The shaduf (Fig. 12) is usually made by erecting two pillars, some 5 ft or more high, joined near the top by a short beam. Over this a long pole is balanced, which has at one end a vessel to hold water and at the other a counterpoise. A man standing at the water's edge fills the receptacle by dipping, raises it, and empties it into an irrigation channel. With this device a man can raise about 600 gallons to a height of 6 ft in a day. Rather later, shadufs were arranged in series, of which all except the first dipped into a trough filled by the preceding shaduf. Their first serious rival was perhaps a continuous chain of buckets—such as was apparently used to raise water from a well beneath the famous Hanging Gardens of Babylon. The ox-driven water-wheel, which can irrigate half an acre a day, is not known to have been in existence before c. 200 B.C., when the use of gearing to link a vertical shaft to that of a horizontal wheel became established.

Men must have dug for water in early times as the bedouin still dig in Arabia, deepening a hole in a likely place until either the water is found or patience is exhausted. For a permanent water-hole there

would be a lining of rough stone or other hard material and probably
a rope and tackle erected over the mouth of the well, so that the
water could be drawn by a downward haul. Since 1500 B.C. at latest,
such tackle—and the shaduf—has often been equipped with a simple
pulley. Wells in the wadis were not usually more than 15 ft deep;
in cities they often went deeper, and at Nimrud excavation of the
Assyrian palace of the ninth century B.C. has revealed a well, still
holding water, more than 300 brick courses deep. But it seems likely
that deep wells were first dug by percussion drilling when the ancient
Egyptians, in their efforts to exploit the desert oases, discovered the
possibility of making an artesian well; that is, one in which the water
is forced upwards from a deep bore-hole by its own pressure.

The conservation of water by damming occasioned some of the
earliest of the surviving large-scale works of man. The Orontes
valley in Syria has a stone dyke 1¼ miles long, dating from about
the year 1300 B.C.; an Assyrian dam above Nineveh still stands in
part at a height of nearly 10 feet. There are also innumerable remains of cement-lined tanks and stone cisterns used for storing
water, including cisterns hollowed underground in the rock to
diminish evaporation, not to mention traces of vast engineering
structures, such as aqueducts and underground conduits of stone or
baked clay, which brought water to the cities (p. 163), often from considerable distances.

In Egypt and Mesopotamia alike the main problem of settlement in the great valleys was irrigation. The annual rise of the Nile
between July and September is an event at once so punctual and of
such paramount importance that the making of the relevant calculations as to date and height were two technical functions which
largely gave the priesthood its power. Menes, the legendary first
pharaoh, is supposed to have dammed the Nile; history, however,
cannot identify the moment at which man first attempted to retain the life-giving waters with a barrier of stone and mud. The
system that evolved was the division of the cultivable area of the
valley into rectangular basins of between 1,000 and 40,000 acres
apiece, which were fed with water from the annual inundation by a
system of sluices. Each of them in turn was flooded to a depth of
from 3 to 6 ft, the water being held for a month or more to saturate
the soil, after which the surplus was drained off to a lower level and
returned eventually to the Nile. Areas to which the flood water would
not flow naturally were fed by a system of canals.

The Tigris and Euphrates presented a different problem from the Nile, requiring a different solution. Their flooding is both dangerous and irregular; the Tigris rises before the Euphrates, which carries twice as much water and recedes more rapidly; and between them they carry five times as much sediment as the Nile, which choked the canals. Moreover, the flood ends at the beginning of the hot season, so that it is not enough to soak the ground thoroughly once, as in the Nile valley. Agriculture depended therefore upon a system of constant irrigation.

The lower valleys of the Tigris and the Euphrates were inter-sected by a series of large canals, the most famous of which, the Nahrwan, was 400 ft wide and probably more than 200 miles long. From them the water passed through feeder-canals into a network of smaller water channels and irrigation ditches, and from these last a trickle of water would be run into a single plot at a time. To main-tain a flow through the system the main canal must have had its water-level a little above the general level of the land, and its flow must have been so regulated that it would neither wear away the banks through excessive speed nor become choked with silt and weeds as a result of sluggishness. At their heads, the canals depended upon great brick-built barrages and river weirs. Besides the use of brick and of reed-matting to strengthen banks of alluvial mud, the main requirement for constructing this vast irrigation system was a mass of workers equipped with picks and shovels. The countryside there-fore flourished when a strong ruler like Hammurabi could compel each district to carry out its due share of such work, as his letters show he did, and the laws enforced a meticulous respect for the irrigation rights on which the value of the closely-defined landed property depended: Herodotus reports that, though it might sound incredible, the Babylonian farmer commonly obtained a yield of 200- and sometimes 300-fold on his corn. But a water system so elaborate and so rewarding was also extremely vulnerable: it is said that the Land of the Two Rivers has not yet recovered from the dis-repair into which the canals fell during the Mongol invasions of the thirteenth and fourteenth centuries A.D.

GROWTH OF TILLAGE IN EUROPE

Irrigation was the dominant factor in the agriculture of Mesopo-tamia and Egypt: the rivers, when properly controlled, provided the necessary moisture and even carried deposits of rich new soil, which kept the land in good heart. The Romans, too, practised irrigation on a large scale in Algeria, as the Arabs did later in Spain and Sicily, when they introduced rice, cotton, and the sugar-cane. But the Mediterranean area as a whole, and still more the heavy soils of northern Europe, required the application of quite different agricultural techniques.

Such countries as Greece and Italy have in the main light soil, torrential rivers, and a climate that combines regular drought in summer with short but heavy winter rains, which tend to wash essential plant nutrients out of the soil. Stock-raising land is scarce,

FIG. 13. Greek plough, from a cup, sixth century B.C.

so that soil fertility cannot readily be replenished with animal manure. The average crop yield in Roman times was not more than about fourfold, and to obtain this the land had to be left fallow in alternate years and pulverized before every crop. If labour costs permitted, the ground was dug, and in any case there were at least three ploughings—successively at right angles to each other and sometimes obliquely. It has been calculated that this method of preparing the ground doubled the quantity of moisture retained in the dry summer months.

The Greeks and Romans used a light plough (Fig. 13), consisting of a pole to which the draught animals were attached; a curved beam joining the pole to the stock, which lay horizontally along the ground; and a single-handled stilt fixed at the plough-tail to guide it. The vulnerable part was the stock, which divided the soil and passed along the furrow. This was commonly made of oak, and its sides were sometimes protected by the insertion of pebbles into holes in the wood; but it was more important to protect the cutting-point with a suitably hard shoe or share. The Egyptians are believed to have used flint for this purpose but not, apparently, copper or bronze; the earliest iron ploughshares have been found in Palestine and date from the end of the second millennium B.C. Rather surprisingly, no iron shares have been traced to Hellenic sources, but they were widely used among the Romans, who had both a socketed and a less common tanged-spearhead type; they came to Britain in advance of Caesar.

The expansion of the Roman empire coincided with the climax of ancient Mediterranean agricultural technology, when advanced methods with better tools were being employed first on some of the great slave-worked estates and subsequently spread over the empire by tenant farmers. These advanced methods included a special attention to drainage, both to check the washing-away of valuable soil constituents in the rainy season and to render more cultivable such marshy areas as the Campagna or the Po valley. The Romans were, therefore, well able to organize the drainage of waterlogged areas in northern conquests like Holland and eastern Britain, where the main problem was not that of water conservation, as required in a region of low rainfall, but that of the inconveniences caused by abundant and irregular rains. The ploughing that was needed, however, was of a different kind from that suitable for the Mediterranean.

In the north, pulverization might ruin the ground; the proper object there was succinctly defined by James Small in 1784 as being 'to cut a slice of soil, to move it to one side, to turn it over'. Roman ploughs were, indeed, sometimes fitted with projecting ground-rests, which pushed the loosened sod aside, or with a large iron coulter, which was wedged into a slot in the plough-beam and made a vertical cut, in contradistinction to the horizontal cut of the share. Nevertheless, there are finds in northern Europe, which may be pre-Roman, to suggest that the heavy plough was developed independently in the north to suit the needs of the heavy land which such peoples as the Belgae had set themselves to wrest from the primeval forest. Its characteristic features include a heavy square frame with plough-beam above and share-beam below, joined by a stilt at the back and by a brace or sheet immediately behind the share. A disputed passage in Pliny appears to state that a pair of wheels to support the beam was first introduced in the country south of the upper Danube and was in his day used also in Cisalpine Gaul. But the wheeled plough seems still to have been largely confined, even a millennium later, to the heavy clay soils won back from the forests, and has never completely ousted the swing plough: in 1523 Fitzherbert noted the greater cost of 'the ploughs that go with wheels'. Another very important innovation in Europe from the eleventh century onwards was a device that the Chinese appear to have adopted in an improved form 2,000 years before. This was the use of a mould-board of curved wood (Fig. 14) to overturn the sliced sod, which was often too heavy to be turned merely by the strength of the ploughman's arms. The shape varied greatly according to the nature of the soil and the crop to be grown in it.

In England, horses were little used in ploughing until the sixteenth century. Teams of eight oxen were a unit of reckoning rather

FIG. 14. Early fourteenth-century plough with mould-board, from an English Bible manuscript

than an instrument of regular agricultural practice, and it was the four-ox team with ploughman and driver—the latter walking backwards in front of the team, plying his long goad—which slowly subdued the heavy lands of southern Britain. The process was effectively begun under the influence of the demands of the Roman corn-market, acquired a new impetus in the later Saxon centuries, and had been in the main completed by about 1300.

As regards other farm equipment, the influence of the Romans was strong, especially on the estates of the Church, which inherited their practice of repeated working of the soil. The Romans had harrows, developed from a frame of thorn branches. They were used first to tear out weeds, later for covering the seed, and in the Middle Ages to break up difficult ground and to supplement the work of the plough; much clod-crushing was also done with mallets. Rollers for improving the tilth were not used, except in a form of harrow consisting of a cylinder of wood fitted with iron spikes. Wooden rakes were common in the Middle Ages, and from Roman times there were iron-shod wooden spades and iron picks and forks. A more important consequence of the use of iron was the development in succession of a balanced sickle, a short-handled scythe, and then the long scythe, which by the twelfth century already had the handle of the modern type. There was a striking difference from modern manual methods in the common habit of cutting corn near the top; Pliny even tells of a machine reaper, which worked on the principle of pushing a large comb and container breast-high into the corn.

The grain was separated from the ears by threshing with the hooves of animals, or with a board studded with flints, or with the jointed flail, which is first mentioned by St Jerome in the early fifth century A.D. The chaff was then removed by means of a winnowing fan, which was not originally a draught-making implement but the basket in which the grain was shaken. Four other items of farming equipment, which have scarcely changed since medieval, and indeed Roman, times are the hurdles of the sheep-fold; small drying kilns for corn that had been harvested unripe or wet; single-handed sheep shears; and the wooden ladder.

PREPARATION OF FOOD AND DRINK

The history of technology is concerned not only with the growth of foodstuffs but with the subsequent processes of preparation, to which mankind has devoted increasing ingenuity and skill. Under the early civilizations the diet of the masses came very largely from cereals or pulses, varied to some extent with fish (p. 62): the flesh of animals was beyond the means of the poor save for special occasions. Animal foods are nowadays more important: a large proportion of our cereals therefore goes in fodder. But the economy of Rome, for instance, depended upon the cheap import of wheat by sea, and the population—in the time of Augustus, nearly one million—lived mainly upon a poor-quality flour which came from wheat that had been coarsely ground and sifted, and not very thoroughly cleaned.

Pounding the grain to get rid of the husks and then grinding the kernels to make flour were originally processes carried on separately in every household. Pestle and mortar gave place to the saddle-quern, used by the Egyptian housewife 4,000 years ago (Fig. 15). The second stage in the development of the quern, commonly met with in classical Greece, was the so-called pushing mill, in which both stones were flat and grooved, and grain was fed from a hollow in the upper surface of the top stone through a slit on to the grinding surfaces below. Then came the rotary hand-mill, one of the first important new uses of the principle of rotary motion since the potter's wheel (p. 76). A handle rotated the upper stone, which was perforated in the centre to admit the corn and had a wooden or iron bridge fixed across the perforation, so as to transfer the weight of the upper stone to a spindle fixed in the middle of the lower one.

These rotary querns came to Rome from the Near East, and are associated with the growth of the class of professional millers, but their spread was a result of the fact that the armies of Rome were accustomed to grind their own corn, every group of ten men being provided with a mill. Larger mills were known as donkey-mills, from one common source of animal

FIG. 15. An early form of saddle-quern, Egypt, c. 2500 B.C.

power; their survival at Pompeii suggests that they were a regular feature of urban civilization, and it was not until the fourth century A.D. that water-mills began to take their place (p. 251).

The empires of the Near East and the Mediterranean made great use of the fig, the olive, and the grape: the plants which bear them take some years to come into full bearing, but their deep, widespread roots tap the subsoil moisture, which enables them to withstand drought, and they crop plentifully for many years. The fig-tree, indeed, may bear two or three crops a year, and was always a staple food for the poorer classes, including slaves. The olive was the main source of oil for all classes: indeed, the word 'oil' is believed to have come, through the Latin and Greek, from the ancient Semitic word for olive oil. Oils or fats from animal sources came to predominate in northern Europe, however, where the olive will not flourish and the expensive importation of olive oil was largely confined to ecclesiastical requirements. There were two main processes in preparing the oil. The first separated the pulp from the kernel without crushing the latter, for which purpose the Romans used an oil-mill —two cylindrical stones turning on a central pivot with a sufficient (variable) clearance to separate the pulp from the olives spread evenly in a flat trough below. The second process was the extraction of the juice from the pulp, which in the earliest times was done simply by twisting the top of a porous bag so as to squeeze its contents. In the last millennium B.C. the principle of the lever was brought into use, weights of all kinds being attached at the loose end of a hinged beam so as to extract the juice from pulp which lay in a bag under the beam (Fig. 16). Pliny knew of four types of presses, worked by beams which might be as much as 50 feet long, or by screws. The screw principle, associated with Archimedes, was

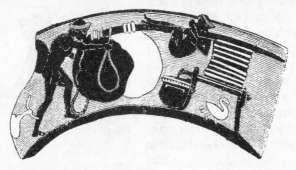

FIG. 16. Simple beam-press for olives and grapes, from a Greek vase of the sixth century B.C.

applied first to force down the beam, and a little later to work directly on the top of a press.

The press was used also for the grape, but the initial processes of viticulture were much more elaborate than those of growing the olive-tree. It was an art which came to Greece from the Near East, but one which the Greeks raised to its full height. The wine which they exported westwards was a determining factor in the growth of Celtic culture, and it is claimed that Hellenistic culture spread eastwards precisely as far as the vine would grow. In Greek vineyards the plants lay generally along the ground, their growth helped by careful hoeing, the pruning of unnecessary leaves during the summer, and an occasional use of green manure. In September the baskets of grapes were brought in to be trodden on cement or wooden floors, the first product—especially the juice squeezed from the grapes by their own weight—being the best. It was the second yield and quality of grape juice that was extracted by the press. The must was then stored for six months to ferment in huge pottery vessels, the type of the so-called tub in which Diogenes made his home. These vats were smeared inside and out with resin, which gave a characteristic tang to the liquid that was taken from them, and finally filtered into amphorae for sale. Greek wines remained the best, though for quantity—running up to 1,600 to 1,700 gallons an acre —Italy became for a time the chief centre of the industry, followed by Spain. The Romans propped or trellised their vines, and took much trouble to vary the conditions of fermentation for different types of grape and to modify the flavour. But the biggest change was the introduction of the wooden cask with metal hoops, which came to Italy from the Celts about the beginning of our era, for barrelled wine kept much better than that in clay-stoppered amphorae. In return, the Romans established vine-growing in France, the Rhineland, and even southern Britain.

The vineyard, like many of the amenities of life, made but a slow recovery from the Dark Ages. A revival began about the time of Charlemagne, helped by the desire to have wine available for ritual use and for medical purposes. In the absence of sugar, grape-must was valued as a sweetening-agent where honey was scarce, and viticulture was promoted by the great monasteries; by the end of the twelfth century vineyards were being planted as far to the east as the valley of the Oder.

The preparation of malt to produce a fermented drink from corn was a common practice in the early empires: the Sumerians, for example, listed nineteen types of beer. The Greeks and Romans, however, regarded it as a barbarian drink characteristic of the Celts and, later, of the Germans: it was the latter who, by the thirteenth century A.D., had introduced the modern type of beer, flavoured and preserved with hops, which were not grown in England until about 1400. There was no other major innovation in brewing until the introduction of porter early in the eighteenth century. Perry and cider were made at an early date from wild fruit, but cider-making from improved apples spread from Normandy to England in the thirteenth century, providing country districts with a drink which made no inroads upon valuable supplies of grain.

Alchemists were familiar with the process of distillation (p. 262) at least as early as the first century A.D., but a thousand years seem to have elapsed before it was applied to the preparation of strong potable spirits. A consequence of this development was the preparation of liqueurs, often a product of monastic herb-gardens, which acquired a new importance in the time of the Black Death (1348), when physicians are said to have commonly prescribed strong alcoholic drinks, perhaps for psychological rather than purely physical reasons. Hence came the distilling of gin with the juniper berry, brandy distilled from wine, and finally the much cheaper *aqua vitae*, 'the water of life'. This name seems to have meant originally almost pure alcohol, but was later attached to the brandy made from yeast-fermented barley, which in the fifteenth century became the characteristic and all-too-familiar means of alleviating the northern winter. Regulations against the abuse of strong drink testify to the existence of a serious social problem even before 1300.

Literature, before the days of the modern realistic novel, had little to say about the diet of the masses. It seems clear, however, that in the earlier Middle Ages it continued to be farinaceous and dull and was varied more often by fish than by meat. But from the thirteenth century onwards town workers, at least, had more frequent access to meat and other supplements to starchy foods. The introduction of a more varied diet must have helped to diminish the incidence of diseases, such as rickets and scurvy, which arise not from lack of food but from the absence of essential elements (vitamins) for maintaining health: such deficiency diseases were, indeed, rife among all classes. Where rye was the staple cereal, fearful plagues of ergotism occurred in hot, damp seasons which favoured the infestation of the crop by a poisonous mould: in 994, for example, 40,000 people are said to have died from this cause in Aquitaine alone, and as late as the eighteenth century there were two severe outbreaks within six years.

FISHERIES

Fishing is the most important of the food-gathering techniques which still survive from the very earliest days, and the methods employed are in principle unchanged. Direct attack by hand and spear was probably tried first; then, perhaps, the use of a fixed trap and experiments with different kinds of bait; next, the baited line, made more effective by the addition of a thorn or bone hook; and finally, the mobile trap or net, appropriate to deep water and able to contain large hauls of fish. But even the net is believed to have been in use during the Mesolithic stage. The pioneer ventures of man as a boat-maker and as a seafarer were both influenced by the search for fish, though in some regions freshwater supplies secured from the bank of river or lake may have sufficed for a thin and scattered population.

The usefulness of fish as a food is limited by the fact that its flesh rapidly decomposes. In the earliest days, therefore, it was normally eaten soon after it was caught, except where it could be naturally preserved by frost. But drying, salting, and smoking of fish were all practised in the Bronze Age, and when civilization began, fish became an important article of commerce, traded by primitive peoples for manufactures. The Phoenicians and Greeks ate much salt fish,

FIG. 17. Fish-traps in mill-pond supplying overshot water-wheel,
from the Luttrell Psalter, c. 1338

especially tunny, from the Black Sea and the mouths of the Russian rivers, while the Romans imported supplies from Spain and Egypt and even from northern Europe. The Carthaginians, who preceded the Romans in the Atlantic coastal waters, went there in search of seals and whales as well as fish; but it is possible that, at least until the Middle Ages, the meat, oil, and bones of the whale became available most commonly as the result of stranding. The Faroese still have a system of hunting small whales by driving them ashore.

Fisheries developed rapidly during the Middle Ages. The fast-days—Wednesdays, Fridays, and the season of Lent—gave the upper classes, including the members of the influential and widespread monastic orders, a keen interest in the supply of fresh fish: salmon-weirs and other fish-traps (Fig. 17) and carefully stocked fish-ponds therefore abounded. The lower classes could, of course, fast without fish, but from the twelfth century onwards the growth of towns beyond the capacity of a local food supply made it imperative to find cheap food imports which were readily transportable. The solution was the large-scale harvesting of herring and cod, which are not Mediterranean fishes but teem in northern waters, and their exchange for minimum supplies of corn (to the far north) and urban manufactures.

The herring, which feeds mainly on plankton and lives in shoals near the surface of the water, makes an annual migration southwards through the shallow North Sea but is much less predictable in its choice of a coastal region for spawning. Since the fish in prime condition is 70 per cent edible, its value has long been recognized: Yarmouth, for example, was already famous for its herring-fishery in the sixth century A.D. But until near the close of the Middle Ages the biggest seasonal fishery was off the coast of Scania at the entrance to the Baltic. This reached its height in 1275–1350, when the international distribution of the catch provided the merchants of the Hanseatic League with a remarkably profitable monopoly, since the salted product remained in good condition for twelve months, provided the gutting of the catch was prompt and complete and the packing sufficiently careful. The barrels were filled in two stages, to allow for the shrinkage of the fish during the first ten days; the layers of salt with which the fish were interspersed had to be large enough to saturate the flesh; and the barrels were finally rendered as airtight as possible to prevent the oil in the flesh from turning rancid. In a good year about 13,000 tons were processed, involving the use of some 2,400 tons of salt, some of which came from nearby Lüneburg but most from the great French saltpans in the Bay of Bourgneuf.

From about 1400 the control of the Hanse was challenged with increasing success by the Dutch. A Dutchman, William Beukelszoon, had recently made some improvement, how fundamental is not known, in the accepted method of preparing the fish for salting; a more definite factor was the desertion of Scania by the herring shoals throughout the long period 1588–1748, so that the main fishery was in the North Sea, where the Dutch easily outmatched English and Scottish rivals. In 1416 they introduced drift-nets, 50 to 60 fathoms long, which are towed along at night, when the shoals may be detected by their luminosity; the net resembles an enormous curtain, the size of the mesh being such that the fish are trapped by the gills as they attempt to swim through. The Dutch also replaced the open boats used for coastal fishing by decked vessels of as much as 100 tons having two or three masts; these 'busses' (Fig. 18) carried salters and coopers in their crew, so that the catch could be packed at sea. By 1620 there were believed to be 2,000 such ships exploiting 'the Dutch gold mine' off the English coast. This was a potent cause of the three Anglo-Dutch wars of that century, but as

late as 1805 an English commercial writer was still proclaiming the
desirability of capturing the fishery from the Dutch.

The principal European cod-fishery was, and is, off the Lofoten
Islands in north Norway, where the cod, which live off other fishes
on the sea-bottom, came inshore for a brief annual season to spawn

Fig. 18. Dutch herring-busses, 1792

and were caught with hook and line. The fishermen gutted and split
the fish, which were then spread on the rocks or hung on lines to dry.
The result was a leathery but non-perishable product, which could
be stacked in open boats for dispatch to Bergen, where the Hanseatic
merchants established a second monopoly, which lasted until the
middle of the sixteenth century. The name 'stockfish' is of Dutch
origin, but there were big sales as far south as Italy.

John Cabot's voyage of 1497 advertised a larger source of supply
on the great banks off the coast of Newfoundland, which quickly
attracted fishing fleets from England, France, Portugal, and Holland,

and later gave New England its first major export. Profits were increased by the introduction of a type of line which could be baited with as many as 5,000 hooks, and Newfoundland itself was valued chiefly as a seasonal fishing base and place to dry the catch. The French, however, having a plentiful supply of cheap salt, salted much cod on board ship, and kept their position in a trade which, like the herring-fishery, was nursed by governments throughout the period of mercantilism, not so much to secure the food supply of the people as to secure a reserve of seamen for their war fleets.

EFFECTS OF THE GEOGRAPHICAL DISCOVERIES

The era of the geographical discoveries brought about a transplantation of crops in both directions—from Europe as well as into it—and a modification of diet, taste, and habit, which became fully effective only with the development of modern means of transportation in later centuries. Pride of place must be given to the potato, which had been cultivated in South America for at least 2,000 years before its conquest by the Spaniards, who first introduced the plant to Europe in or before the year 1570. It was probably first brought to England independently, though not by Sir Walter Raleigh. From England it reached Ireland, though we cannot exclude the possibility that it came direct, as it figured among the plunder from Spanish ships wrecked along the coast of Connaught. The English in turn introduced it to Virginia, where it was originally called 'the Irish potato' to distinguish it from the sweet potato. In the eighteenth century the potato began to be used commonly for the preparation of alcohol by fermentation. But its spread as a foodstuff was the direct product of necessity: it became staple diet in Ireland during the seventeenth century. In the rest of Britain, and in France, it was not much used before the late eighteenth century, when Britain needed it to feed a growing industrial population. In Prussia its use was commanded by Frederick the Great, but in central and northern Europe as a whole the potato did not become one of the main crops until the nineteenth century. Maize, or Indian corn, was also brought at an early date to Europe. Magellan is believed to have spread its use to the Philippines and the East Indies, and the Portuguese also took it to West Africa, where it was apparently first grown for ships' stores for slavers. It was not adapted to the climate of northern Europe, but flourished in the south-east, where maize porridge quickly became a staple food.

In the reverse direction, sugar and rice were the two most important food crops introduced by Europeans to American soil. The latter, requiring a hot climate and irrigation, had been brought by the Muslims to Spain in the eighth century, whence its cultivation spread to Italy, and from there in turn it was transplanted to South Carolina about 1700. Sugar (an Arabic word) had a rather similar early history, but in the later Middle Ages its importation from the Near East had been an increasingly important feature of Genoese and Venetian trade, though the cane itself was also grown in Spain and Sicily. It was taken to the New World on Columbus's second voyage, but large-scale cultivation became common in the middle of the seventeenth century, when slave-owning planters in the French and British West Indian islands copied the methods and appliances of the Dutch. By 1700 sugar could be bought in England at 6*d*. a pound; honey had finally lost its pre-eminence as a sweetening agent, which dated from time immemorial (p. 48).

The raw sugar was made in West Indian factories, where the pieces of sugar-cane were crushed in a roller-mill, which might be worked by wind- or water-power. There were then successive boilings, in which the juice was reduced to a syrup and the scum and dirt removed at intervals. This finally produced a solution so concentrated that it would crystallize on cooling; the syrup or molasses from which the crystals separated provided the basis for the manufacture of rum by fermentation and distillation. The further refining of the sugar was done in Europe, a solution of the unrefined product being boiled in a mixture containing lime-water and blood until it became completely clear. After being filtered through cloth and concentrated by evaporation, it was allowed to crystallize in pottery moulds, which gave it the characteristic sugar-loaf shape.

Tea, coffee, and cocoa have never been grown in Europe. The first-named belongs to China, the last to the New World. The stimulating qualities of coffee, however, appear to have become first known in Ethiopia in 1450. It spread via Aden to the Mohammedan world, and thence to the Christian, reaching Paris in 1643 and Oxford in 1650. The strong influence which coffee-houses soon exercised upon society and politics illustrates the far-reaching consequences of minor innovations. The Dutch took coffee shrubs successively to Java, Guiana, and finally Brazil. In the course of the eighteenth century, tea—first shipped to Europe, so far as is known, by the Dutch East India Company in 1609—became a drink familiar to all classes in England, as coffee did in other European countries. The vogue of drinking-chocolate, however, depended upon the plentifulness of sugar, for it was unpalatable if drunk unsweetened. Although a slab form of chocolate suitable for eating was known in Spain as early as 1520, its popularity as a cheap and convenient eatable in Britain dates at the earliest from Gladstone's free-trade budget of 1853.

Tobacco likewise came from the New World, and was indeed offered to Columbus on his first landing. It was first used in Europe as a medicine, in the belief that the natives of Brazil employed it to 'carry off the superfluous humours of the brain'. It was being cultivated in Europe as a cash crop by the end of the sixteenth century—in Spain in 1558, and in Gloucestershire by emigrants returned from Virginia in 1586. Although the growth spread from Europe to Turkey and the Near East, the main line of development was that which began when seeds from Spanish-American plantations were brought to Virginia in 1612. Powdered tobacco was brought to Portugal for snuff-taking in 1558, and an important sale developed. The making of tobacco and snuff involved no new developments in technology, but their prominence in the Stuart and Hanoverian scene runs parallel with the increasing use of spirits. Much *aqua vitae* was made from fermented corn; gin crossed from Holland to Britain; wines were commonly fortified with brandy; and whisky distilled from Irish and Scottish barley became an important feature of English sideboards. Hence there arose a widespread interest in distillation apparatus.

Trans-oceanic produce, however, did not for a long time replace the staple cereals of Europe, where flour-milling was a major industry, employing both water- and wind-power. Although the basic principles of the milling process remained unchanged—that is to say, grinding between a fixed and a rotating stone—there were many refinements of detail. The grooves, incised in both stones, were a key feature, since they both cut and ventilated the meal as it passed out to the circumference, and various characteristic patterns were evolved (Fig. 19). The dressing of stones was done either by the miller or by a skilled itinerant craftsman, and the stones themselves were often brought from remote sources, their texture being of the first importance. Thus some English stones came from Andernach on the Rhine, and French stones were even exported to America. Mills were numerous and correspondingly small, each serving its own locality, since before the industrial revolution there was no strong inducement to transport grain long distances for grinding.

Printing soon produced the cookery book, which must have tended to standardize the way in which food was eaten as well as the way in which it was cooked. The sixteenth century saw the use of the spoon established; the seventeenth, the use of the three- or four-pronged fork to convey food to the mouth, its two-pronged late-

FIG. 19. Dressing millstones by hand. Insets show some traditional designs. (A) Late Roman; (B) eighteenth century; (C), (D), and (E) nineteenth century; (F) and (G) right-handed and left-handed stones in 'four-quarter' dress

medieval prototype having been used mainly for serving. Individual receptacles for food and drink also became customary, with a consequent growth in the pewter, pottery, and glass industries: to drink from a glass became common among the well-to-do about 1650. As regards kitchen equipment, the most important improvement was in the roasting spit. This was turned by the pull of a weight, by clockwork, by a dog in a 'dog-drum' (a kind of treadmill which survived into the nineteenth century), and even by means of power from a fan turned by the hot air rising in the vast kitchen chimney.

PROGRESS OF AGRICULTURE, *c.* A.D. 1500–1750

Agricultural progress in Europe was extremely uneven. The superior diet of the English and Dutch, denounced by their neighbours as gluttons, corresponded to a superior technique. Germany required a century or more after the ending of the Thirty Years War in 1648 to restore her agriculture to the prosperity it had had at the close of the Middle Ages: the real wages of a German in 1700 are said to have been about one-half of those of 1500. The two principal developments were that sheep took the place of pigs as the forest area gradually declined, and that the introduction of winter fodder for cattle, a practice which came from Italy via Flanders, enabled more stock to be kept through the winter. The soil of France as a whole was less well cultivated than might be supposed from the glorification of the farmer by the eighteenth-century physiocrats. Except for intensive small-scale farming round Paris and in the west and north-west, France remained a country of medieval rotations of crops, unselected animals, and old-fashioned implements. The Netherlanders, on the other hand, imported the corn supply for what was then the most densely populated region in Europe, while they themselves grew barley and hops for brewing, tobacco, and a variety of industrial crops (part of which was exported), and were already famous for their market gardens, fruit-trees, and bulbs. Apart from the winning of new land from the sea, to be considered in a moment, their secret was the careful husbanding of small portions of ground—there was even a complicated nine-year cycle of crops— and the regular application of fertilizers obtained from stock-keeping and from industrial and general urban refuse.

In England the sixteenth century had seen the rise of market gardens and of an important, but empirical, agricultural literature. Nevertheless, it is noteworthy that even the efforts of the Royal Society did not produce any general change in crops or agricultural methods, although the improvement of arts and industries was one of its principal objects and a Georgical Committee was set up to investigate agricultural practices within two years of the Society receiving its first royal charter in 1662. The later seventeenth century also witnessed a great investment of commercial profits in landed estates, and a better balance established between corn growing and wool production. This prepared the way for the work of such pioneers as Jethro Tull, Charles Townshend, and Robert Bakewell, who brought in improved practices and useful new crops from abroad, including the turnip as a field crop from the Netherlands and clover from Spain. Where the English excelled was in the fact that their social system gave the improving landlord, who had the capital with which to experiment, a prestige which stimulated imitation by lesser men.

In considering implements particularly associated with the agricultural improvements of the eighteenth century, pride of place may be given to the 3- and 4-ton wagon, both the deep-bodied box-wagon (Fig. 20), which was common also on the Continent, and the wide bow-wagon of the west of England (Fig. 21). These were used on the larger farms, which also developed standard patterns of horse harness. By the end of the eighteenth century the harness of horses was much the same as today, with the carefully designed collar as the most essential item; since horses work by pushing against the collar, a lighter and closer-fitting type was evolved in hilly districts to suit the frequent changes of gradient. Hedging-hooks and the smaller bill-hooks, made by local blacksmiths to the traditional local patterns, belong mainly to the newer England in which common, waste, and strip were giving place to hedged fields, so that laying and plashing were becoming important crafts.

FIG. 20. Nineteenth-century box-wagon from Lincolnshire

FIG. 21. Bow-wagon from Wiltshire

Important though they were, such innovations were secondary to the more scientific system of cultivation introduced by Jethro Tull in his struggle against the uneconomical habits of farm workers. His main invention, in 1701, was a drill to plant seed in rows (Fig. 22). This gave results far superior, not only to those of casual broadcasting—though that method, too, lived on into the late-nineteenth century—but to the existing practice of dropping the larger varieties of seeds into a series of holes prepared one by one with an iron-pointed dibble. The horse which pulled the drill also pulled a bush harrow behind it to cover the seed. The regular drilling of seed in rows in turn made it possible to use the horse-hoe, which Tull introduced from France in 1714. His general plan of keeping the soil clean and loose by continuing tillage after sowing was particularly successful with turnips, but he even showed that he could grow above-average wheat crops from one-third of the average quantity of seed on unmanured land for thirteen years in succession. The straight lines of the modern harvest field and its abundant crops— the productivity of wheat has been trebled since the Middle Ages— owe much to Tull's admirers and imitators, both among the English

FIG. 22. Jethro Tull's seed-drill, after the original plans, 1701

nobility and gentry and among the hard-headed Scottish Society of Improvers.

LAND RECLAMATION

A dramatic development of the sixteenth and seventeenth centuries was the progress in land reclamation, which changed the face of large areas of the Netherlands and extended the agricultural resources of Italy, France, and England. In the Netherlands, land reclamation had been a great problem throughout the Middle Ages, for the period in which the Roman works fell into disuse coincided with an increase of rainfall and the sinking of the land-level by an estimated four inches a century. The Zuider Zee had reached its greatest extent about 1287, in which year 50,000 people were engulfed by it in a single storm. The Dutch had perforce become experts in the construction of dykes and the leading away of water by canals, and as early as 1106 were being invited to practise their arts farther east, in Germany. Nevertheless, down to the close of the Middle Ages they lost more of their homeland than they regained.

A general work on dyke-building, written in Holland about 1578, shows that in its author's time methods of dyke-construction and protection were roughly comparable to those of the present day. Boulder clay provided the usual basis, having the seaward face protected first by clay and osiers, seaweed, straw, or reeds, and later with palisades of short piles, the interstices of which were filled with bundles of faggots. In the sixteenth century the Dutch developed a new technique of dry laying, by which drowned land in inland districts was systematically reclaimed for agriculture. The area to be drained was ringed with a strong bank of earth, the making of which automatically created a deep channel surrounding the bank. A series of drainage mills was placed on the bank, and these pumped the water from inside the bank to the channel outside, whence it flowed away through a river or canal. The windmill-driven scoop-wheel used for this purpose was a fourteenth-century invention.

One of several abortive plans for draining the malaria-infested Pontine Marshes, about 300 square miles in extent, was that prepared by Leonardo da Vinci: in many other parts of Italy there were similar problems of regulating rivers in the interests of health and navigation as well as of food supply. Thus it came about that from an early date Italian scientists interested themselves in studying the behaviour of rivers. Galileo was at one time superintendent of the waters of Tuscany; later Italian scientists continued his studies, and before the end of the eighteenth century an Italian mathematician could write that 'hydraulic architecture arose, advanced, and almost reached perfection' in Italy.

In this respect France and England both owed more than Italy to the Dutch. Henry IV of France sent to the States General of the Netherlands for 'four qualified individuals, experienced in the art of dyking' to help him in his military operations, but later decided that land reclamation was also one of the ways of restoring prosperity to his distressed country. An Association was established under a series of edicts—imitated from a similar Board of Control in the Netherlands—and its work was continued until the revocation of the Edict of Nantes in 1685.

The English fenland covered an area of about 700,000 acres, largely protected by ancient embankments on the Lincolnshire coast, and drained by four slow-moving rivers; until 1540 it was looked after, to some extent at least, by the great fenland abbeys. The hope of a rich return from capital investment was what then, and for a long time to come, attracted attention to the draining of the Great Level between the Nene and the Norfolk uplands. A survey of 1589 had made clear that almost the whole of the land was above sea-level, so that reclamation was basically a problem of digging adequate canals along short tracks to the sea: machinery would not be required. But it was not until 1630 that a group headed by the

Earl of Bedford put the work in hand, with the famous Dutchman, C. Vermuyden, as their principal engineer; he had already drained 70,000 acres in Yorkshire (Hatfield Chase). The scheme, which was completed in 1653, depended upon drainage by gravitation; its very success quickly proved its undoing, for as the water was carried off, the peat-lands and even the silt-lands shrank, with the result that the surface of the land fell and the water ceased to flow.

By this time, however, drainage mills of the Dutch type were becoming well known in Britain. A book called *The English Improver Improved* (1652) refers to horse-mills as well as windmills, and describes the raising of the water by a scoop-wheel 'or else by a good chain-pump or bucket work'. Before the end of the seventeenth century the windmill was fully established in England for pumping water, but even this important and highly relevant technological advance did little to benefit the fens in an age when political opinion was antipathetic to the setting up of any central board, such as had been formed in the Netherlands and France.

3

PRODUCTION FOR DOMESTIC NEEDS

EARLY POTTERY

POTTERY may have grown out of basket-making, and certainly could not become an important factor in human affairs until Neolithic man had adopted a settled mode of life: game had been roasted on a spit, but the cereals and pulses which now made up a large part of his diet required slow cooking in a container which could stand heat. Then, and only then, would he have occasion for large-scale use of containers which were as easily broken as made. They are easily manufactured, since clay is plentiful and the hardening effects of fire upon it could be discovered whenever primitive man happened to use a patch of clay for a hearth. The fact that pottery is fragile, readily discarded, and yet ultimately imperishable, is, of course, the combination of qualities that has given it so large and prominent a part in the archaeological record. But although pottery occurs in Neolithic settlements before the growth of urban cultures, its development is primarily associated with the latter; it was a product that settlers and colonists introduced to remoter areas, and that commonly suffered a setback when the urban influence declined. Britain, for example, in the second millennium B.C. had much good pottery of Mediterranean origin; for the greater part of the next millennium, very little.

Nevertheless, pottery deserves pride of place among the domestic arts as one in which the product and its uses have changed comparatively little in the course of the ages. One great invention, that of the potter's wheel, was made about 3000 B.C., but no further technical advance of revolutionary importance was made until the nineteenth century A.D. The potter has always had three main tasks to perform: the selection, mixture, and moistening of clay; the forming and shaping of the vessel; and the execution of the drying and firing processes by which the finished product is made hard and durable. Very little is known about early methods of selecting, washing, and kneading the raw material with water. It is the second process, the shaping, that was transformed by the invention of the potter's wheel.

The lump of clay which the potter is ready to shape, when placed in the centre of the fast-turning wheel—at least 100 revolutions a minute—will rise easily and assume any desired circular shape at the lightest pressure of the potter's hand. The potter with the wheel can do in a few minutes what would take an amateur without it several hours, at the same time achieving perfect symmetry. Thus

FIG. 23. Potters with turn-table and kiln, Egyptian model, *c.* 1900 B.C.

the momentum of the spinning wheel, which reduces the muscular effort on the part of the potter to almost nothing, gave man one of the first of the long series of labour-saving devices out of which modern industry has been developed. No early wheel survives complete, and we have no means of determining how the device originated, though it may have grown out of the practice of using a turn-table so as to have all sides of a pot under modelling conveniently to hand (Fig. 23). In its simplest form the wheel turned on a pivot which fitted into a socket in a stone. Spun by hand, such a wheel could be given sufficient momentum for the shaping of one pot, but enlarging it to increase the momentum caused the small disk in the centre, on which the pot itself was supported, to be placed less conveniently for the potter's hand. Hence the practice, which seems to have grown up by 2000 B.C., of deriving the necessary momentum from a second wheel placed under the first and generally turned by the foot of the potter, or possibly with a stick, or by an assistant using a band. By the sixth century B.C. the wheel was also being used as a lathe (p. 90), for instance to cut grooves and mouldings.

In order to make the vessel less porous it was usual to cover it, when dried but not fired, with a slip of a finer clay which could be burnished with a pebble or other implement to close the pores and make the product watertight. From a very early period, large pots were commonly made in two sections, in order that their weight should not cause them to sag before drying; when partly dried they were fitted together with a slip. The same method was used for pots with narrow necks.

During the firing a complex series of changes occurs in the clay, the nature of these depending upon many factors, but particularly upon the final temperature reached. Primitive man probably had to be content with firing-temperatures in the range of 450 to 700° C., which did no more than drive off all the moisture from the clay. At rather higher temperatures (750 to 800° C.), such as can be attained in large open fires or simple kilns, chemical changes take place in the clay, making it stronger and less porous. At higher temperatures still it is vitrified (fused into a glassy substance), but such a degree of heat is readily attainable only with furnaces of comparatively modern type: in ancient times firing-temperatures above 1,000° C. were very rare. Firing is a long process and consumes much fuel, and a good supply of the latter is essential for any sort of large-scale work. Wood must have been the principal fuel, but dung, peat, and grass were also used when appropriate. Some pottery may have been sold or bartered unfired, the purchaser completing the process himself.

Pots must originally have been dried on the domestic hearth, then in a special fire of brushwood, and later in a fire burning for several days under cover of earth or other air-excluding matter, after the pattern of the charcoal-burner's fire. It is believed that this last type of fire could attain a temperature of 750 to 800° C., about 150° below what was required for the kiln-fired Athenian vases. When the kiln began we do not know, but examples can be traced from the fourth millennium B.C. Until modern times the vertical kiln was commoner than the horizontal: it was developed, mainly in brick-using countries, as a domed structure, from which the hot gases generated in the hearth escaped eventually through a chimney. The pots to be fired were placed on a perforated clay floor and the kiln was then sealed: indirect heating prevented them from being contaminated by smoke and smuts from the fuel. The two problems, of retaining the hot gases long enough for them to be fully effective and of equalizing the temperature at the top and bottom of the kiln, were partly solved in the horizontal kiln, where the flue is laid horizontally between hearth and chimney, which are at opposite ends of the kiln. Specimens are found in Roman Britain, but the vertical kiln remained commoner until modern times, except in China.

The nature of the processes made the potter at a very early stage a whole-time specialist. The aesthetic sense which he developed, and which gives such interest to the study of early pots, was both a result and a cause of his special position. Painting was one early form of decoration, mixtures of natural earths being used before firing, and either organic or inorganic colours at a later stage. Shapes were, to some extent, an imitation of wood- or basket-work, and later there was sometimes a rather odd imitation of sheet-metal products. It is claimed that the pleasurable excitement of the spinning process and the ease which it imparted to the potter's work had much to do with the development of a sense of form; indisputably, pottery developed with remarkable speed both as art and as craft. First at Corinth and later at Athens, pottery manufacture for a wide overseas market achieved a degree of industrial concentration which almost rivals those of modern times, while the beauty of the best Attic products has remained unequalled. The achievements of some of the early metal-workers, for instance at Ur (p. 119), were also dependent in part upon the skill of the potter, who supplied the casters with moulds made of fired clay.

EARLY TEXTILES

The nimble fingers which moulded clay had from earliest times a parallel task in the entangling of vegetable or animal fibres so as to make some things serviceable to man. It is probable that baskets, mats, and even ropes were made by Palaeolithic man at an earlier stage than textile fabrics, which require the use of a twisted or spun thread and the criss-cross weaving pattern of weft and warp: this, however, is conjecture. Our earliest specimens, which are Egyptian and from the early part of the fifth millennium B.C., include mats, coiled basketry, and primitive fabrics; the earliest examples of rope in Egypt occur a few centuries later.

Except for the fact that ropes at the present day are sometimes manufactured from man-made fibres for the sake of durability, it is true to say that basketry, matting, and ropes have a continuous history of at least 7,000 years in which some of the materials, main techniques, and even patterns have shown no change. A specimen of coiled basketry from about the year 3400 B.C. illustrates both a method of fabrication, that of sewing the coil in shape from the base upwards, and a form of decoration, with vertical coloured stitches passing over two coils, which are still in vogue. The same is true of the use of plaited material for baskets, the making of rush mats, and the more complicated basketry built up on a frame of stakes. The making of ropes, on which sea transport and large-scale building operations depended, was not a domestic art, but may be included here because the process is one of spinning. Reed, leather, palm fibre, and esparto were among the materials anciently used. Normally, there were three distinct processes involved—twisting the fibres into yarn, the yarn into strands, and finally the strands into rope; in order to prevent the completed rope from untwisting itself, the strands are twisted internally in the opposite direction from that in which they are twisted together. In an Egyptian rope-walk, two men respectively twisted the strands and closed them as they walked with the rope held between them, while a third man in the middle packed it tight with a marlinspike.

Reeds, rushes, sedges, and grasses were all used in ancient basketry, but the principal textile material of the ancient Near East was flax, which was grown also for its oil-containing seed and was well established by 3000 B.C. To prepare it for use, the fibres had to be separated from the rest of the stem by soaking it to loosen the structure before scraping and combing. Hemp was the first fibre-plant of the Chinese and was known in eastern Europe by 500 B.C., but its main use in Europe has been for rope. Cotton, though it may have been derived originally from Arabia, appears first in India, and silk in the Far East. Wool was thought unclean by the Egyptians, and, although there was much woollen cloth made in Mesopotamia and northern Syria, the earliest considerable remains are from Scandinavia about 1000 B.C. The colder climate doubtless stimulated demand for it in Europe.

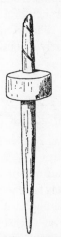

FIG. 24. Wooden spindle from Kahun, Egypt, c. 1900 B.C.

In order to make a usable thread, fibres from any natural material have to be drawn out parallel and twisted together so as to form one continuous narrow thread. This process, which we call spinning, will first have been done experimentally by rubbing between the palms of the hands, then between one hand and the cheek or leg, leaving the other hand free to control the bundle of tangled fibres: the spun thread was then wound on a stick. The use of the stick, which was intended originally simply to avoid entanglement, developed into the use of a spindle of wood (Fig. 24) or other material, which was twirled to spin the thread. The spindle, which until the fifteenth century A.D. was virtually the only mechanical aid to spinning, might be kept in rotation by the human hand; but usually it was suspended with a weight on it, the whorl, which would keep it turning for some time like a top. The action of the spindle produced

a more uniform thread than the unaided hand, but it was nevertheless common in early times to double the thread for increased
strength before it was used for weaving. Another, less important,
implement was the distaff, a larger stick used to hold the fibres ready
for spinning. That spinning was normally work done by women is
shown, not only by early illustrations, but by the continuing use of
'spinster' for unmarried women and 'distaff side' for the female
branch of a family.

The essential feature of the loom, which seems to have been a very
early Neolithic invention, is that it provides the frame on which

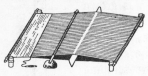

separate threads are stretched parallel
to each other (the warp) to be interlaced at right angles by a continuous
thread (the weft). The bedouin still use
a loom pegged out on the ground, such
as was common 5,000 years ago. This
already contained the two essential

FIG. 25. Horizontal ground-loom

features of the rod-heddle and the shed-rod. Every second thread
was fastened to the heddle, the raising of which would provide a shed
through which the weft could be passed; the alternate threads passed
over the shed-rod, which could be turned on edge to make the
counter-shed through which the weft passed back again (Fig. 25).
The rows of weft were then 'beaten up' with a stick to make the
weaving more even. The same form of loom set upright would
enable the weaver to sit more comfortably, but of course required a
more permanent structure. A third type of loom, which was still
used in Iceland less than 100 years ago, had loom weights of pottery
or stone, of which specimens survive at Troy from the middle of the
third millennium B.C. The warp threads were tied in bunches to
these weights, the weaving went downward, and the positions of
rod-heddle and shed-rod were consequently reversed. The simplest
form of weaving, known as the tabby-weave, was also the oldest, single
threads being passed over and under single warps—as in darning;
it is still practised. When weft and warp were doubled or otherwise
equally increased, this became canvas-weave. Variety could be introduced in two main ways: by the use of coloured threads as in
tapestry weaving, where the colour variation is in the weft, and by
the process known as 'floating', where particular threads are made to
pass over more than one thread, either in warp or weft. A multi-
plicity of variations was rapidly achieved.

As we might expect, the earliest textiles remaining to us are in plain weave. Elaboration begins about the middle of the third millennium B.C. and develops so fast that the tomb of Tutankhamen shows us fine linen with counts as high as 280 × 80 to the inch; its marvellous tapestry pieces include a robe decorated with rosettes and a lotus border, having a collar in three colours shaped as a vulture with outspread wings. Two centuries later the girdle of Pharaoh Rameses III displays the most intricate of weaving techniques, with two qualities of weave in the one textile, and a count of 340 × 61 to the inch. Bronze Age Scandinavia, in contrast, yields only coarse plain weaves with counts not exceeding 13 × 10 to the inch, but surviving garments are interesting because they are made exclusively of wool. A sixth-century Greek vase shows us both spinners and weavers; the loom, which is believed to have been about 5 ft wide and a little higher, is of the kind which Homer pictured in the hands of Penelope or Circe. No fragment of cloth from ancient Greece survives. As for the looms, only the Chinese had anything better than the type depicted, and the weaving knowledge implied in their fabrics of silk, dating from about the year 1000 B.C., did not begin to influence the western world until after the beginning of the Christian era.

IVORY, WOOD, LEATHER, GLASS

Ivory. Ivory-work resembles basketry in that it was brought quickly to perfection, but, unlike basketry, it began and has continued as a luxury craft. In Egypt, Phoenicia, Crete, and Greece alike, it was used especially for decorative knife-handles, toilet articles, and statuettes, and in furniture for panels, as at the tomb of Tutankhamen, though we also hear of Solomon's 'great throne of ivory' and the luxurious ivory beds denounced by the prophets. Ivory combs and inlaid trinket-boxes were made in Syria 3,000 years ago, much as they are made today, while no modern hand has surpassed the skilfulness of certain small Cretan figures.

The methods of the craft were clearly handed down from father to son. This was the case even in modern times, when the first exploration of the Ivory Coast, west of what is now Ghana, by the seamen of Dieppe gave that port an ivory-carving industry which endured for 500 years. Ivory panels were commonly attached to a wooden base by small tenons, which were fastened in a mortice with a pin, and were often marked on the back to facilitate assembly. The pins themselves were usually of ivory, as they still are, because metal tends to corrode and so cause stains. The work was apparently done with small saws, chisels, and drills which had bits of a type still used to place the pegs for piano-strings. A simple form of lathe assisted ivory-working in Asia, but it was the Romans who first employed the file. The high cost of the material encouraged careful workmanship, jointing of small pieces to make composite figures, and the plugging of flaws.

Wood. The supply of wood was not restricted in anything like the same degree as that of ivory, but accurate work was not possible without close-grained timber such as was not to be found in quantity in Egypt. Cedar, cypress, and yew were therefore common Egyptian imports from Syria and the Lebanon, while the timber tribute paid by the Sudan gives us the name of ebony, which is Egyptian. With this limitation, we may say that wood-working as understood today was practised from the time when copper tools were introduced into Egypt, about 4000 years B.C.; the standards reached by the Egyptians were not equalled by Europeans until the Renaissance.

Important works of art in wood seem to have been designed either by priests or by other educated persons attached to the court. But the craftsmen appear to have had a many-sided skill in carpentry, joinery, and inlaying (Fig. 26). Pull-saws and bow-drills were used, and the final smoothing was done with sandstone rubbers. In the earliest times parts of furniture were fastened together by lashing with thongs, but by about 2000 B.C. the methods of making a joint were very far advanced. The glue of 1600 B.C. resembles that of the present day, and was presumably made similarly by boiling down bones, skins, and hooves of animals. The tomb of Tutankhamen displays such refinements as pegs capped with granulated gold buttons, which were used decoratively to fasten an ivory veneer to a casket; veneering was much practised to economize in the more valuable woods.

The development of fine wood-work among the Egyptians seems to have proceeded from statuary to the making of strong-boxes and chests; for these purposes the reeds in many ways employed were obviously unsuitable. With an interest in furniture came the problem of devising bed- and chair-frames to take the strain of a separately-woven mattress or seat. Apart from furniture, there was also the exacting task of making corn measures, held together by hoops of bent wood. A royal tomb dating from about 2690 B.C. shows us a craftsmanship that was already traditional. A thousand years later, the royal tombs of Egypt yield us amazing coffins of cedarwood, carved to a uniform thickness of $1\frac{1}{2}$ in., which not only show the human form on the outside, but have every contour repeated on the inside in reverse form with complete exactitude. A little later we have such astonishing, if florid, triumphs as the deeply carved furniture of Tutankhamen, including an ebony bed, shaped to allow for sagging of the woven mattress, which has not warped appreciably in all the intervening centuries.

Leather. Palaeolithic man used the skins of the animals he killed, or whose bodies he found, for clothing and, to some extent, for tents

FIG. 26. Furniture-making, from a tomb at Thebes, Egypt, *c.* 1440 B.C.

and containers. But we do not know when man first learned to make durable leather by scraping and treating the skins with fats or in other ways, which gave him a ready-made equivalent of a textile material that had also some of the qualities of pottery. There is plenty of archaeological evidence for the early use of skin-scrapers of bone and stone, but the desirability of preserving only the central layer—as distinct from the epidermis, to which the hair or wool is attached, and the layer of fat or flesh below—would be learned only over a long period of time, and to find a satisfactory method of preserving it would take even longer. The Eskimos still cure their skins by smoking them, and it is said that the teeth of their women are often worn to the gums in the preliminary task of chewing the skin so as to soften it beforehand. Other primitive methods of preservation are salting, sun-drying, and the working of fats into the tightly-stretched hide, a method described in the *Iliad*. Tawing was a method widely used in ancient Egypt, and still important in the Middle Ages, which involved the application of alum, often combined with salt, to produce a stiff white leather which was then worked over a curved frame to soften it. The most important process, however, employs tannin, and is thought to have originated from the steeping of skins in forest pools, or from the practice of vegetable dyeing; the main source was oak bark or oak galls. The tanning was done by soaking the skins in a series of pits or vats, the oldest, and therefore the weakest, liquor being used first; in ancient times the whole process might take fifteen months.

Finishing processes were of three kinds. For durability, sole-leather was hammered, and harness-leather curried—that is to say, impregnated with grease while still damp after tanning. For appearance, goatskin was rubbed to produce what we call morocco leather, and the same process produced the creasing of willow calf. For colouring, there was the red produced from the insects of the kermes oak, black from copperas, and the use of many vegetable dyes.

From the Mesolithic stage onwards, leather played an enormous part in the ancient economy. Leather of varying degrees of hardness and suppleness served many of the purposes to which pottery and textiles were later adapted. The leather bucket of the type still used in the shaduf, the stitched leather play-ball, the dagger-sheath, the leather jerkin, and many types of glove, sandal, and shoe illustrate a continuity reaching to our own times, which was perhaps greater with leather-working than with any other important handicraft. A Greek bowl (Fig. 27) shows us a shoe-maker of the sixth century B.C. cutting his leather: the half-moon knife which he is using had been in use in Egypt a thousand years before; a knife of identical pattern is to be seen in the hands of the shoe-maker of today. Down to 1900 at least, the saddler's was another very conservative leather-working trade of fundamental importance to society.

Glass. Glass is a rigid non-crystalline substance, suitable for many of the uses of pottery but having the special quality of transparency or at least translucency. Its earliest use was for the glazing—that is, coating with glass—of other objects, while in more recent times it has provided windows, mirrors, and the essential parts of optical instruments. Glass was generally made by heating a clean mixture of soda, lime, and sand (or ground flint) until it fused into a vitreous fluid, requiring to be slowly cooled or annealed to prevent cracking and crystallization. The history of glass resembles that of leather inasmuch as the best processes and products of antiquity were not substantially improved upon until quite recent days. The glazing of soap-stone beads dates in Egypt from about 4000 B.C., and the making of small solid glass objects, which may be regarded as imitations

of precious stones, dates from about 2500 B.C. both in Egypt and in
Mesopotamia. Glass vessels, however, do not make their appearance
before about 1500 B.C., while the technique of glass-blowing, which
we tend to think of as the fundamental process of glass manufacture,
was new, but spreading very rapidly, at the dawn of the Christian
era.

Glaze was composed of the same constituents as ancient glass, but
with a larger proportion of sand and a smaller proportion of lime. It

FIG. 27. Shoe-maker cutting leather, from a Greek bowl of
the sixth century B.C. Insets show: (A) Egyptian; (B) Iron
Age; (C) medieval European; and (D) modern knives

was usually applied as a moist powder and then fired. For glass-making
proper we have very little evidence as to how the two basic processes
—the heating and raking of the raw materials to get rid of some of the
gas and to mix them effectively, known as fritting, and the process
of melting and annealing—were conducted originally. Soda-glass
becomes fluid at about 1,000° C., which can be achieved with a charcoal fire and is, we have noted, the maximum temperature attained
by ancient potters. Potash-glass, then less common, melts at a rather
lower temperature. With either type, bubbles of gas often remained
because the available heat had been insufficient to expel them, and
the glass might also crystallize and become brittle if the cooling in
the annealing oven were not slow enough. Glass made from pure
soda, lime, and sand is colourless, but is coloured by even small
traces of certain mineral impurities—a fact of which advantage was

taken from an early date: copper, for example, gives a deep blue-green. Most sands contain compounds of iron, which impart a greenish-brown colour to glass; the fine colourless glasses of antiquity, especially those of Alexandria, must have been made by using pure silver sands.

The first glass objects, including some quite elaborate figurines, were shaped in clay moulds, while seals and even larger articles were made by grinding or carving the glass, treated as if it were stone. But the general practice for making a glass vessel was to dip a core of sand, tied up in a cloth bag, into a crucible of molten glass, roll it into shape on a stone bench, perhaps add blobs and rings of different coloured glass to the outside for decoration, and to pour away the sand from the finished vessel when cold. This last technique probably grew out of the practice of making glass beads by surrounding a wire core with viscous glass, withdrawing the wire when the glass had cooled, and cutting the product into appropriate sections.

Such was the glass-making technique of the second millennium B.C. By about 1350 B.C. Egypt had factories producing glass in quantity; the art was spread, no doubt by migratory workers, all over the Near East, but has left no traces north or west of Greece. After an apparent interruption which lasted for some 400 years, glass vessels become common again in the eighth and seventh centuries B.C., when they were brought by Phoenician traders to the Atlantic coast, while the making of glass beads spread across Europe, perhaps even as far as Britain.

THE CONTRIBUTION OF THE GREEK AND ROMAN WORLD

In this period the most revolutionary developments were in glass-making. The sand-core technique went out of fashion, while Egypt took the lead with an output of mould-pressed ware, beautifully finished by grinding and polishing. Coloured rods or 'canes' were fused together and then cut transversely in order to make polychrome glasses; this culminated in mosaic glasses and bowls such as graced the Roman emperors' table. But the biggest change came not from the Alexandrian centre but almost certainly from Syria, whence it spread across the Roman world with astonishing speed in the early years of the empire. This was the art of glass-blowing, which probably began with the blowing of vessels within moulds; as skill improved, moulds were dispensed with. Free-blown glass was produced as a bubble on the end of a blowpipe, and shaped with pliers; transferred while still molten on to the end of a second rod, the pontil, which was thrust into (but not through) the glass at its base; the process was completed by detaching the blowpipe, leaving a mouth to be trimmed with shears. Reheating his glass when necessary, the blower could blow and spin it into almost any shape, from flat dishes 2 ft in diameter to a small jug inserted into a larger one. By the second century A.D. the glass industry had spread from Italy to important new manufacturing centres with improved techniques round Cologne and Trier, whence it also reached Britain. Minor technical changes were diffused so fast that there must have been a constant movement of skilled glass-makers from the Near Eastern centres all across the empire. Finds ranging from Afghanistan to the Sahara, Scandinavia, and the northern highlands of Scotland show the popularity of imperial glass even among the outer barbarians.

The centuries of the Pax Romana, with its widespread opportunities for trade, are likewise something of a landmark in the history of ceramics, textiles, and furniture, to which we must now briefly turn. Greek pottery reached its climax in the Athenian vases of the sixth and fifth centuries B.C., both as regards decoration—by which alone we can judge the glories of the long-vanished mural and panel paintings of the Greeks—and technique. Decoration was applied after the vase had dried leather-hard but before it was fired, a method facilitated by the toughness of Athenian clay, and one which helped to achieve smoothness in the lines of the drawing; fresh clay could be applied for details. The whole surface of the vase was covered with a thin wash of clay, on which the design was sketched out with a blunt tool. The figures were then painted in, lines drawn inside the silhouettes, and the background given a contrasting colour—usually red on black, or black on red (Figs. 28, 29). The exact coloration depended on conditions within the kiln, the practice being to fire the vessel in three successive stages, in which air was respectively freely admitted, then limited, and finally admitted freely again. With the decline of Athens early in the fourth century B.C. there arose the potteries of southern Italy, using the same technique. But farther north, in Tuscany, the Greeks had a rival in the famous black Etruscan pots, bearing a design in relief, such as became common with Greek ware a century or two later. This involved the preparation of a thick-walled mould, on the inner side of which a design was cut; this was then fastened to the potter's wheel, and a bowl was spun inside it, pressure being applied from within by hand to secure the relief. The products of two or more moulds were often combined to form such articles as jugs.

The Romans of the first century B.C. produced their Arretine bowls by the same system of relief-moulding (Fig. 30) at the former Etruscan city of Arezzo. The glaze, both of the Arretine vases and of a very common type of pottery derived from them, which archaeologists call *terra sigillata*, was a brilliant coral red in colour. The Romans also produced a blue-green glazeware, which is likewise found in many parts of the empire. This was a lead glaze, melting at a definite

FIG. 28. The return of Hephaistos to Olympus, from an
Athenian wine bowl of the fifth century B.C.

temperature, into which the vase was dipped to coat the outside, while a thinner coating was applied to the inner surface. Much domestic ware was, however, left unglazed. The making of terra-cotta statuary (Fig. 31) and reliefs was another Greek, Etruscan, and Roman practice, in which the use of the mould replaced free modelling. Not only did the use of moulds, several for each figure, make it possible to produce identical figures quickly, but the figures themselves could be hollow.

The contribution of Greece and Rome to the textile industries lies first and foremost in their choice of raw material. Their finest flax came from Egypt, but they had their own wool, which they improved by selective breeding. Sheep shears of a modern type, meant for use in one hand, were probably a Roman invention. Silk is first recorded in the west in the first century A.D. as an expensive eastern fabric;

descriptions of the source of raw material are confused. Cotton, however, had been brought from India and was now grown on the south-eastern periphery of the Mediterranean, and there was large-scale manufacture of cotton goods in Roman Malta. Important changes in the textile processes, however, were very few, and in no case fundamental. The dyes used continued to be mainly vegetable, but the Romans attached importance to the costly purple dye of Phoenicia—a dark violet inclined to brown. This 'imperial purple' was obtained, a few drops at a time, from a gland in several species of molluscs; for the best results *Murex brandaris* was used. Twentieth-century chemists have found that this costly dyestuff, which gave

FIG. 29. Preliminary sketch for the bowl shown in Fig. 28

a pound of wool a value of £40, is closely related to the vegetable dye indigo.

In furniture, too, classical civilization introduced no radical changes, though the improved tools of the Iron Age encouraged an increasing mastery of technique. The Greeks contributed to furniture only a new type of chair, having a woven seat supported upon curved legs and with a curved back—a chair which, unlike its Egyptian predecessors, was not completely rigid but could be varied to suit the comfort of the individual. The Romans were the first makers of strong tables and of shelved cupboards. Armies returning from the Asiatic campaigns of the last two centuries B.C. brought with them to Rome the idea of many oriental luxuries, including the sideboard, and with the general trend towards luxury and ostentation, there was extensive use of costly veneers and of metal furniture-fittings and furniture.

The most important new tool was the lathe which perhaps dates back to about 1500 B.C., but was brought into wide use for wood-turning by the Greeks. No ancient specimen is extant, but it was probably developed out of the bow-drill, or perhaps the potter's wheel, and made a special appeal to a people who loved geometrical perfection. Iron hand-tools had been much developed by the Assyrians in the eighth century, and the Greeks probably had proto-types of the tools which were in common use among the Romans.

FIG. 30. Arretine mould, with incised design, first century B.C.

In nearly every case the tool of iron was an improvement upon its copper or bronze predecessor: iron saws were the first to have raked teeth; modern files and rasps supplemented the plane. Working with such tools for a luxury-loving society, the Romans used most of the techniques and many of the exotic materials, such as tor-toise-shell and ivory, which made their next appearance to meet the demand of wealthy patrons in western Europe after a gap of more than a thousand years.

Little is known of the wood-working crafts of northern Europe during this long period, but the word 'carpenter', which comes to us, through the Latin, from the two-wheeled Celtic cart (*carpentum*) which the Romans greatly admired, is a reminder that the men of the most forested areas were not inactive. It is hardly too much to say that the peasant wood-working crafts, often carried out in the home in the darkness of the northern winter, represent a living tradition (or, at least, one of only yesterday) which goes back to a Neolithic practice of wood-working distinct from that of the Mediterranean world. The men of the north made much more extensive use of their plentiful timber, eating off wood rather than pottery, and living in wooden houses rather than in ones of stone or brick. Moreover, they had plenty of soft woods, such as pine, beech, and birch, which could be worked more easily than the hard woods favoured by Mediterranean craftsmen and were suited to more primitive needs. The nor-therners, in short, were better at carpenter-ing than at joining, and were wielders of the axe, the adze, and the knife rather than the more accurate saws and planes of the south.

FIG. 31. Etruscan warrior, in terracotta (life-size), sixth or fifth century B.C.

THE MIDDLE AGES

The history of production for the home during the Dark Ages is little known, and there was perhaps little new to record. The techniques of the later Middle Ages, on the other hand, are relatively well known to us, because they survived to find a place in the printed litera-ture of the sixteenth century, and in the woodcuts by which it is illustrated. One common factor running through the period is the debt of the west to the east, to the Greeks or Byzantines, to the Islamic world, and to the Far East. In the case of pottery, which we make our starting-point, this ascendancy of the east over the west lasted far beyond the Middle Ages. It was not until 1709 that western potters were able to rival the glories of the translucent porcelain which had been made in China since the days of the T'ang dynasty— a period of almost exactly one thousand years.

One consequence of the fall of the Roman empire in the West in the fifth century was that in many areas the potter's wheel fell into disuse, and pots were again built up by hand from lumps or coils of clay. This was true, for instance, of Britain, except perhaps for Kent, up to the ninth century; then the wheel came back from the Rhine-land, which, together with parts of Gaul and Italy, had kept the Roman ceramic tradition uninterrupted. The kick-wheel was charac-teristic of the Middle Ages (Fig. 32), the potter being left with both hands free to shape the vessel. Another new development was in the design of the kiln. The correct firing of pottery requires a slow raising of the kiln temperature, a higher maximum temperature than is readily attainable with wood fuel, and a slow cooling-off. Better design made it easier to fulfil these requirements while at the same time saving fuel. By the middle of the sixteenth century the use of an

FIG. 32. Potter using kick-wheel. Agricola, *De re metallica*, 1556

hour-glass by the master-potter for timing the operation presages the instrument-control of modern times.

Among the useful modifications of design introduced by the medieval potter was the convex base, formed by working the inside of the soft clay with hand or pad. This made the base itself stronger, while the convex surface cracked less readily under changes of temperature. Another was the tubular spout, which was formed by wrapping a strip of clay round a finger or stick, used also to make the hole to which it was fitted. A good deal of elaborate ornament was moulded on to the pots without the help of a wheel, and there was even a device for casting screw-tops for the necks of pottery bottles. But the only independent development of first-class importance in western Europe was its stoneware, which was not derived from the earlier Chinese manufacture, though this was imitated in the Near

East. Stoneware requires a fine plastic clay and a kiln which can be fired at a high temperature of about 1,250° C., which causes partial vitrification and so gives a non-porous vessel without glazing. Ware of this kind was being made in the Rhineland from the time of Charlemagne onwards in quite simple kilns, success being probably due to the extreme plasticity of the local clay. In the fourteenth century Rhenish potters learned to throw salt over the pots at a late stage in the firing so as to produce a salt-glaze. Dutch Limbourg rivalled the Rhineland, but stoneware like this was not produced in England until about 1684.

Some of the eastern influence was Byzantine. The use of lead glazes, for example, which had been discontinued in the west after the fall of the Roman empire, owed its revival in the eleventh century in part to its continuance in Byzantium during the Dark Ages. Polychrome decoration, of which specimens are found in tenth-century Bulgaria, may also be supposed to have come partly from Byzantine sources to Italy and thence to France. But the most important influence on western potters was that of Chinese ceramics imported through the Islamic world.

White, translucent, metallically resonant porcelain was being made in China from fine white clay and china-stone, fired at high temperatures, from about A.D. 700. Within a century porcelain from China reached Baghdad. To imitate this creamy porcelain, which they coveted but of which they could not find the secret, Mesopotamian potters developed a white opaque tin-glaze—composed of powdered potash-glass, oxides of lead and tin, and salt—in which to dip the once-fired vessel. The result was not merely a reasonable imitation of Chinese porcelain, but the production of a surface on which a brush could paint most delicate work. The ceramics of Baghdad, and later of Cairo, to which Baghdad potters migrated in the eleventh century, inspired imitation in Spain and Italy, leading by the fourteenth century to the majolica ware, probably named after the island of Majorca, but a characteristic achievement of the Renaissance period at Faenza (whence came the name faience) and other Italian centres. This was made with the glaze described above, and painted with colours derived from Islamic practice, such as cobalt blue, which was smuggled into Italy from the Levant in the fifteenth century.

Meanwhile, in the twelfth century the whiteness of Chinese porcelain was imitated in Persia by a new composition of powdered quartz and glass; this gave Persia a high position in ceramics, but did not directly influence Europe. In the fifteenth century, however, the blue-and-white porcelain of China gave a new impulse to pottery-making in the Near East, and hence indirectly in Europe, with the result that majolica pottery spread in the sixteenth century from Italy to the Netherlands; and when the Dutch East India Company in 1609 began to import Chinese porcelain direct, the craftsmen of Delft imitated it in the tin-enamel ware with which the name of their town is for ever associated. From 1615 onwards the Dutch exported it all over the western civilized world.

The revival of brick-making was also a characteristic of the later Middle Ages in Europe. After the fall of Rome it had continued in Byzantium and north Italy, and among the Mohammedans of Spain. Between the eleventh and thirteenth centuries it spread from southern France to eastern Britain, and became the main basis of medieval architecture in the region from the Low Countries to the Baltic, which has very little stone. Bricks, made in large rectangular kilns, were cheap: at Hull, by about 1400, three or four unskilled men were able to do all the work of digging and kneading the clay, shaping the bricks, and tending the kiln, for an annual output of about 100,000 bricks, the product of ten five-day firings with dried turf as fuel. Besides the common clay tiles for roofs, inlaid paving-tiles and orna-mental relief-tiles on walls were also characteristic of the later Middle Ages. From the fifteenth century onwards these found a new use in covering the large heating stoves of the cold north, where relief ornament added incidentally to the surface available for heat radia-tion; particularly beautiful effects in painted tin-glazed tiles were achieved by the Dutch. Once again the inspiration came from the east—the tiles which decorated the mosques and mausoleums of Islam.

The medieval glass-maker's craft may be dealt with more briefly, for after the fall of the Roman empire in the west there are serious gaps in our knowledge. The medieval industry in northern Europe centred upon the Rhineland and Normandy, used potash instead of soda for its alkali, and was based accordingly upon the forests, which also supplied the necessary fuel. The change had taken place by the ninth century, but there is no clear evidence of its being caused by a disruption of the industry in the Dark Ages. The pagan Jutes made glass of a sort in Kent, and there were attempts to bring back the lost art from the Continent to the Northumbria of Bede's day, but it is not until 1226 that we hear of workers from Normandy establishing glass-houses in forest areas of Surrey and the Weald. A similar mystery surrounds the development of soda-glass in Italy. Sites of glass factories belonging to the eleventh century have been found at Corinth, but we have little knowledge of Italian, or even of definitely Byzantine, glass until the thirteenth century, when Venice became a great glass-making centre, from which the craft spread in Italy and elsewhere. The impetus seems to have been given by the Crusades, which may have encouraged the movement westwards of workers from the Near East, with their skill in cutting and enamelling the glass. But it was not until the middle of the sixteenth century that the Venetians, whom the waning fortunes of their city now tempted to emigrate, took the manufacture of crystal glass as far afield as England.

As late as the twelfth century, the windows of English churches were not always glazed, and even in the later Middle Ages it was only the larger houses whose windows might have such protection. Glass for the former was obtained by splitting a large blown cylinder with a hot iron, and opening it out in the furnace; for the latter, 'crown glass' was made by the simpler course of rapidly spinning a hollow globe of molten glass until centrifugal force caused it to open out suddenly into a flat, circular sheet, with the 'crown' by which it was attached to the pontil as a distinctive blemish. The manufacture of coloured glass, of which the oldest English examples date from 1170-80, required, as we have remarked, specific additions of mineral substances to the molten material and very careful control of conditions within the kiln. Greens and reds were produced by the use of copper, though the finest red required gold chloride—as it still does today. Browns and yellows were made by adding iron, the best yellow with metallic silver, and the blue was obtained with *zaffre*—an Arabic word for a mixture containing cobalt. Conversely, the art was learned of producing a colourless glass, either by using the purest materials or by getting rid of the green or brown tinge from iron by an addition of 'glass-maker's soap' (manganese dioxide).

The use of stained-glass windows in churches began in the Mediterranean lands in the twelfth century, with the exclusion of the hot sunshine as one of its main objects. Within a hundred years this developed into one of the greatest of art-forms, the supreme glory of the Gothic cathedrals of France and England. Though the finest work was done in the period 1280-1380, the technique of coloration continued to improve until about 1550, when the world lost an accomplishment which many believe has never been fully regained.

MEDIEVAL TEXTILES AND LEATHER-WORK

In the Middle Ages flax was grown all over Europe; indeed, it continued to be the main vegetable fibre in use in the west until the eighteenth century. It was so efficiently processed that fine linen, almost alone among medieval western goods, found a market as far away as Pekin. But the only important technical development in its manufacture was the flax-breaker—a fourteenth-century invention, probably of Dutch origin, which broke the woody tissues of the stalk between pieces of wood.

Far more important were the developments in the use of wool. By the fifteenth century there were fifty-one grades of English wool, the best being those of Shropshire, Herefordshire, and the Cotswolds. It was sold chiefly in the great manufacturing centres of Flanders, where in the good years of the early fourteenth century as much as 15 million pounds was needed as the main basis for an estimated annual output of 150,000 28-yd pieces of cloth. Fine English wool was also an important export to north Italy, but until near the close of the Middle Ages English cloth enjoyed less esteem, partly because it was believed, with some reason, that the English sorted the wool for its manufacture rather carelessly.

Wool required to be washed, dried, beaten, and oiled before the fibres could be disentangled for spinning. This disentangling or carding process had originally been done with thistle (Latin *carduus*) or teazle heads, but by the thirteenth century the French were using a pair of wire-toothed boards (not unlike very stiff hairbrushes), the wool being worked from one to the other by hand; these are still used by hand-weavers. Combing was another traditional practice, alternative to carding; it was probably derived from the linen industry, and was certainly common in western Europe by the twelfth century. The combs had metal teeth mounted in horn on a wooden handle, and were heated before use so that the comb might slip more easily through the wool: one comb was fixed to a post and the wool was then drawn from it with long strokes, the object being to collect the long fibres for spinning separately from the short. There was also a third method, alternative to carding, in which the fibres were disentangled by the vibrations of a bow-string. Both carding and combing are mentioned, though not described, by classical writers, including Pliny; but bowing, which is still practised in India and parts of Europe, may rank as a medieval invention.

The three major innovations associated with the medieval woollen industry are the spinning-wheel (Fig. 33), the horizontal frame loom, and the fulling-mill. In using the spinning-wheel, the right hand turned the wheel, which was connected with the spindle by a belt and pulley; as the spindle turned, the yarn slipping off the end was drawn away in the left hand. When the arm was fully extended, the yarn had to be held out at right

FIG. 33. Spindle-wheel, from the Luttrell Psalter, *c.* 1338

angles and the spindle reversed for a few turns, so that it might be wound properly on to it. Before the close of the Middle Ages the machine had been further elaborated by the flyer, which made it possible to spin and wind simultaneously.

According to Adam Smith the spinning-wheel, with its continuous rotary motion, doubled the productivity of labour. The horizontal frame loom, on the other hand, was a matter of convenience to the weaver rather than of any fundamental advance. The weaver was provided with treadles, to raise and lower the heddles (p. 80) as he passed the shuttle to and fro (Fig. 34); the reed, with which the lines of weft were beaten tight, was hung from the frame on a heavy batten; the release of a lever enabled the workman to pay out

FIG. 34. Four-heddle loom as used about 1400

the warp as he needed it from the warp-beam at the back of his loom; and the woven cloth was wound on the cloth-beam in front.

The trampling or fulling of cloth to thicken it by matting the fibre is analogous to the felting of unwoven wool, fur, or hair, a process which was probably older than weaving itself. Fuller's earth and various cleansers, such as wood ashes (but not soap), were used in this process by the ancients; what was new in medieval times was the substitution of power-driven mallets for the wetting and often noisome labour of the human foot. The power was supplied from the water-wheel as in the corn-mill; the turning of the shaft of the wheel caused tappets to engage in the shafts of two large wooden mallets, so that their heads fell alternately upon the cloth, which lay soaking in a trough of water containing fuller's earth and other alkaline materials. The cloth had to be rearranged from time to time to secure uniform treatment, but the economy of labour, as compared with the old method of treading and beating, may be judged from the fact that a fifteenth-century mill in Kent was able to treat simultaneously three pieces of cloth each 12×2 yd. Since the fulling-mill profoundly influenced the organization of the woollen industry, causing it to move out of the older towns to hilly districts well supplied with fast streams—and giving the English industry a corresponding advantage over the Flemish—it is remarkable that so little is known of its origins. There is a mention of it in an eleventh-century French charter, but the earliest English reference—to two mills, in Yorkshire and the Cotswolds respectively—dates from 1185. In the thirteenth century the fulling-mill became so common that the word 'mill' in documents was usually given further definition; no complete description or illustration, however, is found until considerably later.

The drying of fulled cloth on tenters (Fig. 35), the raising of the nap with teasels, its subsequent cropping and pressing to ensure a smooth surface, and the dyeing, were all processes of great importance in the medieval economy, but the practices were seldom new. There was, however, an interesting development in the preparation of alum (p. 266), which had been used from very early times as a mordant to enable the dye to attach itself properly to the fabric.

The history of cotton and silk in the Middle Ages emphasizes once more the all-important connexion with the east. Cotton manufacture was developed on a large scale in Spain by the Moors, whence it spread across Europe in the twelfth to fifteenth centuries as far as England, particularly in the form of fustian, a cheap cotton cloth with a linen warp, which derived its name from the Cairo suburb of Fostat. Cotton itself was to some extent grown in Italy, but the raw material came mainly from Syria, Egypt, and Cyprus. More interest attaches to the development of the silk industry. There had been silk-weaving in Europe under the Roman empire from the second century onwards, but the raw material came exclusively from the Far East. Although the production of raw silk was attempted at Byzantium under Justinian in the sixth century, when silkworm eggs were smuggled out of China—reputedly hidden in the staffs of two

FIG. 35. Cloth finishing in a monastery: (*right*) correcting faults; (*left*) stretching on a tenter-frame.
From an Italian manuscript of 1421

Nestorian monks—it was not until the twelfth century that it became firmly established in south Italy in imitation of the Muslims of Spain. Lucca became the chief centre of manufacture, which flourished in many of the north Italian cities, and had begun to spread to France: silkworm eggs were among the trophies of the Italian wars of Francis I. Britain, which never succeeded in producing the raw material on any appreciable scale, had no important silk manufacture until the great influx of Huguenot workers to Spitalfields and elsewhere when the Edict of Nantes was revoked in 1685.

Under suitable conditions, 1 lb of spinning caterpillars yield about 12 lb of silk in a year, but the filament loosened from the cocoons when they are stirred in warm water is extremely delicate, making it a day's work by traditional methods to reel 1 lb of silk by winding from three to eight filaments together. The thread, which at this stage is so fine as to be almost invisible, is then twisted to prevent the filaments from separating, and wound upon a spool, two or three threads being wound together to obtain uniform strength. But a further process intervenes between the spooling of the silk threads and the weaving—a twisting and doubling process in which the continuous silk filament is given any required degree of thickness. In thirteenth-century Italy the demands of this process gave rise to the first factories, silk-throwing mills operated by undershot water-wheels. Their secret was closely guarded, but a fifteenth-century sketch shows that the system was already that which (Sir) Thomas Lombe patented in Britain as late as 1718. A fixed wooden framework held rows of spindles, with reels above, which were rotated by rubbing against the laths of an inner wooden frame turned by the wheel. The silk-throwing mill received no substantial improvement until the nineteenth century. Its appearance is a great landmark in industrial history, since it required only two or three operators to operate many hundreds of spindles and reels, which did the work that had previously been done by some hundreds of hand-throwsters. It is interesting to note that China, the original home of the silk industry, had had a reeling-machine in the first century B.C., to which a flyer was added by A.D. 1090, but the first use of water-power in the industry there seems almost exactly to coincide with its use in the west.

The improvements in textiles during the Middle Ages are not paralleled in the case of leather, the manufacture of which remained fundamentally unchanged (Fig. 36) though its uses continued to be extended. Two examples may be taken: one from its more strictly utilitarian purposes, which included clothing, bottles and jugs, and most forms of luggage; the other, from an instance of the way in which leather served the arts. The shoe-maker was called the cordwainer because shoe-making was the principal use to which the superior *cordovan*, or Spanish leather, came to be put. This was originally made by the Moors from the skin of the moufflon, a hairy sheep now confined to the Mediterranean islands, but it was imitated in goat-skin all over Europe. In spite of his prestige in the community, what the cordwainer produced was very like the modern slipper. The welt did not begin to come in until the fifteenth century; there were no heels until towards 1600, and the regular use of the high boot came even later. Cheaper footwear was made from oxhide.

Our other example is from bookbinding, a craft where both the techniques and the styles developed in the Middle Ages still play a large part. It is to the monasteries that we owe such superb examples of leathercraft as the seventh-century Stonyhurst Gospel which once lay in the coffin of St Cuthbert, and other glorious relics of the Dark Ages. As protective as it was ornamental, this decorated leather binding on boards was originally worked with small tools and without regard to the time taken. By the fifteenth century, however, binding was being done commercially, and metal templates were used so that designs could easily be re-peated. But it was not until about 1600 that binding achieved its greatest splendours, when Europe learned, apparently from the Moors, the art of gold-tooling. The leather is marked out first, and the gold-leaf impressed with a hot iron, all excess being wiped away and carefully recovered. Gold was applied to edges in much the same way, but had subsequently to be polished with a small tool—which even in the mid-twentieth century is often made of the humble primeval flint. The use of so costly a metal was made possible only by its remarkable extensibility, which enables the gold-beater by re-

FIG. 36. Removing hair from hide in a tannery, from a sixteenth-century woodcut

peated hammerings between sheets of vellum to turn one ounce of metal into 250 sq. ft of gold-leaf. The art of gold-beating was known to the ancient Egyptians.

Although stretched leather had been used for chair seats in ancient Egypt, leather furnishings and upholstery in Europe belong not to the Middle Ages but to the sixteenth and seventeenth centuries. They may, however, be mentioned here for convenience. Embossed Spanish leather for a time enjoyed a great vogue for hangings and nailed-on wall-coverings. It was not, however, proof against certain insect pests, and lost favour in France when Colbert, in the later seventeenth century, revived tapestry-making. In England, too, it was replaced, by a wallpaper that looked like leather, but leather screens remained in favour, although they were eventually painted rather than gilded and embossed. Leather for the seats and backs of chairs was introduced in the sixteenth century, though its characteristic modern use for upholstery cannot be traced back farther than about 1650.

FURNITURE

Turning to furniture in general, the effect of the fall of the Roman empire was to restore the supremacy of the carpenter. He built the houses of the early Middle Ages, just as he built almost everything else, and into the houses he put the essentials of heavy, clumsy furniture. It was only in Italy that the art of the joiner lingered on: there is in the Vatican a cabinet, fitted with small drawers, which is named in an inventory of the eighth century. By contrast, the joiner was not seen in England until the thirteenth century, when planes reappeared, and the use of panelling, of which there is an eighth-century specimen at Ravenna, had reached as far as Germany and the Low Countries. Panelling could be used to make furniture lighter and to save wood, but in the damp, cold north it had a particular use for lining the walls with the wainscot oak imported by the Hansa merchants. To carry the wainscot overhead and so complete the lining of the room was the original meaning of 'ceiling'.

Carving, painting, and gilding were ancillary crafts, the first of which was often practised by the joiner. The use of joined construction made the work of carving easier, and much of the carving was repetitive, as when the gouge was employed to provide a pattern of flutes. But the turner was an independent maker of chairs, stools, and beds, whose common products changed little during the thousand years from early Saxon times to the seventeenth century. At the end of that time wheel-lathes were becoming more common, but the pole-lathe, which some authorities think dates back to the Mesopotamian Bronze Age, was still in use (Fig. 37). The turner commonly decorated the legs or posts of the better-class furniture produced by the joiner, but he also made his own dowel-jointed furniture, which was much cheaper.

Wicker chairs, of young willow shoots or osiers, were among the products of the basket-maker, whose trade was plied by many of the Huguenot refugees to England in 1685. A very special type of chair, having an X-frame which could fold, had a seat of stretched leather and much rich decoration, and was produced by the coffer-maker alongside his leather trunks. At the other extreme there was the stick-furniture which carpenters put hastily together for the poor. It was made of thick slabs of wood, with splayed legs, which penetrated the seat and were fixed in position with wooden wedges, as was also the back. Beech, ash, elm, and oak were the commonest material, and much of the work was done with the simple two-handled draw-knife. Stick-furniture was to be found all over Europe throughout the Middle Ages, in an unchanging functional style affected only by local materials and tastes. Meanwhile, from the superior craftsmen of Italy such arts as inlaying and veneering, as well as the use of mortise and tenon and dovetail joints, which had been highly

Fig. 37. Joiner and turner at work, Low Countries, *c.* 1600

developed in Egypt as early as the third millennium B.C., spread slowly northwards. Even in the Middle Ages, Paris was the centre of an important luxury trade: during the Renaissance, French work-men began seriously to vie with the glories of the Italian style, which under the aegis of Louis XIV they finally surpassed. The vogue of large cupboards to house sumptuous clothes and of grandiose beds called mainly for traditional skills, but the new processes of enrich-ment included gilding—leaf gold laid over many successive coats of size and adhesive mixtures—and marquetry carried out with varie-gated woods or other substances such as ivory and painted horn, tortoise-shell, pewter, and brass. A. C. Boulle's method of inlaying was to glue shell, brass, and other materials on to a framework of deal, but these tended to come unstuck; *appliqués* of gilt bronze, added for ornament, often served to strengthen the piece. Upholstered chairs of different degrees of comfort played an important part in the etiquette of Louis XIV's court, but the rest of his furniture spread a fashion to lesser courts and more modest residences than Versailles. The Gobelins manufactory, presided over by Le Brun, even had a special department for *ouvrages de la Chine*, a taste that was to recur at intervals for centuries: the lacquer used at this time had been invented by Dagly of Liège, but a more perfect imitation of the Chinese and Japanese material was achieved by S. E. Martin in 1744.

TEXTILES AND GLASS, 1500–1750

It will have been noticed that this account of the domestic arts has already more than once strayed from the Middle Ages into the first centuries of modern history: there is, in fact, no clear dividing-line. The working of wood and leather continued mainly along traditional lines, throughout the early modern period and far on into that later modern history which we think of as transformed by the industrial revolution. Even in the case of pottery, the discovery of the secret of Chinese porcelain at Meissen, near Dresden, in 1709, did not take full effect until the Wedgwood era, which lies well beyond our arbitrary dividing-line at 1750. There are, however, two of the domestic arts which must now be considered further, namely textiles and glass-making, since both of them underwent developments of the greatest importance between about 1500 and the middle of the eighteenth century.

In the case of textiles, progress was not due to the use of some new material. Instead, the driving-force was the increased market for old materials—a larger market at home due to a rising standard of life from the Renaissance onwards, and the huge expanding market overseas which followed the great geographical discoveries. Linen continued to be more important than cotton: most of the calico used in Europe was imported from India, while the most widespread cotton manufacture of the Continent was the making of fustian. Though heard of in England in the later Middle Ages, the fustian industry was probably reintroduced by Flemish immigrants at the end of the sixteenth century; it is known to have existed in Lancashire in 1621.

For the linen industry there were, as we have already noted, two main preliminary processes: the soaking of the woody stalk of the flax, and the separation of the fibre from the wood. Attempts at mechanical separation began in 1664: by the early eighteenth century water-driven rollers were in use for breaking the flax, and the action of the knife or scutching blade, used to separate out the fibres, was reproduced by a series of spikes on a wheel, which was likewise driven by water-power. Wool-combing, in contrast, remained purely a hand-operation, but the carding of the shorter fibres of wool was mechanized by three machines, all patented, significantly enough, in the same year, 1748. Two of these were hand-machines made by Lewis Paul. Daniel Bourn's invention, on the contrary, envisaged the possible use of rollers driven by water-power, and, though it did not succeed, provided the pattern followed by later machines which were successful.

Spinning, in contrast with weaving, remained the slowest of the basic textile processes. The only important change after the introduction of the flyer in the later Middle Ages (p. 97) was the treadle-wheel, which seems to have originated in England, or possibly Brunswick, in the early decades of the sixteenth century. The treadle worked from the front legs of the spinning-wheel. When it was pressed down, a loop of cord at the other end operated a connecting-rod and crank which turned the wheel. Two cords could be used, so as to drive the flyer as well as the bobbin on which the thread was wound; alternatively, the yarn itself dragged round the flyer. But it still took from three to five spinners to supply one weaver, a disparity which was increased (as we shall see) by the invention of the flying shuttle in 1733, so that only five years later Lewis Paul, together with John Wyatt, patented a scheme for machine-spinning. The thread was to be drawn out through pairs of rollers, each pair of which turned faster than its predecessor, and one pair at least would also impart a twist. Attempts were made to work this machine by donkey-power and by a water-wheel: they were unsuccessful, but a portent of things to come.

In weaving, the increasing luxury of the age caused increasing attention to be given to the draw-loom, with which it was possible to produce all kinds of figured fabrics. It was first used in the east for silk-weaving, and came into Europe in the later Middle Ages in the silk-weaving industries of Italy, and later of France. A pattern could be created by varying the number and position of the warp threads to be raised each time the weaver passed the weft in its shuttle to and fro. In the draw-loom this was done by means of a figure-harness raised above the loom, from which cords descended, enabling a draw-boy to draw up the appropriate series of warp threads, which were held down by weights, for each successive passage of the weft. Although there are no medieval illustrations of draw-looms, the basic figured weaves were all developed then, mainly by imitation of

Islamic practice, though there was also a Byzantine influence and a little direct imitation of Chinese weaves. Thus satin tissues, damasks, and figured velvets, the last chiefly Italian, were established as luxury fabrics long before modern times.

The first important improvement was made about 1600 by the Lyons weaver Claude Dangon, who introduced two devices which rendered the use of a very complicated machine easier. Firstly, the cords were brought to the side of the machine, so that the draw-boy might work from there, instead of perching precariously on top. Secondly, a lever was introduced to make it easier for the draw-boy to lift the weights on the warp, and the number of loops which could be used to move the warp-threads was increased to 2,400. The appropriate loops were knotted together to form the required shed for each passage of the weft, as selected by the assistant with the help of a paper pattern. There was naturally an interest in producing an automatic loom which would save both the expense and the possibility of error involved in the employment of the draw-boy. Between 1725 and 1745 three devices were made in France, where figured weaves were in great demand, in each of which the desired pattern was arranged to correspond with the perforations in a roll of paper or card passed round a perforated cylinder: the cords were attached to a row of needles, which were raised through the holes wherever a perforation occurred, thus automatically selecting the required warp-threads and forming the pattern. After each passage of the weft the cylinder was turned to bring the next series of perforations into position. The latest of these devices was constructed by a famous inventor, Jacques de Vaucanson, and though (like its predecessors) it proved too complicated for practical use, it is important as the foundation for the well-known Jacquard loom of the following century.

Meanwhile there were other forward-pointing inventions. The origin of knitting is unknown, though it is clear that the firm texture of cloth woven on primitive looms would encourage the development of a more elastic alternative, if one could be devised from the same materials. Knitting on frames was practised among the Arabs before the Christian era, and is believed to have led gradually to the modern technique; the first knitting-needles were hooked, a type still to be found in use among the shepherds of the Landes. In 1589 a Nottinghamshire clergyman, William Lee, devised the stocking-frame, in which the knitter manipulated a series of movable hooks so as to draw the stitches over a series of fixed hooks. For fear of creating unemployment the inventor was discouraged by Elizabeth I and James I, and took refuge in France; nevertheless, by the eighteenth century the 'frame', which was never power-driven, had become the basis of an important new domestic industry in England, especially in the east Midlands. Another significant development at the end of the sixteenth century was a ribbon-loom, invented in Danzig, which required no skill beyond the working of a bar and could produce up to half a dozen narrow weaves simultaneously. Although it seems to have been in use in London in 1616 and at

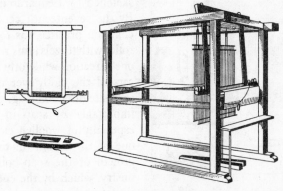

Fig. 38. Kay's flying shuttle, 1733. (*Right*) complete loom; (*left*) batten on which the shuttle travels; (*below*) shuttle

Leiden in 1620, its spread was handicapped both by popular rioting and by restrictive legislation; more than a hundred years later, an inventor at Basle, who devised a method of harnessing water-power to the narrow ribbon-loom, found his device prohibited.

Finally, there was the flying shuttle (Fig. 38), patented by John Kay, a Lancashire weaver working in Colchester, on 26 May 1733. This enabled the seated weaver to pass the shuttle in both directions across a piece of cloth far wider than the span of his own arms. It was operated by pulling alternately the ends of a cord, which were attached to two leather drivers or pickers made to slide along a metal rod. These knocked the shuttle, which ran on wheels from side to side along a batten. One weaver could now do the work of two, provided he was energetic enough to tend the threads of a double width of cloth as well as to throw the shuttle; he was encouraged to be so by the fact that his posture at the loom became for the first time healthily upright. Kay derived little profit from this famous invention, which was denounced by prejudiced weavers and pirated by unscrupulous employers: yet its immediate effect was to increase the pressure upon spinners to keep up with the weaver's demands for yarn, and in the long run it stimulated the development of the power-loom, to which it was successfully adapted.

The profitableness of the textile industry likewise produced improvements in the finishing process. Gig-mills for raising the nap on

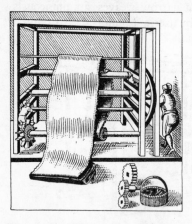

FIG. 39. Gig-mill for raising the nap on cloth, shown by Zonca, 1607

cloth were in existence in the fifteenth century, and were first sketched by Leonardo da Vinci. By the seventeenth century the common practice was to cover a roller with teazels; this rotated in one direction while other rollers carried the cloth over it in the opposite direction (Fig. 39). The importance of soap in fulling, especially of woollen cloth, was one of the factors in the rapid growth of the soap-boiling industry, which by the end of the seventeenth century had begun to use whale-oil, though the best qualities were still made with the olive oil of Mediterranean countries. In dyeing, there was an important advance when it was discovered about 1615 that red cochineal could be turned into a bright scarlet by the use of a salt made by dissolving pewter in nitric acid: the active principle was the tin present in the pewter, which might then contain up to 90 per cent. of this metal. Bleaching methods, however, were not substantially improved until just after 1750 (p. 536).

The history of glass-making to a great extent resembles that of textiles. This period witnessed the spread of the highest craftsmanship from Italy into the north; an important growth in the market for the finished product, though for obvious reasons export played a smaller part; and a series of technical improvements. In the case of glass, these last have the additional interest that they were not superseded at the coming of the industrial revolution.

Italian glass-making, of which the main centres were the Venetian suburb of Murano and Altare, near Genoa, owed its reputation at the end of the Middle Ages to three factors. Firstly, whereas northern Europe made its glass of local sands and alkali derived from vegetable ashes, the Italians used purer sources of both silica and soda. Secondly, they inherited the more refined technical tradition of the Mediterranean. Thirdly, and as a consequence, they were making a beautiful clear crystal suitable for the finest vessels, while northern Europe continued to concentrate upon window-glass. This Italian crystal, which was, however, seldom completely colourless, was gilded and then enamelled, coloured by the 'cane' technique (p. 86), or given a crazed surface by dipping it while still hot into cold water. The only enrichment not commonly applied was engraving: much of the glass was too delicately thin for any engraving-wheels available before the second half of the seventeenth century. Such glass had a great vogue abroad, and Italian glass-workers were eventually induced to emigrate, in spite of penalties, so that by the third quarter of the sixteenth century their art had spread across the Continent as far as Sweden and England.

What glass-making looked like at this time is depicted in a Tuscan wall-painting, in which the irons, shears, and tongs can be seen, with blowing in progress; in a big compartment above the furnace the glasses are slowly annealed by cooling. The expertness of the Italian glass-making deserved such commemoration, for the bottle- and window-glass of the mid-twentieth century is virtually identical with the mixture that they had been using for their glass since the Middle Ages.

As we have seen, it was well known even in Egyptian times that rich colours will be imparted to glass by adding certain minerals to the melt. Over the centuries the art of glass coloration steadily improved, although it necessarily remained on an empirical basis until the development of modern chemistry made possible a proper understanding of the processes involved. When so much of the glass industry was concerned with the manufacture of luxury articles, great attention was naturally paid to the production of clear colours. By medieval times the principal spectral colours could be achieved (p. 95), and intermediate ones by suitable blending, but red long presented a particular difficulty. While there is some evidence that the Assyrians knew how to make a ruby glass by incorporating gold in the melt, the use of gold for this purpose is essentially a seventeenth-century development. Glass-makers at Murano made a good red glass by adding copper oxide to the melt and heating it slowly in the absence of air. This glass was called *avventurino* (meaning 'chance') and is an excellent example of the fortuitous element in technological progress—an element which is of the first importance even today.

In England it became necessary to develop an independent line in glass-making as a result of a proclamation of 1615, which sought to economize timber by forbidding its use for glass-furnaces. Hence the development of the coal-burning furnace, with the fire laid on a grill of iron bars, which proved to yield higher temperatures than with wood. This in turn must have promoted the use of a covered pot, since sulphur compounds and smuts from the coal would be liable to discolour the glass. More important, however, was the work of George Ravenscroft, who from 1675 onwards rivalled the Venetian crystal with his flint-glass, made from a mixture of potash, lead oxide, and calcined flints. This heavy lead crystal received a severe check, however, when the British government in 1745 began to tax glass by weight. Germany and Bohemia meanwhile produced another rival to the Venetian crystal in a potash-lime glass, heavy and colourless, and particularly suitable for engraving. A huge demand for deeply-engraved glass was met by the use of a series of copper cutting-wheels, ranging from about 1 to 10 cm in diameter, on which dripped a mixture of oil and abrasive. The wheels were usually foot-driven by a treadle, although water-power was sometimes employed.

The most important new trade demand of the later seventeenth century was for the provision of plate glass in large sheets, only to be produced by casting. Colbert brought Italian workmen to blow glass for mirrors—such as are to be seen at Versailles, built up from small sections and by no means free from distortion; others set up the manufacture at about the same date in Lambeth. But the method of casting plate glass, though known to the Venetians, was first developed by the glass-makers of Normandy under royal patronage. For this, about 2,000 lb of glass was introduced by stages into a crucible as big as a large hogshead, heated sufficiently to disperse the bubbles, and then poured out on to the casting-table, which had movable guides to determine the size of the sheet. While still molten, a state in which it remained for scarcely a minute, the glass was rolled to produce a sheet of even surface and uniform thickness. After annealing for about ten days, the surface was ground with a smaller plate of glass, and polished with a felt-covered board and roller.

In making mirrors, which had acquired a practical importance for use in instruments of survey and navigation, besides their use for decoration and the toilet, the production of sheets of glass with absolutely plane surfaces, to give an undistorted image, was not the only difficulty. True silvering—the deposition of a bright film of metallic silver by chemical methods—was not practised before the mid-nineteenth century; instead, the necessary reflecting surface

FIG. 40. The German glass-furnace, 1752

behind the mirror was made of tin. This was a Venetian process, in which the clear and polished glass was coated with sheets of tinfoil, and mercury was poured on it, forming an amalgam. After several days the surplus mercury was drained off and the back of the mirror was varnished to protect it.

By the eighteenth century a cone-shaped glass-furnace had become usual in England. Its merits were conceded by the French Encyclopaedists, as it brought all the air currents into a single upward movement, which made for a uniform and economical provision of heat; it also produced a cooling draught for the workers. But the German furnace, described by the metallurgist Agricola two centuries earlier, was still the most usual type elsewhere (Fig. 40). This had a single stoke-hole for the fire; a floor above, in which the glass was melted in pipe-clay pots; and a cooler chamber above that, in which glass-ware was annealed.

Not all the uses of glass in this period can be called domestic. Mention has already been made of the importance of mirrors in optical instruments; that of the lens was still more fundamental, and may be allowed to conclude this chapter.

Although the nature of light was quite unknown until quite recent times, the study of optics is an ancient one. The law of reflection was certainly known as early as the fourth century B.C., and in the second century A.D. Ptolemy recognized that refraction was governed by a definite law, although the exact form of this was not known for another 1,500 years. In the tenth century the Islamic philosopher Ibn al-Haitham (Alhazen) was familiar with the properties not only of lenses and plane mirrors but also of spherical and paraboloidal mirrors. This knowledge was passed on to the west through Latin translations of his work: among those it influenced were Robert Grosseteste and his younger contemporary, Roger Bacon. Although Bacon certainly experimented with the use of convex lenses for correcting defects of vision, the inventor of spectacles is not known. The invention was probably made about 1286, and by the early fourteenth century their manufacture was well established at Venice. Early lenses were all convex and so could assist only long-sighted people: the concave lenses, necessary for the short-sighted, came nearly two centuries later. From the use of lenses to correct defective vision, instruments were developed designed to extend the power even of perfect eyesight. The origin of the telescope is obscure: although it was certainly Galileo who, in 1609, first made this into a scientific instrument, there is no doubt that there was a prior Dutch invention. The modern compound microscope, too, stems from the work of Galileo, though again he may have been anticipated by others. Theoretical optics developed rapidly and the underlying causes of two major defects of lenses were quickly discovered. In 1637 Descartes showed that spherical aberration (failure of the lens to give a rectilinear image) could be avoided if it were possible to grind lenses with paraboloidal surfaces; in 1671 Newton's famous experiments with the prism revealed the cause of chromatic aberration (light of different colours coming to a different focus).

These developments made new demands on glass technology. Firstly, it was necessary to remove all traces of cloudiness from glass used for optical purposes; and secondly, great care had to be taken to eliminate flaws and bubbles. Galileo, and his pupil Torricelli, much advanced the techniques of grinding lenses with spherical surfaces, using manual grinding and polishing, but paraboloidal surfaces were not achieved until the eighteenth century. The cure of chromatic aberration, by using compound lenses made from two different types of glass, also was not found until the eighteenth century: in the meantime, however, a way round the difficulty had been found, in the case of optical instruments, by employing mirrors —which reflect light of all colours in precisely the same way—in place of lenses. Lens-grinding machines were in use by the middle of the seventeenth century.

4

THE EXTRACTION AND WORKING OF METALS

THE EARLIEST USE OF METALS: THE BRONZE AGE

THIS subject has already been anticipated both by the use of the terms 'Bronze Age' and 'Iron Age' to cover main divisions of human history, and in our accounts of food and other production for domestic needs, which was seen to advance beyond the most primitive stage only through the use of metal tools. The history of metal-working resembles that of textiles and pottery in the astonishingly high artistic achievement of the early period. But the mining of the ores underground also marked an important new stage in the boldness of man's exploitation of his physical surroundings. To the author of the book of Job, writing in about the fourth century B.C., probably with the copper-mines of the Arabah and Sinai in mind, the work of the miner was still a superb example of technical ingenuity:

> He putteth forth his hand upon the flinty rock;
> He overturneth the mountains by the roots.
> He cutteth out passages among the rocks;
> And his eye seeth every precious thing.
> He stoppeth the streams from flooding;
> And the thing that is hid bringeth he forth to light.

The history of metal-working begins well before that of the extraction of metals from their ores, for a number of metals, such as gold, occur naturally in their uncombined state. The precious metals probably first attracted man's attention by their glitter and the same quality led to their extensive use for decorative purposes. Of metals useful mainly for strictly practical purposes, iron was literally heaven-sent, for iron from meteors was greatly prized for tool-making: much more recently, the iron in a meteor that fell in Greenland was utilized by Eskimos for more than a century. Copper was another metal originally known in its elementary state, though deposits of this kind were soon exhausted and extraction from ores became necessary.

The utilization of ores involves two separate processes: first, the separation of the metal from other elements with which it is chemically combined; and second, the working-up of the metal into useful articles. Metallic ores are, in the chemical sense, extremely varied, but in a large number of them the desired metal is combined with sulphur or oxygen. To separate the metal it is necessary to provide an alternative partner for this sulphur, oxygen, or other constituents of the ore. In many instances carbon is most satisfactory for this purpose and, since the chemical reaction usually takes place only at high temperatures, the furnace plays a paramount part in metal extraction processes. Carbon, which within the period we are now considering means almost invariably charcoal, provides both the means for reducing metals to their elementary state and the heat necessary for the reaction to take place. A further consequence of the high temperature is that the metal may be obtained in a molten condition and so can be run off from infusible impurities which remain behind as a slag; sometimes a flux is added to facilitate slag formation.

How such a relatively complicated process was first evolved by primitive man must be a matter for speculation, but there is at least plausibility in the suggestion that the first ore smelted was malachite, a green carbonate of copper. This ore occurs fairly widely in the Middle East, and from at least as early as the fifth millennium B.C. was used as a pigment, especially as a cosmetic for painting the lower eye-lid. Malachite is particularly easily reduced to copper, and if a little of the ore were dropped into a fierce wood fire a bead of copper would result. From such a chance discovery might have arisen the deliberate smelting of malachite and thence of other copper ores.

As regards the working-up of the metal, there were two main possibilities. One, which went back to the very earliest days, when man experimented with finds of pure metal which needed no smelting, was simply to shape the metal with hammer and anvil; at a very early stage it was discovered that hammering hardened the metal, but that if desired it could be made soft again by renewed heating. The other way of shaping the metal for use was to pour it while molten into a mould, giving it a rough shape which could be finished with the hammer. It appears that the ancient practice was to remelt metal for casting rather than to cast it straight from the furnace.

The above description applies to the principal metals and their alloys, except for iron, which will be considered later (p. 120). Of the others it may be appropriate to begin with the preparation of gold and silver, since, although the use of gold in the Near East did not necessarily precede that of copper, it quite frequently occurred in a form pure enough for immediate working. Gold in small quantities was to be found in many parts of the ancient world, such as the Caucasus, where the practice of straining alluvial deposits through wool is believed to be the origin of the legend of the Golden Fleece. Egypt, however, had something like a monopoly of its production —more than a hundred gold-mines in the Nubian desert, and others in the Eastern desert. Silver was the characteristic product not of Egypt but of north-east Asia Minor, the district associated with the Hittites, the name of whose capital was written with the ideograph for silver. Silver and lead were found together in the mineral galena (lead sulphide), which could be converted into a lead-silver alloy by roasting it to get rid of some of the sulphur and then heating it to a higher temperature, which further reduced the sulphur content and caused the alloy to form at the bottom of the furnace: the charcoal fuel prevented reoxidation. Sometimes, too, metallic silver underlay the seams of galena. The silver-lead alloy was melted in a porous clay crucible (the cupel) and a blast of air was blown upon it. The lead was thus oxidized and removed, the completion of the process being indicated by the sudden appearance of a shining button of silver. Cupellation, which was probably introduced about 3000–2500 B.C., was also employed to refine gold. The impure gold was mixed with lead and fused in the cupel; the lead and impurities were then removed by the air blast.

Silver and gold became standards of value, but weights and bars of copper and lead were used even earlier for the same purpose and continued to be circulated more frequently than the precious metals in actual payments. Copper was the first of the useful metals. Since native copper is rarely found in quantity, although lumps weighing several hundred tons are not unknown, its widespread use presupposes widespread mining, such as occurred in Asia Minor, Armenia, and Elam, from which the Sumerians received it as early as 3500 B.C.; in the island of Cyprus, whence the peoples of Italy imported it and named it *cuprum*; in the Egyptian centres described in the book of Job; and in many parts of Europe. In the earliest days stone tools were used by the miners; later, bronze ones. The vein of ore was by preference followed horizontally into the rock, occasionally for as much as 50 yds; but relics in Hungary reveal vertical shafts up to 6 ft in diameter, sometimes duplicated to provide ventilation, with access by notched tree-stems and even, in one case, a three-spoked wind-lass. Miners worked by the pillar-and-stall method, leaving pillars of ore intact to support the roofs of the passages which they cut into the vein. Where rock was a serious obstacle they broke it up by fire-setting, that is, lighting a fire to heat the rock, which could then be splintered by throwing on cold water. Early methods of mining metallic ores doubtless owed much to the practice of flint-miners, who had learnt to work at depths of about 30 to 40 ft (p. 6).

The extraction of metal from the widely different types of copper ore involved complicated smelting processes. In the eastern Alps, for instance, where some 20,000 tons of copper are believed to have been produced in the period 1300–800 B.C., ore and fuel were piled together for smelting, and after three successive stages of re-finement, the copper was still only about 95 per cent. pure. For fur-ther purification, it was necessary to melt the copper with charcoal and apply a blast of air.

Although there was apparently a true Copper Age in Egypt up to about 2000 B.C., that is to say, a period during which pure copper was utilized, the history of the use of this metal was from a very early date inextricably linked with that of tin. Copper of such purity as was yielded by ancient processes is a relatively soft metal; certain of its alloys therefore had far greater practical value. Outstanding among these was bronze, the alloy of copper and tin, its precise properties depending on the relative proportions of the two metals. The origin of bronze is uncertain, and may well have been different in different places, but it is reasonable to suppose that it was first discovered by the accidental smelting of mixed ores of copper and tin, such as are known to occur; not until very much later were different species of ore clearly distinguished. Before long, however, copper and tin ores were being deliberately mixed in predetermined proportions by European smelters.

An alternative way of obtaining bronze is to melt together definite quantities of metallic copper and tin, and this course seems to have been followed in the Near East. It is easy to extract quite pure tin from its principal ore, cassiterite, and the making of tin seems by 1500 B.C. at latest to have been well established in Europe, whence it was exported to the Near East. The notion of mixing tin with copper may have been another accident: it was not clearly distinguished from lead, which was already being added to copper to render its casting easier.

Another metal often alloyed with copper to make a bronze was antimony, derived from Caucasian ores; arsenic, too, was sometimes used by the Egyptians. Zinc-containing bronzes are well known, but as this metal was not clearly distinguished until the sixteenth century A.D., at earliest, its presence in ancient bronzes is presumably accidental. Analysis of such bronzes reveals the occurrence of many other metals that must have been present as impurities in the original ore and were simply carried through the smelting process: their presence must often have influenced the properties of the alloy.

As compared with flint implements, those of copper or bronze were not necessarily sharper, but they lasted longer, were much less brittle, and could be made in any shape desired. The smallest and simplest copper implements were forged direct from a lump of metal, but it was more usual to pour molten copper into a mould of stone or clay to give it its rough shape: for this purpose bronze was more convenient than copper because of its lower melting-point. Then the material was worked up by a series of hammerings, interspersed by annealings when it became too work-hardened; a careful final hammering gave the edge to axe, dagger, or other implement. Casting from a two-part mould (Fig. 41), which could give an all-round impress to the metal and then be opened up for its removal, was difficult with pure copper, because it absorbed gases which made blow-holes on cooling and so spoilt the castings: with bronze, however, it was fully practicable. The parts of the mould itself might be made of bronze (for accuracy) as well as the more usual stone, clay, or pottery; a tool or weapon could also be provided with a socket for a handle by the insertion of a clay core in the mould.

The finest bronze castings were made by the *cire perdue* or waste-wax process, the basis of which was the use of modelled wax inside the clay mould to fill the volume intended for the metal. When the mould was baked, the wax melted and escaped, leaving prearranged channels to admit the molten bronze; the mould was broken off after the metal had cooled.

The Bronze Age was characterized by the production of many of the craft tools of today: for example, the heavy sledge-hammer, the shaft-hole chopper-axe, the cold chisel, and the carpenter's rasp. As for weapons, the sword developed out of the dagger early in the Bronze Age; socketed spear-heads were introduced; and the decoration of battle-axes, to be judged by specimens from both Hungary and Persia, crosses the border-line between implements of use and works of art.

The contents of the royal cemetery of Ur, dating from the first half of the third millennium B.C., show that all but half a dozen of the metal-working processes of today were already in use. Three- or four-pieced clay moulds were commonly employed. Clay models sometimes provided the original shape for the mould, and where a

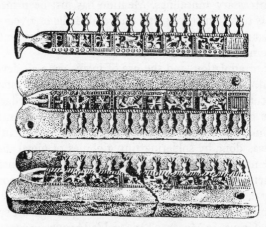

Fig. 41. Syrian double mould and a gold casting made from it, Ugarit, *c.* 1300 B.C.

large figure was concerned a core of some cheap substance was placed inside, so that the casting was hollow. For the largest castings of all, such as the huge basin of bronze which Hiram of Tyre made for Solomon's temple, the mould was excavated in a convenient patch of clay: 'In the Plain of Jordan did the king cast them, in the clay ground between Succoth and Zarethan' (1 Kings vii. 46). A thousand years or more of expert bronze-founding made possible the Egyptian renaissance in the seventh century B.C., and the bronze-work of classical Greece which followed. Bowls were beaten from sheet metal by cold-forging, with frequent annealings to diminish work-hardening, and a type of statue was laboriously worked and chased from copper sheets nailed to a wooden core or frame. The earliest examples are some figures of bulls, about 2 ft in height and length, together with a panel in relief, all in copper and made in Mesopotamia in the fourth millennium B.C.; from Egypt, in the same material, there is a (now fragmentary) life-size statue of an Egyptian pharaoh who reigned about 2300 B.C.

Much more might be said about the advanced technology of this early period. There was, for instance, extensive use of *repoussé* work—reliefs in sheet metal built up by punching from the back. Thus the cemetery at Ur contains a number of gold figurines of animals made of sheet gold a few thousandths of an inch thick, worked into high relief by a series of beatings and burnishings interspersed with the necessary annealings. Mention has just been made of the use of nails to fasten sheet metal on wood: nails or rivets were also used to fasten together pieces of metal, but brazing or soldering was the commonest method of joining.

Filigree, granulation, and the use of inlays were all developed in this period. The wire for the filigree had in the first instance to be made by cutting a continuous narrow strip from the edge of a circular sheet of metal: drawing wire through dies was known in 2500 B.C. Granulation is less common, but occurs in Tutankhamen's tomb: it was done by soldering tiny globules of metal to a base, a task of the utmost delicacy. *Cloisonné* work, formed in open-fronted cells of metal strip, was used as settings for precious stones. First devised by the Sumerians, it was brought to a climax in Egypt, as, for instance, on Tutankhamen's collarette. This prodigal art spread also to Europe. Graves at Mycenae have yielded bronze daggers from the sixteenth century B.C., with metal inlays portraying in gold, electrum (gold-silver alloy), and silver such scenes as a lion-hunt; but Homer himself, whose distant heroes sleep in those graves, belonged to the new age in which 'the iron of itself draws a man on'.

THE EARLY IRON AGE OF GREECE AND ROME

The Bronze Age had rested upon two difficult techniques: the miner's work in the dark bowels of the earth, and the smelting together or mixing together of two metals (one of which, tin, was always in short supply) to form an alloy. Since iron ore, in the form of bog-ore, was plentiful enough on the surface to dispense for a very long time with any need of mining, and since the metal had multifarious uses without admixture, it is at first sight surprising that the long Iron Age dawned so late. For it does not really begin until about 1200 B.C., when the destruction of the Hittite empire scattered the smiths, though a few pieces of man-made iron were in circulation before 2500 B.C., and iron ornaments and ceremonial weapons soon after 2000 B.C. Two reasons may be suggested for the delay. The early finds of meteoric iron (p. 114) would not prompt any inquiry into the iron ore of the earth, with which they had no obvious connexion. Moreover, an experimental smelting of iron ore to see if it behaved like ores of copper or other known metals would be most discouraging: because pure iron melts at 1,535° C. (compared with 1,083° C. for copper), experiments in smelting it would produce only a mass of slag and cinders concealing unmelted globules of iron. Until the introduction of the blast-furnace in the Middle Ages there was no means of producing molten iron for casting, though from pre-Christian times the furnace temperature was increased either by securing a better natural draught or by using bellows. Repeated hammerings at red heat were required in order to beat most of the slag out of the bloom of crude iron, before it was usable.

But the wrought iron so obtained, though tougher than other available metals, would not take a satisfactorily sharp edge: this was obtainable only with steel, iron containing approximately 0·15–1·5 per cent. of carbon and no residual slag. The problem was only half solved by the invention of cementation, apparently by the 'Chalybes' of Asia Minor, a subject-tribe of the Hittite empire, in about 1400 B.C.; this was a process for steeling wrought-iron bars by repeated hammerings and heatings in direct contact with charcoal, which diffuses carbon into the surface regions of the metal. Some exceptional iron ores yield steel directly if the smelting process is sufficiently elaborated; it was obtained in this way—but much later, about 500 B.C.—in the central European region of Styria and Carinthia, the Roman Noricum. Meanwhile, it had still to be learnt that steel required to be further hardened by quenching the hot metal in cold water, the effect of which upon copper or bronze, which had already been in use for a thousand years or more, was to make it softer. This tempering process seems to have originated about two centuries after cementation. Thus it was not until the last millennium B.C. that ancient iron metallurgy reached its height, and even then it was the metallurgy of the smith with his hammer and his bellows, cast iron being virtually unobtainable with the small furnaces and low temperatures of that period.

Iron began as an ornament, and then slowly became the material for swords and daggers. Iron spear-heads were difficult to make because of the need for a socket, not easily achieved except by casting, and iron battle-axes seem to have been rare, though one has been found in Syria dating from about 1300 B.C.; it had a socket of gold and copper. But the sword was the main gift of the early Iron Age, for bronze was comparatively brittle. The force of the stroke was now limited only by the strength of the human arm; hence the great power of the iron-girt Assyrians when they came down 'like the wolf on the fold'.

New tools of the Iron Age included the hinged tongs without which the smith's work would have been impossible, anvils for making nails, wire-drawing dies, and frame-saws almost identical with the modern hack-saw. The iron file was useful in every kind of metal-working, whereas the earlier bronze file had been little more than a carpenter's rasp. In general, as iron could be made harder, so the older types of tools were improved, until most small hand-tools had something of the quality as well as the traditional shape that they have today.

But we must beware of exaggeration and anticipation. The new metal was used first for weapons; then for the hoe and the axe and pick of the farm and mine; lastly, for the improved tools that we have been describing. Words are deceptive: the iron of early classical Greece, which was not considered suitable, apparently, for plough-shares, was evidently a very inferior metal compared with the properly hardened and tempered material that served the Roman legions about the beginning of the Christian era. Nevertheless, the Greek civilization of the sixth century B.C. was founded upon iron, while the spread of Roman power, which eventually carried that civiliza-tion to the farthest limits of the western world, was associated with iron throughout its long history. Iron-mines which the Etruscans started in Tuscany and Elba about 900 B.C. early attracted the covetousness of the Romans, and there were few of the imperial provinces from Spain to alpine Noricum and Dalmatia where iron-mining was not among the certain rewards of, and probable incen-tives to, conquest.

In a survey, however brief, of mining in the classical world, pride of place must be given to the silver-mines of Laurion, which the Athenians worked from 600 B.C. after a much earlier Mycenaean exploitation. Large mines were nearly always worked by prisoners, including prisoners-of-war, whose lives and limbs were deemed en-tirely expendable. But the imagination is caught by the contrast between the admired democracy of Athens and these slave-worked Attic mines, from which that democracy derived a considerable part of its wealth and consequent leisure. The ore was mostly galena, producing about 60 oz. of silver to the ton. Extraction was in two stages. First, the silver-lead alloy obtained by smelting was repeatedly melted and allowed to crystallize, when almost pure lead first separated. When the silver content had risen to between 1 and 2 per cent., the silver was extracted by cupellation. It was not very efficiently done, however, and the slag-heaps were subsequently re-worked with profit more than once, as in many other old mining areas, including the lead-mines which were worked for three centuries on Mendip during the Roman occupation of Britain.

FIG. 42. Greek miners, from a Corinthian clay tablet of the sixth century B.C.

By about the end of the first century A.D., when work at Laurion ceased until modern times, some 2,000 shafts had been sunk, the deepest reaching to about 350 ft. Access was by a series of ladders or notched tree trunks, fixed to the sides of the shafts, the ore being hauled up by rope and pulley in the middle. The roofs of the galleries were supported by leaving pillars of poorer ore unworked. Ventilation was achieved by having parallel galleries, ventilation doors, and sometimes fires to increase the draught. The miners worked by lamplight with pick and basket (Fig. 42). On reaching the surface, the ore was ground to powder and then washed to separate the heavy particles of ore from lighter rock: this process of ore-concentration had been practised by gold-miners in Egypt as early as 3000 B.C.

Roman mining is distinguished above all by its scale and extent (Fig. 43). Even in remote Britain they regularly exploited lead (with its silver), copper, iron, and tin. Condemned criminals (*damnati in metallum*) and slaves were probably a declining element in the total labour force as compared with the free native labour available in every province; a miner began to be recognized as a skilled craftsman. The most important technical advance made by the Romans was to apply both the Archimedean screw and the scoop-wheel to mine drainage. The former may have originated for irrigation in Egypt before the time of Archimedes; in any case it was the Romans who made the *cochlea* (water-snail), as they called it from its shape, into a regular mining instrument. As for the latter, at one of the Rio Tinto copper-mines the water was raised to a total height of nearly 100 ft by employing eight successive pairs of scoop-wheels powered by tread-

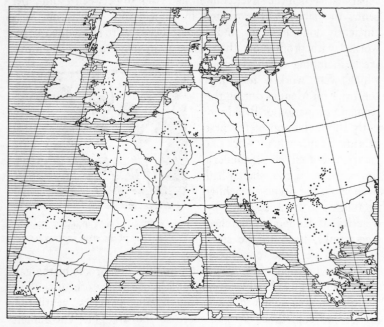

FIG. 43. Positions of Roman mines in Europe

mills. Few surface deposits of ore were overlooked by the Romans, but deeper strata, even if located, could not be profitably exploited when shortage of labour became an acute problem, as it did in the last centuries of the empire's history. Moreover, the extraction of metals from their ores, to which we now turn, still depended upon charcoal smelting, which became increasingly expensive with the serious deforestation of the Mediterranean area.

One important development in Roman metallurgy was the use of mercury for the extraction of gold. About the beginning of the Christian era mercury was produced for the first time in Spain by distillation, its ore (usually the sulphide) being roasted in a furnace fitted with a simple device to condense the vapour. Gold occurs not only in the alluvial form already mentioned (p. 116), which can be separated by the panning methods still employed in the gold rushes of modern times, but also as an ore sparsely distributed in hard rock. To extract this gold the Romans crushed the ore and then treated it with mercury, in which the gold became dissolved as an amalgam. The mercury was then filtered through leather and distilled: the gold was left behind in the still, and the distillate of mercury recovered for further use. The Romans also increased their production of gold and silver by extracting them from copper by the liquation process. This depends on the fact that, when copper is melted together with a large quantity of lead, they do not dissolve in each other but form two immiscible liquids, like oil and water. Precious metals present in the copper become transferred to the lead, from which they are recoverable by cupellation.

In the mining of tin the most important change was the closing of the Spanish mines about the middle of the third century A.D., and the exhaustion of sources of stream-tin generally. In consequence the vein-ore in Cornwall, which had been mined since the third millennium B.C., giving rise to the name 'the British metal', began to be exploited with a new vigour. Some of the tin was compounded with 30 per cent. of lead to make pewter, which was popular for vessels used in Roman households; in the Middle Ages the proportion of tin in pewter was a good deal smaller. But most of it was devoted to the making of bronze, for which the Romans exploited a very rich supply of copper in Spain. Copper was exported as far afield as India, and the making of copper- and bronze-ware was developed on a factory basis at Capua, the uniform products from which are found not only throughout Italy but even as far away as Finland. A new alloy was brass. This, a variably composed alloy of copper and zinc, may possibly be identified with the 'white bronze' that was used to embellish the palace doors of Sargon II, but it did not reach the west until the time of Augustus, who struck a brass coinage: even then, it continued to be at least six times as expensive as copper, and in some parts of the ancient world it was more highly valued than silver. Until the sixteenth century A.D. pure zinc was unknown; brass was made by a cementation process, in which calamine (zinc carbonate), copper, and charcoal were roasted together.

European iron metallurgy had its first main centre from the tenth century B.C. in Noricum, to which it had spread from the Hittite empire. After about 400 years the centre moved to the Celtic lands, and especially to Spain, where the smiths developed the

Catalan iron furnace, in which two pairs of bellows were used alternately so as to maintain a constant blast. There were also two-storied shaft-furnaces, the narrow lower part being filled with charcoal, the wider upper part with ore and charcoal mixed. The Catalan furnace produced a malleable iron direct, the shaft-furnace a more highly carbonized bloom, which required subsequent forging; in neither case was the temperature high enough to produce liquid iron for casting. Some steel was produced direct from the iron-ore of Noricum; more was made by the cementation process already described (p. 121). But the best steel known to the Romans was the so-called 'Seric iron', which they supposed to be Chinese; it was actually 'wootz'—a high-carbon crucible steel, made in round cakes a few inches in diameter, which reached Rome via Abyssinia from southern India, its name being probably a corruption of the Kanarese word for steel.

Though the exploitation of metals by the Greeks and Romans involved relatively few new processes and was never conducted on a sufficiently large scale to produce an industrial revolution, or even a concentration of industry in the modern sense, it nevertheless left important marks on the arts both of war and peace.

The defensive armour and shield of the Greek hoplite were made of bronze, but his main weapons were a 9-ft spear tipped with iron and a short, straight iron sword. The Romans were originally equipped as the Greeks, but the legions eventually developed the use of an iron cuirass, made of jointed plates and strips overlapped for extra strength. They used a longer sword, but their main weapon was a throwing-spear of the same length as the Greek spear, but divided equally between a wooden shaft and an iron head. The two halves were originally riveted together, but later a wooden pin, which broke on impact, was used in order that the weapon should be rendered useless to the enemy; the same object was afterwards achieved by making the iron soft enough to bend below the point. The use of cavalry was taught to the west by the east, but the famous cavalry squadrons of Alexander the Great wore heavier armour than the hoplites. Three centuries later the Parthian cataphracts who defeated the Roman attempts to extend their empire beyond the Euphrates, were not only fully armoured themselves but had similar protection for their horses. Both their armour and their bow—with which on retiring they fired the famous Parthian shot—were subsequently imitated by the Romans.

Neither the cross-bow nor the various forms of twisted-rope artillery, in which the Romans followed Carthaginian, and especially Greek, practice, were built of metal, though the arrow had an iron tip and the catapult sometimes fired an iron-headed dart weighing about 6 lb (p. 248). In the days of the Assyrians, however, sieges had been dominated by the battering-ram with its heavy iron head. They generally mounted it on wheels; the Greeks added a high timber framework for swinging the ram pendulum-fashion, the Romans a *terebra* to bore into the battered wall or gate. But resistance to siege was an art in which the Romans were past masters. The great walls which they left behind them between the Danube and the Main and across northern Britain are a reminder of this. So are the marks of the temporary encampments, each with its ditch and rampart, which the legionaries were taught to erect for themselves almost as a matter of course with the iron tools they carried on the march.

The structural use of iron in the classical period is mentioned elsewhere (pp. 165, 166); greater interest attaches to the use of metals in small works of art, where the Greeks and Etruscans set an astonishingly high standard of production for Rome to imitate. Inspiration still came from the east: the Greeks of the fifth century B.C., for example, were deeply influenced by the jewelled metal-work of the Persian court. But the Greeks and the Etruscans often improved upon their oriental masters—as, for instance, in the delicacy of their granulation and filigree work. The work of the Romans is perhaps less subtle, though they understood how to do *repoussé* work on silver so as to maximize the play of light: the massive gold medallions of their emperors are a more characteristic achievement.

As regards new techniques of ornamentation, Europe in the late Mycenaean period provided the first specimens of true enamel-work, that is, vitreous material fused on to a metallic base, which appears in the decoration of some gold rings preserved in Cyprus. They were made by firing tiny fragments of broken glass, arranged as a disk inside the round *cloisons* of gold. Similar small spots of enamel were used by the Greeks from the sixth or fifth century onwards, and later by the Celts. New in scale and material, if not strictly speaking in technique, were the great Greek chryselephantine statues (p. 15), the Parthenon Athene and Olympian Zeus. Ivory was used to simulate flesh, and the draperies were made of sheets of beaten gold, and could be removed. In the third century B.C. the same kind of *repoussé* work was used for the bronze plates which were laid over columns of stone to form the 124-ft high image of the sun god, known as the Colossus of Rhodes. The Greeks also achieved remarkable success in the casting of large figures in bronze, using a number of clay moulds and afterwards riveting or welding the parts together.

The use of coins, which appears to have developed at about the same time, but independently, in the Far and Near East, became known to the Greek merchants of Asia Minor as a practice introduced by Lydian kings, who had stamped their lion's-head badge upon ingots of electrum having a standard weight and fineness. According to tradition, the mainland Greeks first minted silver soon after 700 B.C. at Aegina, where silver pieces of a given weight were stamped with a turtle. The device was cut in reverse form with hammer and chasing tools on to a piece of bronze or iron, which was recessed in an anvil; a disk of the metal to be coined was then struck into the recess with a plain punch. But within a century it was thought desirable to mark both sides of the coin, so a second device was cut, into the head of the punch. The blank disks for coining were cast by pouring metal into a series of shallow depressions in baked clay or stone. The design being in very high relief, it required great force to bring it out properly. Nevertheless, it seems remarkable that traditions of die-cutting and minting, unlike many of the finer techniques of classical metal-work, did not survive the fall of the Roman empire in the west, an event which was foreshadowed as early as the third century by a decline in metallurgical output.

METAL-WORKING IN THE MIDDLE AGES

Practically nothing is known about mining in the Dark Ages, not even whether the coins issued by Anglo-Saxon and Carolingian monarchs were made from old metal or from the products of new mining. By the time of Charlemagne, the great Spanish mines had passed into the hands of the Moors; output at first declined, but it was the Moors who discovered means of utilizing sulphide ores of copper, from which they obtained copper sulphate by oxidization. When the sulphate was dissolved in water and run over iron, pure copper was deposited. But the severance of Spain from Mediterranean Christendom is perhaps more important as part of the process by which, when the scene becomes clear again, the centre of European mining is found to have been transferred to the Saxon miners of central Europe. They were at work in the Harz mountains

before A.D. 1000, at Freiberg about 1170, and in the following century as far afield as Hungary.

By a fortunate chance the mining methods in vogue in the later
Middle Ages have been thoroughly recorded by an outside skilled
observer—such as is almost wholly lacking in the earlier history of
technology. The observer was the physician Georg Bauer (commonly
Latinized as Agricola), a Saxon who had studied medicine in Italy
but practised in the Bohemian mining district of Joachimsthal. In
his day this was famous chiefly for silver, which had been found there
in 1516 in such profusion that the valley gave its name to a silver
coin known as the *thaler*, the eponym of the modern dollar. But as the
district had long been famous for the mining of base metals (it is
today famous for uranium), the twelve books of the *De re metallica*,
published in 1556, are a fair guide to late medieval methods in a
strongly traditional industry.

Agricola tells us that the section of the mine-shaft was normally
about 10 ft by a little over 1 ft. His fine illustrations of equipment
show that it was not very different from that of earlier periods, except for a truck designed to run in a groove (p. 212). He regards the
windlass as the normal means of hauling the ore up the shaft, and
records the use of geared wheels and the horse-whim for large loads
(Fig. 44). He is aware of problems of mine ventilation, of dangerous
conditions in which 'burning lamps are also extinguished', and of
workings abandoned on account of poisonous 'damps' or bad air;
he reports the use of revolving fans and bellows. It is clear that the
water-wheel was a normal source of power (Fig. 45).

From the standpoint of later history, however, most interest
attaches to Agricola's very detailed consideration of problems of
mine drainage, which had held up development, especially in Saxony,
in the preceding century. He mentions as a 'seventh kind of pump
invented ten years ago' a sequence of three suction pumps raising
the water in succession, all of which had their piston rods drawn
up by a single water-wheel 15 ft high. Since about 30 ft was the
maximum height to which the suction of a single pump could draw
water (p. 313), resort was had to the rag-and-chain pump, which
had been in existence long enough for six different varieties to be
described by Agricola. The carefully stuffed balls were fixed at intervals on the chain, and on entering the barrel of the pump each in turn
acted as a one-way piston, driving up the water before it. Agricola instances a series of three such pumps at Chemnitz, in the Carpathians,

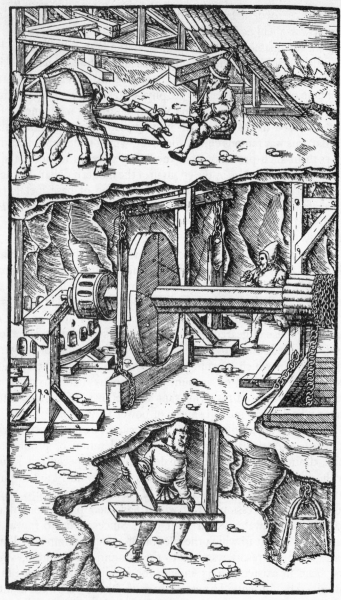

FIG. 44. Use of horse-whim in mining. Agricola, 1556

worked by ninety-six horses to a depth of 660 ft. 'These horses go
down to the machines by an inclined shaft, which slopes and twists
like a screw and gradually descends.' Such elaborate contrivances
are evidence that, by the close of the Middle Ages, mining had become a highly profitable industry. They are also evidence that
among the miners themselves there were groups of technicians competent to develop and operate complicated machinery.

In metal-working, as distinct from the mining of metallic ores, a
decline began before the fall of the Roman empire in the west and
continued in the Dark Ages. Surviving material has not yet been at
all fully examined, but it would appear that the working of other
metals was interrupted more seriously than that of iron; no darkness
could obscure the need for tools and weapons. Skills that had been
practised in Roman Gaul survived in Merovingian France, and there
were some Syrian experts working in western Europe, while by the
eighth century there were books in circulation describing Byzantine
skills. Great skill was expended on the forging of swords and the
decoration of their handles and scabbards. The most remarkable surviving product of the age is a type of pattern-welded sword, which
contained strips of iron rod, about $\frac{1}{100}$ in. thick and $\frac{1}{8}$ in. wide, twisted
in either direction and running the full length of the blade, giving
worm-like markings on the surface. Such welding required great
skill, and the works of Burgundian and Frankish smiths were even
imported by the Arabs.

Two of the most interesting medieval uses of metals may be
traced from the revival of western Christendom in the age of Charlemagne. One is the building of church organs with pipes of copper or
bronze. The organ had been well known in the ancient world: the
problem of providing an even wind-pressure by mechanical means
had engaged the attention of both the great Alexandrian mechani-
cians, Ctesibius and Heron. Its use in Christian services appears to
have begun at Constantinople in the fourth century, and St Jerome
tells of an organ at Jerusalem, with two elephant-skins for a wind-
chest, which was audible a mile away. The Franks received their
first as a gift from the Byzantine emperor in 757, and by the tenth
century organs were fairly common in England as well as in France
and Germany: St Dunstan, for instance, installed two, and there was
one in Winchester cathedral said to be furnished with 400 bronze
pipes and 26 bellows. The pipes were at first operated by pulling
rods, but a keyboard was employed at Magdeburg cathedral before

FIG. 45. Overshot wheel used for raising water from mines. Agricola, 1556

1100; the pedals were added before the end of the Middle Ages. By the time of Samuel Pepys, who longed to buy one, small organs were a not unusual amenity in private houses.

The casting of church bells in bronze likewise dates from the eighth century, their predecessors having been made of sheet-iron, like the small Roman table-bell. Probably the *cire perdue* process

FIG. 46. Foundry for casting bronze cannon, with power supplied by treadmill, sixteenth century

was used at first; later, the bell was cast between a core and an out-side cope, the former being covered and the latter lined with a care-fully dried loam mixed with horse-hair and manure. In the eleventh century a bell weighing 2,600 lb, at Orleans, was still thought large, but the size of the mould increased—hence the 'bell-fields' adjoining some great churches, where bells have been cast on the spot—so that the experience of the bell-founder eventually prepared the way for the casting of cannon (Fig. 46).

Meanwhile, Charlemagne's contemporaries were learning to ap-preciate the importance of armour in war, especially for the horse-man. Not many of the Germanic peoples who overran the Roman empire in the west had originally adopted the armour and armour-making of the Romans, which survived chiefly in the Byzantine empire: interlaced chain mail was at first brought from the east. But the medieval smith came to be above all an armourer, who equipped the feudal knight with anything up to 100 lb of mail or plate. Rings of iron wire were welded or riveted together to form the mail,

FIG. 47. Chain mail, from the effigy of Aymer de Valence (d. 1324) in Westminster Abbey

which was shaped to cover the feet and arms and even the head (Fig. 47); by the twelfth century the latter might be completely cased (apart from holes for eyes and nose) in a helm of steel. By the fourteenth century plate armour, which was originally a reinforcement of chain mail, was taking its place. The skill of the smith was then shown both in finish and in inlay, but most practically in contriving protection where the plates were jointed (Fig. 48).

A key event of the Middle Ages was the gradual colonization of large regions in east central Europe, in which German and other settlers developed not only mining but the working of metals. Ores containing silver attracted the most eager attention, as we might expect. But in addition to the steel-yielding iron ores of Styria and Carinthia, there were important developments in the production of copper in both Saxony and Sweden; of lead, produced about equally in central Europe and England; of Cornish tin; and eventually of zinc. Smelting and cupellation, however, were largely conducted by the old methods, and new developments are to be found chiefly in the metallurgy of iron.

The older types of iron smelting continued throughout the Middle Ages, often at hillside sites where a good natural draught was available. Both the Catalan furnace and a rather simpler Corsican type continued in use, side by side with the *Stückofen*—basically Roman in origin—of Styria and the Rhineland. This was a furnace ten or more feet high, in which the ore underwent continuous reduction by charcoal. The forging process was assisted by the use of water-driven hammers, and by the fourteenth century there were water-driven stamping-mills to crush the ore. Since water-power was also needed to work the bellows of large furnaces, the industry tended to move away from the mining areas toward the neighbourhood of fast-moving streams—a change which militated against the use of coal in forges.

FIG. 48. Armourer's workshop of the early sixteenth century, showing some of its products and the tools used in making them

Coal had been so used at Liège before 1200, and in the later Middle Ages was found among blacksmiths and iron-smelters in England and other countries of western Europe, but never on a scale to rival the use of charcoal. A more decisive innovation, which slowly established itself between the thirteenth and fifteenth centuries, was the casting of iron, made possible by higher furnace temperatures and the production of an iron having a relatively high carbon-content: cast iron was a virtually new commodity, which came into its own with the rise of artillery. Extraction processes were still very inefficient, however, and it must have been rare for as much as half the iron to be recovered from the ore. Meanwhile, from the eighth century onwards, steel-making, chiefly by the cementation process, was the speciality of Styria and Carinthia, the product being sold as far away as Turkey and England.

The iron implements of the Middle Ages included the tools of the farmer, the craftsman, and the soldier, made for the most part in the traditional way. The best swords, for instance, were at one time forged

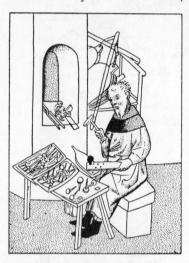

in the north of Italy, and the art was carried thence to Solingen in the Rhine valley as a consequence of the Italian wars of Frederick Barbarossa. Scythes, on the other hand, were especially a Styrian product, and iron needles—first with a hook and then with a true eye—were first made in south Germany, where water-power was applied in the fourteenth century to the making of iron wire by the draw-plate method. The nail-maker also was a specialist (Fig. 49). A specialist tool-maker likewise provided the more elaborate equipment of the mason and the carpenter, especially the drill-bit

FIG. 49. German nail-maker, late fifteenth century

and the brace for turning the drill. Nevertheless, the tools of medieval tradesmen, including those whose trade was war, were made chiefly by the blacksmith, who wrought the iron in his forge and was encouraged to imitate, and compete against, the specialist by the high cost of long-distance transport.

That the fine metal-work of the Greeks and Romans continued into the age of the barbarian successor states in the west is shown convincingly by the treasures of the mid-seventh-century ship burial at Sutton Hoo, Suffolk. These include a number of hanging-bowls with enamel decoration; a purse-mount of gold, ivory, and garnets, said to be the greatest surviving jewel of that age; garnets set in gold *cloisonné* with such refinement that there is even patterned gold-foil laid at the bottom of each cell to enhance its brilliance; and no less than ten round bowls 9 inches in diameter, made by spinning on a lathe a sheet of silver nailed to a recessed piece of wood. Inlaying has a continuous history from the fifth-century sword of Childeric, through the enamel plaques on the crown which was set on the head of the emperor Conrad II in 1027, to the bronze doors inlaid with silver which decorated the great medieval churches of Germany and Italy.

Enamel-work is found commonly, not only of a *cloisonné* type with the glass held by narrow metal strips or wire but also with the space for the enamel sunk or carved in relief, or even with the enamel painted—though this last process belongs to the later fifteenth century. The richest early example is the superb Ardagh chalice, which has enamelled grounds to its silver bosses and panels of enamel on the foot, but the most famous is the 'Alfred jewel'. Enamelling was applied chiefly to enrich the sacred treasures of the Church, and practised first in workshops attached to monasteries, fine work being produced especially at Limoges and in the valleys of the Rhine and the Meuse. Later, however, there was cheaper work in gilded copper, made in lay factories by craftsmen who, like the bell-founders, brought their skill and their tools to new places, stimulating demand by the availability of their products.

Casting of gold and bronze continued without interruption from the Roman period. Moulds from the Viking age found in the Ork-neys, for instance, were formed by joining together two clay im-pressions of a model wooden sword; after hard baking, they were buried in a casting-pit to be filled with molten bronze. At the begin-ning of the twelfth century, by way of contrast, we find such a marvel of the *cire perdue* process as the Gloucester candlestick, an 18-in. stand with most intricate carving, cast in bronze from a single mould and subsequently chased and gilded (Fig. 50). Thereafter the chief limitation was the problem of handling molten metal in quantity: thus the goldsmith who cast the early bronze effigies of the English king Henry III and his daughter-in-law Eleanor of Castile, which are 4 in. thick, is believed to have had the help of bell-founders. A century or so later the demand for objects of cast metal resulted in the adoption of the modern practice of casting in sand and using linked moulding-boxes. As with so many of the more obvious in-ventions, the adoption of this one had been delayed by the circum-stances of sporadic production, for the travelling caster, who could always be sure of finding local clay, would not want to add moulding boxes to the equipment on his back.

The crude designs of early medieval coinage bear witness to a break of continuity with the fine engraving of imperial Rome (p. 128). By 850 the coinage of gold had been completely discontinued in western Europe, and though reckonings were still made in silver pounds, silver pennies were the only western coins in circulation. Dies were made in local mints by largely untrained workers (Fig. 51), and both the device and the lettering came to be formed by punches in a limited range of shapes. The design was in low relief and therefore easier to strike, and, to avoid the risk of striking through, many of the large thin coins were struck on one face only, a reversion to the most primitive practice. By the thirteenth century love of heraldic display and commercial pride were producing finer work as increasing supplies of silver became available for minting, and by the mid-fourteenth century all the richer states had also begun to coin gold in emulation of Florence, which struck its first florin in 1252. But the engraving of dies did not return until the Italian Renaissance.

FIG. 50. Gilt bronze candlestick from church of St Peter, Gloucester, early twelfth century

The Black Death (1348–50) caused a labour-shortage, wage crisis, and price rise, all of which helped to precipitate a decline in metal production and working, lasting until the middle of the following century. The Hundred Years War (1337–1453) was another contributary factor, at least in France, and, more generally, the exhaustion of the more easily worked mines; yet it is in this very period that metal-working acquired the particular importance which has attached to it throughout modern times in connexion with fire-arms. Apart from the production of armour already mentioned, the smith had served the warrior of the Middle Ages above all through his skill in the forging of sword-blades of improving quality. Otherwise, the chief new contribution of metal to the older art of war was the introduction about 1370 of the steel cross-bow, an extremely powerful weapon that was bent mechanically. This was not ousted from the battlefield by the hand-gun for about a hundred years,

FIG. 51. Striking coins, from a twelfth-century Norman carving

and was still used for hunting in the early seventeenth century.

But the record of medieval metallurgy may be appropriately closed with the invention of the cannon, which came into common use in the second quarter of the fourteenth century. Its immediate antecedent may well have been an iron bucket with a small touch-hole near the bottom, employed by the Moors, perhaps as early as 1250, to propel a load of stones by the explosion of an underlying charge of 1–2 lb of gunpowder (p. 268). To begin with, cannon were very small, some only 20–40 lb in weight, but about the middle of the century they began to be cast from bronze, possibly

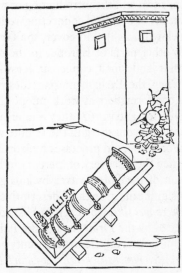

FIG. 52. Fourteenth-century cannon

also from copper or brass. Then came the forged iron guns, such as Richard II bought for the Tower of London, which might weigh as

much as 600 lb; these were made from iron bars, arranged longitudinally upon a core and then welded together: after removal of the core the
barrel was bound with iron hoops (Fig. 52). This in turn was followed
early in the fifteenth century by the casting of iron cannon in a mould,
a process which spread from western Germany with the rise in
blast-furnace temperatures (p. 135). It was already clear, not only
that feudal chivalry and the stone castle were doomed, but that the
emerging modern state, through its reliance upon artillery, to say
nothing of the newer hand-gun, would have a direct interest in the
progress of metallurgy.

EXTENSION OF THE USE OF METALS, 1500–1750

The early centuries of modern history, however, record little in
the way of spectacular changes in metallurgical techniques. Instead,
they are marked by the impact of rising capital, which stimulated
the use on a large scale of methods already known or foreshadowed.
Two examples from sixteenth-century Germany are the increasing
of the supply of silver by a widespread application of the liquation
process to copper ores, which had been practised by the Romans
(p. 125); and the introduction of water-power to high-level mines by
means of overland connecting-rod systems from wheels in the valley
below (p. 258). Moreover, the Germans carried their technical skill
to other parts of Europe: in the reign of Elizabeth I they began to
mine and smelt copper at Keswick, so that before the Civil War
(when the Parliamentarians destroyed their buildings) there were
4,000 foreigners at work among the mountains of the English Lake
District; and in 1623 they established silver-mining on a considerable
scale at Kongsberg in the remote wilderness of Norway. In the New
World, too, old processes took on a new lease of life, as, for instance,
when the discovery of mercury in Peru about 1550 facilitated extraction of the Potosi silver by amalgamation (p. 125). There was also
a significant growth of descriptive literature. Agricola's great work,
De re metallica (p. 129), published posthumously in 1556, was preceded by the *Pirotechnia* of the Italian Biringuccio, and followed at a
similar interval—less than twenty years—by the *Beschreibung allerfür-
nemsten mineralischen Ertzt- unnd Berckwercksarten* of the Bohemian
German Lazarus Ercker, giving more detailed information on
assaying. Iron, however, though by then enormously important,
receives little attention in these books, and it was not until 1722
that iron-making processes were reliably described by Réaumur,

in his *L'Art de convertir le fer forgé en acier et l'art d'adoucir le fer fondu.*

Certain minor metals became more familiar in this period. Thus the preparation of the semi-metal arsenic was precisely described for the first time in 1641, although, as we have noted, arsenic-bronzes had been made by the Egyptians; it was used with copper and tin in the making of metal mirrors. Antimony is easily smelted from stibnite, its principal ore, and was well known to the ancient world; it was an ingredient of bronzes, but for long was not clearly distinguished from lead. Bismuth was employed in type metal before 1500.

Lead was very widely used, not only as before in building, but for the making of shot (often in an alloy with arsenic), and after 1670 for the sheathing of boats, where it had the unwelcome and then inexplicable effect of corroding the iron rudder fixtures, as copper did later. There was also widespread use of tin in the manufacture of a variety of small wares, and for the tinning of sheet iron to make tinplate, which was originally a German manufacture, first imitated elsewhere with any success in France under Colbert. In the early eighteenth century, however, it was made at Pontypool by rolling red-hot bar iron in various thicknesses, tinplate being particularly in demand for food-containers and other utensils on shipboard. The British process involved steeping the sheets in a solution of sal ammoniac and standing them in an infusion of bran and water; the sheets were then dipped in molten tin (covered with whale oil or tallow to prevent oxidation of the surface), and the final irregularities were removed by cold-rolling. Molten lead or tin could be formed into cast sheets by running it down a sand-bed; but in the seventeenth century lead sheets were produced more cheaply and evenly in rolling-mills. Except for some uses of the precious metals—in certain gold coins, for example, or in gold-leaf—the main employment of all these metals was in alloys.

A tin-lead alloy was used for soldering, but the more important alloy was pewter, the best qualities of which had the highest proportion of tin, together with brass and bismuth. It was easily cast in clay or sand moulds, the better qualities of pewter-ware then being finished with the hammer. The simplicity of the casting process almost certainly influenced the early printers, using moulds of soft stone or metal, to favour a special quality of pewter for their type (p. 239).

Throughout medieval and Renaissance times, brass continued to be produced in crucibles containing calamine, charcoal, and copper scrap, heated by a conical furnace below ground. Zinc for alloying with copper to make brass was imported from the Far East, chiefly by the Dutch, or collected as a by-product from furnaces in which silver and lead ores were smelted, but it was a surprisingly long time before the metal was recognized as being the essential constituent of calamine. In the sixteenth century Paracelsus identified it as a bastard form of copper, but it was not until the early eighteenth century that the metal won from calamine was identified with the *calaëm* brought from the east. The smelting of zinc was established at Swansea about 1720 and at Bristol in 1740, two cities which are still the principal British centres for its manufacture. Later in the same century it was also begun in Silesia and in Belgium.

Germany and Flanders had been the main centres of the manufacture of brass, whence came, for instance, the sheets for the ecclesiastical brasses that adorn the English churches of the later Middle Ages; brass manufacture first became established in England in the reign of Elizabeth I. In spite of its tempting resemblance to gold, brass was still used mostly on a small scale: Biringuccio's book in 1540 describes a brass-foundry in Milan, where 1,200 small objects could be made in one mould—an interesting early example of mass-production. Another use was to add 5 per cent. of brass and 8 per cent. of tin to copper to make a bronze. Bronze had long been used for large castings such as statues and bells; to these the modern world added cannon (see p. 150), because the copper alloys corroded and fractured less readily than the iron then available. For melting the large weights of metal which were required, a reverberatory furnace was employed from the sixteenth century onwards, the heat being thrown downwards from a low roof, so that there was no direct contact between fuel and metal.

Copper, together with the precious metals and their alloys, was widely used for coinage. The quantity and quality of the coinage became a burning issue in the sixteenth century, when the Spaniards occasioned a rapid rise in price levels throughout Europe by the importation of unprecedented amounts of silver from the West Indies, Mexico, and, in 1553, from Peru. To debase the coinage became the natural resort of governments which could no longer pay their way with a revenue fixed by tradition. Henry VIII, for instance, ruthlessly reduced the precious-metal content of both gold and silver coins throughout the last twenty years of his reign. Edward VI and Mary tried to restore their values, but it was left to Elizabeth I to undertake the big task of calling in the base money and organizing a recoinage. Her success did not solve the problem of the Crown's finances, which became one of the main causes of the Civil War, but the new English currency of 1561 was both honest in content and skilfully designed. For a time the clumsy method of manufacture by hammering was superseded by the use of a screw press under the supervision of a Frenchman, Eloye Mestrell, formerly employed at the Paris mint; it was abandoned after his execution on a charge of counterfeiting in 1573. Even when the press became regularly established in the middle of the following century, it took two strong men to work it.

Good coins, however, contained some alloy. In the case of the German gold crown, 6 to 7 per cent. was considered a reasonable proportion, at least if the alloying metal was composed of two parts of silver to one of copper. The sterling silver of Elizabeth I, which continued for several centuries, likewise had a standard alloy content of 7.5 per cent. The smallest Elizabethan silver coin was a half-penny, but copper coins were introduced in 1613; they had been used in Ireland in the fifteenth century.

FURTHER DEVELOPMENTS OF THE IRON INDUSTRY

We may now return to the development of the iron industry, which by the close of this period was beginning its momentous association with coal, an association that did much to shape the course of the industrial revolution. The three dominant factors were these. In the sixteenth century, after a long period during which the price of iron had changed little, it became rapidly dearer. At the same time the frequency of war and the new means by which it was waged increased the demand for iron—Tilly, for example, expended from 12,000 to 18,000 cast-iron cannon-balls every day of his two months' siege of Magdeburg in 1631. Nor, in an age of rising populations, was it difficult to employ this increased iron production in time of peace, as, for example, in the making of farm implements, fire-backs, fire-irons, and the cooking equipment of the home. A third factor was the growing scarcity of wood for charcoal, with a consequent increase in the price of the latter, which caused the shifting of the industry from district to district and even from country to country, so that by the eighteenth century Sweden was in the lead. This concentrated attention, especially in Britain, upon the possibility of replacing charcoal with pit-coal.

Higher productivity and greater economy of fuel were achieved in the first instance by developing the *Stückofen* of the later Middle Ages (p. 134) into a blast furnace. This involved raising the height of the furnace and increasing the force of the blast enough to raise the temperature to the point at which the metal could be run out to be cast as molten pigs of cast iron. The use of water-wheels solved the problem of the blast, and by the end of the seventeenth century it was possible to work with furnaces over 30 ft high. Such a furnace could be continuously fed at the top with supplies of ore and fuel, and could be kept in use for as long as forty weeks on end. It was this readily available supply of cast iron that gave England a virtual monopoly of the cast-iron cannon for a century, from the time of Henry VIII when, according to tradition,

> Master Huggett and his man John
> They did cast the first Can-non,

until the rise of the Swedish industry in the Thirty Years War. In 1682 cast iron was used for the water-pipes connecting Marly with Versailles, and soon after 1700 the Swedish ironmaster, Christopher Polhem, in his very varied manufactures at Stjärnsund, was employing large cast-iron rolls as backing for small wrought-iron rolls which used less water-power. Slitting-mills were also in use in Sweden in the early eighteenth century (Fig. 53).

But the usefulness of the product of the *Stückofen* was severely limited by its inacceptability as a source of wrought iron. For although the blast furnace succeeded in reducing the total of impurities in the ore, the high temperature at which it worked caused both sulphur and phosphorus to be found in the final product; the blooms produced in the old way at lower temperatures were therefore still preferred by the forge-masters. Wrought iron continued to be in more extensive use than cast iron. The work of the forge might now be assisted by the *trompe*—an Italian invention (*c.* 1500) which replaced the bellows by forcing the air into, and out of, a closed wind-chest by the suction of a water-chute. Hammer forges were commonly powered by water-wheels for the tilt-hammers; wire-drawing apparatus and roller- and slitting-mills, using the same source of power, made bar iron and iron wire readily available.

Steel continued to be made by various—all of them small-scale—processes. For farm-tools the smith often produced his own steel by reducing a suitable ore in a hearth. A standard method was to forge blooms of wrought iron that had been carburized by dipping in molten cast iron which had a high carbon-content. Bars of wrought iron up to 5 ft long were also cemented to give steel, by firing with charcoal for a period of from three to seven days in a furnace made like a baker's oven. Lastly, steel was made in crucibles by heating iron with charcoal, a method used in India for making wootz steel

FIG. 53. Water-driven slitting-mill, from Swedenborg, *Regnum subterraneum*, 1734

(p. 126) and known in England in the seventeenth century, but first launched commercially in the west by Benjamin Huntsman, a Doncaster clockmaker, who set up his works near Sheffield in 1751.

Since every one of these processes required fuel, it is easy to see the steadily growing relevance of coal to the problems of metallurgy. Its use for the working of wrought iron in smithies involved no major technical problem—it is even possible that in suitable districts coal had been mixed with charcoal in the forge, for producing horse-shoes and other simple iron wares, long before its use there as a separate fuel. In England and Scotland there was some consumption of coal in the later Middle Ages, chiefly as a domestic fuel and especially in the neighbourhood of outcrops and other easily acces-sible deposits. But in the Low Countries, coal-mines of considerable size were developed specifically to serve the iron-finishing and other metal industries which made Liège in particular a great armoury, especially in the first half of the sixteenth century. It was in the second half of that century, in the reign of Elizabeth I, that the shortage of wood—said to have been intensified as a result of quick sales of woodland at the dissolution of the monasteries—in relation to the growth of population, shipbuilding, and industrial needs gave an impetus to the coal-mining of Tyneside and other districts in England, Scotland, and Wales. It is calculated that by 1660 these areas were producing five times as much coal as the rest of the world put together, a lead which continued with little modification through the eighteenth century.

The important relationship between Britain's lead in coal-mining and her ascendancy in transport developments and in the development of a great new prime-mover are considered elsewhere. We have already had occasion to see how the requirements of the new fuel brought about the use of the covered pot in glass-making (p. 110). There were a number of other industries, including salt-making by evaporation, the production of alum, lime-making, the baking of bricks, and brewing, for which the adoption of coal as a fuel involved no fundamental change, because the coal merely supplied heat and took no part in the actual processes. But iron, even more than glass, presented a complicated problem and one which was not so quickly solved, for at all stages in iron-making coal tended to impair the quality of the product. In 1614 a method was discovered (by two Englishmen) for using coal in the conversion of bar iron into steel, and by that time a little coal was commonly mixed with charcoal for the forging of bar iron. Yet for almost a hundred years no advance towards the use of coal in the all-important blast-furnace was made except indirectly—through a problem which arose in brewing.

It was found that when coal, already a common fuel in breweries to warm the wort before fermentation, was used by brewers to dry their malt, the coal ruined the taste of the beer; the main reason, as we now know, was the presence of sulphur. But about the time of the Civil War the brewers of Derbyshire, where a special kind of hard coal was to be found, had the idea of charring their coal to make coke, just as wood was charred for charcoal. The result was a coke-dried malt and a famous Derbyshire beer, the method of preparation of which might be expected to impinge upon the consciousness of the thirsty iron-master. Nevertheless, the seventeenth century ended with the problem of iron still apparently insoluble, although the new reverberatory furnaces had by this time made it possible to use coal directly for the smelting of lead ore, and a mixture of coal and charcoal had been introduced for copper smelting. So far as is known, the first successful experiment was conducted by Abraham Darby—who had served his apprenticeship to a malt-mill manufacturer—at Coalbrookdale in Shropshire in 1709. But his use of coke in the blast-furnace, which seems to us a belated discovery, was not taken up in the trade at all quickly: in the next fifty years only six other coke furnaces were built in all Britain. The Quaker family at Coalbrook-dale did not presumably advertise a secret from which it derived some profit, but the main factor was probably a lack of interest among its rivals: this would be encouraged by the fact that success could not be attained without a careful selection of the type of ore and of coal used, as also by the rather slow advance in the use of coal-fuel for other purposes. As long as they had to use large quantities of charcoal for the further process of converting pig into bar iron, ironmasters were reluctant to leave the wooded areas in which they were already established, for others where coal was readily acces-sible. In 1748 Abraham Darby II began to study seriously how to make a cast iron acceptable to the forges: he succeeded by careful selection of ores with a very low content of phosphorus. Thus the coke-smelting of iron became finally established, an event which opened a new phase in the long history of iron-making.

ARMAMENTS

Though David Hume, writing in the 1750's, claimed the cast-iron cannon, along with shipbuilding, as the great speciality of English manufacturers, the weapons of war taken as a whole provide a good illustration of the uses to which Europe put its metallurgical skill. Up to about 1700 the main infantry weapon was the pike, a steel head mounted on a shaft which might be as much as 18 ft long, an effective protection against cavalry. It was superseded by the bayo-net, first employed by the musketeers in the armies of Louis XIV. The sword, which the pikemen carried for hand-to-hand fighting, could then be dispensed with by the rank and file, though it con-tinued as the thrusting (and duelling) weapon of their officers. The standard cavalry weapon was now the sabre, designed for a slashing downward stroke, and there was also a lighter and shorter version of the medieval knight's lance. It is perhaps evidence of the minor part now played by all these weapons, at least in warfare between civi-lized nations, that the steel of which they were made was apparently inferior in average quality to the best products of the earlier age, when immense care had been taken because faulty metal might spell disaster.

Yet the first thing to be said about early hand-guns is that they were inaccurate, being designed only for short-range warfare between close formations; the incentive to the gunsmith to improve them came rather from the popular demand for a superior sporting piece. Leaving aside the stock, which was the wood-worker's concern, to produce a successful hand-gun required the means of forming a reasonably true barrel and the device of the lock to fire the charge. The barrel was commonly made from strips of iron: either a single strip was bent round a cylinder and then welded at the edge, or a number of short strips were rolled into tubes and welded end to end, one advantage of the second method being that the metal could then easily be tapered towards the muzzle, where relatively less strength was needed. In either case the roughly-formed barrel was then bored by means of a bit turning on the end of a long shaft pushed gradually into the barrel; by the eighteenth century such machines were commonly driven by water-power (Fig. 54). How the value of spiral grooving of the barrel was discovered is uncertain: experience would show that the spinning projectile has both a longer and more accurate flight. Nevertheless, as late as the middle of the eighteenth century a writer in the great French *Encyclopaedia* still thought that the object of rifling a gun-barrel was simply to procure a tight fit for the ball, not to cause it to spin, though the physics of a spinning projectile were expounded to the Royal Society by B. Robins in 1747. At all events, rifles were well known by 1525 and may have come into existence half a century earlier, to judge by armoury records at Turin and Nuremberg. They do not appear to have been used for military purposes until the Thirty Years War; their vogue was chiefly among wealthy sportsmen, who could afford to pay for accuracy, a quality which mattered much less for troops fighting in close formation and firing at short range. The difficulty of loading a rifled barrel from the muzzle was met by using a lead bullet a little large for the bore; this, when hammered home with a ram-rod, would fit the rifling exactly. That this was necessarily a slow process must have been a strong deterrent to its military use.

The early hand-gun was fired with a slow match applied to a touch-hole in the barrel so as to ignite some fine priming-powder on the firing-pan. The matchlock which superseded it had an arm which, when the trigger was pulled, brought the match down on to the priming; but the firing still depended upon keeping the match alight —a feat not always easily achieved in field conditions with a piece of coarse twine, however heavily impregnated with saltpetre to secure a steady glow. For the horseman it would be particularly difficult, which is one reason why the wheel-lock, which is believed to be an Italian invention made about the middle of the Franco-Italian wars of 1494–1559, was a favoured device for the horse-pistol. In this a key was used to wind a spring, the release of which turned a rough-edged wheel against a piece of pyrites; the resulting sparks touched

FIG. 54. Water-powered machinery for boring gun-barrels, from Diderot's
Encyclopaedia, 1777

off the priming. The winding made this a weapon that could not be fired twice in quick succession, and its use was therefore confined chiefly to the cavalryman, who would fire once and then charge in. It had important rivals from about 1580 onwards in the Dutch snaphance and the Spanish lock, which survived to the time of the Peninsular War, when it was known as the miquelet. The next decisive change was the introduction of the flintlock, perfected in France by 1630. The flint was pulled back (cocked) and, on the release of the trigger, was driven by a strong spring against a roughened metal plate over the firing-pan, into which the sparks fell. The mechanism was stronger than that of the wheel-lock and could be fired more rapidly. The flintlock was essential for the novel French sport of shooting birds on the wing, but was at first deemed a luxury for the infantryman. Louis XIV re-equipped his army with it in the 1660's; in England the change was in progress at the Revolution of 1688.

An improved flint-lock was fitted to Brown Bess, the 10-lb, 62-in. weapon that served the British Army from Blenheim to Waterloo. A percussion-powder, patented by a Scottish clergyman, A. J. Forsyth, in 1807, brought about its eventual replacement (p. 501), but flintlock guns are still to be found in parts of Africa, where Norfolk flints continue to be exported from what is in a sense Britain's oldest industry.

The standard cannon of the sixteenth and following centuries were smooth-bore muzzle-loaders cast in bronze, brass, or iron. Iron was cheapest, but bronze was considered to be best because least liable to corrode or burst. The development of the blast-furnace made it possible to make large iron castings, but for three centuries the general method continued to be the same as had been used in the making of the great bronze cannon, one of which weighed almost nineteen tons, employed by the Turks against Constantinople in the siege of 1453. To a large extent, too, it was, as we have already seen, a continuation of the art of the medieval bell-founder.

Cannon-founding involved three distinct processes. The first was the making of a tripartite clay mould. One part was an exact reproduction of the outside of the cannon, including its decorations and the gudgeons on which it would be pivoted; the second part was the model of the breech; the third was the core representing the space to be occupied by the barrel. The clay model was then reinforced with iron bars, assembled, baked, and lowered into a pit. The second process was the filling of the mould in the pit by tapping a furnace of molten metal; the mould had then to be broken to extract the casting, which meant that each barrel must be made individually. The third main process was the boring, necessary because the casting could not give sufficient precision; this was done with a bit mounted on a long shaft, usually driven by a water-wheel, supported at one end only—an inaccurate method which would not correct, and might even exaggerate, any misalignment of the core in the original mould. It was only the Dutch who, by 1747, had made it their universal practice to bore from a solid-cast gun-barrel; in Britain this development awaited the invention of Wilkinson's boring-engine (p. 350).

There was a remarkable increase in the use of artillery about the middle of the eighteenth century, when the field-gun really came into its own; but long before this, in the time of Marlborough, fortress warfare had turned upon the slow assembly of the heavy siege-batteries. But the impact of artillery upon naval warfare was still more incisive. In place of the immemorial tactics of boarding and ramming, success in a naval battle came to depend upon the weight of fire which could be brought to bear upon the enemy line. Thus the ability of the founders to provide heavier guns played a considerable part in those exchanges of broadsides by which the fate of Europe

FIG. 55. Roman locksmith at work, second century A.D.

from the days of de Ruyter to those of Nelson was so often determined.

Such words as matchlock and flintlock are reminders that the gunsmith's craft was closely associated with that of the locksmith, that of the latter being of far greater antiquity. The craft of the locksmith was well established in Roman times (Fig. 55). Once man began to have a permanent home and to acquire personal possessions attention was necessarily directed to securing valuables against theft. Locks activated by weighted tumblers are to be found on Egyptian mummy cases of 2000 B.C., but there was no provision for re-opening what guarded the possessions of the dead. A jewel box of 1350 B.C. incorporates a simple lock, in which rotation of a knob causes a cross-bar to engage with a slot. For many

FIG. 56. Iron Egyptian key of the third or second century B.C.

purposes, however, such as the safeguarding of treasure-stores, the early Egyptians seem to have relied more upon seals—the breaking of which entailed severe sanctions—than upon locks.

The so-called Egyptian lock appeared much later, under the Ptolemies. In this (Fig. 56) a series of prongs, at right angles to a cross-bar on the iron key, was used to lift the tumblers: a similar lock, of wooden construction but again with a metal key (Fig. 57), is known from the monastery of Epiphanius, at Thebes, and dates from about 800 A.D. As this type of lock is used even today in humble Egyptian

dwellings, it can be assumed to have an unbroken history of over two millennia. Nevertheless, the ordinary modern lock seems to have derived from another source altogether: the tumblers of medieval European locks are arranged in a single row and the web of the key that lifts them is attached directly to the shaft instead

FIG. 57. 'Egyptian' lock and key from Thebes, *c.* A.D. 800

of to a cross-piece. The Egyptian keys that survive are of metal and they certainly could not readily have been fashioned from wood; the modern type of key, by contrast, could easily be made from wood, and wooden examples are known from such widely separated places as The Faeroes (Fig. 58), the Greek islands, Zanzibar, China, and India. Such little evidence as there is is not inconsistent with the view that the modern lock is derived from a very ancient Asiatic prototype of wood.

Simple though the mechanism was in principle, locksmiths of the medieval and early modern periods—who also made latches, handles,

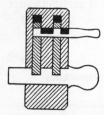

and ornamental ironwork, such as was required for chests and drawers—produced some elegant mechanisms and many very elaborate cases. Henry VIII, for example, had a 14×8 in. lock bearing the royal arms, which is said to have been screwed to his bed-chamber door wherever he went. In Eliza-bethan England the manufacture of door-locks, padlocks (a fifteenth-century word), and cabinet-locks was already concentrated

FIG. 58. Primitive wooden lock, The Faeroes

in three Staffordshire towns, though it remained predominantly a handicraft industry almost until 1900. Modern locksmiths, however, devised a series of improvements to make the task of the picklock more difficult. First, pivoted plates were introduced that had to be aligned by the key before the bolt could be shot, and later, as in Robert Barron's lock of 1778, the ends of the tumblers were elaborated where they engaged with the web of the key. Bramah's achievements are mentioned elsewhere (p. 350), but the two most influential innovations were those of Jeremiah Chubb, who patented a lever lock in 1818, from which a big English manufacture developed (*see* Fig. 165), and—in the next generation—of the American, Linus Yale. By separating the lock mechanism from the lock itself, he was able to produce the cylinder lock: the prongs of the Egyptian lock reappear in the five notches of the yale key, cut automatically to eight different depths in a milling machine, which gives 32,768 variations.

INSTRUMENT-MAKING

Growing skill in the working of metals is further exemplified by the development of the instrument-maker's craft. To many of the early products of this we make reference elsewhere—for example, clocks (p. 225), navigational instruments (p. 205), and balances (p. 221)—and here we can consider only the general line of development. We must further restrict ourselves to some instruments of direct practical application to technology: the making of scientific instruments is, of course, of the utmost importance—by 1776 there are half a dozen instances of instrument-makers becoming Fellows of the Royal Society—but they had an effect on technology only in so far as the researches for which they were used found practical application. Navigators, gunners, and surveyors were the chief buyers of such instruments during our present period.

The modern tradition of instrument-making dates from approximately the middle of the fifteenth century, when Nuremberg became the first great centre of instrument-making for western Europe: craftsmen there inherited little from the Middle Ages, but the influence of Alexandria was still felt. The traditions of Alexandrian scientists—which culminated in Ptolemy, who gave a detailed account of the instruments of his day in the *Almagest*—were not transmitted to the Byzantine empire and were only slowly recovered from their true heirs, the astronomers of Islam. The making of astronomical instruments enjoyed a temporary revival at Oxford (Fig. 59) and Paris in the fourteenth century, but it was not until about 1440 that the craft became permanently established; three astronomical instruments purchased at Nuremberg in 1444 still exist.

Nuremberg perhaps owed its instrument-making originally to the fact that it lay astride the great trade-route from Italy to the Nether-lands and was already a centre for skilled metal-work, but its ascendancy is certainly due to the fact that Johann Müller (Regio-montanus), the pioneer of modern astronomy, settled there in 1471. Within a short time Augsburg, too, had a famous school of instru-ment-makers. Many of the instruments made in these two cities are of such exquisite workmanship that they are prized today not only for their technical interest but as works of art. From Germany the

FIG. 59. Division of an astronomical circle by Richard of Wallingford (d. 1335), from a fourteenth-century manuscript

craft spread to Louvain, and there was also some activity in Italy, but political events on the Continent eventually led to London's becoming for many generations by far the most im-portant centre in the world for the making of instruments. The devastation of the Low Coun-tries by the 'Spanish Terror' led to the eclipse of Louvain, and the decline of the German cities in the Thirty Years War led to the virtual extinction of the craft there.

German techniques had been introduced to England in the early sixteenth century by the Bavarian craftsman, Nicholas Kratzer, some of whose instruments appear in Holbein's well-known painting, 'The Ambassadors', and Thomas Gemini, who came from near Liège, brought with him a highly developed skill in engraving on brass. This last was a timely innovation, for sheet brass was then becoming available in England for the first time, through the Eliza-bethan Mineral and Battery Works. Among those associated with this venture was Humfray Cole, who may have been apprenticed to Gemini and was the first English expert in instrument-making. Cole established himself in London as a maker of 'Scales, compasses, and sundry sorts of Geometricall instruments on metall'. Among his customers were Drake and Frobisher: for the last-named he made all the instruments for the first voyage in search of a North-West Passage in 1576. Cole began a long line of distinguished instrument-makers in London, of whom there were at least thirty before 1650.

Increasing and more exacting demands led to greater emphasis being put on performance and less on ornamentation: by the beginning of the eighteenth century the exquisite workmanship of earlier generations had been discontinued, except for special presentation models, and scientific instruments had begun to assume the severely practical appearance of those of today. At the same time the craft became increasingly decentralized, makers of navigational instruments establishing themselves in the principal ports and those supplying artillerymen tending to move near the armament works.

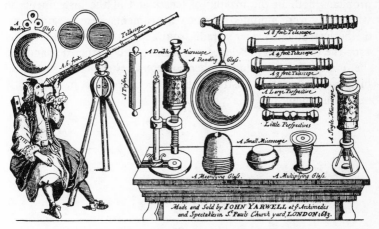

FIG. 60. Instrument-maker's trade-card, London, 1683

Brass, ivory, and close-grained woods, such as box and pear, were the principal materials of the instrument-makers, with brass becoming increasingly favoured because of its rigidity and permanence. For the shaping of metal the lathe (p. 102) was a valuable tool, and the clock-makers in particular developed it greatly for precision work. The engraving of scales was, of course, a most important part of the work: until the advent of mechanical devices, this was done with simple engraving tools and punches, the design being first set out by geometrical methods.

The earliest products of the instrument-makers were made mainly for astronomical purposes or to apply astronomical methods in navigation: they included astrolabes, cross-staffs, quadrants, sundials, and orreries, as well as basic geometrical instruments such as compasses and rules. From the seventeenth century, however, a variety of new instruments, or much improved versions of old ones, began to appear. The needs of surveyors led to elaboration of the hodometer—an instrument ascribed to Vitruvius, but probably never used in ancient times—enabling land distances to be measured by recording the number of revolutions of a wheel as it was pushed along. Improvements in artillery called for the more accurate sighting of cannon (see Fig. 10), and by the beginning of the seventeenth century the gunner's level had been highly developed. The invention of the telescope and microscope (p. 112) introduced new problems both in the making of lenses and of the instruments in which they were mounted: the new instruments were a regular part of the instrument-maker's trade from about 1660 (Fig. 60). From 1700 the revolution in science was making still further demands on the craft, and air-pumps, thermometers, barometers, electrical machines, and other instruments were called for in constantly increasing quantities.

5

BUILDING CONSTRUCTION

THE most familiar fact about Palaeolithic men is that they often inhabited caves; but when there was no cave, they improvised an equivalent. There are (disputed) wall paintings which show their light summer huts of boughs, and actual remains from the less insubstantial winter-quarters of mammoth hunters in Russia, Siberia, and Czechoslovakia. These might be described as imitation caves, since the floor-level is as much as 9 ft underground. Hearths can be identified, and it is supposed that the roofing was timber, perhaps covered with earth, though it is tempting to think that the mammoth bones which lie strewn around played their part in the construction, much as whale bones have been used in the far north. In Mesolithic times it is rare to find, as in Denmark, a people who occupied their semi-sunken dwellings all the year round; still rarer to find, as in Hanover, a hut which was entirely above ground. Regular technological progress necessarily awaited the settling down of Neolithic man, though in the early days of Egypt a type of framed wooden house, made of overlapping planks lashed together with hide, was designed to be dismantled and re-erected in the desert during the annual flood.

From the Neolithic stage onwards, Europeans, as we might expect, built houses and whole villages of timber, such as the so-called lake villages, which were raised on piles either to secure the permanent protection of water or as a precaution against seasonal flooding. The low stone huts of Skara Brae in the Orkneys, with their stone furnishings, are an exception appropriate to those wind-swept, treeless islands. The Bronze Age craftsmen of Stonehenge towards the middle of the second millennium B.C. fitted their huge trilithons together by the mortise-and-tenon technique of the wood-worker—it is possible that there was also ritual building in timber, both in Britain and in other lands, from which the builders of Stonehenge may have taken their model. In the early Iron Age, too, it was not only lake-villages like Glastonbury and Meare which were of wood. Hill forts had timber revetments and palisading, and the huts inside them—even as late as the end of the first century B.C.—had their roofs supported by timber uprights.

The Near East, in contrast, had less timber, though it had reed and palm-leaves instead, but from the earliest Neolithic period— before the use of fired pottery—villagers east of the Tigris were building their houses of dried clay, and from Jericho there are examples of mud-brick walls, one of them socketed to take timber cross-beams. In the dry climate, such buildings would last long. In the flat alluvial plain of Mesopotamia, clay remained the staple building material for 6,000 years; the valley of the Nile, in contrast, had stone, but this was a state monopoly, and clay was the building material of the multitude. There were clay buildings also in Asia Minor, although there was plenty of wood and stone there, and even in the forested island of Crete. Thus rammed clay or *pisé*; its natural successor, sun-dried brick; and its artificial successor, kiln-fired brick, played a very large part in the history of the early empires.

The clay was prepared by adding water and treading-in chopped straw or dung to prevent warping or cracking; the bricks were then shaped, usually two at a time, in a rectangular wooden mould with no top or bottom; and were afterwards left to dry, being turned over from time to time. With a larger addition of water, the same clay mixture was used both for mortar and for plastering. So far as build-ing is concerned, the kiln came into use originally for special pur-poses, such as the making of pavements, and where the brick needed to be watertight; in Egypt it was not used at all until classical times. In Mesopotamia, both the shapes and method of laying of bricks were quite different from those which became customary later. The upper surface was convex, like the top of a loaf, and the bricks were laid on end at a slight angle; alternate courses sloped in opposite directions, giving a herring-bone effect such as may sometimes be found in stone walls in the west of England today.

In the plains of Mesopotamia brick-building reached its climax with the places of worship known as *ziggurats*, about the year 2000 B.C. These huge staged-towers met the effects of shrinkage and sub-sidence—any sort of prepared foundation was rare—by having courses of reed matting running across the faces at intervals. At Ur, where the *ziggurat* (Fig. 61) was 75 yds long and 60 yds wide, with a height of 30 yds, the revetment was 8 ft thick, composed of kiln-baked brick set in bitumen (asphalt): Strabo records that higher up the Euphrates, at Hit, lumps of bitumen were found in abundance in the river. Arches were already in use—both the corbelled false arch, with which small domed burial chambers were built up of limestone rubble, and the true arch surmounting gateways through walls.

Further developments in Mesopotamia awaited the introduction of stone by the Assyrians from the north, but in Egypt early in the third millennium B.C. we find buildings, beginning with the famous step-

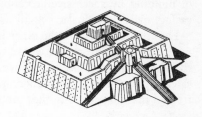

FIG. 61. Reconstruction of *ziggurat* at Ur, *c.* 2000 B.C.

pyramid of Zoser, which show the kindred arts of the quarryman and the stonemason already in an advanced stage of development. To obtain the blocks of stone, tunnels were driven upwards from a cliff face, if necessary for several hundreds of yards. Crouching in a deep recess made just below the ceiling of the stratum to be worked, a man outlined blocks in the floor of this recess, cut them one course deep, and then split them by inserting wooden wedges which would be wetted to make them expand. The recess was gradually extended, the rock being cut away in steps. All this was apparently done with a mason's pick, while even more astonishing is the fact that single blocks, weighing as much as 1,000 tons, were moved from quarry to building site without benefit of wheels: levers, sledges, rollers, ropes, and a remorseless

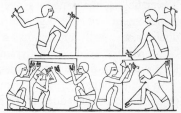

FIG. 62. Stone-dressing, from a tomb at Thebes, Egypt, *c.* 1450 B.C.

expenditure of human effort carried the material to and from the Nile waterway (*see* Fig. 111).

Both the small blocks, used in the time of King Zoser, and the larger masonry of later dynasties were squared and dressed by hand with chisel, mallet, boning-rod (for straightening), and mason's square (Fig. 62). According to Herodotus, the total labour required for the Great Pyramid, built about 150 years after Zoser's, was equivalent to $7\frac{1}{2}$ working days per cubic foot of masonry, which, when quarrying and transport are taken into account, may not be an absurd exaggeration. It is 150 ft higher than St Paul's Cathedral and, though it covers upwards of 13 acres, deviates from a perfect square by only $\frac{8}{10}$ inch in length and 12 seconds in angle. The method of building by successive accretions, each with its own limestone casing, makes the final result all the more marvellous.

Egyptian temples, on the other hand, since they lacked the arch, were for a long time restricted to a space of 9–10 ft between columns, that being the maximum distance which a limestone block could safely span; but the introduction of Silsila sandstone eventually trebled that distance. Another problem which the Egyptians solved was that of jointing three architraves so as to rest them all on the head of a single column. The columns themselves were often built up from a series of drums, as, for instance, in the great temple at Karnak, where it took several blocks to build up even a single capital, so vast is the scale: the foundations, however, as in many Egyptian structures, were weak and careless, as was revealed in A.D. 1899 when eleven columns collapsed.

FIG. 63. North–south section through the pyramid of Sahure, c. 2400 B.C.

Nevertheless, mankind has never ceased to be impressed by the achievements of the Egyptians in building construction—their obelisks, the walls and ceilings of their temples, and, above all, the extraordinary accuracy of pyramids planned apparently with very little aid from mathematical theory (Fig. 63).

In the early part of the first millennium B.C., both limestone and gypsum were being added to the brick-building tradition of Mesopotamia. Sennacherib's stone canal, which brought water to Nineveh from a point 50 miles away, with a fall of 1 in 80, is a particularly impressive example. Not only did it cross a wide valley by a limestone aqueduct 300 yds long, but the stone pavement was accurately graded throughout, apparently in order that blocks for successive sections might be conveyed on wheels or rollers along the canal itself from the quarry at its head. The structure was rendered waterproof with bitumen. Of the 20-ton bull colossi with which Assyrian kings delighted to adorn the gates of their palaces, we know only that the carving was completed on the site after they had been pulled into position on enormous sledges, but it seems clear that they were first

floated down the Tigris. Most building was still in brick, and arching was employed to make brick vaults, in which each successive
semicircle of bricks was tilted slightly backwards, so that no temporary wooden framework was needed for centring. The use of
glazed bricks reached its climax at Babylon, where the figures on the

Fig. 64. Foundations of the Ishtar gate, Babylon, sixth century B.C.

Ishtar gate (Fig. 64) have been modelled in this way in a clay panel,
which was afterwards divided into bricks, glazed, and fired. What is
most remarkable is that these figures are repeated on the gate- and
street-walls underground, where only the eye of a modern archaeologist would ever behold them—a circumstance the more extraordinary because in Mesopotamia, as in Egypt, the quality and
depth of foundation was by modern standards one of the weakest
features of their building construction.

Since the Hittites have left no important structural feature in
their ruins that is not to be found elsewhere, we may turn to Crete.
There is something strangely modern about the appearance of its

two- or even three-storey houses, of which we have representations dating from about 1700 B.C., and even in the planning of the palaces with their many-sided activities, at Knossos and Phaistos; these were unfortified, as befitted a sea power, and in general were more elaborate versions of their private houses. The Cretans made the bottom part of their walls of stone rubble, and the upper of sun-dried brick; stone piers supported the first floor, but the framing was of timber. The rooms faced inwards upon light-wells approached

through columned cloisters; the use of upper rooms and terraced flat roofs for the first time gave staircases a place in domestic architecture. Bathrooms, water-flushed conveniences, terracotta water-pipes, and well-conceived sloping gutters, to the design of which a rainy climate gave the necessary impetus, likewise fore-shadow the later civilization of Europe and America.

FIG. 65. Ruins of gateway, Mycenae

The centres of Mycenean civilization on the mainland, such as Tiryns and Troy, had their palaces surrounded necessarily by a fortress wall. The palace itself at Tiryns, for instance, had all its main rooms on one floor, with the light coming in through high windows. There are recognizable units consisting of a porch en-trance, sleeping-chamber, and columned living-room, the last of which contained a permanent hearth, the focus of the European home. The pitched roofs were another homelike feature. But the great 'beehive' tombs—pointed stone domes, built up of horizontal corbelled courses in a cylindrical shaft underground, with access by a highly ornamented doorway having a corbelled arch above (Fig. 65)—are important, not as foreshadowing the Greek future, with all that it was to mean for Europe, but as stirring the Greek imagination with pictures of a dimly comprehended past. Our own Stonehenge in its completed form probably dates from much the same period and may even have been influenced by Mycenean style, for a Bronze Age dagger, carved on one of the sarsens, resembles the Mycenean type (p. 14). Here, too, it is impossible to escape the sense of mys-tery surrounding a technical marvel—the fetching of the 40-ton blocks, some from a distance of 150 miles, the dressing, the erection

—which stands apart from any continuous technological development.

It is more to our purpose to notice the beginnings of bridges, waterways, and roads. Early civilizations made use for the most part of fords, temporary boat-bridges, or bridges of timber, which have perished even from memory. But there was a 36-ft wide bridge at the palace of Minos, and Nebuchadnezzar was traditionally the builder of a timber structure resting on more than a hundred brick piers, which linked the two parts of Babylon across the Euphrates. Contemporary with Sennacherib's great aqueduct (p. 160), there was a 12-mile underground conduit, 9 ft wide except at the intake end, built for supplying water to Erbil, the temple-city of Ishtar. As for roads, Herodotus ranks the making of the stone-paved road which carried the material for the Great Pyramid as 'a work not much inferior to the pyramid itself'. Both Egyptian and Mesopotamian towns were paved with flagstones, and there are short lengths of paved road to be found in Crete and other regions under Minoan influence. But no processional route is known earlier than that which the Hittites made about 1200 B.C. at their capital at Bogazköy; then come those of the Assyrians and Babylonians, Babylon itself having a Sacred Way built high above the plain and paved with red and white slabs of stone, each more than 3 ft square. The roads of the early empires, however, were routes made by usage and improved on occasion, as described in the imagery of a sixth-century Hebrew prophet: 'Make straight in the desert a highway for our God . . . and the crooked shall be made straight, and the rough places plain' (Isaiah xl. 3, 4).

GREEK AND ROMAN BUILDING

The building construction of the Greeks and Romans, like their literature, is part of the common aesthetic inheritance of Europe. Systematic town-planning, for instance, usually on the 'gridiron' pattern, began with Hippodamus of Miletus, who reshaped the Piraeus, and it flourished in Alexandrian Egypt, where the Greeks imbibed the tradition of the ancient empires. From the present standpoint, however, there is more to be learnt from Rome than from Greece, for, with the honourable exception of Herodotus, the great Greek writers show little interest in the way in which the glories of their architecture were produced. Our knowledge of Greek quarrying comes indeed from a Greek, Pausanias, but one who lived in the second century A.D. For details of building methods we are largely dependent upon Vitruvius, a Roman architect, military engineer, and writer in the reign of Augustus.

Greek architecture, for all its grandeur, had its origins not in the great buildings of the Near East, nor even in the domed Mycenean tombs, but in the timber-framed house of European type, with its three chambers and hearth. The earliest Greek temples were of mud-brick with a thatched timber roof; to make a greater width possible, a row of posts was placed down the middle to hold the transverse beams, and for the same purpose rows of posts were likewise inserted in the mud-brick walls. Such were the humble beginnings of the trabeated architecture of the age of Pericles: the columns of the three classical orders derive from structures of wood.

The hard limestone of Argos had been used in the Mycenean age. The classical architects used a different variety from the west and north of the Peloponnese, which had a surface suitable for plastering with fine stucco (of burnt limestone) that was afterwards colour-washed. But the marble used for the great public buildings at Athens came from the near-by quarries on Mount Pentelicon, rectangular blocks being obtained by chiselling a groove round each, and then forcing them out with wedges. This Pentelic marble had a close, fine grain and a milky whiteness to which the traces of iron in it added a rich brown patina after long exposure; since it also made fine joints and finished smoothly, it was obviously superior to stuccoed limestone. Greek taste, unlike Roman, did not favour brightly coloured marble: the Parian, much used for sculpture, was white, the Naxian grey. The inferior marble of Hymettos and the huge limestone quarries of Syracuse did not come fully into use till the third century B.C., though the latter, which has one rock-face 90 ft high and more than a mile long, was the scene somewhat earlier of the Athenian captivity immortalized by Thucydides.

Trabeated architecture was possible because beams and lintels of limestone and marble could be as much as 15 ft long. The columns were built up of drums, as in Egypt, fixed in position with small pins fitting into sockets at the centre. At the Parthenon these were as much as 6 ft in diameter, lifted by small projecting bosses of marble, which were afterwards chipped off, and brought up to the Acropolis in carts drawn by some thirty or forty oxen. When soft stones were used the drums were sometimes turned on a lathe. Very fine jointing was achieved by grinding the blocks together. But clamps were used of various metals, including iron, and a remarkable feature was the employment of wrought-iron beams—for instance at the Parthenon, where they acted as cantilevers to hold up the heaviest statues on the pediment. The low-pitched roofs of these great buildings had a timber framework (which does not survive) supporting tiles of terracotta or marble. Before the end of the sixth century Corinth could supply tiles for repair work, each numbered according to its correct position on the roof of a temple.

The contribution of the Romans to building construction is really threefold. They adopted and adapted the work of the Greeks, embellishing their city and empire with temples and other public buildings which were in appearance a rather florid imitation of the Greek. Secondly, they took over and developed the use of the arch, which had enabled the Etruscans, a millennium before the Roman empire began, to build, for example, a 24-ft bridge of wedge-shaped unmortared blocks. Thirdly, they used the four centuries of their empire in the west for vast programmes of public works, with which the modern traditions of civil and military engineering might be said to begin.

Augustan Rome was not built of marble, but marble was used for dressing and finishing of work to an extent which made it important both as an import and as a product of Italy itself. The pure white marbles of Carrara are still the most famous in the world; among imported marbles peculiar prestige attached to the imperial porphyry from Egypt, first quarried under the Emperor Claudius and retained as imperial property because its colour was the true imperial purple. Two other local stones used at Rome were travertine, of which the ancient walls of the catacombs and much of the Colosseum are built —this came largely from Tivoli—and a hard basaltic rock used to pave some of the roads leading out of the city. But the Romans, of course, worked the stone in every part of their empire—from Baalbek in Syria, where Antoninus Pius in the second century A.D. had incorporated in a temple three blocks of stone measuring $63 \times 13 \times 10$ ft, which still constitute a record for any building—to the gritstone of Hadrian's Wall. It is claimed that there is hardly any English building-stone which the Romans did not use: they even took Bath stone as far as Colchester.

In quarrying the Romans too used wedges, which were inserted into deep chiselled furrows and then saturated with water, so as to create pressure by swelling. They were particularly skilful in

maturing their stone in the quarry: in the famous multangular tower
at York the Roman stones for this reason survive in far better condition than larger stones laid in the same place a thousand years later.
Saws of copper fed with sand and emery were used for cutting,
though much shaping was done by pounding with stone balls. In
the last phase of the empire water-driven saws by the Moselle are
recorded in Ausonius's *Mosella*.

Returning to the age of Augustus, we must notice that Roman
builders worked in other substances besides stone. Kiln-burned
bricks now became widely available, the largest being about 23
English inches square, and the normal thickness $1\frac{1}{2}$ in. Though
generally covered with plaster or marble veneer, bricks were used
as a facing for rubble and flint walls. Nevertheless, Rome itself was
made chiefly of concrete. The Romans were fortunate in having
available a volcanic earth called *pozzolana*, which when mixed with
lime formed a cement that resisted both water and fire. Blended with
brick or stone, it made a concrete as hard as the brick or stone itself.
Such concrete was employed not only for foundations and walls,
cast between timber shuttering, but also to make vaults and domes,
and the use of concrete between brick arches or ribs served in particular to reduce the weight of a vaulted structure.

An arch of wedge-shaped stones, requiring little mortaring, can
be extended to form a vault merely by the provision of additional
material and additional timber framework for support during construction. The result, however, was not only dark but dangerous,
because of the outward thrust upon the walls on which the vault
rested. The Romans therefore constructed cross-vaults to buttress the
walls, thus making possible such a span as the 100 ft of Diocletian's
palace. The same problem of the outward thrust also confronted
them (and their successors) in the domes which were among their
greatest architectural triumphs. They were designed chiefly for
garden-buildings or the hot rooms of baths, such as the Bath of
Caracalla, where the diameter was 116 ft; this structure also employed T-shaped iron girders, apparently for a framed floor. But the
largest Roman dome adorned a temple, the Pantheon (A.D. 110–25),
which has an internal diameter of 142 ft, with the dome—of which
the precise composition and mode of construction are still a mystery
—resting upon a wall of concrete, strengthened by a system of
built-in brick arches. This magnificent building, which has served in
modern times as a royal mausoleum, had doors of bronze and a roof

of gilt bronze tiles. Tiles, usually of terracotta, were also important, not only as a roofing material, but in the construction of the famous hypocausts, the rooms over which were usually floored with large tiles about 23 in. square. In one type of hypocaust, small tiles were used for the columns, through which the heat rose, and, whether it was circulated by this method or by channels under the floor, the heat escaped eventually by means of flue-tiles set in the walls.

In communications, hydraulic engineering, and fortification, the popular view which stresses the achievement of the Romans is almost certainly right. Nevertheless, harbour construction may not be the only case in which the achievements of earlier Mediterranean civilizations were so far obliterated by the Romans that it is difficult for us to judge. Thus the ancient Egyptian canal to the Red Sea (renewed by Ptolemy Philadelphus in 285 B.C.), though used by Roman emperors, attracts little attention in comparison with the great Roman road network; and what the Roman road itself may

FIG. 66. Greek rut-road with side-branch

owe to earlier Etruscan ideas is quite obscured. As the Greeks possessed scarcely any well-built roads until Roman times, their contribution in this respect is limited to the prepared wheel-rut (Fig. 66), though even of this there are some earlier examples in Malta. These ruts have a fairly regular depth, width, and gauge, run often through shallow cuttings, and are specially provided for in the few places where there are stone setts. Seen at their best on pilgrimage routes and the road to Delphi, they were a device for easing the passage of wheeled traffic which reappears many centuries later in the approaches to mines and quarries.

The construction of the great Roman roads was a far more arduous process. Thus a contemporary poet, Statius, gives the following description of the making of the Emperor Domitian's new road linking Campania with Rome:

The first task is to begin the furrows and to open out the track, and then with deep digging to hollow out the soil. Next, they fill in the hollow trench with other materials, and prepare a lap on which the road-surface may be laid, lest the ground should give way or the spiteful earth provide an unreliable bed for the rammed blocks. Then, with close-set curb-stones, on both sides, and with many cramps, they bind the road together.

The reference to the hollow trench is a reminder that in Italy, as distinct, for instance, from Britain, the roads were not usually banked-up above the surrounding land. In Italy, too, the roads were less straight than when laid out in newly conquered territory, and were for longer distances paved with blocks of hard stone. But the gravel roads about 6 metres wide, which are the type usually met with in the provinces, except in the vicinity of important towns, retained the essential features of good drainage and generous thickness. The Romans had surveying instruments for computing angles and measuring out distances, but it is uncertain how they achieved such a *tour de force* as the alignment of Stane Street on its ultimate destination at Chichester from the point at which it leaves the Thames just east of London Bridge.

What is true of roads is true of streets. Classical Greece was in this respect inferior to Knossos: a place of assembly might sometimes be 'fitted with huge stones set deep in the earth', as Homer pictures it, but the streets which led to it would be narrow, muddy, unpaved, and undrained. The Romans had pavements of basalt slabs from an early period, and cleared the surface-water from the streets by sewers, which they imitated from Etruscan practice. Under the empire new colonies and cities were generally laid out in squares, and the heights of buildings were restricted to the equivalent of five storeys. But streets continued to be narrow by our standards in order to give better protection against wind, which was thought of as a bearer of disease as well as of rain.

Roman roads occasionally passed through cuttings made in the solid rock and even through tunnels, but the most important engineering features, apart from the road-bed itself, were the bridges, essential to a network of fast communications running right across Europe. The earlier ones were of wood, and timber superstructures continued to be used by the military engineers in outlying provinces, as with Trajan's famous bridge near the Iron Gates on the Danube (Fig. 67), to which the contemporary London bridge is believed to have borne a broad resemblance. But the characteristic feature was the semicircular arch, with a span ranging from 16 to 65 ft; on the Via Flaminia, north of Rome, there was even one span of over 100 ft.

The usual material was large stone blocks or (later) brick with a concrete inner core, piers being built up of *pozzolana* cement after excavation inside a tightly packed ring of iron-tipped piles. There were often projecting cut-waters on the upstream side of the piers to reduce erosion by the water, and earthen embankments were raised where necessary to construct the approaches. A bridge still usable, which once sustained the tramp of the legions, is a most vivid reminder of Rome's work in uniting the European world: such is the bridge over the Marecchia at Rimini, built in the first century A.D.

FIG. 67. Trajan's twenty-pier bridge near Orsova, *c.* A.D. 99, from a relief on Trajan's Column

For reasons of necessity, the empires of the Near East had developed great works of water conveyance. The Greeks were their imitators, and Herodotus, who thought the aqueduct of Samos was one of the three greatest Greek constructional achievements, caused its designer, Eupalinus of Megara, in the sixth century B.C., to be the first hydraulic engineer named in history. The aqueduct in question, however, was two-thirds tunnelling and the tunnel, bored simultaneously from each end, was originally 16 ft out of alignment in the middle. The Greeks excelled rather in mechanical devices. For instance, they adopted the principle of the siphon to carry water in pipes over intervening heights: in the second century B.C., at Pergamum, the maximum pressure approached 300 lb to a square inch, and the supply was driven up 500 ft into the citadel. The genius of Archimedes may not have originated the water-screw (p. 123), but Arab sources associate him with surveys and dams in Egypt, and a rather later Greek mechanician, Ctesibius, is associated with the invention of a pressure pump.

But the Romans, who spread city life so widely and based its amenities so largely upon a lavish supply of water—it has been estimated that Imperial Rome received over one million cubic metres a day, much of it brought into private houses by standardized lead

FIG. 68. Roman aqueduct near Nîmes, first century A.D.

pipes—were as naturally builders of aqueducts as Victorian Britain was of the railway viaducts which so often resemble them. The capital itself was eventually supplied by at least a dozen aqueducts, with largely underground courses except for the last ten miles across the plain, where it was desired to maintain height for the sake of distribution. The construction of a single aqueduct by the Emperor Claudius involved the transportation of 40,000 wagon-loads of tufa annually for fourteen years. In the provinces they often march across deep valleys, as at Nîmes, where the 900-ft long Pont du Gard (Fig. 68) has a maximum height of 160 ft, and at Segovia in Spain, whose aqueduct-bridge half a mile in length still carries water. Of the several minor aqueducts in Britain, perhaps the most interesting was one 8 miles long, which supplied water to wash gold in Carmarthenshire. The Romans also dug canals to improve the drainage of rivers all across Europe from the Po to the Cam, and less frequently with navigation for the main object, as in the case of the 23-mile Rhine-

Meuse canal, which eliminated a sea-passage. In this connexion their most spectacular achievement, however, was the drainage of Lake Fucinus, which added 50,000 acres to the Emperor Claudius's estates in a land-locked basin in the Apennines. For this they drove a 3½-mile tunnel through the mountains—a record in tunnelling which stood unsurpassed until 1876.

The oldest known harbour works are those of Tyre and Sidon, and very impressive installations existed at Carthage before the Romans captured it: 'Two Ionic columns stood in front of each dock', writes Appian, 'giving the appearance of a continuous portico to both the harbour and the island.' Athens had at the Piraeus a great wharf, which was used by merchant ships 200 ft in length, but the striking feature was the slipways for the warships; these had raised ramps and colonnaded roofs and could accommodate 372 vessels. A still more spectacular Greek achievement was the great lighthouse at Alexandria, built about 280 B.C., which was more than 250 ft high and with the aid of polished metal mirrors threw from a fire of resinous wood a beam reputedly visible for about 35 miles. This structure on the island of Pharos gave both a generic name and a common stepped form to other lighthouses of the ancient world.

The artificial port of Rome, the Portus Romanus, was developed on an adjoining site after the silting-up of Ostia in the time of the early emperors. Its six-sided inner harbour, having a depth of 13–16 ft, was half a mile wide, with concrete and brick quays, and a bottom of hard stone blocks to facilitate dredging. At Leptis, the terminus of the Sahara caravan-routes, 60 miles east of Tripoli, the quays of large limestone blocks were backed by colonnaded warehouses, some of which had a platform built out just above water-level to keep ships clear of the actual quayside. In both these cases, two great moles had been built out to sea as a protection, with the lighthouse on the extremity of one. There are remains of great breakwaters at other Italian ports, such as Puteoli, the main port for Rome, and as far away as the Straits of Dover the Romans built at least three lighthouses—two at Dover, of which one survives, and a very famous twelve-storey structure at Boulogne (Fig. 69).

The dry stone walling of Troy, whose surviving fragments almost certainly antedate the famous city of Priam, is a reminder that forti-fications have a longer history than cities. The classical Greek and Hellenistic periods saw the general replacement of wood and brick fences by stone, the use of ditches to keep besieging bowmen at a distance, and the growth of the practice of mining walls by timbered underground galleries which caved in when the besiegers set fire to the supporting woodwork. The Romans, having at their disposal the organized manpower of the legions and the directed labour of newly conquered peoples, built very complex fortifications, so that an enemy could enter a city of importance only by carrying several successive lines of wall, each of which was protected by formidable towers and ditches. This system perhaps reached a climax in the east Roman capital at Constantinople, where the land approach was restricted, and the triple fortifications could be correspondingly lavish (p. 28). But the Romans did not build strong defences only around their cities: every camp was fortified in proportion to its degree of permanence; and in Germany and Britain great walls barred the way respectively from river to river and sea to sea.

Fig. 69. Pharos at Boulogne, from a sixteenth-century English wall-painting

THE MIDDLE AGES

The decline of the building arts is a marked feature of the Dark Ages. In England, for example, both public and private buildings with few exceptions were made of wood up to the time of the Norman conquest. Where stone was used, as in the famous Anglian crosses of Northumbria, the softer types were preferred; apparently tools were lacking with which to cut, for instance, the magnesian limestone of the north. Brick-making was virtually a lost art, and such stonework as there was in England seems often to have been executed, or at least supervised, by masons brought from France or Italy. The surviving split-log walls of Greenstead church, Essex, represent what must have been a common type of church building for some four centuries; the hall of the Saxon thane, we may be sure, would be no better.

Italy, and to a lesser extent the Frankish empire and even Visi-gothic Spain, had a stronger tradition of stone building, based on the development of the Roman basilica. This had been the public hall of the Romans, divided by columns into nave and aisles, and, from the fourth century onwards, it provided the pattern for the early Christian church. A semicircular apse was provided at the east end, and a railed-off portico or ante-nave at the west, while the columns, which had formerly been in two tiers, were now set in a single row on each side of the nave, supporting nave walls that were pierced with windows to form clere-stories. This early Romanesque architecture, however, has left few traces, and it is significant that its outstanding creation, Charlemagne's cathedral at Aachen, is modelled upon the Italian Byzantine church of San Vitale at Ravenna.

FIG. 70. Tomb of Theodoric

This is a reminder that what was best in the west came from the uninterrupted Roman build-ing tradition of Constantinople. It was in 537, when western Europe was at its most barbar-ous, that Justinian's great brickwork cathedral of Santa Sophia was dedicated, with its arches of 100-ft span and astonishing pendentive dome, so called from the use of inverted spherical triangles to convey the weight to the corners of a square tower, 180 ft above the pavement. Dedicated to the Divine Wisdom, it still bears witness to the sublime ingenuity of man. Brick was used in Byzantine practice as a facing material, or in alternate courses with stone; and stone was jointed so accurately that some stone building was unmortared. The Byzantine influence was naturally strongest in north Italy, where the church of San Vitale in Ravenna had for lightness a dome con-structed of hollow earthenware pots, while the famous mausoleum of Theodoric (Fig. 70), built in the same city and at the same period (second quarter of the sixth century), was surmounted by a flattened dome made of a single block of limestone 35 ft in diameter. About the time of the Norman conquest of England, the same Byzantine style found splendid expression in the rebuilding of St Mark's at Venice.

Romanesque architecture, which began to spread across the Alps as the result of the visits of the higher clergy to Rome and some migration of Italian workmen, was developed more vigorously from the beginning of the eleventh century. The Norman abbeys of Bernay and Jumièges were the achievements of an Italian Benedictine abbot, and the latter building seems to have inspired the work of Edward the Confessor at Westminster. From the time of William I onwards, the style which the Normans themselves had only just acquired was stamped with increasing thoroughness upon the England they had conquered—the change can even be traced in the frequent references to quarrying rights in legal documents. The best material was obtained from Northamptonshire, south Yorkshire, and Somerset, but there was a natural preference for local stone or stone which was easily accessible by water; consequently, many important buildings in south-east England came to be built of limestone from Caen in Normandy. Transport difficulties likewise required blocks of stone to be kept as small as possible: thick walls were given a core of rubble, and very often the rubble was merely plastered at the surface. The characteristic feature of church and castle alike was the semicircular barrel-vault of Roman origin, the outward thrust of which was at first combated not by buttressing but by thickening the wall or by introducing a second vault at right angles, as in the lower aisles of St John's Chapel in the Tower of London. Windows also had semicircular heads, often referred to as 'Norman'.

Though the building of St Denis's abbey church near Paris, which was begun in 1137, is generally regarded as marking the first burgeoning of the style to which a later age gave the derogatory name of Gothic, in England the starting-point is the rebuilding of Canterbury Cathedral by a French architect fully a generation later, and it is not until the early thirteenth century that the introduction of the pointed arch can be seen to have its full effects. The great advantage of the pointed arch was that the height of the arch was then no longer fixed by the width it spanned; this made it possible to apply the principle of cross-vaulting used by the Romans. The soaring roof, which was the supreme glory of a Gothic cathedral, reaching its climax in the $157\frac{1}{2}$-ft high choir of Beauvais, came to be supported by ribs which might spring from a single pillar in three directions to form arches of different angles reaching the same height. Moreover, the more sharply pointed the arch the greater its thrust towards the ground and the smaller the dreaded thrust sideways. In aisleless churches,

such as King's College Chapel, Cambridge, the thrust of the stone
roof could be resisted satisfactorily by buttressing the walls; otherwise it was necessary somehow to bridge the aisles, a problem which
French architects solved triumphantly by the invention of the flying
buttress, as seen at Westminster Abbey. In the structure of Salisbury Cathedral, in the middle of the thirteenth century, it is already
possible to foresee the skeleton-form of building which was not

developed to the full until after
1500. By then the walls had
become mere frames for the
beauties of stained glass (p. 95),
while narrow pillars culminating
in fan-vaulting enhanced the
sense of spaciousness.

All this depended upon the
work of the mason. By the fourteenth century at latest, all types
of English stone were being
worked, from that of Portland,
which had already made its London début in Henry III's rebuilding of Westminster Abbey,
to the alabaster (gypsum) of the
north-east Midlands, used for
the carving of effigies and the

FIG. 71. Sack of a cathedral, from a
twelfth-century English miniature: note
variety of tools

retables of altars, and extensively exported. To save transport much
of the shaping of the stone was done at the quarry, which was the
common training-ground of masons and even of the master-builder
who, like the jobbing-builder of modern times, worked alongside the
men he supervised. There were three grades of workmen: the free-
masons, so called because they were qualified to carve freestone (i.e.
ungrained stone, especially sandstone and limestone, which could be
worked in any direction); the rough-masons, who squared the stone
and did straight mouldings; and labourers, who fetched and carried.
This last was both an arduous and a dangerous task, because although
the mason's tools were not very different from those of today (Fig.
71), for lifting heavy material there was nothing better than a simple
hoist with a fixed pulley and a windlass, while scaffolding consisted
only of lashed timbers and beams let into holes in the wall (Fig. 72).
The labourers, about whom the records are usually silent, were

doubtless the most numerous class: when a Welsh castle was built
in a hurry, 1,000 labourers and 230 other workers were needed to
support the efforts of 400 masons.

The craft of the mason must not be allowed to obscure that of the
carpenter, without whom the oak roofs, which were a particular
feature of the English Gothic building, could not have been made.
These were greatly strengthened by the abandonment of the old

FIG. 72. Building in stone, from a French fifteenth-century manuscript

practice of resting the rafters upon the outside of the stone vault. A
tie-beam was necessary in order to prevent the rafters from thrusting
the sides of the building outwards, but with a high-pitched roof it
was difficult to bring this low enough without obstructing the view
of the east and west windows: hence the elaborate carpentry of the
so-called hammer-beam truss. This compromise structure, peculiar
to England, had the middle part of the tie-beam cut away to clear
the view, but carried much of the outward thrust to a lower and
therefore securer position on the walls by means of a curved strut
which pressed upon a vertical jack-leg.

The roofs of large buildings were usually lead-covered. For more
ordinary roofing, certain districts had their own slate or stone, and
in 1212 the use of tiles instead of thatch or wooden shingles was
declared compulsory in London as a precaution against fire. In
the course of the same century, bricks began to come into use again

for domestic architecture, at first as a foreign import and later as a
native manufacture in foreign hands; they were used chiefly in
the eastern counties, where Flemings or Dutchmen settled. In the
fifteenth century a Lincolnshire castle (Tattershall) was even built
in brick, but by then the castle itself was becoming no more than
a fortified dwelling-house, and greater importance attached to the
city wall, built and rebuilt by local masons.

The evolution of the stone church and castle, dominating the mud
and timber buildings of the people, is a story which leaves untold
much of the varied development of the medieval builder's art. For
example, some lighthouse towers of masonry began to be constructed
soon after the year 1000, and from the thirteenth century onwards
the profitableness of trade encouraged work on worn-out Roman
roads and other traffic routes. By 1237 the most direct way across
the Alps had been opened to pack-animals by the construction of a
track with bridges through the St Gotthard Pass; a second north–
south Alpine road, passable for small carts, was made a hundred
years later. Causeways over marshes were often built and maintained by religious houses; less charitable motives influenced warrior
kings like Edward I, who twice ordered the widening of the passes
into Wales. Sometimes roads were surfaced with mortared blocks,
more commonly with cobbles or broken stone laid on loose sand,
making them easy to repair, well suited to horse-drawn traffic, and
not rapidly disintegrated by northern frosts.

There was also much work done in bridge building, especially,
it appears, in England, though most English bridges were nevertheless narrow and steep and suitable only for horses and pedestrians.
Old London Bridge (1176) with its four arches and drawbridge
belongs to the same period as the famous bridge of Avignon with its
twenty-one elliptical arches; but the general practice, as we might
expect, was to imitate the semicircular arches of Roman bridges,
though the spans were less uniform. Where the rush of water made
it impossible to place a pier, the span of the arch was sometimes
greater than in any Roman bridge. A fourteenth-century duke of
Milan bridged the Adda with a 236-ft arch; the bridge was destroyed
during a siege in 1416 and was not equalled for more than 400 years.
Bridges, by converging traffic, stimulated the growth of town life.
At the same time the larger towns were becoming more clearly
differentiated from mere villages by the revival of paving, which had
been a feature of Moorish Cordova in the ninth century. Paris laid

rough slabs of stone at the royal behest to reduce dust as early as 1185; a hundred years later the aldermen of London were instructed to pave their wards; and it gradually became usual to give at least the main streets a surface of stone or brick. There were parallel improvements in urban water supplies through the repair of aqueducts and introduction of lead pipes, as at Canterbury Priory (Fig.

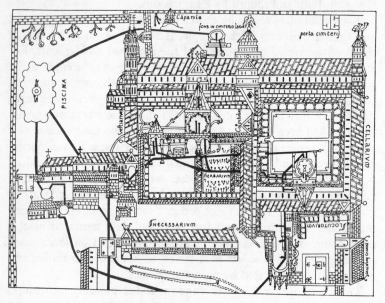

FIG. 73. Part of plan of Canterbury Cathedral and Priory, showing systems of water-supply and drainage, *c.* 1153

73); by the end of the fifteenth century some south German towns used for this purpose piston-pumps driven by water-wheels.

But the enterprise which looks forward most clearly to modern times is the beginning of canal development. The growth of trade in later medieval Europe, increasing the activity on navigable rivers, proceeded side by side with the increased use of water-mills for power. From the end of the thirteenth century, and perhaps much earlier, this conflict of interest was being met by the introduction of navigation weirs (stanches) to maintain the depth of the water, free passage being ensured by having a barrier that could be lifted and turned to one side. The flow was not interrupted, however, as in a lock, and boats had to be dragged through against the current. The earliest record of such a weir on the Thames is from 1306; by the sixteenth century there were twenty-three weirs on the sixty-two miles of river between Oxford and Maidenhead.

It was, however, in Holland that a more elaborate type of sluice was developed on the drainage canals; when the tide was at the right height to balance the pressure of the canal-water on the other side of the gate, this could be wound up, enabling boats to pass to and from the river into which the drainage canal emptied. By 1373 at latest, the Dutch had learned to build two sluice gates, between which lay a large basin, equivalent to a lock but operated more slowly, because of the great volume of water, and at long intervals. In the last decade of the century this was followed by the first lock of modern dimensions, capable of being opened and shut for each boat which passed, at Damme near Bruges. The development of the modern movable lock-gates, worked in pairs and containing small sluices to control the flow of water into the lock, seems soon to have followed. It was in a district farther east, but no doubt under Dutch influence, that locks were used for the first time, not merely to circumvent the effects of the tide, but to carry boats over a ridge of land between two lower water-levels. The watershed between the Elbe and the Stecknitz was surmounted in 1391 by two locks with a rise of 16 ft, followed by a 12-ft-deep canal cutting, making an inland water route from Lübeck to Hamburg. Similarly, in north Italy an irrigation canal, completed in 1209, had later been deepened, equipped with stanches, and dubbed the Naviglio Grande; soon after 1400 a sluice was made, enabling the marble from Lake Maggiore to be brought from it along the moat to the side of the new Milan Cathedral—an enterprise which prepared the way for the larger canal projects associated with the Italian Renaissance.

BUILDING FROM THE RENAISSANCE TO THE EIGHTEENTH CENTURY

In general building construction the greatest impact of the Italian Renaissance is clearly that revival of classical styles, and even of classical methods in architecture, which by 1450 had swept through all Italy except Venice, and by 1750 had completely ousted the Gothic in the remotest parts of Europe. The brick dome which Brunelleschi erected in Florence in 1420, with its two separate brick-work shells connected by 24 stone ribs along the sides of the octagonal vault, is generally thought of as the starting-point of Renaissance architecture. The double dome, however, is neither Roman nor Byzantine, but Persian in origin. Brunelleschi was among the first to turn back to the architecture of the ancients, and it was in his time (1414) that a manuscript of Vitruvius (p. 164) was found in a Swiss monastery, though it was not until 1486 that the printing of it made it easier to imitate the principles of classical architecture without seeing examples. Thus the classical orders of columns were revived, at least for decoration, in the building of splendid Renaissance palaces, which were spacious, light, and grand in the classical tradition. Rome in particular underwent a complete transformation, between the preparation of the first master-plan of the city for Pope Sixtus IV (1471-84), through the revolutionary reign of Sixtus V (1585-90)—when the great architect, Domenico Fontana, transformed the layout of the principal streets and piazzas—to the completion of the colonnaded Piazza of St Peter's by Bernini in 1667, which made the Papal City the crowning glory of this last great age of Italy. It was Fontana who organized the removal, from the square behind St Peter's to a central position in front of it, of the 75-ft Egyptian obelisk weighing 327 tons, which the emperor Caligula had brought to Rome from Heliopolis (Frontispiece). Although the new position was lower than the old, the transportation engaged the efforts of about 800 men and 140 horses working 40 capstans, with a public executioner available on the site—methods hardly distinguishable (except for the capstans) from those by which such obelisks had been first erected three and a half millennia earlier on the banks of the Nile.

Of St Peter's itself it may be noted that the general design for the reconstruction, Bramante's masterpiece, was inaugurated only eight years before its author's death in 1514. Michelangelo's famous dome, completed a generation later, bears a very striking resemblance to the Florentine structure: in both cases the stone ribs took the main weight of the lantern, poised so gloriously 300 ft in the air, though at St Peter's the tendency for the dome to spread had to be counteracted by the use of three iron tie-rings. Two centuries later the appearance of serious cracks caused Pope Benedict XIV to appoint a committee of three mathematicians, who calculated that the existing rings were insufficient to withstand the thrust; on their recommendation five more were then added.

The new impulse which Italy gave to European architecture goes beyond the profusion of her Renaissance buildings. In Alberti's *De re aedificatoria*, printed posthumously in 1485, description of the techniques newly practised in Italy extends to such matters as canal locks. The universal genius of Leonardo da Vinci, interested from an imaginative and theoretical point of view in almost every problem of the architect, builder, and engineer of his day, left in his studies much that still arrests the attention of later generations; and his ideas may have had at least an indirect effect upon Galileo. It is to the Italian astronomer, forced in old age by the Inquisition to turn aside from the more dangerous study of the machinery of the heavens, that we owe the first exposition of many of the problems of mechanics and statics, published, significantly enough in Holland, in 1638. Not only did Galileo put together whatever the sixteenth century had learned in the sciences affecting building construction, but from his study of the bending strength of a beam there dates a new branch of science—the theory of the strength of materials.

In France, which the Italian wars of 1494 onwards made familiar with the new tendencies, there were many imitations of the Italian dome and secular architecture which rivalled—and at Versailles surpassed—Italian achievement. The buildings of Louis XIV spring readily to mind, but it was his grandfather, Henry of Navarre, who began to shape Paris into a planned city by means of a programme of public works, designed as an act of restoration after the wars of religion and to create employment for his people. The Mansard roof, with its double slope on each side, though taking its name from a French architect born in 1598, was actually in use at Hampton Court, the Louvre, and in Italy half a century before his time. Its importance, perhaps greatest in France, was that it made it possible to combine the steep medieval roof—characteristic of north Europe with its heavy snowfalls—with the provision of good, well-lighted attics to accommodate a growing urban population. Gothic architecture was, however, more firmly rooted in the north than in Italy, so that many of its features died hard, and the building of half-timbered houses and stone houses in older traditional styles, like those of the English Cotswold villages, continued all through the sixteenth and seventeenth centuries.

In England, indeed, the impact of Renaissance architecture is associated chiefly with two architects, both of the seventeenth century. It was in 1617 that Inigo Jones erected the first buildings that were in the Italian style throughout, as distinct from having Italian features superimposed on Gothic structure. At Greenwich, Whitehall, and Covent Garden he introduced the classical orders (p. 164), together with large windows, low-pitched roofs, and hidden chimneys; the importance of the chimney was increasing with the increasing use of coal (p. 146). But the taste of the English gentry had scarcely advanced beyond the decoration of the fronts of manor houses with classical cornices and pilasters when the civil wars and their consequences checked building enterprise, so that even at mid-century Renaissance ideas were still making little progress.

One of the minor works of Inigo Jones was the portico which he added to the west front of old St Paul's Cathedral, which was in course of slow restoration for a generation before the Great Fire of London in 1666. This makes an interesting link between the man who brought Renaissance architecture to England from his empirical studies at Rome, and Sir Christopher Wren—already famous as astronomer and scientist before he turned to architecture—who created the vogue for it nearly a generation after the main work of his predecessor. Apart from his training, Wren was well acquainted with the ideas of contemporary natural philosophers such as John Wallis and Robert Hooke: nevertheless, his designs seem to have been largely empirical and intuitive. Wren built fifty-two London churches, and left his mark also in both Oxford and Cambridge, but the new St Paul's Cathedral transcends all his other achievements—a triumphant introduction into England of the dome brought at second remove from Italy, for Wren himself never saw either Brunelleschi's work at Florence or Michelangelo's St Peter's. Like its Italian prototypes, this is a double dome, but the space between the inner dome of brick and the outer of lead-covered timber is greatly increased, so as to combine the beauty of a hemisphere inside with the maximum effect of a towering height visible then from all parts of the city. Wren's dome solved the problem of the weight of the stone lantern by the inclusion of an unseen intermediate cone of brick.

The Great Fire, which had completely devastated an area of 436 acres around the cathedral, had important technological consequences outside the sphere of ecclesiastical architecture. Fire-engines, consisting of a portable cylinder and piston pump arranged for continuous operation, such as had been described by Heron in the first century A.D., had been introduced to England from Nuremberg in 1625 and manufactured at the rate of about two a year; the idea appears to have reached the American colonies in 1654. In the first fifteen years after the Fire, the use of leather pipes, enabling the engine to play from a safe distance, was introduced from Holland, as was also that of iron-wired suction-hose instead of replenishing the engine from a chain of buckets filled, passed, and often spilt, by hand. Building regulations for London were given the authority of Parliament, requiring uniformity in roofing and construction in brick or stone, and fire insurance companies began to develop in Britain a full century ahead of other countries. Yet public opinion did not give sufficient support to carry through Wren's bold scheme for the rebuilding, under which the city would have become a planned urban centre with vistas comparable to those of Paris, and some of the light and air let into narrow streets by Hitler's bombers would have become permanent amenities nearly three centuries earlier. As it was, the formal town planning which Inigo Jones had begun at Lincoln's Inn Fields and Covent Garden was allowed to expand only westwards and north-westwards, in the West End squares, of which Leicester Square alone had been completed before the Fire. By the middle of the eighteenth century their classical façades were beginning to reach as far as Oxford Street.

If England was slower than Italy or France to appreciate the benefits of town planning, she had, on the other hand, the advantage that, on an island enjoying strong naval protection, the sites of towns were less hampered by the needs of fortification. Though the Elizabethan fortifications of Berwick are among the earliest specimens of the elaborate town defences which all over Europe replaced the medieval castle, the siege of Londonderry in 1689 was the last occasion on which urban fortifications played any important part in British domestic history. On the Continent the age of Vauban was then just dawning. The great French marshal brought to a fine art the system of carrying the defence works far beyond the city wall, and developing that wall into a series of platforms for artillery—a problem to which Italians like Machiavelli and Leonardo da Vinci had given their attention during the Franco-Spanish wars in Italy. The theory of the polygonal shapes which provided the most complete network of lines of fire from a given fortress area became part of mathematical studies.

Vauban, whose contributions were regarded with respect as late as the nineteenth century, began with a 'first system'. This combined the various devices for projecting the means of defence far in front of the original wall, such as the outlying fort or *demi-lune*, and the smaller outlying position between two bastions called the *tenaille*, which had been worked out in the wars of the two preceding centuries. He later developed defence in depth, with a second ditch and wall behind the works of the 'first system'. These were flanked by two-storeyed strong-points, containing well-protected cannon, which could fire at both the inner ditch and the outer bastions. Even if Vauban himself had not been associated with Louis XIV's great canal works and equally appreciative of their possibilities for commerce and defence, it would be easy to see that the great development of civil engineering was helped by the accurate surveying, careful accounting, and competent assembling and organization of material and personnel required of the military engineer.

This is true, for instance, of the important bridges, such as the Pont Royal (1685) in Paris, designed by Mansard's great-nephew, J. Hardouin-Mansard, for Louis XIV, and the original Westminster bridge, completed by a Swiss architect, C. D. de Labelye, in 1750. Old bridges often collapsed owing to insecure foundations; alternatively, the foundations had been placed on artificial islands (starlings), as with the old London Bridge, which so constricted the channel as to make the rush of water dangerous to boats. Better results followed the introduction of the coffer-dam—a watertight building-area on the river-bed, from which the water was extracted by pumping, and inside which it was possible to dig down to a firm foundation upon which to build the piers of a bridge (Fig. 74). It is believed to have been de Labelye who first improved on this method by sinking a caisson on an area of river-bed that had previously been levelled by dredging. The caisson at Westminster, which had a wooden base 30 × 80 ft, contained the first courses of masonry for a pier, and had 16-ft side walls, so that it could be drained and used as a coffer-dam; when the pier had been built up sufficiently, the sides of the caisson were withdrawn for further use, leaving the wooden base and masonry in position. The work also benefited from the use of pumping and pile-driving machinery worked by treadmill or water-power. The great attention that bridge-builders needed to give to the security of their foundations reflected the situation in building generally, for throughout ancient and medieval times builders had been remarkably casual about this aspect of their work. Thus the craft guilds commonly gave no more than a ten-year guarantee against structural collapse.

Bridge-building materials, however, did not change greatly. Although difficulties of jointing prevented timber from being used satisfactorily where the relation of beam to beam was one of pulling rather than compressing, the use of a timber superstructure was proposed for Westminster bridge in the 1730's and was the plan adopted for the Rhine bridge at Schaffhausen in 1757. Wooden truss bridges are illustrated in Palladio's *I Quattro Libri dell'Archi-tettura* (1570), but their constructional advantages were not widely appreciated before the nineteenth century. One important improve-

FIG. 74. Coffer-dam made of interlocking piles. Ramelli, *Le diverse et artificiose machine*, 1588

ment certainly was the spread of the use of the waterproof Italian *pozzolana* cement (p. 166) for underwater construction, which, for instance, provided the watertight masonry for the Pont Royal. But the biggest improvement was that the wider employment of cranes made it possible to build with large, accurately-dressed stones, comparable to the masonry of the Romans. Joints became closer, particularly those of the wedge-shaped voussoirs forming the ring of the arch, while the arches themselves had longer spans (390 ft by the second half of the eighteenth century), narrower intervening piers, and a thickness at the crown which fell from one-twelfth of the span, as recommended by Alberti, to a mid-eighteenth-century figure of one-twenty-fourth. In general, bridge construction became lighter and more graceful.

Alberti, it will be remembered (p. 180), had written also about canal locks. When he wrote, an Italian engineer had just completed a 12-mile canal, which made a descent of 80 ft by eighteen locks (1458), and from then onwards a considerable network of canals grew up in north Italy. Before the end of the century Leonardo da Vinci, who was for a time ducal engineer of Milan, had for this purpose replaced the portcullis gate (Fig. 75), the superstructure of

FIG. 75. Lock with portcullis gates, from a Florentine manuscript, *c.* 1470

which impeded navigation, by the modern mitre-gate for which his drawings survive. By the middle of the sixteenth century, mitre-gate pound-locks are found outside Italy in the river improvements of France, Brandenburg, and England. Thus the malt-boats from Ware passing down the river Lea to Elizabethan London entered a lock which was of modern type in every respect except its material of construction. The Hertfordshire poet, Vallans, in 1577 describes it as follows:

> This locke contains two double doores of wood,
> Within the same a cesterne all of Plancke,
> Which onely fils when boates come there to passe
> By opening of these mightie dores.

By 1600 the lock had reached as far as Sweden, where the first attempts were being made towards the construction of a through waterway between Stockholm and the west coast, taking advantage of the great lakes.

By the middle of the eighteenth century, although England still had no true canals, comparable to those of the Continent, the length of English rivers which had been made navigable by artificial means was roughly equal to the whole of that which was naturally navigable. Most of these inland navigations had been made since 1600: for example, the Wey, the Warwickshire Avon, and the Worcestershire Stour were all opened up in the second half of the seventeenth century, and in the following fifty years there was a significant growth of engineering works on the main Yorkshire rivers, on the Mersey and Irwell, and on the Weaver navigation across Cheshire to the Mersey estuary. The last of these, completed in 1732, was within two decades carrying an annual cargo of more than 50,000 tons. The first British-built summit-level canal was not completed until 1745; it was a comparatively modest enterprise in Ireland, designed to carry coal from Newry to Lough Neagh for shipping to Dublin.

Most continental countries lacked the relatively long coastline, well supplied with sheltered harbours and deep estuaries, which enabled England and Scotland to rely mainly on coastal shipping for their internal trade. Where the alternative was road transport, there was an adequate incentive to canal-builders in the reduction of freight charges to one-quarter. The first important canal outside Italy was completed in 1561, with a fall of 34 ft, to link Brussels with the river Rupel; its five locks were large enough to accommodate small sea-going vessels. This was followed by other important works in Flanders after the Twelve Years Truce was signed between Spain and the Dutch in 1609: a 44-mile canal linking Bruges and Dunkirk, built about 1622, was both enlarged and extended in the following half-century. Canal-making in Germany was similarly interrupted by the Thirty Years War, but by 1669 an Italian and a Dutch engineer in the service of Frederick William, Elector of Brandenburg, had provided Germany with its second summit-level canal, which linked the Spree with the Oder above Frankfurt. The greatest developments, however, were in France, where the possibility of a canal from the Mediterranean to the Atlantic was discussed by Francis I with Leonardo da Vinci, who accompanied him on his return from the Italian wars. This grand project was not lost sight of in the troubles of the wars of religion, but Henry IV and his great minister Sully decided upon a more modest project to link Briare on the Loire with a tributary of the Seine. In 1604 Sully set 6,000 troops to work, and in seven years the work was virtually completed; there was a rise of 128 ft from the Loire and a fall of 266 ft to the Loing. Final completion was delayed until 1642, however, largely for political reasons, the only additional engineering difficulty being the need to provide a 13-mile feeder channel to increase the supply of water at the summit. This led into a storage reservoir at summit level, and the same device was used forty years later when the Loire traffic was found to justify the construction of a second canal, giving direct connexion between Orleans and the Loing.

But the reign of Louis XIV had what Voltaire called 'its most glorious monument' in the construction of the Languedoc canal, following the more southerly of the alternative routes by which Francis I had originally contemplated joining the two seas. In 1661 the engineer Riquet worked out a scheme for supplying water at the summit; this involved damming a valley by a wall 105 ft in height to provide a storage reservoir of 250 million cubic foot capacity, which was filled in winter for use in summer. The scheme being supported by Colbert and approved by the king, a well-organized labour force of more than 8,000 men brought the canal into use by May 1681, seven months after the death of Riquet. The canal had 100 locks in a length of 150 miles, with a climb of 620 ft from the Mediterranean and a descent of 206 ft to the Garonne at Toulouse. The enterprise included a staircase of 8 locks, a 180-yd tunnel (the first to be blasted with gunpowder), culverts passing underneath the canal for many streams, and three big aqueducts, of which those over the rivers Cesse and Orbiel were designed by Vauban. With a width at base of 32 ft and a depth of 6½ ft, the canal could take a barge of as much as 200 tons from the Mediterranean to the Atlantic. No such feat of civil engineering had been achieved in western Europe since the fall of the Roman empire; it anticipated the triumphs of the nineteenth century, though the use made of it by through-traffic remained small.

The highly centralized government of France under the *ancien régime* had also taken the lead in road-building. As trade and travel increased, the tendency was for the roads of Europe to deteriorate because local populations were indifferent to the needs of through traffic: bad roads favoured brigandage, and in some regions landowners were lawfully entitled to all spilt merchandise. Unbroken stone and bundles of faggots therefore continued in use for making and repairing roads long after Renaissance enthusiasts had drawn attention to the far superior structure of the Roman roads. In France, however, the post of Grand Voyer became permanently established in 1645: there were grants for new roads, a service of state coaches (1664), and a widespread use of stone setts to make the *pavés du roi*. In 1720 the French Regency established the first body of technical civil servants to look after roads and bridges, which started an organized system of trenched roads. By the middle of the century an official training school, the École des Ponts et Chaussées, had been set up in Paris with the result that—if we look forward as far as

1776—France had some 25,000 miles of highways under state control, of which one-half was then being reconstructed or aligned as avenues. Moreover, the French method of superimposing the small surface stones upon layers of larger stones laid in the trench had found imitators even before 1750 in some of the smaller German states and in the empire under Charles VI, who linked Vienna with Trieste.

6

TRANSPORT

BEGINNINGS: THE WHEEL AND THE HORSE

PROBLEMS of transportation are not peculiar to human beings, as we are reminded, for instance, by the astonishing spectacle of beavers conveying felled timber along miniature canals of their own construction. Nor are they peculiar to the inhabited world, since the most sensational scientific ventures of our own day are concerned with transportation into outer space. With so vast a theme it is not surprising that there is no obvious starting-point. Women, we must suppose, were the first human burden-bearers, carrying infants and gathered food while the men acted primarily as hunters and protectors. Thus the tying of a bundle on the back or the dragging of it along upon the outspread twigs of a convenient branch are contributions to technology which probably had a feminine origin.

We do not even know at what remote time the burden was first transferred from the back of the woman or the contraption she pulled behind her to the back of a domesticated animal. Some have supposed that the dog was the first to be used in this way because he was tamed first; others have given precedence to the reindeer, because it would be easy to make him pull a burden over the slippery snow. It might also seem likely that, once cattle had been domesticated, the idea that the strength of the ox could be used for rough haulage quickly suggested itself. There are, however, no relevant facts covering the early period of the domestication of animals (p. 45), which may even antedate by as much as two millennia our first certain evidence of a pack animal at work—the ass, which was so used in upper Egypt at the beginning of the early dynastic period (about 3000 B.C.). Since by that time it had also, in Mesopotamia, been harnessed to a vehicle, we may perhaps infer that the ass had already been carrying its burden for many centuries. It is certain that by 2000 B.C. caravans of pack-asses were in regular use in the Near East for tribute payments and merchandise.

Two other lines of advance are of immemorial antiquity. The yoke and the litter were obvious developments from bundle-carrying; and the practices of dragging a bundle on a branch and dragging slaughtered animals over the ground in their skins must soon have combined to suggest the possibility of shaping a tree-trunk into a rough sledge.

We do not know when runners were first added to facilitate the haul over grass, bare earth, marsh, or snow, but in Scandinavia the earliest sledges belong to the Mesolithic Age and skis (Fig. 76), which are based on the same sliding principle, existed there as early as the late Neolithic Age. In Egypt and Mesopotamia, too, it was

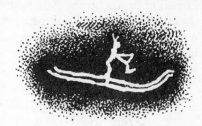

FIG. 76. Man on skis. Stone Age rock carving, north Norway

the sledge which, together with the rope, enabled men to erect the first colossal figures of gods now long forgotten (Fig. 77).

Equal obscurity surrounds the development of the boat from the time when man, a clumsy swimmer, first seized upon floating objects to support him in the water. The hollowing-out of a log of wood, in order to sit inside instead of astride it, seems to us the most natural first step, but the infant Moses in his ark of bullrushes and the modern Welshman in his coracle of leather-covered wickerwork are reminders of some of the other materials from which mankind evolved the boat. When multiplied, the original single float

FIG. 77. Transport of statue by sledge, from a tomb at Saqqara, Egypt, c. 2400 B.C.

quickly became the raft, but to make an effective boat two further advances were required. One was to achieve manœuvrability by increasing the length in relation to beam, the other was to extend the hollowed-out space so as to add to both buoyancy and capacity.

Four further devices gave land and water transport its characteristic form and pace down to the industrial revolution. These are the wheel, the sail, the made way (p. 163), and the utilization of the strength and speed of the horse. Of the origin of the sail, which has an obvious prototype in a waterborne, windblown leaf, we can say little. Early Egyptian drawings show us reed-built vessels equipped to carry a square sail spread from a short yard on a bipod mast; that mast was placed well forward, the ship being designed to be carried upstream on the Nile before the prevailing north wind. By the middle of the third millennium B.C. ships of reed and, in greater numbers, ships of wood traversed the eastern Mediterranean; after the mast had been stepped more nearly amidships it was easier to sail across the wind (Fig. 78). The Tigris and Euphrates were early

homes of the inflated skin-float and the coracle, but it is not known at what period ships first sailed from there to the Red Sea ports of Egypt.

FIG. 78. Egyptian model boat, c. 2000–1800 B.C., from a tomb at Beni Hasan

In the wheel we have one of the greatest as well as one of the oldest technological advances. The cart wheel seems to have come into existence at about the same time as the potter's wheel (p. 75) and certainly had comparably far-reaching results. Thus the earliest indication of the use of wheeled vehicles—a conventionalized sketch in a Sumerian account tablet, which shows a sledge mounted on four solid wheels—can be dated not long after 3500 B.C. Cart, wagon, and chariot then quickly became characteristic of the early civilizations, though it was not until the second millennium B.C. that the chariot was a horse-drawn vehicle of the type described in both Homer and the Old Testament.

The wheels of these early vehicles were solid. This might be held to support the common notion that the idea of the wheel originated from the use of the roller by primitive man for moving heavy objects, such as the trilithons of our own Stonehenge (pp. 162–3). But in fact the solid wheels are nearly always tripartite disks, three wooden planks being carved to form a circle and clamped together by a pair of transverse wooden struts. The axle was made separately; but we do not know whether the wheels at first turned with it, as they still do, for example, in Sindh. It has been argued that the three-piece wheel originated in a country where large trees, enabling large wooden disks to be produced readily by transverse slicing, were not numerous and among a people who had metal saws, two indications that Mesopotamia is a likely place of origin. A second feature of the earliest wheeled vehicles is paired draught, which may have resulted from the transfer of the pole of an ox-drawn plough to the pulling of a sledge on wheels. Thus it may well be that the tripartite wheel and the pole both spread from a common origin in lower Mesopotamia.

The spoke and the horse make their début together before 1800 B.C., when a light and easily manœuvred horse-drawn chariot became a decisive factor both in the great wars between the ancient empires

FIG. 79. Egyptian wheel-wrights, from a tomb at Thebes, c. 1475 B.C.

and in the upkeep of internal communications upon which their survival depended. There is little archaeological evidence to support the theory that the spoke suggested itself as a result of the carving-out of holes in the solid wheel: it is safer to regard the radially-spoked wheel as a new invention, one whose full possibilities for the bearing of heavy loads were not realized until the later Middle Ages. Four spokes may have been the most usual number at the outset, but six and eight and even more occur in specimens belonging to the first six centuries of the spoked wheel's known existence—a period during which its use spread westwards as far as Crete and became widely diffused throughout the Near and Middle East. The Egyptian wheel-wrights (Fig. 79), the first of whom we have accurate knowledge, made composite hubs and felloes of separately carved wooden segments; these were connected by mortise and tenon joints to form a circle. The spokes themselves were made of two pieces of wood glued together end to end, and trimmed to fit with precision into the appropriate holes on hub and felloe.

The carts and wagons used in the early empires are known to us chiefly from the splendid examples preserved in royal tombs, but their general use was for the humdrum purpose of the carriage of foodstuffs, building materials and metals, and migrant peoples.

During the third millennium B.C. efficient types had come into use, which—apart from the introduction of spoked wheels—underwent

FIG. 80. Greek country-cart, from a vase of the fourth century B.C.

little further change among the ancients and, in some parts of the world, survive to the present day. Except for their clumsy cross-bar wheel, Greek country-carts of the classical period (Fig. 80) look not very different from some of the cruder types of modern times. But the chariots, which are likewise depicted on Greek vases, represent a high technical achievement that once shaped the course of history but has long fallen completely into disuse.

Egyptian chariots, such as that found in Tutankhamen's tomb, are the oldest wheeled vehicles that still survive complete. They are

FIG. 81. Greek war-chariot, from a vase of c. 500 B.C.

masterpieces of ingenuity, with heat-bending used to shape both pole and felloes. The floor was made of interlaced leather thongs, the yoke rested on a saddle on the horse's back, held in place by a girth-strap to which the breast-harness was also attached, with a loop for the reins. These were fixed to a nose-strap, which with five other straps formed the bridle; the horses had blinkers, but no bits survive. The linchpins leave a play of about 1 cm. for the wheel, which itself is fitted together with extraordinary deftness and accuracy. The type of chariot from which Homer imagined his heroes dismounting to contest the fate of Troy was broadly similar to this (Fig. 81).

THE GRAECO-ROMAN PERIOD

In classical times the art of war was changed by the use of the horse for riding, a practice which, together with equestrian hunting, came from the steppe lands of Asia about 800 B.C. But the effectiveness of early cavalry—and the convenience of riding in general as a means of transportation—was severely limited by the paucity of the horse's equipment. Not until the fourth century A.D. did the Romans replace the primitive horse-cloth by the padded saddle, adopted from the east. Though loose loops were not unknown as an aid to mounting, there were no metal stirrups to give fuller security to the rider's seat, and this must have made the use of the prick-spur often risky. Horse-shoes, apart from a type which was tied to the hoof in slippery conditions, do not appear to have been common in civilized countries much before the first century B.C., when the Romans partly adopted light shoes of iron, with nail-holes stamped through from one side and the free ends turned down to improve the grip. They were known much earlier among the Celts and other peoples by contacts with the east, but the regular use of heavy horseshoes in Europe was a medieval innovation.

The pressure of the reins on the bit has from early times been important for the rider's control of his horse. The earliest snaffle-bits were of two links. These were commonly replaced later by three-link bits, in order that it should be less easy for the horse to take the bit in his teeth; it is probable that the bit was often cruelly roughened. The manœuvring of cavalry formations led to the development of a simple form of curb-bit, a loop of metal under the chin which could be pulled upwards and forwards by a rein on a lever. Later the Romans began the development of a curb or flange inside the horse's mouth which could be pressed against the roof of the mouth, with the same object of forcing its head up so that its run would be effectively checked. But the metal stirrup, which enabled the cavalry-man to brace himself for the charge, was not seen in Europe until the sixth century A.D., when the Avars rode in from the trackless Asiatic steppes.

Meanwhile, the wheel begat the road. There are known to have been some lengths of paved road in ancient Mesopotamia, Egypt, and Crete, and the short-lived Persian empire undertook the paving of parts of its famous network of tracks that were used as postal routes. But the first great road system (p. 167), originally designed by the Romans as an instrument of conquest, could not enable the cart, and still less the heavy four-wheeled wagon, to compete against the ship. In the time of the emperor Diocletian the land carriage of a load of hay for 30 miles doubled its cost, whereas the carriage of a shipload of wheat the full length of the Mediterranean added only one-quarter to the price. Thus, although roads enabled the power and influence of Rome to spread far beyond the Mediterranean hinterland, it remained true throughout the classical period that civilized life depended mainly upon the ships that followed the path of the Ithacan 'over the wine-dark sea'.

Even in the Homeric age the ship of war and the merchantman had already become distinct. The warship was of light construction

FIG. 82. Greek sailing merchant-ship and war-galley, apparently a bireme, from a vase of the sixth century B.C.

and propelled mainly by oars, though it is still unclear whether terms like trireme and quinquereme in descriptions of its more elaborate later forms refer to multiple rows of oars or a multiplication of rowers at each oar. Both trader and warship (Fig. 82) had a well-developed keel and were carvel-built, that is, the planking, which was secured with wooden pegs, met edge to edge; but the trader was broad-bottomed, partly decked, and had hurdle-work for protection at the low waist. Moreover, the trader depended upon its square sail set on a single mast, for the simple reason that freightage would hardly ever have justified oarsmen's pay, or even the capital cost and upkeep of a crew of slaves.

It was only natural that the establishment of the Roman empire, which brought peace to the whole Mediterranean area, should be accompanied by great developments in Mediterranean shipping. The Romans guarded the seas with strongly built war-galleys. These were propelled by oars set in two tiers, though a small mast set right forward made it possible to use a sail to take the ship out of action if the oarsmen were disabled. They mounted a ram, but their most important battle equipment was a hinged, spiked gangway, which could be let down to grip the enemy for boarding. There is reason to believe that the heaviest type of Roman war-galley was as big as one of Nelson's ships of the line, though far more lightly constructed: it had no armament to carry more powerful than the catapult, nor had it to cope with the Atlantic swell. Since the emperor Caligula possessed a pleasure-galley which was no less than 450 ft long, it seems safe to conclude that the only check upon considerable further growth of the war-galley among the Romans was the fact that they had no technologically equal enemy to build against, though some limit was imposed by the use of wood as a structural material (pp. 209, 371).

But the large cargo-carrying vessel was essential to the life of Rome: it provides the motif for many stone carvings which make clear its character. The hull was very strongly built with three or more protective wales, and was rounded like that of the modern sailing trawler, the length of the ship being 3½ or 4 times the beam. The stern would lift well to a following sea, and only the two quarter-rudders, one on each side of the ship, look clumsy to the modern eye. There was a mainmast amidships and a foremast in the bows, both sharply raked forward, with a square-sail on each mast and one or two topsails on the mainmast only. It was lower in the bows than any modern sailing-ship; but that was because the general practice was to sail mainly before the wind and trust to Providence to escape such storms as that which shipwrecked the apostle Paul on Malta. Safely arrived at their destination, the heavier cargoes were often distributed inland by barges, the grain for Rome, for example, being towed in this way from the mouth of the Tiber by oxen. The ancient world had a standard type of river barge, keelless, with a flat floor formed of half-a-dozen wide and heavy planks, the floor-timbers being pegged to large knees and these in turn fastened to a heavy line of inside planking above water-level. It is thought that boats of this kind of construction, from which the modern barge derives, had been carrying stone and, no doubt, other heavy building materials along the rivers of Europe long before the days of the Romans.

Indeed, it would be most unwise to assume that in the period of the classical civilizations the barbarian world necessarily lagged behind where transport was concerned. It is more probable than not that the horse-drawn, spoke-wheeled chariot, which we first encounter in Mesopotamia, came there originally from some unidentifiable Bronze Age culture of the steppe lands. It was certainly from that area, the habitat of the wild horse, that civilized man learnt the art of riding: the Gauls had horseshoes several centuries before the Romans. There is also the fact, to which Julius Caesar gave such lasting publicity, that the Greek chariot, which the Roman used only for racing and processional purposes, had undergone an astonishing development among the Celts against whom he fought. The sort of chariot which figures so much in *De Bello Gallico* was a masterpiece of joinery, smith's work, and enamelling. An even more striking achievement of the Celts before their conquest by Rome was a type of wagon of which the front pair of wheels was mounted on a swivel: this precedes by at least 300 years the appearance among the Romans of even a much simpler innovation, long known in China, namely, the use of shafts. These are first shown to us in a sculpture of a child's miniature chariot found in a provincial town of the third century A.D. As regards ships, too, it was the barbarians of northern Europe who developed the clinker build, that is, construction from a series of overlapping planks fastened together by clinched iron rivets, although they were very slow to adopt the principle of the keel, on which the strength and stability of a ship mainly depends.

TRANSPORT IN THE MIDDLE AGES

The fall of the Roman empire in the west meant that life in western Europe became for a long period decentralized, localized, and restricted, alike in outlook and in physical relations. Trade between one region and another—particularly in valuable imports from the east—was never wholly interrupted, but its volume was not enough to stimulate enterprise. On the contrary, the roads built by the Romans fell slowly into decay and their artificial harbours (p. 171) were allowed to silt up. But it is claimed that the more widespread use of the iron horseshoe was an important mitigating factor, because it enabled pack-horses to tackle the roughest paths. Where four feet could not climb, it was possible to use serfs or slaves as human burden-bearers. Harbour facilities, too, mattered less than might be supposed in an age whose commerce was largely conducted by small boats plying on small rivers. The hazards of war and piracy discouraged distant exchanges on any large scale; indeed, the first important technological advance of the period was in the arts of war rather than of peace.

The Viking ship has probably been over-written for want of material with which to compare it, not with the shipping of western Europe, but with the Byzantine war fleet, for the latter was the true heir of the Mediterranean shipbuilding tradition. However, if we accept the Gokstad ship (Fig. 83) as being a Norwegian vessel of state of about the year 800, it follows that the Vikings of that era were as skilful as they were certainly warlike and adventurous. The

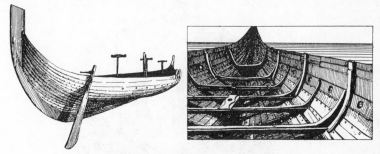

FIG. 83. The Gokstad ship, *c.* 800, after restoration

vessel has a true keel, single steering-oar with tiller handle, well-raked stem- and stern-posts, sixteen rowing-ports cut in each raised side, and a square-sail to be rigged on a single mast amidships. The whole is clinker-built, light, and buoyant; and, as the name 'long-ship' suggests, the length was a striking feature—at least five times the beam. In the course of two centuries these vessels grew until they had thirty and even sixty oars a side, and in them the Vikings made their raids, their conquests, and their far-reaching explorations from the Russian rivers to the American coast.

But the builders of Viking warships had no monopoly of invention. The Irish had braved the Atlantic waters before them in skin-covered boats of which practically no details survive. There is, too, a possibility that the longships built by King Alfred were not mere works of imitation but derived their efficiency from some know-ledge of Roman ship-construction. Moreover, the sagas seem to indicate that for trade purposes the Vikings themselves preferred a different type of vessel; at all events, the merchant ships of the later Middle Ages were based on quite other models than theirs. In the thirteenth century a broad-beamed sailing-ship, called a cog (Fig. 84), made its appearance in northern waters, meeting the demand for cheap freightage of bulky, mainly low-priced, commodities. This was clinker-built, with a single square-sail, and is thought to have been an enlargement of the 'round ship', which had been long in use in North Sea trade.

Meanwhile, two important inventions, both of eastern origin, had come into vogue, first in the Mediterranean galleys, used both for

FIG. 84. Hanseatic cog

war and for the carriage of such small but costly cargoes as spices from the Levant. The lateen (that is, Latin) sail was the first triangular fore-and-aft sail, the use of which made it possible for the vessel to beat into the wind. The Moslems are believed to have brought it from south-west Asia: it is found in Greek ships of the ninth century and in Italian of the eleventh century, after which it became common on all the European coasts. The second important innovation was the stern-post rudder, the traditional high stern being lowered and a port cut into it, through which the tiller passed from the head of the rudder to the helmsman's hand. This, of course, made for greater accuracy in navigation and facility in tacking, and we may perhaps connect it with the enterprise of the Genoese, who in the early thirteenth century began to undertake regular winter sailings, and before the end of the century had inaugurated a definite sea-route between Italian ports and those of the North Sea.

The use of the magnetic compass was becoming common by then; it seems to have begun about the end of the first millennium A.D., and an early tradition connects it with Amalfi. Originally the needle was floated on straw to give a rough indication of direction, but by 1269 at latest it began to be mounted on a pivot. Charts had been made for the Mediterranean and Black Seas; A.D. 1270 is the date of the first recorded use of a chart on board ship. In the fourteenth century the lure of the Baltic trade caused the passage round the Skaw to the Sound to be established as the first regular open-sea route for shipping.

Meanwhile, the central Middle Ages had seen the spreading into general use of a major improvement in land transport, comparable to the use of the lateen sail at sea. Its origins, too, are partly Roman and Byzantine, though there is also an important influence, difficult to trace, from models originating farther east. Horse-power, as our modern use of the term implies, was the most universally available source of power known in the pre-industrial world; but when men first harnessed the horse, their pattern was the primeval ox-yoke, which they applied unsuccessfully to the ass and horse, neither of which has the prominent and powerful shoulders of the ox. Hence the use of a breast-band, which they tried to hold down by a strap passing between the legs to the girth-band: chafing was the least of the evils which resulted. When the horse pulled hard, there would be a choking pressure on the windpipe and a compression of blood in the veins of the neck. The ancients had only a limited knowledge of anatomy, and though various experiments were made in improving the harness, particularly under the Roman empire, it was not until the twelfth century A.D. that the modern type of horse-harness became usual in Europe.

There were three main improvements. Shafts, which could be attached well down the breast-band, had been only occasionally used in vehicles by the Romans; they now became general. Traces, which had been used to some extent by the Greeks and Celts, served in the same way as shafts to bring the pressure to the middle of the breast-band. When they came into common use in the form of ropes, it became a regular practice, as it had not been before the Middle Ages, for a team of draught animals to be used in the most effective way—that is, in file (Fig. 85). But the most vital trans-formation was that of the breast-band into the stiff, padded horse-collar. When this, too, became established in the course of the twelfth and thirteenth centuries, the effective tractive power of the animal had been multiplied by as much as five.

Thus, the horse began to come into its own. The modern type of cart-horse was first bred in France at this time, its original service being to carry the medieval knight in panoply, a heavy burden. The use of the collar enabled the horse to be substituted for the ox at the plough, albeit very gradually. More immediately, the wagoner and

FIG. 85. Two-wheeled cart, from the Luttrell Psalter

the carter became key figures in the life of the age, though this was not because the vehicles themselves had notably improved: the wheelbarrow was the only striking medieval innovation. Even such a convenient device as the swivelling front-axle, once used by the Celts, seems to have been completely forgotten until revived in the fifteenth century. Nor was it until then that the wheel was further improved, by 'dishing' it—that is, giving it a concave shape—to achieve better balance. All the more remarkable is the effectiveness of horse traction. In England, what has been called the 'peasant reserve of carts' made it possible to secure conveyance at a penny per ton per mile in any normal case where the return journey could be made within the day. As bridges became more numerous, land transport could even, in favourable circumstances, compete with water transport—between Southampton and London, for example, to avoid rounding the dangerous Kentish coast; or for the grain imports of the German Hansa towns, when the normal route became affected by high river-tolls. But speeds remained very low: when the king of Scotland's ransom had to be brought south to London in all haste in 1375, it travelled no more than 36 miles a day.

THE PERIOD OF THE GREAT GEOGRAPHICAL DISCOVERIES

It is believed that in the Middle Ages transport costs were a smaller proportion of total costs than at the present day: in other words, the industrial revolution has produced relatively greater economies in production than in carriage. If this view of medieval conditions is correct, it helps to explain the persistence of commercial enterprise in Europe, even under the discouraging circumstances of the earlier Middle Ages, and the wealth of commercial activity that characterizes the thirteenth and earlier fourteenth centuries. Yet it was in the middle of the fifteenth century, after a long period of declining trade, that the full-rigged ship came almost suddenly into existence—the first ship that was fit for great voyages of discovery and new transoceanic trades.

The northern merchant-ship, the cog (p. 200), had been imitated in southern Europe, so that the new ship which grew out of this, the carrack, seems to be neither wholly northern nor wholly southern in type. It is clearly anticipated in the little Portuguese caravels, lateen-rigged ships with two or three masts, which Henry the Navigator, from about 1415, sent on early voyages of exploration down the African coast. Since the shipwrights of the region round Bayonne had most to do with developing the new features, it has been proposed to call the carrack an 'Atlantic' ship. The earliest dated picture of a fully developed carrack is on a French seal of 1466: it shows what is essentially a modern sailing ship.

The carrack (Fig. 86) was carvel-built, according to the southern practice (p. 196); but the rudder hung from the stern-post, as in the north, and a tiller passed into the hull of the ship through a port above main-deck level. There was a forecastle-head or deck in the high bows and two or more decks were built up behind in the poop. Though the waist was comparatively low, the hull had sufficient room for cargo, stores, armament, and crew. They grew rapidly in size: by 1500 a vessel of 600 tons was becoming quite common, and Henry VIII's ship, the *Great Carrack*, better known by its later name of *Henry Grâce à Dieu*, was originally a 1,500-tonner carrying 195 guns and 900 men.

The three or four masts—for a second mizzen-mast soon became quite usual—mounted a variety of sails. The mainmast had a large square mainsail and a small topsail on the light topmast, which rose above the halyards and lifts for the big square-sail yard. The foremast, which was shorter and no longer raked forward, carried a second square-sail. These two were the driving sails or 'courses'. The mizzen-mast or -masts had lateen sails running fore and aft, and there was also a spritsail on the bowsprit. These smaller sails at the two ends of the ship could be easily furled or set and were especially helpful for manœuvring in narrow waters.

Fig. 86. Three-masted carrack, from a late-fifteenth-century Flemish engraving

The full-rigged ship such as we have described was now the ship *par excellence*: in a list of Henry VIII's navy made in 1546, 'ship' means 'carrack'. By 1550 the big trading-galley, in which Venice had specialized, was ceasing to be profitable. Its good timekeeping, possible because the oars were brought into use whenever the wind failed, could not save it, even for expensive cargoes. But the slave-rowed war-galley, mounting guns and sail, survived much longer in Mediterranean waters. Four of them, indeed, came up the English Channel with the Spanish Armada, only to be defeated by the

English weather. There was also the galleon, which deserves description as one of the first types of sailing-ship to be regarded primarily as a warship. Though readers of Charles Kingsley think instinctively in terms of Spanish galleons, they were actually a Portuguese invention, and an English galleon, the *Ark Royal*, was flagship in the Armada year.

Galleons were rigged like other big sailing-ships of the period, but their length was about four times the beam. They also had lower castles fore and aft which, together with their relative narrowness, made them fast, though the reduction of the castles also made them more vulnerable to boarders. But the main difference from the ship of commerce was that the galleon, not needing cargo space, was built with a gun-deck which could support a heavy main armament of cannon, discharged through ports in the ship's sides. Thus naval warfare ceased to be a matter of ramming or grappling with an enemy. In the new age of the broadside, warships learnt to keep their distance, but the successful use of the armament still depended upon speed and manœuvrability.

Ocean voyages in bigger and better ships were both a cause and an effect of improved methods of navigation, such as had been unnecessary while shipping could find its way satisfactorily by landmarks along the coastline of the Mediterranean and the north-western seaboard of Europe. The use of compass and chart, dead-reckoning, and sounding were no longer adequate for such tasks as Prince Henry the Navigator imposed, when he ordered his ships to voyage due south and in a given latitude turn at right angles to make the coast of Africa. The essence of the problem was how to adapt astronomical instruments, which in such forms as the astrolabe were already highly developed, for use by seamen under shipboard conditions, thus enabling latitude to be determined. Dates of inventions are very uncertain, since seamen were seldom writers, but there is good evidence that the sea-quadrant came first; the earliest account is dated 1456–7. From the engraved plate the sailor measured the angle of elevation of the pole star, observed through the pin-holes, by a plumb-line passing over an engraved scale. The measurement was corrected by reference to the changing position of the Guards, two stars in the Lesser Bear. The circling of the Guards had long been used for time-keeping, and early in the sixteenth century this was facilitated by an instrument called the Nocturlabe or Nocturnal, which was set to indicate the number of hours before or after midnight. Latitude was also determined by observing the height of the sun at noon and taking the necessary reading from a printed table of daily solar altitudes.

Two other instruments which seem to have come next after the quadrant were the sea-astrolabe, a modification of the astronomer's instrument and difficult for unskilled observers to handle, and the cross-staff; both were used for taking an altitude. The cross-staff was the simpler and cheaper instrument, particularly useful in rather low latitudes, and more apt for determining stellar altitudes than solar ones. A transversal was drawn to and fro along a staff until one end covered the horizon and the other shot the star or the sun: the altitude could then be read off from graduations on the staff. From 1595 onwards this in turn began to be superseded by John Davis's back-staff, known to foreigners as the English quadrant, a more precise instrument which had among its advantages that the user turned his back to the sun and so was less dazzled by it. English navigators had also been responsible a few years earlier for the introduction of the log and line—the first major English contribution to the art of navigation. The log was a wooden board thrown from the stern of the ship; the line, which was attached to it, had a series of knots at 7-fathom intervals. Each knot paid out from the reel in a period of half a minute, measured by a sand-glass, represented a speed of one sea-mile per hour. Observations were to be made whenever the wind changed, and entered in a book, later called the log-book.

Although its wandering was then, and indeed still is, uncertain, the secular variation of the position of the North magnetic pole was charted by 1702 and in consequence a ship's course could be accurately measured. This, with the development of the log, made possible navigation by the method of dead reckoning, in which direction and distance is plotted systematically on a chart. Although this method has serious limitations—in particular those resulting from sideways drift—it was, and continues to be, of the greatest importance, for in a ship at sea it may well happen that celestial observations cannot be taken for days, or even weeks, on end. The problem of determining longitude at sea, however, still remained unsolved, for it depended upon the development of a really accurate chronometer that was robust enough to work perfectly on board ship.

Contemporary developments in inland transportation were much less sensational; perhaps the most important was the spread of canals and improved river navigations (p. 186). The four-wheeled wagon, which in medieval England had been used chiefly as the occasional carriage of the great, now came into more general use, as it had long since been on the Continent, a 4-ton carrier's wagon being a common sight on the roads in the time of Shakespeare. Its size was increased later, but the 4-tonner survived to provide the model for the wagon used on the big farms of eighteenth-century improvers (p. 71). A development of the still more distant future was foreshadowed by the first appearance, in the prosperous continental mining industry at some time before 1550, of wooden rails used to facilitate the haulage of heavily laden trucks.

Of more immediate importance, at any rate to the upper classes of society, was the coach, which is supposed to have been introduced to England in 1564 by a Dutchman who became coachman to Elizabeth I. The name, which is common to most European languages, comes from the village of Kocs in north-west Hungary, but what features of the coach were actually invented in Hungary is not known. The covered wagon was employed in the Middle Ages and earlier, but the coach from the first made the traveller less sore, though perhaps not less sick, by having its body suspended on straps. It also had a bogie or turning-train: that is to say, the front axle was attached to the chassis through a pivot, a device that had been revived for war-engines in the preceding century.

Early coaches struggling through miry roads made practical use of postilions armed with whips, such as are occasionally to be seen astride the horses in state processions at the present day; they had been employed with humbler vehicles since the twelfth and thirteenth centuries. The word 'postilion', however, was originally a name for the post-boy, who rode with official dispatches and other documents from post to post or stage to stage on the roads of England and the Continent. The horses used for this purpose, which in cases of urgency might maintain an average speed of about 10 miles an hour, could also be hired by private persons.

DEVELOPMENT FROM 1600 TO 1750

The growth of wealth, trade, population, and colonies in the next century and a half (1600–1750) was not accompanied by any particularly sensational advances in the means of transportation. The duration of an average voyage across the Atlantic did not become appreciably shorter, nor did the tempo of a continental grand tour become very different. A Dutch or English East Indiaman, the pride of their respective navies, would be unlikely, even in the days of Clive, to exceed 800 tons; such a vessel kept the sea for a generation or more, journeying 10,000 miles in the year without breaking bulk and carrying sufficient armament to protect ship and cargo in unpatrolled waters. Ships of the line, however—the 'great ships' of Pepys's diary—were enlarged to take more guns, all lesser tasks being relegated to the smaller and speedier frigates, which could not face the enemy's broadside in battle. Accordingly, the building of the big warship, such as the 1,500-ton *Sovereign of the Seas* which Charles I built with the ship money, gave shipwrights in all the leading naval countries a chance to develop new devices which were later transferred to the trader.

The longer, lower lines of the galleon type of ship were, on the whole, preferred. It became usual to have a flush deck running from end to end of the vessel, and, as the lowered poop caused the ship to labour less in a seaway, it became common practice to fit galleries and windows to improve accommodation in the stern. Capstan, chainpump, galley, and hammocks all became common features of ships at this time, but the chief development—carried farthest, of course, in the warship—was in the size of mast and spread of sail. The addition of a fourth mast became less rather than more frequent, but in a big ship each of three masts had a topmast and topgallant mast above it and the fore- and main-mast also had royals (short for topgallant-royals), making eleven masts in all, as in the *Sovereign of the Seas*,

> Whose brave Top top-top Royal nothing bars,
> By day to brush the Sun, by night the Stars.

The sail area was further increased by setting triangular fore-and-aft sails on the stays between the masts, and there were also studdingsails added to increase the area of the square-sails in fair weather. A warship built on such a scale required the felling of some 2,000 oak trees—50 acres of woodland, which would not bear a second harvest for at least a century. Even the launching of so heavy a vessel from the dry docks, in which they were usually built, presented great problems, as did subsequently their careening, to burn and scrape off marine growths, and for repair (Fig. 87).

Ships were very carefully designed with the help of a large mouldloft, on the floor of which sections for the timbers could be drawn without reduction. The original drawings were worked out by the master-shipwright at his table (Fig. 88), commonly on a scale of ¼ in. to the foot; every curve of the timber was then transferred full size to the mould-loft floor with the help of large divided compasses called sweeps. Although the growing interest in mathematics and science undoubtedly helped to formulate the proportions and sail-spread for the designs, methods remained almost wholly empirical; Pepys's contemporary, Sir Anthony Deane, is reputed to have been

the first naval architect who could compute in advance the exact depth of water required to float a new vessel. Most ships were in fact based upon the midship section of some notably successful vessel previously built by the same individual or firm, as recorded in the careful scale-model—of which many examples still survive—that shipwrights in early days often preferred to a plan as guidance for their work.

FIG. 87. Careening at Batavia, from a Dutch painting of 1699

Ships of the eighteenth century are also known to us in many cases from surviving plans. The steering-wheel came in about 1705; the topsails became bigger in comparison with the courses; and a new type of sail, known as the flying jib-boom, replaced the spritsail in the bows. More interesting is the fact that the big ship was coming to be of international type, though the Dutchman was still made shallower and broader in order to negotiate the Zuider Zee. This tendency towards standardization resulted from the almost perfect adaptation of design to function that had now been achieved in the sailing-ship.

So long as the chief constructional material was wood, 2,000 tons was about the maximum size of ship that could be built. But it was only the ship of the line, followed at a considerable interval by the merchantman engaged in distant and hazardous trades, that aspired towards this maximum. The bulk of the mercantile marine of every seafaring nation consisted of much smaller craft: as late as 1800 the average tonnage of English merchantmen was no more than 100 tons. Here, as in the design of their fishing fleets (p. 64), the Dutch long took the lead. In the first half of the seventeenth century the *fluitschip* undercut the English and French in the carrying trade by 30–50 per cent., and when the Navigation Acts intervened, the 'fly-boat' or 'flute' became anglicized by devious means to work in large numbers under English ownership and the English flag.

This *tour de force* of Dutch shipbuilding represented a combination of favourable factors. Building costs were reduced by the prevalence of low rates of interest in Holland and by the well-established Dutch control of the market for timber and other ship's stores in Norway and the Baltic lands. Labour was saved by the use of wind-driven sawmills and great cranes; the latter particularly impressed

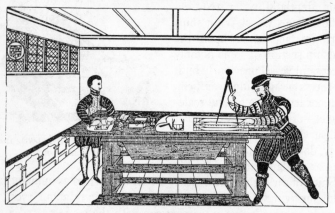

FIG. 88. Tudor ship-designers at work, after an English manuscript of the late-sixteenth century

emissaries from Colbert. Above all, there was the skill in adapting craft to function which the Dutch had acquired in dealing with their native problems of inland navigation: they had thirty-nine types of river and canal boat. This enabled them to design a ship with a very large hold; narrow lines and light timbers (200–500 tons was the normal burden); three short masts; and a 'tumble-home' to reduce bulk and wind-resistance above the water-line. Barring accidents, to which they were somewhat prone, these ships sailed so fast in comparison with more orthodox types as to make possible an extra voyage to the Baltic within the sailing year; moreover, carrying simplified rigging and no guns, they were worked with less than half as large a crew.

The growth of science brought with it improvements in the seaman's equipment. Perhaps we may include under this heading the work of Edmond Halley the astronomer, who in 1686 published the first wind-chart of the trades and monsoons and in 1699–1702 charted also the global variation of the magnetic compass. This was the earliest isometric map, and was twice revised in the following century as better observations became available. The quadrant and back-staff were greatly improved upon by a method, anticipated by Isaac Newton, which was demonstrated before the Royal Society by John Hadley in 1731. This used an octant, in which the image of the sun or a star was reflected by a mirror on to a second mirror already aligned with the horizon; the angular observation of the altitude was made by a telescope moving over a graduated scale. A very great advantage of the octant was that it was not affected by the motion of the ship. Admiralty tests in 1732 showed Hadley's instrument to have an accuracy of not less than 2′. Simultaneously and independently Thomas Godfrey, of Philadelphia, devised a similar instrument, while Caleb Smith in Britain designed one which used prisms in place of mirrors, a valuable feature in view of the scarcity of good mirrors, though his design was in other respects inferior to Hadley's. With an extended scale, the octant developed into the modern sextant.

Meanwhile, the extreme importance of the problem of determining longitude at sea had been emphasized by the setting up of a Board of Longitude in Britain, empowered to make an award of £20,000 to 'such Person or Persons as shall discern the Longitude at Sea'. This was in 1714, seven years after disaster had befallen a British fleet off the Scillies, when the loss of the flagship with all hands was believed to have been due to the inability of the Master of the Fleet to fix its longitude. But it was not until 1762 that a chronometer made by John Harrison, his famous No. 4, fulfilled the exacting requirements of the award, and the problem of a precise determination of longitude at sea was finally solved. Nine years later a smaller version of this accompanied Captain Cook on his second great voyage, in which he charted the mysteries of the south Pacific ocean.

The development of roads and of vehicles is obviously closely interrelated: thus in England during Charles I's reign there was even a period in which the use of stage-wagons was banned in order to protect the public highways from wear and tear. For a very much longer period the minimum width of the iron tyre was prescribed by law—at one time it was as much as 16 in.—and in the middle of the

eighteenth century the use of broad-wheeled vehicles was still encouraged by making them free of the toll-gates which were then
becoming numerous. At that time the average width was 9 in., but to
circumvent the regulations designers began to build bevelled wheels,
of which only about 3 in. normally touched the road. For heavy goods
the 8-ton wagon drawn by as many as twelve horses was the only
rival to the river barge and the pack-horse train. It also carried the
poorer passenger: in an aristocratic age technical progress ministered
mainly to the needs or ambitions of the rich. From 1665 or there-

FIG. 89. Miner's truck, with pin to engage
in grooved plank. Agricola, 1557

abouts the roughness of the road
was mitigated for the coach
traveller by the introduction of
the first springs, which supported the body of the coach on
C-shaped ιstrips of tempered
steel; lighter travelling vehicles
with two wheels also began to
make their appearance. Since the
seventeenth century, the rival to
the coach for town use had been
the sedan chair. But now the
growth of properly paved streets
and squares, which resulted from eighteenth-century town planning,
encouraged the construction of all kinds of fancifully named experimental vehicles, such as the titiwhiskey in which Jeremy Bentham
in his youth set out from London for Paris and the *pot de chambre* in
which apparently he arrived there.

Systematic progress in design, however, depended upon the improvement of road surfaces. Here, in the period immediately preceding the industrial revolution, France clearly led the way: England
had nothing to compare with the French organization (p. 188).
It would have required more than human insight to attach any
special significance to the development in seventeenth- and early
eighteenth-century England of the rail-way which, as already noted,
had appeared in its most primitive form among the German miners a
generation or two before (p. 207). The Germans at first had a pin
underneath the truck, which moved along a groove in a plank so as
to keep the front wheels on a straight course (Fig. 89), but it is
possible that before the end of the sixteenth century flanged wheels
of wood were also in use (Fig. 90). The earliest English reference to

rails occurs in a colliery account of 1597-8, but wagon-ways laid with timber 'tilting-rails' developed fast: the coal trade was growing rapidly, and much of it was horse-drawn for long distances down from the mine to river- or sea-level. As with the rut-roads of the ancients (p. 167), the wagon-wheel ran in a groove at the outset, but the success of the system encouraged adaptation to different forms both of rail and of wheel, as we shall see later.

FIG. 90. Transylvanian coal-wagon with flanged wheel, probably sixteenth century

Meanwhile, the Britain of Daniel Defoe—of which we get a far clearer economic picture than of any one country on the Continent—was still a land in which even gentlemen rode more than they drove and the poor travelled on foot. Fast-trotting horses might be used to convey fresh fish from Lyme Regis to London, but much of the capital's food supply walked there from the poultry farms of Norfolk or even from the cattle-grazing districts of Scotland and Wales. For long-distance transport away from the rivers the pack-horse was still the prime goods-carrier, and coal, which was to be the life-blood of the new era, still cost six times its pithead price to deliver taxed in London.

COMMUNICATION AND RECORD

SPEECH AND RECORD

SPEECH, writing, printing, and photography are four stages in the technology of recording. For the purpose of the present history, printing is the most important of the four because its impact on society can be viewed in full, from the stir made among the literate few by the first inventions in the fifteenth century to the effects of almost universal literacy among the western nations 400 years later. By contrast, the impact of photography, especially in the form of the moving image, was only beginning to be felt in A.D. 1900. As for speech and writing, we can but dimly discern what these innovations meant to mankind, since we know relatively little of man's prehistory before he learned to write, and virtually nothing of man in that most remote past when he communicated with his kind only by the sounds, signals, and gestures of the animal.

It has been well said that language is correlative to the tool. Palaeolithic man made words as well as tools, but all is surmise as to the process by which the cries of the animal were developed into the language of man, enabling him to communicate his thoughts in speech. The Australian aborigines, still living in the Palaeolithic stage in the eighteenth century A.D., had, nevertheless, as many languages as there were tribes—perhaps 500 with an average membership of 500 apiece—who then roamed the island continent. The mist does not begin to clear before the Neolithic revolution, when it is easy to see that the growth of specialized activities would lead to the growth of specialized vocabularies—of the potter, the agriculturist, of the women spinning and weaving in the hut. The rise of civilization in its turn would produce new needs of vocabulary, to express ideas both concrete and abstract, and a modification of grammar until it reached a condition of exactness without archaic cumbrousness. Thus we arrive at the stage reached by the classical Greeks, beyond which language has made no noteworthy progress.

Language in itself is the most evanescent of all technologies, since until modern times it left no record on the air. The enduring record begins with Palaeolithic art, though no doubt there were sign messages long before the oldest of the Palaeolithic cave paintings which survive. Cave paintings, it is believed, had probably a magical significance for the hunter, and may have given a purely personal aesthetic pleasure to the painter. At the same time, it is difficult to look at the representation of a hunter gored by a wounded buffalo (Fig. 91) without supposing that its author was deliberately recording the event. But the great step from painting to writing would

FIG. 91. Upper Palaeolithic cave painting at Lascaux, France

only be taken when man, moving into a condition of civilization, required to make quantitative records to maintain the life of the city.

From the temple archives of Sumerian Erech, which Jewish legend numbered among the possessions of Nimrod, the first 'to be a mighty one in the earth' (Genesis x, 8), there survives a set of tablets (Fig. 92) in which pictures are used systematically for record. It is thought that these are the accounts of the temple, and they date from about the middle of the fourth millennium B.C. These word-signs or pictograms express not only concrete nouns, such as bread, but also verbs, such as to eat, represented by a hand and mouth when placed alongside the sign for bread; their interpretation is often uncertain, but it is possible that some of the compound signs depict objects, the names of which are compounded to represent a proper name or a person. Be that as it may, from the beginning the scribes of the Sumerian city temples developed the art of recording by two methods. One was to mark the pictogram with lines so as to modify its meaning: for instance, a line under a chin to convert the sign for head into the sign for mouth. The other was to use the pictogram to represent not a thing or action, but a sound—in much the same way as we, faced with the same problem, might use the sign for 'ass' to represent the syllable 'as'—a change which was all the more valuable because the Sumerian vocabulary consisted mainly of monosyllables. This enabled the number of signs in use to be reduced, so that by about 2900 B.C. a total of 2,000 signs had been reduced to 500 or 600, of which about 100 represented a syllable, that is, a vowel

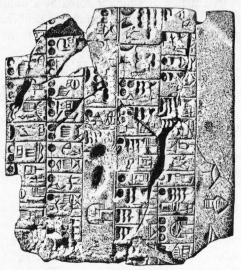

FIG. 92. Pictographic tablet from Erech, Sumeria, *c.* 3500 B.C.

with or without accompanying consonants. Since, however, the consonantal sounds were not distinguished from the syllables in which they occur, the Sumerians never achieved an alphabet.

The development of writing has at all times been greatly influenced by the nature of the material available and the means of marking it: even today blackboard and chalk present different problems of calligraphy from those of paper and pen. Apart from monumental inscriptions on stone or (later) metal, the early Mesopotamian peoples wrote exclusively upon tablets (usually about 3 × 4 in.) and variously shaped blocks of clay, the markings being done originally with a sharp pen of reed—difficult to draw with on the wet clay. But by about 3000 B.C. it had become usual to shape the end of the reed like a wedge, and, with the help of different sizes, to build up the required sign by stamping wedge-shaped marks into the clay. The sign soon lost its resemblance to the original pictogram, all the more so when the Semitic conquerors of Mesopotamia adopted this cuneiform writing (*cuneus*, wedge) to represent their Semitic language. It was also taken over by the Hittites for their very different Indo-European language, and figures as late as the middle of the last millennium B.C. in the Susian inscription of Darius's victories on the Rock of Behistun. In the meantime it had served to spread Babylonian culture widely through western Asia.

It is probable, but not at all certain, that the Egyptian system of writing grew originally out of the Sumerian. Nevertheless, it developed very differently and, it would seem, from different needs. For Egyptian writing begins with the formation of the united monarchy, and its first known use was to help monumental art in recording the names and achievements of the kings. The Egyptian hieroglyphics (or sacred carvings) are also distinguished from the

FIG. 93. King Narmer's palette

Sumerian system in that they never abandoned the idea of the picture, as it first appears in 'King Narmer's palette' (Fig. 93) of *c.* 3100 B.C., which is said to indicate that the god Horus brought to the Pharaoh 6,000 foreigners captured within his land. Hieroglyphics survived for occasional use as late as the Roman period, but for documents, as distinct from monuments, the Egyptians developed more rapid forms of writing (hieratic and demotic), in which the clear outline of the pictorial sign disappears, as with the Sumerian, and the sign commonly represents a syllable. The Egyptians were able even to represent a consonant by a single sign, but were so conservative—their writing, like much else, centred largely upon the rites for the dead—that they refrained from taking what would seem to us the natural step of discarding more difficult methods in favour of a purely alphabetic system of writing.

The Egyptians had no need to resort to cuneiform writing because they had paper and ink with which to write. To make paper, the pith of the papyrus reed was cut into strips, which were laid across each other at right angles, pressed, dried, smoothed, and gummed together to form a roll. They made their ink from lamp-black and gum-solution, their pens—used brushwise at first, but later cut like quills—from rushes. Papyrus was an Egyptian monopoly but convenient to export, and therefore a powerful stimulus to the spread of writing among Egypt's neighbours east and west.

Hieroglyphs are to be found side by side with cuneiform writing among the Hittites, and appear to have influenced the earliest Cretan

FIG. 94. The earliest known Latin inscription, Palestrina, Italy, seventh century B.C.

script, though by 1400 B.C. linear signs were in use at Knossos to express a language now recognized as Greek. But the future lay with the westward spread of the alphabet, from its uncertain place of origin in the Near East. It is thought to have been first introduced by a Semitic people in contact with Egypt soon after 2000 B.C. We know that an alphabet, resembling the Arabic and having eight letters not found in Hebrew or Phoenician, was in use at Ugarit on the north coast of Syria before its destruction by attack from the sea in the thirteenth century B.C. It is suggested that the disappearance of this alphabet is also connected with the fact that it was written in cuneiform, which would not be likely to survive where clay was not the natural writing-material of the country.

At all events, it is clear that before the downfall of Ugarit a linear Phoenician alphabet of twenty-two letters representing only consonants was in use by the kings of Byblos, about 120 miles to the southward. Early in the first millennium B.C. this Phoenician alphabet is to be found in Syria, Palestine, and Arabia; a variant, descended from the same ultimate Semitic source as the Phoenician alphabet, became established a little farther south, and was the ancestor of the Arabic alphabet. But it was the Phoenician alphabet which the trade and colonization of the Phoenicians bore across the Mediterranean as far as Carthage, and which, as the fabled 'Cadmean letters', was brought to Greece, where the linear writing used at Knossos had once existed but had died out. Alphabetic writing began among the Greeks about the middle of the ninth century B.C. The Etruscan alphabet certainly came from the Greek, and the Roman probably from the Etruscan; in the last century before Christ the Latin alphabet (Fig. 94) consisted of twenty-three letters, to which modern English added only *v*, *w*, and *j*.

MEASUREMENT

Many of the original purposes of writing were strictly practical, such as to record important historical events and codes of law and to

FIG. 95. Land measurement, from a tomb at Thebes, Egypt, *c.* 1400 B.C.

keep the accounts required for organized taxation and commerce. The development of systems of measurement was an essential concomitant of the development of writing, and we must therefore consider, though necessarily very briefly, the evolution of measures and weights. As a background to this account it is important to realize that the ancient world knew nothing of such precise and widely used systems as are in use today. The old units varied greatly not only from place to place but from time to time, and in many cases were never very accurately defined until local idiosyncrasies eventually gave way to the uniformity of the metric system.

Although proof is lacking, it seems obvious that measurements of length must have preceded all others: time is an abstract quantity, and weight had little meaning until some form of balance had been devised. By contrast, measurement of length became important as soon as man began to build and to divide up land (Fig. 95). Moreover, as long as only rough measurements had to be made, man had the dimensions of his own body as a readily available standard: a horse's height is still measured in hands, the breadth of a man's palm. Of units based on the body, the most fundamentally important was the cubit: this was the length of a man's forearm from elbow to finger-tips, and the forearm was the Egyptian hieroglyph representing it. The span, from the tip of the little finger to the tip of the thumb when the hand is fully stretched, is roughly half a cubit. The length of the foot was another convenient measure and was most commonly reckoned as about two-thirds of a cubit. Men could also use their own height, approximately equal to the distance from finger-tips to finger-tips when the arms are outstretched: this made four cubits or one fathom.

As men differ individually in stature, and the average proportions of different races differ also, it became essential for individual communities to define units of length more precisely by using some sort of officially approved rule, and this seems to have been done as early as 3000 B.C. The Egyptian royal cubit was approximately 20·6 in., and the variation was probably no more than 2 per cent.; the 'double remen', the diagonal of a square having sides of one cubit, was widely used by the Egyptians in land measurement. There was also a Sumerian cubit of approximately 19·5 in., a Greek Olympian cubit of 18·2 in., and a longer Persian cubit, derived from the Assyrian, measuring about 25·3 in. The Roman foot was based on the Egyptian royal cubit; it was divided into twelve *unciae* (ounces or inches), and was shorter by $\frac{1}{3}$ in. than the modern foot. This became the standard for much of Europe, but a longer 'Drusian' foot of 13·1 in., which prevailed in northern Europe in Roman times and had been known to the Egyptians in the second millennium B.C., was widely used in medieval building work and in the woollen industry. In England, Henry I standardized the yard by the length of his own arm: the present standard dates from 1305.

Longer distances were much less precisely defined, and were normally expressed in terms of days' journeying. In an age when most journeys of any length were made for business reasons this was satisfactory enough, for it was the time taken, rather than the actual distance, that was of interest, although Xenophon recorded in Persian *parasangs* the progress of his great march across Asia to the sea. Eratosthenes, whose measurement of the Earth in the second century B.C. (p. 229) must rank as one of the great intellectual achievements of all time, used as his unit the Greek *stadion*: this was a furlong of

600 'feet', but unfortunately we do not know the exact length of the foot on which he based his calculations. The Romans reckoned 8 *stadia* to their mile of 1,000 double paces, the principal Roman roads being marked with a stone at every mile, both for the convenience of travellers and to simplify the organization of maintenance work. This Roman mile, equivalent to about 1,665 modern English yards, was used throughout the empire, and was the basis of subsequent European miles, although the latter varied considerably from place to place.

Early measurements of area, too, were ill-defined by modern standards, but in accordance with practical needs. Thus the acre came to be defined as the amount of land a yoke of oxen could plough in a day: naturally, it varied greatly according to the character of the soil. An alternative was to measure land in terms of the area that could be sown with a given amount of seed. Not until relatively late was land-area more precisely defined: the English statute acre, for example, in 1305.

For bulk commodities, such as grain, and for all liquids, measurement by volume is relatively easier than by weight. The Egyptian unit was the *hon*, rather less than one (0·84) imperial pint. The Egyptians also used the Syrian *kotyle*, equivalent to 0·62 imperial pint; the term still survives in Greece. The bushel is apparently of Celtic origin: it was, and still is, a very variable quantity, its volume depending on country, commodity, and whether heaped or level measure is prescribed.

It is tempting to assume that early standards of weight were related to the weights of existing standard volumes of water or grain, but the evidence for this is slight. The earliest use of balances seems to have been for weighing gold-dust, a commodity so precious that accurate measurement was of great importance. This use can be dated from the fifth millennium B.C.: the balance (Fig. 96) seems not to have been widely used in trade until at least 2,000 years later. Because of the limitation to the weighing of gold, only small units of weight were at first required; the standard was the shekel, used throughout the Middle East, varying in weight from 7·78 to 14·13 grammes. When larger weights were required the *mina* (25 to 100 shekels) was introduced, and subsequently the talent (60 *minas*). A Sumerian talent of about 2350 B.C. weighs approximately one hundredweight.

The balance in substantially its modern form—that is, a beam pivoted at its centre and carrying the object to be weighed at one end and standard weights at the other—dates from prehistoric Egypt. As early as 1350 B.C. balances could weigh a shekel with an accuracy of 1 per cent. The Roman steelyard (Fig. 97), still widely used, was a form of balance in which the object to be weighed is counterpoised not by varying the weight at the other end of a beam of fixed length, but by moving a fixed weight along the beam: by

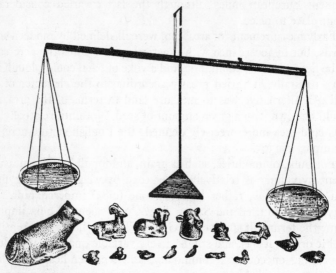

FIG. 96. Egyptian wooden balance, with 30-cm beam, showing typical animal and bird weights. El-Amarna, *c.* 1350 B.C.

appropriately graduating the beam the weight of the object can be read directly.

The measurement of time presents exceptional difficulties. Nevertheless, records of time were among the earliest uses of writing, and the Egyptians, thanks to the remarkable accuracy of their astronomical observations, had established a reasonably accurate calendar by 3500 B.C. For primitive man the day's activities began at dawn and ended at dusk: the division of the daylight hours was of little interest. By contrast, the succession of seasons was always important to him in relation to the ripening of fruits and berries and the seasonal migrations of much animal life, and as soon as permanent settlements were established, the cycle of the seasons determined the times for the various operations of the agricultural year. Thus the early Egyptians recognized three seasons—those of the Nile flood, of sowing, and of harvesting respectively—each lasting four lunar months, and reckoned each year from the time when the heliacal rising of Sirius, the brightest star, gave warning of the imminence of the annual inundation.

The lunar month, however, is of approximately $29\frac{1}{2}$ days, while the year—the period of revolution of the earth round the sun—is approximately $365\frac{1}{4}$ days. Consequently a year of twelve lunar months gets out of step with the seasons by approximately eleven days annually. To rectify this discrepancy the Egyptians at first introduced an extra month every three, or sometimes two, years. To avoid this inconvenience, a civil calendar was introduced some time early in the third millennium B.C. It was based on a civil year of 365 days, found from astronomical observations, divided into twelve months of thirty days each: the remaining five days were introduced as a special period at the start of the year. This civil year was used for secular affairs; the lunar calendar was used by the priests.

FIG. 97. Roman steelyard, A.D. 79

Further revision of the calendar became necessary, however, when the effects became apparent of the six hours by which the sidereal year exceeds 365 days. This was effected by introducing, about 2500 B.C., a special lunar calendar of thirteen months that kept in step with the civil calendar. About 357 B.C. a revised lunar calendar was introduced, based upon a twenty-five-year cycle. As early as 239 B.C. it was realized by the Egyptians that the forward drift of the civil calendar by one day every four years could be obviated by the simple device of introducing what we now call the leap year; nevertheless nothing effective was done until the Roman period.

The Babylonians, the Greeks, and the Jews encountered the same difficulties in reconciling the lunar month with the solar year, and solved it similarly by introducing various intercalary periods that would have the over-all effect of making the year 365¼ days on the average. Our modern calendar, however, had its beginnings in the local calendar of the city of Rome, which was apparently introduced by the Etruscan kings. Like other early calendars, it drifted away from the seasons, and when the gap had widened to eighty days a fundamental reform was decided upon by Julius Caesar, who sought the advice of the astronomer Sosigenes of Alexandria. The new calendar was again based on representing the 365¼-day solar year as three years of 365 days followed by one of 366 days.

The Julian calendar remained in force from 45 B.C. until the famous Gregorian reform in A.D. 1582, which resulted from uncertainty about the proper day for the observance of Easter. The date of Easter, which derives from the Jewish Passover, is determined by the date of the first full moon after the vernal equinox, which was fixed in A.D. 325 as 21 March in the Julian calendar. After some 1,250 years, however, the vernal equinox had receded by some ten days, and in consequence the correct date of Easter—of immense significance to the whole Christian world—was uncertain. This further discrepancy arose because the assumption that the solar year is of 365¼ days is not quite true: the annual discrepancy is about 11 min. By a papal bull of 1582 it was ordained that, instead of having a leap year every fourth year, there should be 97 leap years in 400 years: to eliminate the accumulated error, 5 October 1582 became 15 October 1582. Most continental countries quickly adopted the reform, but it was many years before Britain and some other non-Catholic states would do so. Britain made the change as late as 1752, Russia not until 1918, and Turkey in 1927.

The establishment of a satisfactory calendar is historically of the first importance. While agriculture was the principal activity of civilized nations, the calendar conferred the great advantage of enabling seasonal work to be planned without reference to the phases of the moon, and its value to the trader, tax-collector, priest, and historian needs no emphasis. Much less importance was attached to measuring the passage of time merely between dawn and sunset. The first attempts to do so invariably divided daylight into equal periods: as the duration of daylight is a variable quantity, it follows that hours in the modern sense meant nothing to the ancient world. The first daily timekeeper was probably the shadow-clock (Fig. 98), found in Egypt from about 1450 B.C., and in later centuries in a great variety of forms. From an early date they carried a number of scales (Fig. 99), to be used at various times of the year. The water-

FIG. 98. Egyptian shadow-clock, about 14 in. long, *c.* 1450 B.C.

clock or clepsydra dates from about the same time, or possibly earlier: in this, time is measured by the flow of water from a small orifice in a large container. Analogous to the clepsydra was the sand-glass, of roughly equal antiquity. These three remained virtually the only daily time-keepers for thousands of years. Mechanical clocks (Fig. 100) first appeared in the thirteenth century A.D. when they were driven by falling weights; spring-driven mechanisms, which made watches possible, were not in use before the fifteenth century. Galileo's discovery of the iso-chronous swing of the pen-dulum, reputedly by observing the swing of a lamp in the cathedral at Pisa, opened in 1581 an era of far greater accuracy in timekeeping.

The accurate mechanical measurement of time must be based upon some repetitive movement that occurs with com-plete regularity. The earliest escapement mechanism was the verge, in which a pair of pallets attached to an oscillating arm engage alternately with the cogs of a crown-wheel rotated by a falling weight. The regularity of the verge was much influenced by friction and, although satisfactory

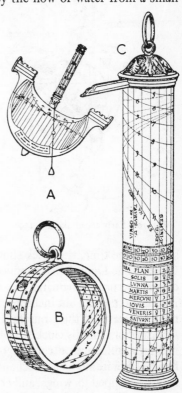

FIG. 99. Sun-clocks: (A) 'ship' dial; (B) ring dial; (C) cylindrical pattern

enough in an age when precision was not of great importance, it was not intrinsically a good time-keeping device. The shaft carrying the crown-wheel was connected through a chain of gears with the hand, or hands, of the clock's face. If the clock was to strike the hours, a second weight-driven mechanism would be incorporated. The earliest surviving clock of this type, in Salisbury Cathedral, dates

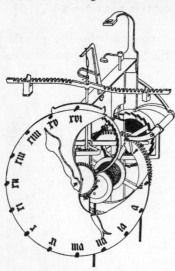

FIG. 100. Early alarm clock, c. 1390

from 1386; clocks very similar to that at Salisbury exist also at Wells (converted at a later date to pendulum control) and Rouen. The close resemblance seems to indicate common craftsmanship; in this connexion it is perhaps significant that Ralph Erghum was Bishop of Salisbury from 1375 to 1388 and of Wells from 1388 to 1400.

The Wells clock illustrates the passion of the day for having elaborate mechanisms in addition to those concerned simply with timekeeping. The striking of the hour is effected by moving figures and at each hour four mounted horsemen appear; in addition to showing the time, the clock shows the age and phase of the moon. Giovanni de Dondi's astronomical clock, built in 1348–62, of which detailed records remain, not only indicated the movements of the sun, moon, and planets but incorporated also a perpetual calendar for the movable feasts of the Church. The design, workmanship, and performance of Dondi's clock were far ahead of its day, however, and it had little influence on contemporary design. Another clock famous for its elaborate auxiliary mechanism—a cock (Fig. 101) that stretched its neck, flapped its wings, and crowed—was that built at Strasbourg in 1354. The clock itself has disappeared, but the cock survives, having been built into a later clock in 1574.

The spring-driven clock appeared in the middle of the fifteenth century. Adoption of this made it possible to construct more compact mechanisms, and indeed prepared the way for the portable timepiece, but demanded a device to compensate for the diminishing force of the spring as it uncoiled: this problem did not arise with weight-driven mechanisms, as the force exerted by the weight at the end of the descent is the same as that at the beginning. The necessary compensation was effected by the fusee (Fig. 102), essentially a conical drum with a helical groove so cut in it that as the spring uncoiled the connecting cord exerted a greater moment on the shaft carrying the fusee.

Early clocks often had a single hand to indicate the hours (Fig. 103) but a second face to indicate quarter-hours soon became common, as did the minutes-hand, and by 1550 a seconds-hand had been experimented with. The seconds-hand did not become common, however, until after the advent of the pendulum.

FIG. 101. Mechanical cock, constructed largely of iron, from the Strasbourg clock, 1354

The principle of the pendulum—that the time of oscillation of a suspended weight is (virtually) independent of the amplitude of its swing—was discovered by Galileo in 1581, but he seems to have made no attempt to use it for timekeeping until 1641, when he instructed his son Vincenzio to construct a clock incorporating both a pendulum and a pinwheel escapement that he had devised: in the event the clock was not completed until both father and son were dead. The principle of the pendulum was developed by Huygens, who detected that the time of swing

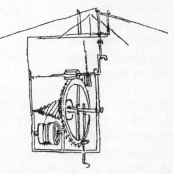

FIG. 102. Fusee, from drawing by Leonardo da Vinci, c. 1490

is not entirely independent of the amplitude—for which deviation he devised a mechanical correction—but, seemingly unaware of Galileo's escapement, adopted the old verge mechanism. Many clocks were made for sale by Huygens' clock-maker in The Hague, Salomon da Coster. In 1673 Huygens published his great work on timepieces, the *Horologium oscillatorium*. Nearly a century elapsed after Galileo's invention before the verge-escapement disappeared. William Clement's invention of the anchor-escapement in 1670 was improved by George Graham about 1715, and remained the standard escapement, especially for astronomical clocks, until almost the end of the nineteenth century. The anchor-escapement produced much less disturbance of the swing of the pendulum than

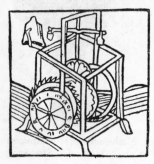

did the more cumbrous verge: it went very close to achieving the ideal of a free-swinging pendulum.

As we have noted, the time of swing of a pendulum is not absolutely independent of its amplitude. Huygens sought to obviate this mechanically, but other clock-makers took the alternative course of lengthening the pendulum and making it swing through a narrower arc. This led to the popular long-case clock, with its 39-in. pendulum beating one second. Still longer

FIG. 103. Clock with single hour-hand, *c.* 1490

pendulums were used for special purposes: thus in 1676 Thomas Tompion constructed two clocks for the new Greenwich Observatory that were fitted with anchor-escapements and 13-ft pendulums, beating two seconds. Three years earlier a long-case clock recording fractions of a second had been built for Thomas Gregory, astronomer at St Andrews University, Scotland.

The advent of much more reliable and accurate clocks stimulated interest in watches. Portable clocks had appeared as early as the last half of the fifteenth century: because of their shape and supposed place of origin they have been called 'Nuremberg eggs', but there is evidence that the first were in fact made in Milan. For such purposes the pendulum was, of course, unsuitable and some new form of isochronous oscillator was necessary. In 1675 Huygens introduced the balance-spring, and the precision of small clockwork mechanisms was much improved with the introduction of jewel bearings—usually rubies or sapphires—in 1704. Huygens hoped that his watch would be accurate enough to be used to determine longitude at sea but, as we have noted (p. 211), the first chronometer satisfactory for this purpose was Harrison's famous 'No. 4' of 1762. George Graham's cylinder escapement of 1721 enabled the works of watches to be enclosed in slimmer cases, and in 1755 Thomas Mudge invented the lever escapement which, although neglected for nearly a century, is used in the best modern watches.

CARTOGRAPHY

Increasing accuracy in the measurement of space and time led to developments in the art of cartography, which—like the geography and mathematics on which they are based—lie outside the limits

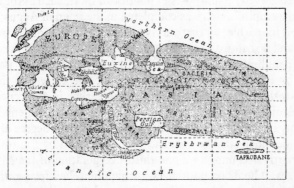

Fig. 104. Map of the world as reconstructed from the ideas of Eratosthenes

set for this book. Modern mapping has, however, very early antecedents, as is suggested by the readiness with which primitive peoples, like the semi-nomadic Eskimos and Red Indians and the South Sea islanders encountered by Captain Cook, draw rough maps to assist explorers. Mesopotamian land maps inscribed on baked clay tablets survive from about 2500 B.C. The Egyptians, as we have seen, had a system of land measurement of great antiquity: this, continuing through many changes of régime, provided the basis of the map used by Eratosthenes in his calculation of the length of a degree of longitude. Helped by the resources of the great library at Alexandria, of which he was the keeper for about half a century (247–195 B.C.), Eratosthenes not only bequeathed to later mapmakers a scientific, and perhaps very accurate, estimate of the size of the earth (p. 220), but his map of the world, known only through medieval versions, employed a system of gridding (Fig. 104). The shape is that of an elongated rectangle surrounded by ocean, but the coverage—from Ushant to the Ganges and from the island of Thule in the northern seas to the supposed sources of the Nile—links up the familiar Mediterranean lands with the conquests and discoveries of Alexander the Great. The map was criticized by the astronomer, Hipparchus (*fl.* 161–126 B.C.), because positions were not astronomically determined, and for the irregularity of the grid; but his proposal for the use of a projection to allow for the curve of the Earth's surface was not taken up until the second century of the Christian era.

The Roman contribution seems to have been severely practical— maps that served the purposes of politics and war, such as the map of the whole empire which was completed in the reign of Augustus and engraved in marble; all that survives is part of a plan of the imperial capital and a road map of the world contained on a strip measuring 745 × 34 millimetres. But the great Alexandrian tradition was continued by Ptolemy, who about A.D. 150 set out 'to reform the map of the world' on the basis of work done earlier in the century by Marinus of Tyre, a geographer otherwise unknown. Ptolemy's map had many imperfections. He believed the length of a degree of longitude to be much smaller than had been calculated by Eratosthenes, which partly accounts for a one-third exaggeration of the Mediterranean sea. The 8,000 positions on which he relied for plotting the known habitable world—180 degrees in longitude and 80 in latitude— were established from itineraries or seamen's dead-reckonings rather than astronomical observation. Although there existed a coastal guide to the Red Sea, he did not know that India was a peninsula nor that the Indian ocean was not a *mare clausum*. His importance lies in the scientific approach, which caused him to expound two methods of map projection. This was to bear fruit in the fifteenth century, when Ptolemy's *Geography*, accompanied by maps that are probably of a much later date, was translated into Latin and later printed; the original Greek version was first published by Erasmus in 1533. In the meantime geographical science passed to the Arabs, while monkish cartographers based their maps upon the interpretation or misinterpretation of Holy Scripture. Only the charts drawn by navigators to accompany the Mediterranean sailing directories or *Portolani* served a serious technical purpose; from the time of the so-called Catalan Atlas of 1375 (see Fig. 9), which gives India its true shape, these sea-charts became incorporated in a decreasingly fanciful version of the *mappa mundi*.

The era of the Discoveries was both a result and a cause of a new interest in the making of maps and charts—and terrestrial globes, a novelty which accompanied both Columbus and Magellan on their voyages—for which new instruments (p. 205) provided new possibilities of accuracy. Gerhard Kremer (latinized as Mercator) surveyed his native Flanders, provided the instruments of observation for the campaigns of the emperor Charles V, and introduced in 1568 the first of the long series of modern map projections; his maps were the first to be known collectively as an atlas. The Low Countries remained pre-eminent in the art for about a century, but the French took the lead in the next important advance, the exact measurement of an arc of the meridian. This was first done by Jean Picard in 1669–70 just north of Paris, but between 1736 and 1745 it was re-measured by French expeditions sent to Finland and Peru, which established the fact that the earth is flattened at the poles. A French map of 1700 first gave the Mediterranean its correct length, and the *Atlas Général* of B. D'Anville, begun in 1737, removed the imaginary lakes from unknown Africa, delineated China in accordance with a contemporary Chinese publication, and abolished the mythical continent from the southern seas. Finally, in 1744 C. F. Cassini de Thury started to map France entirely by triangulation—a process which it took 39 years to complete—on a scale of 1:86,400.

But in all this later development no event was of more cardinal importance than the introduction of engraving, which gave both maps and charts a wide distribution, such as was never contemplated before, and at the same time made their reproduction accurate. Cartography, in fact, was one of the arts that gained most from the invention of paper and printing, to which we now turn our attention.

PAPER

The important Arab manufacture of paper directly prepared the way for the invention of printing. The Greek and Roman world is distinguished far more for what it recorded than for any great originality in the technique of recording. Indeed, the only considerable advance was the increasing substitution of parchment for the papyrus of the Egyptians. The practice was not wholly new: the Egyptians had written on leather at a very early date, and it was not a far cry from leather to parchment, which was in fact in occasional use as early as the thirteenth century B.C. Parchment is made from untanned leather; the best quality (vellum) from the skin of a very young calf or kid. It was washed and soaked in lime to get rid of dirt and much natural grease; dried on a stretching-frame; shaved with a knife; and smoothed to produce a perfect writing-surface. The name is believed to come from Pergamum in Asia Minor, where the material was being prepared at the end of the third century B.C. as a tougher, though dearer, alternative to the Egyptian papyrus, the export of which had been banned by Ptolemy Epiphanes in the hope of checking the growth at Pergamum of a rival library to the Egyptian.

The use of parchment spread rather slowly, the main change-over from papyrus occurring in all probability about the time of Constantine the Great. North-western Europe adopted it first for the service of the Church, last for public legal documents, where its use had been forbidden by Roman law. Originally, for lengthy documents rectangular sheets of parchment were sewn together in long strips which could be rolled up, in much the same way as the sheets of papyrus had been glued or gummed; but early in the second century A.D. the practice began of folding a large rectangular sheet so as to form various sizes of page, and then binding together the folded sheets so as to form a codex or book in the modern sense (Fig. 105). The word 'volume'—from the Latin *volumen*, a roll— like the legal title of Master of the Rolls, is a reminder that a book was originally a record which the reader unrolled, but the newer device was a great deal handier. It was specially favoured by the early Christians, who are said to have invented it, in Egypt, in order to have more than one of the sacred writings in the same book. A very moderate-sized book of 200 quarto pages of parchment, however, would require the skins of no less than twelve sheep, so the writing for a long time cost a good deal less than the material. Thus the adoption of printing on any significant scale presupposed the availability of a cheap and plentiful material upon which to print.

Hence the importance for the western world of contacts which the Arabs made with the Chinese. It was in the middle of the eighth century that they took prisoner some Chinese paper-makers in the course of a struggle for the possession of Samarkand; paper had been in use in China since A.D. 105, or even earlier. Arabic manuscripts written on paper survive from the ninth century, and in the twelfth century the industry was established among the Moors in Spain, and also probably among the Moorish subjects of the Norman kingdom of Sicily. From there it spread to the Christians in Spain and Italy, and in the fourteenth century to Germany and elsewhere, though down to the close of the Middle Ages the most important paper-making centres were in north Italy.

The earliest paper was referred to as cloth parchment, but in fact its raw materials, which must be of a fibrous nature, included straw and wood as well as linen or cotton. The first process was to beat the material to a pulp and mix it with water to disperse the fibres.

Fig. 105. St Luke copying his gospel into a codex from a scroll, from a twelfth-century Byzantine manuscript

As early as 1150 this was expedited by the stamp-mill, believed to have originated at Xativa in Spain, which used a wheel and tappets to raise and drop pestles in mortars. The mill was at first turned by hand, later by wind- or water-power. It was also made more efficient by the addition of spikes to tear to pieces the rags which were the normal raw material. In the seventeenth century this pulp-making process was much improved by the introduction of the 'hollander', in which the rags were shredded with knives mounted on a rotating cylinder.

The pulp was transferred to a vat and kept stirred to ensure a uniform mixture. The paper-maker then dipped into it a rectangular mould, the bottom of which was formed by a number of tightly stretched wires: in the fifteenth century there were about 28 wires to the inch, but this was gradually increased to give a finer paper.

As the water drained from the mould, the fibres felted together to

FIG. 106. Watermark attributed to Tycho Brahe

form a sheet of paper. By 1285 the practice had begun in Italy of sewing a figure of wire into the mould so that the texture of the paper might incorporate some kind of sign—the watermark (Fig. 106). Successive sheets were removed from the mould and laid between layers of felt cloth. When they totalled a gross they were squeezed in a press (Fig. 107), hung up to dry, and perhaps finished by rubbing with a smooth stone. The improvement of the surface by sizing was introduced in the sixteenth century, using tanner's waste, and soon after the year 1700 wooden rollers were employed to

FIG. 107. French paper-makers, mid-eighteenth century

complete the finishing stage. As early as the fifteenth century a sheet of paper (8 octavo pages) cost only about one penny even in England, to which the manufacture came very late; from about 1650 onwards the practice of papering the walls of rooms greatly increased the demand.

ORIGINS OF PRINTING

The impact of printing was tremendous. The output of books in the first fifty years after its discovery was almost certainly greater than in the preceding thousand years. Besides its tremendous significance for religion, politics, and the arts, this was a technological advance which facilitated every technological advance that followed it. It is therefore disappointing, and perhaps surprising, to find that the precise origin of so epoch-making an invention is still uncertain. It is not even possible to determine with any exactness how far the western world was influenced by discoveries which were undoubtedly made first in the Far East.

Printing certainly preceded typography. The Romans, for instance, cut patterns on wooden blocks, with which they stamped designs in plaster and made printed textiles. At the end of the thirteenth century the printed paper currency of the Mongol empire was both described by Marco Polo and made familiar in practice to north Italian traders, who did much business with the East, by its attempted introduction into Persia. The Far East used block-printing also for playing-cards and religious charms. While there can be little doubt that the existence of printing in the East was known in Europe well before the fifteenth century, it is uncertain whether its technique also was known. It remains an open question whether both idea and method derived from the East or if there was an independent European invention of printing. In any event, by about 1400 both playing-cards and prints of saints were being printed in Venice and in the south German towns. As religious prints were sometimes pasted into books, it is natural to suppose that religious block-books—books made by carving pages of lettering in wood—likewise preceded what is commonly termed the invention of printing. But of the block-books which survive, none is certainly earlier than 1470.

There are four prerequisites for ordinary printing. With two of these—a block carrying the desired design in relief, and paper to which the pattern is to be transferred—we have already dealt briefly. The other two are a suitable ink, and a press to transfer the ink from the raised parts of the block to the paper.

The earliest printing was done with a water-ink similar to that used by scribes (p. 264), but the physical properties of this were not suitable for the new process. It is difficult to spread uniformly even on a wooden printing block, and this disadvantage became serious when metal began to be used, for on such a surface watery solutions tend to collect in droplets. Further, an absorbent paper had to be used and, as absorption takes place both laterally and in depth, the result was an impression that was not only smudgy but showed through on the reverse side of the paper. Again, the viscosity of water is relatively low, so that the paper would tend to slide about on the surface of the block while the transfer of the ink was being effected by applying pressure; so further contributing to a poor impression.

FIG. 108. Printers at work, with type-cases and tympan, Frankfurt-am-Main, 1568

Most of these difficulties were overcome by using an oil-bound ink, made by grinding boiled linseed-oil with lampblack or powdered charcoal. It is thought that the linseed-oil may have suggested itself through its use as a varnish by early fifteenth-century Flemish painters, and the discovery may have been applied to the inking of wooden blocks before the time of Gutenberg, to whom it has been generally attributed since 1499; in any event, the result was a standard ink employed for more than four centuries. Originally the pressure needed to transfer the ink from the block to the paper was achieved by rubbing the back of the paper with a leather pad; but a screw-press, with which greater and more uniform pressure could be attained, was soon substituted. For this, oil-bound ink was essential, since without it there would have been too great a risk of the paper moving during the operation.

The press was already familiar, being used, for example, in pressing linen and in paper-making, and required at first only slight modification for its new function. But the actual printing was considerably helped later by the introduction of the 'tympan', a parchment-covered frame to which the paper was fastened before printing. This was hinged in such a way as to bring the paper down exactly level with, and square to, the type (Fig. 108).

What has been said above applies to the origins of relief printing, with which the future lay, but the technique of intaglio printing—

that is, cutting a design into a surface, leaving the ink in the cuts only, and transferring the outline of the cuts to a soft and absorbent surface—is also an ancient one. From the ancient world onwards, goldsmiths and silversmiths had been accustomed to embellish their products with lines engraved by a sharp instrument called a burin; a metal plate engraved in this way and inked could be used for printing. Alternatively, there was the process practised by fifteenth-century armourers of etching the metal. In this, the surface to be decorated was first coated with an acid-resisting film. The design was then cut through the film to expose the metal, which was eaten away by the application of acid; if necessary, parts of the design could be emphasized by working with a burin or by further etching. It is thought that the earliest line-engraving may date from about 1346; the etched engraving, which prepared the way for pure etching, from about 1500. Thus the notion of printing was being developed in the fifteenth century on a second basis quite distinct from relief printing, though the latter in fact proved to be the more economical method for the printing of illustrations as well as for printing from movable type.

Although the makers of printed books were quick to develop the art of adorning them with illustrations, plans, diagrams, and maps, all of which were cut in relief in blocks of wood (usually box) or metal (generally copper, but sometimes brass or lead), it is, of course, the invention of letter-press printing from movable type that at some point in the mid-fifteenth century created the modern book. The relief block made it possible to reproduce a complicated pattern of lines, but each such block, created by much delicate work, served one purpose only. Movable types, on the other hand, had three advantages. Firstly, they could be used repeatedly, their period of usefulness being limited only by gradual wear. Secondly, the supply was easily and cheaply renewed, since each letter, once carefully designed, could be reproduced in a mould (Fig. 109). Thirdly, interchangeability necessitated strict standardization in size and shape of lettering: such uniformity, which is so often an unattractive feature of modern mass-produced articles, is a positive help to the reader of the printed page.

How did this great change come about? The making of single letters or symbols must long have been an established practice. If the inscription under the wood-block of a saint became damaged, letters would be cut out and new ones glued in, so as to avoid remaking the whole block. It would be surprising if no early manufacturer of playing-cards had thought of making a single carved wooden block representing the symbol for each suit, and of pressing out a clay mould, so that he could reproduce the symbol by casting in lead or tin. But in such cases the result would be crude, whereas the printing of books from movable type demands type which fits together with complete regularity on all six surfaces.

FIG. 109. Typefounder pouring molten metal into mould, 1568

It seems likely that the decisive changes resulted from the work of more than one experimenter. Johann Gutenberg, the goldsmith of Strasbourg, who returned to his native Mainz about 1446, is clearly defined as an active and litigious figure; but it may well be that Johann Fust, his fellow goldsmith and sometime partner, who is supposed by some to have stolen the technique from Gutenberg, had in fact experimented independently at an earlier period. Items printed in Holland, which may be earlier than anything produced by Gutenberg and Fust at Mainz, may be the work of a third independent experimenter, Coster of Haarlem, or of several different craftsmen not necessarily confined to Holland: it is known that some work was being done in southern France. What is clear, however, is that the first large-scale printing-office in the modern sense was the one conducted at Mainz and first associated with the names of Gutenberg and Fust. By 1448 at latest, they were using accurate type, which they could produce in sufficient quantity to print a Vulgate Bible.

It seems likely that the Mainz printers began their type-making with the use of steel punches, which would be familiar to them as goldsmiths because of their established use in coining, though copper punches were also in use for type at an early period. The punch was then struck with a hammer into a softer metal such as lead, and the matrix so formed was inserted in a type-mould, the size of which corresponded as accurately as possible to the size of the type to be cast. The metal from which early type was cast in this way is not definitely known, but was in all probability the tin-based alloy containing a little bismuth which was employed by fifteenth-century pewterers. The type was then taken out from the mould and filed at the foot—the end which would be uppermost in the mould—to give it the exact height required: this was approximately 1 in., although it was a considerable time before there was any standardization. Including joined letters and abbreviations, more than 150 characters had to be prepared for each size of type, and the making of a single punch was the work of days rather than hours. As for the composing, it is estimated that to set up a page of the Mainz Bible in this not perfectly regular type would take one man a day. Composing was done much as hand-composing is done today. The compositor picked out each letter in turn with a pair of tweezers and set it line by line in a composing-stick. The lines were set up as pages of type, which were fixed in chases; a proof was taken and corrected; and the work was then ready for the press, from two to sixteen pages, according to size, being imprinted on each sheet of paper.

Such was the technique of the Renaissance printer, bringing new life to a world in which Latin was not yet a dead language. Where so much has changed, it is an interesting link between the twentieth century and the fifteenth that the proof-reader still marks his instructions to the compositor in abbreviations direct from the learned tongue. The name of a type in which the latter composes provides a second link with the past, since roman type was introduced before 1500 as a humanist gesture against the so-called gothic type, which Gutenberg and others had developed by imitation of the thick black-letter handwriting prevalent in their own day. What the Renaissance humanists preferred was the closest approach they could make to the hand of ancient Rome, namely, the ninth-century carolingian hand in which many surviving classical manuscripts had been copied. Some of the earliest roman types were cut with astonishing skill and artistry; indeed, it has been claimed that the designs which the Frenchman, Nicholas Jenson, made in 1470 remain unequalled. At all events, since the introduction of italics—planned as a further imitation of Roman handwriting—by the Aldine press at Venice in 1495, the history of printing style is the story of the very gradual displacement of gothic from its strongholds in central and northern Europe; of much experimentation in detail—under Louis XIV, for example, the French Academy of Sciences had new letters accurately drawn on minutely squared backgrounds; and a fundamental conservatism to which modern industry shows few parallels.

DEVELOPMENTS, 1500–1750

In 1450 book-printing was still in its earliest infancy, but by 1500 there were nearly 40,000 recorded editions of books, and even though more than two-thirds of these came from the presses of Germany and Italy, there were twelve other European countries in which the art of printing was by this time established. In the next two and a half centuries, progress, as we might expect, was much slower: it is calculated that all the minor improvements put together did not enable a given standard of work to be accomplished more than three or four times as fast as in the fifteenth century. What is more surprising is that the average quality of printing at the beginning of the eighteenth century fell far below that of the best work produced at Mainz in the very earliest days.

A sixteenth-century improvement which strikes the reader's eye was the reduction in the number of joined letters, and with the reduction in the number of units required the modern practice quickly grew up of setting type from a pair of cases, of which the 'lower case' included all the minuscule letters arranged in compartments, the largest and most accessible holding the letters most frequently required. It became regular practice to strike the matrix on copper with a steel punch, so that the mould became more accurate and less trimming of the letter was required after casting. A lead-antimony alloy, resembling modern type-metal, came into use, and with the establishment of type-founding as a separate trade the tendency after 1600 was for type to become to some extent standardized.

The wooden printing-press (Fig. 110) underwent various improvements. One was that the bed holding the type was made to run in and out on rails. Another was the introduction of the hose: this was a hollow block of wood through which the screw of the press passed, and to which the platen (the upper half of the press) was attached to avoid the danger of twisting at the moment of impression. At the same time the type-bed came to be made of stone, which could easily be worked to a plane surface, as at the present day. So far as there was any specifically new form of press, it was the so-called Dutch press, introduced by the Amsterdam publisher, geographer, and astronomer, W. J. Blaeuw. This had an improved winding-mechanism and a hose of quite different design; it was widely used in the Low Countries, and was the first to reach North America. But presses in England long continued to have a large square hose of the old type.

FIG. 110. Printing works, *c.* 1590. Stradanus, *Nova reperta*

There were interesting developments in the field of illustration. Two of the greatest artists, Dürer and Rembrandt, made use of an engraving technique from which only a small number of prints could be made. This was what is called 'dry-point' work, done with a steel point, and usually leaving the excised material on one side of the furrow so that more ink is held and the line softened. Rembrandt and his fellow-countrymen are also particularly associated with the growth of pure etching, that is, the technique of drawing lightly with a needle on a metal surface protected with a thin film, to which acid is applied so as to eat away the metal from the lines. The design is developed by recoating the metal, drawing more of the design, and etching again. Then came the mezzotint, which its inventor, L. von

Siegen, demonstrated to Prince Rupert in exile in 1654: it figures, however, as 'Prince Rupert's new way of engraving' in the list of 'exotic and very rare secrets' at the end of the catalogue of trades shown to the Royal Society by John Evelyn in January 1661. This, like the dry-point and the etching, is a system of intaglio work, done with a series of ridged steel tools called rockers, which make furrowed indentations all over the plate, crossing each other in different directions.

Of these other processes, only etching could be used for making any large number of prints, but straightforward engraving came to play an increasingly large part in the illustration of books whenever fine lines were required. They were often printed on separate leaves— hence the name 'plates'—but from the sixteenth century illustrations of this kind began to be incorporated in the text. Intaglio work required strong pressure to make sure that the paper took up the ink, which had to be thin enough to run into the finest grooves. To achieve this the roller press, which was something like a mangle, was devised: the inked, engraved plate and damped paper were placed on a wooden board, and the whole was passed between the rollers by turning the upper one. In two special cases engraving actually replaced letterpress. Music type was too complex for the ordinary compositor, so there were direct advantages in the engraving of music on copper or pewter plates, the staves being marked first with a scoring-tool, and in the course of the seventeenth century this became the regular method for printing music. It was in the same period, too, that the engraved title-page came into use as a graceful embellishment for books.

8

EARLY SOURCES OF POWER

UNTIL man learnt how to domesticate and harness draught-animals his sole source of power was his own muscles. Where power greater than the individual could supply was required, two alternatives, or a combination of both, were open—social devices for bringing the strength of many men to bear upon a single object, and mechanical devices for transforming a small force acting through a considerable distance into a great force acting through a proportionately short distance.

To some extent the social device has been applied at every stage of political development: hunting, agriculture, irrigation, and building are examples of tasks that long continued to require a careful organization of manpower for the completion of urgent work in a limited time by the employment of many hands. Where building is concerned, the construction of the Pyramids shows that vast numbers of men could satisfactorily supply the want of machinery; in a less spectacular field, the use of the *corvée* in road-making did not end in some parts of Europe before the middle of the nineteenth century A.D. But an institution specially characteristic of the ancient world was slavery. It is easy to exaggerate its importance, for the slaves that figure in classical literature and in inscriptions worked for the most part in small numbers, fulfilling the same economic function as free men. Moreover, the employment of slave-gangs for vast agricultural estates, at one time prevalent among the Romans (p. 18), ceased to be common as soon as the supply of slave sfrom conquest declined and they consequently rose in price. It was not, however, until A.D. 1795 that an inquiry on West Indian plantations attempted a statistical estimate of the disadvantage of fear as the sole incentive to labour: it was then found that the output of a slave was at most one-half that of a free man. Nevertheless, there were at least three respects in which the availability of slaves mitigated the effects of the lack of power.

From the earliest days of the ancient empires, prisoners taken in war were used on a large scale by conquering kings in the execution of public works by which they sought to do honour to their reigns: how great was the temptation to use these slaves of the state as easily expendable pioneers may perhaps be judged by the fact that in an age of machinery prisoners of war have been worked to death in railway building, in Europe as well as Asia. Secondly, the city of Rome under the early empire, with perhaps 200,000 slaves in a total population of less than a million, is an outstanding instance of a society where their services made possible a high degree of luxury in the homes of the rich and some important amenities for all: for example, 660 slaves maintained the 280 miles of aqueducts which gave a daily water supply of 38 gallons a head. Finally, there was the exploitation of slave labour in mining, which was used to enrich the kingdom of David and Solomon as well as the fifth-century Athenian democracy and spread as far west as Roman Spain: this won the metals, on which technical progress largely depended, by methods that stretched manpower to exhaustion. We lack the details, but Diodorus Siculus in the reign of Augustus writes that in the Spanish silver-mines the strongest workers were the most unfortunate, because they were slowest to die.

Of mechanical devices for assisting man's strength the lever is by far the most important, and its principle is indeed the basis of nearly all machines. Its origin is unknown, and the law of the lever was not enunciated until the time of Archimedes, but even primitive man must have learned that heavy objects could be moved by pushing a log under them, resting this on some firm fulcrum located relatively near the object, and then exerting a pull on the free end of the log. Archimedes fully realized the enormous force that a lever might generate: 'Give me but a place to stand, and I can move the world.' Four other mechanical devices related to the lever were also well known in ancient times, and are fully described in the *Mechanica* of Heron of Alexandria, who wrote in the first century A.D. These are the wedge, the screw, the compound pulley, and the wheel and axle. All these have the same principle as the lever: a small force acting through a long distance is transformed into a great force acting through a short distance. Put in another way, the greater the work to be done the longer it must take.

The multiplication of force by employing gangs of workers is repeatedly described and illustrated in ancient works (Fig. 111).

Used alone, it is exemplified by lines of men hauling on ropes to shift heavy objects, such as the huge blocks of stone required for the construction of great buildings and monuments. More often, however, multiple manpower was allied with mechanical devices of the type described above. In the rowing of galleys, for example, mass manpower was deployed through levers—the oars. The lever was used in Greek beam-presses as early as 1600 B.C. to express the juice of grapes and olives (*see* Fig. 16). Oil-presses in Pompeii were worked on the screw principle. The principle of the wheel and axle, in which a small force at the circumference is transformed into a

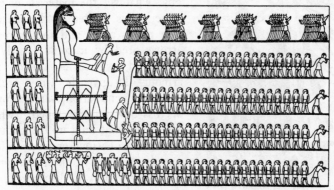

FIG. 111. Large-scale use of gang-labour, Egypt, *c.* 2000 B.C.

large force near the centre, found a practical application in the tread-mill (Figs. 112, 113). Sometimes the effect was still further augmented by trains of gears, also described by Heron, but the usefulness of these was very limited because of the power losses resulting from the primitive methods of construction. The practical limitations did not, however, deter inventors from designing ambitious systems of gears (Fig. 114).

From the earliest times the spring, of which there are innumerable natural examples, has been a most important means of accumulating energy and releasing it suddenly when required. Its first known use, and one of continuing importance for very many centuries, was in the bow used to shoot arrows in hunting and in battle. The first unequivocal representation of it, dating from later Palaeolithic times, is from North Africa. In its simplest form, the bow consists of a single strip of some springy material such as wood or horn, tapered from the centre towards the ends. In more elaborate forms a variety of materials, glued and lashed together, was used. The short 'Turkish bow' was a composite one designed to be fired from horseback, and to it the Asiatic invaders of Europe owed much of their remarkable military success in the Middle Ages. Its range is said to have far exceeded that of the famous and deadly English long-bow, which is reputed to have originated in south Wales and was commonly made of yew.

FIG. 112. Crane powered by tread-mill, from a Roman carving, c. A.D. 100

The effectiveness of the simple bow, whatever the materials of construction, is limited by the strength of a man's arms, and the power of arrows fired by it could largely be countered by heavier shields and armour. To give the arrow greater power of penetration, various forms of cross-bow were developed, in which the tension was built up by means of some kind of winch or lever. A lock was also necessary to keep the spring loaded until it was discharged; although this gave a far more powerful weapon, the comparatively slow rate of discharge offset the advantage.

Weapons of this kind were at an early date developed for use both in the hand and as artillery. One of the earliest mechanical hand weapons, the 'scorpion', which was probably a development of the cross-bow, seems to have been widely used in the second century B.C., for we are told that 2,000 were handed over to the Romans at the fall of Carthage. The catapult, an artillery weapon, was apparently made even earlier: Dionysius of Syracuse, who was the first Greek to employ it, may have obtained the invention from his enemies, the Carthaginians, in about 400 B.C.

The materials available for the bow-string limited the power of such artillery. For still greater power, the force of twisted cords—preferably made from women's hair and sinews of animals—was

FIG. 113. Crane used at Bruges, probably early fifteenth century. Comparison with Fig. 112 shows how little machines of this kind had changed in the course of well over 1,000 years

FIG. 114. Fanciful design for developing sufficient force from the wind to uproot a tree, using gearing, 1680

used, as in the torsion-catapult (Fig. 115). This took two main forms, designed to dispatch arrows and stones respectively; its first known use was by Alexander at the siege of Tyre (332 B.C.), although the Phoenicians may have been his masters. Heron, Vitruvius, and Philo of Byzantium were among those who made close studies of the design of these weapons: the last-named proposed to introduce bronze springs as the source of power, and also designed a quick-firing device for arrows. The use of bronze springs had earlier been suggested by Ctesibius, who also proposed the compression of air in cylinders to give the necessary power. Although this imaginative weapon was deemed impracticable at the time, it may be remarked that its principle is the same as that of the blow-gun of primitive tribes of Asia and South America, and of the air-gun of modern times. A later variant of the torsion-catapult was the onager—so called because liable to 'kick'— a siege weapon dating from the fourth century A.D.

The power of these artillery weapons is difficult to assess, but in the fourth century B.C. they seem for a time to have put the attack ahead of the defence, until solid city-walls of dressed stone had replaced those of brick and wood; they then became weapons of defence rather than of attack. Vitruvius records catapults as having launched stones of up to 300-lb weight, but this was certainly exceptional, for these weapons normally proved incapable of breaching solid walls: the average missile was probably a 5 to 6-lb arrow with an iron head, or a stone of perhaps 10 lb (Fig. 116). Catapults were also used to throw inflammable materials and, later, 'Greek fire'. Because of frictional losses and the necessarily cumbersome wooden construction, the velocity of discharge did not exceed about 200 ft a second. That they were used in considerable numbers is shown by the fact that in the Roman army in the fourth century A.D., as

FIG. 115. Mobile catapult, from Trajan's Column, c. A.D. 110

described in the *De Re Militari* of Vegetius, every legion had a mobile catapult with a crew of eleven men to every century, and for siege warfare an onager to every cohort.

The spring as a source of continuous power for small machines did not appear until much later. Its first use, perhaps as early as the fourteenth century, was in clocks, which had previously been weight-driven: hence the present generic name of clockwork for spring-driven mechanisms.

Other devices for exerting great force were also well known to the ancients. The splitting force of wooden wedges, for example, could be increased still further by wetting them when they had been driven home as far as human strength permitted: the resulting swelling of the wood created still greater force. Similarly, use was made of the contraction of ropes that occurs when they are wetted. In mining, rocks were broken by first heating them with fire and then dashing water on them: the resulting contraction set up great internal forces that fractured the rock. The expansion that takes place when water freezes was made use of in agriculture, although without understanding of the principle, when winter frosts crumbled the clods of freshly broken earth.

For many centuries little fundamental change was made in these devices of the ancient world. They became bigger and more elaborate, but the use of wood as the principal material of construction limited

FIG. 116. Siege cross-bow and projectiles. After Ramelli,
Le diverse et artificiose machine, 1588

their development. The most important change was in the basic source of power: manpower was gradually replaced, first by the power of draught-animals, and later by the power of water and wind. Donkey-driven mills, for instance, were employed as early as the fifth century B.C. to crush ore from the silver mines at Laurion, and their use had extended to the grinding of corn in Greece by about 300 B.C. But limitations of harness and shoe (pp. 201, 195) profoundly affected the economic value of the horse. In good harness the horse can pull roughly fifteen times as strongly as a man, but in harness of the type used for oxen it could pull barely four times as much. At the same time, a horse cost roughly four times as much to feed as a man, who had the advantage of being much more adaptable. In such circumstances there was no great incentive to replace men by horses as a source of power.

THE WATER-WHEEL

The earliest water-mill of which we know is the so-called Greek or Norse mill. It differs from the type with which we are now familiar in that the axle was not horizontal but vertical: at the lower end of the axle was a series of scoops or vanes that were immersed in the stream. Such mills were used mainly for grinding corn. When so employed the axle passed upwards, through the lower millstone, and was fixed directly to the upper one, which it turned. Mills of this kind required a rapid stream of water, and apparently originated in the hilly regions of the Near East; they are not known to have been used in Egypt or Mesopotamia, doubtless because the rivers there are in the main slow-running and subject to great rise and fall. Pliny refers to water-mills for grinding corn, presumably in northern Italy, and these were probably of the Norse type. They were widely used in Europe in medieval times and in some regions up to the late-nineteenth century; in the Shetland Islands, where they at one time numbered about 500, one remained in use at Sandness in 1933 (Fig. 117). They may, indeed, be looked upon as precursors of the water-turbine, a nineteenth-century development, and on this view may be said to have been in use continuously for well over 3,000 years. Norse mills were generally small and slow, since the millstone revolved no faster than the wheel; they were suitable for grinding only small quantities of corn, and their use must have been purely local.

An alternative design for the water-mill was advocated in the first century B.C. by Vitruvius, who made the axle horizontal and the wheel vertical. The inspiration of this may have been the water-lifting device known as the 'Persian wheel' or *saqiya*, which consisted essentially of pots arranged around the circumference of a wheel, turned by man- or animal-power, that dipped into the water. It was used in Egypt in the second century B.C., and must have been well known to Vitruvius, who described a more efficient modification known as a scoop-wheel. The Vitruvian water-wheel is essentially a scoop-wheel working in reverse. Designed for grinding corn, its wheel was connected to the moving millstone through wooden gearing, generally giving a reduction of about 5:1. The earliest mills of this type were undershot—that is, the lower part of the wheel dipped into the stream and was made to turn by the force of the current; later, it was found that an overshot wheel was more efficient. In this, the water falls on the top of the wheel and fills some of the buckets fitted round the circumference; the weight of the water causes the wheel to turn; as it does so, the full buckets discharge their contents and empty ones are brought under the water supply.

Although more efficient, such wheels generally demand considerable ancillary equipment to provide the necessary water supply. Commonly the stream was dammed to form a mill-pond, from which a chute carried a regulated flow of water to the wheel (see Fig. 17). This type of mill provided a source of power greater than any previously available, and it not only revolutionized the grinding of corn, but opened the way to the mechanization of many other industrial operations.

The power of such mills is difficult to compute, but can be deduced approximately from their output. Thus a Roman mill

Fig. 117. Norse-type water-mill, Shetland

at Venafro, of the undershot type, with a wheel some 7 ft in diameter, could grind about 400 lb of corn an hour; this performance corresponds to about 3 h.p. on modern rating. For a comparison, a donkey-mill, or a mill worked by two men, could grind barely 10 lb an hour.

By the fourth century A.D., water-mills of very considerable size had been installed in the Roman empire. At Barbegal, near Arles, for example, sixteen overshot wheels were in use for grinding corn in about A.D. 310, the wheels being some 9 ft in diameter and a little less than 3 ft wide. Each of them drove, through wooden gearing, a pair of millstones: the total capacity was nearly 3 tons of corn an hour, sufficient to meet the needs of a population of 80,000. As the population of Arles at that time was only about 10,000, it is clear that this mill served a wide area.

It is rather surprising that the Vitruvian mill was not commonly used in the Roman empire until the third and fourth centuries A.D.: the explanation is perhaps to be found in social conditions. While slaves and other cheap labour were available there was little incentive to undertake the necessary capital expenditure: indeed, the emperor Vespasian (A.D. 69–79) is said to have opposed the use of water-power because it might create unemployment. When manpower was not available it was easier to use donkeys or horses than to build water-mills. The possible danger of this policy was, however, demonstrated as early as the first century A.D., when corn-grinding, like

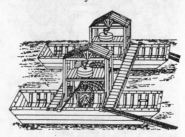

FIG. 118. Floating mill. After Verantius, *Machinae novae*

the baking of bread, had already become a specialized industry in Rome. At that time the corn-mills on which Rome depended were driven in the main by horses and donkeys: Caligula having confiscated the horses, shortage resulted. By the fourth century A.D., however, circumstances had radically changed and there was a great shortage of manpower, so that the construction of water-mills became a matter of public policy. These circumstances, it may be remarked in passing, found a close parallel in the nineteenth century, when shortage of labour in the United States provided a powerful stimulus to the use of machinery there.

Strategic considerations led to the development of a type of water-mill known as the floating mill, employed by Belisarius when the Ostrogoths, during their siege of Rome in 537, attempted to cut the aqueducts that supplied both drinking-water and power for the corn-mills; the great inconvenience resulting from the cessation of the water-mills is an indication of the degree of dependence on water-power. This floating mill consisted of a water-wheel placed between two boats, moored in a fast current, in each of which was placed a mill, an invention that may well have been prompted by the much earlier one of a ship propelled by a paddle-wheel turned by oxen: the anonymous author of *De rebus bellicis*, who lived about A.D. 370, proposed a device of this kind. Floating mills (Fig. 118) were widely used in Europe, some surviving until recent times. Tide-mills are known to have been in use as early as the eleventh century, when one is recorded, for instance, at Dover, but most date from the eighteenth: as sources of power they never became of great importance.

Although the grinding of corn gave the main stimulus to the development of the water-wheel, it was widely used throughout medieval Europe for a great variety of industrial purposes: the Domesday Book, for example, records no less than 5,624 water-mills in England south of the Trent, mainly of the Vitruvian type. Water-power came to be used for sawmills, fulling-mills, ore-crushing plants, hammer-mills for metal-working (Fig. 119), mills to operate the bellows of furnaces, and a great variety of other concerns. It had an important effect on the geographical distribution of industry, causing the fullers, for instance, to move into rural areas in search of suitable streams and encouraging the growth of larger units in mining and metal-working. The harnessing of water-power for multifarious uses also gave an impetus to the improvement of gearing and machinery in general. The importance of water-wheels to the community is reflected in almost all European countries in complex legislation relating to the control of rivers; in the Muslim world, however, their use was largely restricted to irrigation.

FIG. 119. Water-driven trip hammer for working metals. Swedenborg, *Regnum subterraneum*, 1734

The water-wheel retained its immense industrial importance long after the invention of the steam-engine, one of the commonest early uses of which was not to drive machinery direct but to pump water to provide a constant head for water-wheels (p. 319). From the sixteenth century until well into the nineteenth, water-wheels were the most important sources of power in Europe and North America: London, for instance, pumped a water-supply from the river by water-wheels installed at London Bridge from 1582 to 1822 (p. 419). Indeed, the industrial revolution, so far from rapidly making the water-wheel obsolete, led to considerable improvements in it after a long period of relatively little change.

THE WINDMILL

As a source of power the windmill is nothing like as ancient as the water-mill. Apart from a phrase in the works of Heron of Alexandria, of questionable interpretation, there is no evidence that the windmill was known to the ancient world. As a source of mechanical power it seems to have originated in Persia in the seventh century A.D., and was possibly derived from earlier wind-driven prayer-wheels used in central Asia. It is a reasonable, but unproved, assumption that it was inspired by the sails of ships. It was firmly established in the Persian province of Seistan by the tenth century, and was there used to pump water for irrigation; by the thirteenth century at latest, it was being used to grind corn. Significantly, the Persian windmill had a vertical axle, analogous with that of the Greek or Norse water-wheel, which is also believed to have originated, as we have noted, in the Near East. The early Persian windmill for grinding corn was a two-storey building. In the upper storey were the millstones; the lower contained a wheel, driven by the sails—six or twelve in number and covered with fabric—which turned the upper millstone. This arrangement of the millstones above the driving shaft is, it will be recalled, characteristic of the Norse water-mill, and further evidence of a relationship with it. At an early stage shutters were introduced on the sail so that the speed of rotation could be controlled, since excessive speed generated so much frictional heat that the grain, and even the mill-stones, could be damaged.

As the Persian windmill seems to have derived from the so-called Norse water-wheel, so the western type, with the axle horizontal, may have been inspired by the Vitruvian water-wheel, for the eastern and western types of windmill appear to have been independent inventions. A curious kind of windmill, found particularly in Crete and the Aegean, may be an intermediate type, but is more probably a local variation of the western tower-mill. These Mediterranean windmills have eight or twelve canvas sails, like those of a ship, set on a light framework, their rate of rotation being controlled by furling the sails as required.

The first mention of the western type of windmill is from a Norman deed, drawn up about 1180, and windmills seem to have been common in the north-European plain by the end of the thirteenth century. Basically, the western type is a much more efficient one, for the pressure of the wind acts continuously upon the whole surface of the sails, whereas in the Persian type only a part of the sail-area is effective at any given time. Its construction was somewhat more elaborate, since provision had to be made for turning the sails into the wind. For doing so two methods were used. In the post-mill—the earlier type—

the whole superstructure, carrying both sails and machinery, was carried on a stout vertical post and could be turned about it (Fig. 120). By the late fourteenth century, tower-mills were in use; in these only the top of the mill, carrying the sails, is turned, thus saving considerable effort. The body of the tower-mill could be of stone or brick, obviating the need for the massive timbers of the post-mill and giving added resistance to the great force of the wind on the structure as a whole: wooden tower-mills are, however, also well known. The invention of the hollow-post mill in Holland in

1430 was a notable step forward. In this the size of the rotating structure is reduced, and a shaft passes down through the centre of the post to drive the machinery in a fixed building below.

A variation of the post-mill was the so-called 'sunk' post-mill, in which the lower part of the structure was sunk in the ground: these are referred to in a twelfth-century source. The

FIG. 120. Post-mill, from an early four-teenth-century Italian manuscript

object was apparently to strengthen the mill against the force of the wind, but a disadvantage was that with the sails relatively near the ground it was often difficult to take full advantage of what wind there was; the timbers also were liable to rot. This type never became very popular, but remains have been excavated in various parts of England and examples are also known from Russia, Brittany, and the United States.

The supposition that western windmills derived from Vitruvian water-wheels is strengthened by the existence in Russia of windmills in which the millstones are located above the driving-shaft. Among the disadvantages of this design are that the sails are too low to catch the full force of the wind, and that there is no adequate storage space for grain at the top to enable the stones to be fed by gravity.

Although the principle of the windmill is very simple, early illustrations show that its construction was often as elaborate as it was massive. The post-mill was constructed wholly of wood, the framework being made weatherproof by shingles or weather-boarding. Except in the simplest types, the bottom of the mill was often enclosed in a fixed round-house, which provided additional storage space. Even when it was well balanced, much effort was required to turn a post-mill into the wind. For a long time the turning was done manually, simply by pushing on a long tail-pole extending downwards, almost to the ground, from the rotatable superstructure. Because of the heaviness of the work, mechanical aids were soon introduced, the earliest being a winch, first simple, and later geared—cast-iron gears were used for this purpose about the middle of the eighteenth century—that could be fixed to any one of a series of posts driven into the ground round the base of the windmill. An important step forward was the fan-tail, patented by Edmund Lee in 1745, which consisted of a set of vanes mounted on the tail-pole and driving a pair of road-wheels. The vanes were so set that when the mill was facing into the wind it exerted no force on them: when the wind changed, the vanes of the fan-tail rotated and drove the road-wheels, so orientating the mill automatically to its proper direction.

Similar methods were used to turn the caps of tower-mills. Sometimes the tail-pole was simply fixed to the inside of the cap, but more often an external bracing was used. Simple or geared winches were often employed, or the cap could be worked round by means of a crow-bar fitted into a series of sockets on its inner circumference. The fan-tail was also used, but was not applied outside England for a century after its invention there, and even then was limited largely to Denmark and the Netherlands.

As their name implies, the sails of windmills were originally of canvas fixed on frames, as in a sailing-ship. Their rotation could be controlled by furling the sails to an appropriate degree, and by altering the angle of set; such sails were difficult to manage, however, in sudden storms. Wooden shutters, which were more robust and more easily adjusted, were also commonly used. The shaft carrying the sails was normally inclined upwards at an angle of 5 to 10° to the horizontal, to enable the tips to clear the main body of the mill. The number of sails was very variable: while four was a common number, as many as sixteen were sometimes employed and six were quite usual, especially round the Mediterranean and in Russia.

The first windmills were used for grinding corn, but from the fifteenth century their most important use was in pumping water, especially in the Zaan district of Holland, where alone there were 700 windmills by the end of the seventeenth century (Fig. 121), and as many as 900 just before the advent of steam-power. At the peak, the United Provinces altogether had 8,000 windmills. Further uses of windmills were to drive mechanical saws—the first in Holland in 1592—and to hoist materials from mines. The introduction of windmills as a general source of power for industry did not always proceed smoothly, however, since they brought with them fear of unemployment, as the water-wheel had done in Roman times: for

FIG. 121. Post-mills and tower-mills in the Low Countries, *c.* 1590. Stradanus, *Nova reperta*

example, a wind-driven sawmill in Limehouse was wrecked by the mob in 1768.

One of the limitations of both the water-wheel and the windmill was that it was usually necessary for the power they generated to be utilized on the spot. There were, nevertheless, systems for transmitting power over land, often for quite considerable distances, but the power losses must have been considerable: one such device is illustrated in Fig. 122.

As with the water-wheel, it is difficult to estimate the power output of windmills. A large Dutch windmill of the eighteenth century, with a 100-ft sail-span, probably generated about 10 h.p. in a 20 m.p.h. wind. Smaller mills, with a 24-ft span, probably yielded about 5 h.p. Theoretical considerations show that the windmill in its traditional form could not, at best, yield more than 30 h.p. It was not, therefore, a powerful prime-mover by modern standards, and a substantial proportion of such power as it did develop must have been dissipated in the clumsy transmission system, even after iron gearing had been introduced. This is the less surprising when it is realized that the millwrights, who built and maintained these

FIG. 122. Long-distance transmission of power, seventeenth century

structures, worked mainly by the light of nature. The earliest full technical description of a windmill occurs in the second edition of a French treatise on carpentry, dated 1702; sail design was scientifically investigated for the first time by Smeaton in 1759. Yet the millwrights, who employed no equipment more elaborate than a heavy-duty lifting-jack and block and tackle, were the ancestors of the modern mechanical engineer.

The power of the average windmill was evidently in the region of 5 to 10 h.p., and this is, as we have seen, approximately the power of the average water-wheel. As water-wheels and windmills were the only important prime-movers of early times, it is fair to say that the industrial revolution was launched with power units capable of generating no more than 10 h.p. Not until the industrial revolution was well under way did the much more powerful steam-engine play a major role.

9

THE BEGINNINGS OF THE
CHEMICAL INDUSTRY

ALTHOUGH the chemical industry as we know it today really
began in the second half of the eighteenth century, many
processes that have already been discussed under other headings involve chemical changes. Among them, to mention but a few,
are dyeing, tanning, smelting, the glazing of pottery, and the making
of glass. That such processes were far advanced long before the
chemical revolution of the late eighteenth century began to put
chemistry on a scientific basis, is an important reminder that technology and applied science are two totally different things; by empirical methods, technologies may be far advanced long before there
is any clear understanding of the fundamental principles on which
they depend.

Although chemistry as an exact science is relatively modern—if a
specific date is to be set, it may be said to have begun with Robert
Boyle's clear definition of a chemical element in his *Sceptical
Chymist* of 1661—it would be quite wrong to suppose that there was
a sharply defined transition from empiricism to science. Chemical
theory was built on a strong foundation of knowledge laboriously
built up over the centuries by practical men and, on a level more
detached from reality, by the alchemists with their fruitless preoccupation with the transmutation of base metals into gold and the
preparation of an elixir of life. More realistic than the alchemists,
though more limited in ambition, were the so-called iatrochemists of
the sixteenth-century Paracelsian school, who looked on chemistry
as primarily the handmaiden of medicine.

Technology is largely concerned with processes of transformation
—the transformation of raw materials into useful or aesthetically
pleasing articles. Hitherto we have in the main considered essentially
physical processes, in which the raw material changes its form but
not its identity; this broad generalization applies to such varied processes as the flaking of flint to make an arrow-head, the conversion

of timber into furniture or ships, the casting of molten iron into cannon, or the transformation of a blob of glass into a finely carved goblet. By contrast, chemical technology is primarily concerned with the transformation of one substance into another having a different constitution and different properties: typical examples are the conversion of fat into soap, salt into soda, and aniline and related substances into dyes. The separation of substances from associated impurities, for example, the extraction of alkali from the ashes of plants, is also an important branch of chemical technology. Although it will be convenient to consider chemical technology as largely comprising processes of chemical transformation and purification, it should perhaps be remarked that even today there is no general agreement about the precise limits of the chemical industry and we shall, therefore, be transgressing no agreed definition if the opportunity is taken of discussing also some allied topics. With metals we need not concern ourselves here: apart from the fact that the ancient world made extensive use of metals found in their native state, the extraction of metals from ores, in which they are chemically combined with other elements, is, for no very logical reason, not normally considered as being within the province of the chemical industry. We have followed convention and described elsewhere the extraction of metals from ores.

THE CHEMICAL INDUSTRY IN ANCIENT TIMES

No beginning can be set to the chemical industry, for at the earliest times for which we have either archaeological evidence or written records a considerable number both of chemicals and of chemical processes were in use. In ancient times, as today, relatively few chemicals were required by the population at large: by far the greater quantity is utilized by other technologies. It is therefore logical to consider the chemical requirements of some of the major industries of the ancient world. In so doing, we may deal first with the industries that provided man with his basic requirements of food, shelter, and clothing, and then with those that met the needs of permanent and increasingly sophisticated settlements.

At the food-gathering stage, chemical processes had little significance, the only notable exception being the use of fire. This deserves brief mention here, because combustion is a chemical process of combination with oxygen: elucidation of this simple fact was one of the great discoveries of the late eighteenth century. Primitive man probably first gained control of fire by making use of natural conflagrations, but knowledge of how to obtain it at will came at a very early date (p. 3): chemical methods of making fire, however, exemplified by the match (p. 552), are comparatively modern. The first use of fire was presumably for warmth and as a protection against wild animals, but the possibilities of making food more digestible and palatable by cooking must very quickly have been realized. This was a development of the first importance to our present theme, for the kitchen was unquestionably the cradle of many chemical processes; moreover, cooking begat pottery vessels, the glazing of which demanded chemical skill.

An early consequence of the custom of cooking food, especially meat, was an increased demand for salt which, apart from making food more appetizing, is a biological necessity. While meat and fish were eaten raw, man's essential salt requirements were naturally met, but many cooking processes remove salt: it is extracted in boiling and runs out with the juices in grilling or roasting. In hot climates in particular—and it was in these that civilization dawned— much salt is lost in sweat, and the need of replenishment is correspondingly great. For these reasons the salt trade is one of the most ancient in the world.

Fortunately salt occurs abundantly, though not ubiquitously. Near the sea it is always obtainable by solar evaporation of sea water in shallow artificial lakes or pans, though this process is readily carried out only where the sun is hot and the coastline suitable. Inland, saline springs whose waters can be similarly treated are of frequent occurrence. In addition, there are many deposits of rock salt, the residue of ancient seas, that can be mined: salt mines were worked at both Hallstatt in Austria and in Spain from at least the first millennium B.C. Occasionally the ash of salt-rich plants, such as *Salicornia*, was used. Unlike many early chemicals, salt was often very pure, although it must sometimes have been contaminated with earthy impurities.

Although the first important use of salt was for seasoning food, it was also used at an early date to preserve both meat and fish. This was certainly linked—though whether as cause or effect is obscure— with the intense Egyptian concern with the preservation of the body after death: for this purpose salt was sometimes used, although natron (an impure form of soda) was preferred for religious reasons (Fig. 123). The production of natron, derived from three main natural sources in Egypt, and especially from the Wadi Natrun, was a state monopoly in Ptolemaic times: it was exported to Europe right up to the nineteenth century A.D. (p. 531).

While the roasting and grilling of food became possible as soon as mastery of fire had been won, boiling had to await the availability of

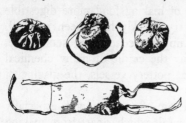

vessels that would withstand the heat of the fire. With the evolution of these we have dealt elsewhere: in the present context we need recall only that the process of glazing pottery, and especially the production of coloured glazes, depended upon the availability of a considerable range of chemicals. A form of salt-glazing was practised in Meso-

FIG. 123. Bags of natron and chaff used for the embalming of Tutankhamen, c. 1350 B.C.

potamia and beads from Ur appear to have been glazed with soda. Babylonian potters used lead oxide to form glazes and natural cobalt compounds were used to produce a blue coloration. In the

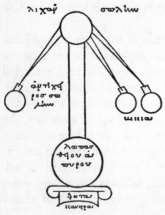

second millennium B.C. an artificial lapis lazuli was made in Egypt by heating sand, chalk, soda, and malachite (a natural copper ore); it was widely used as a glaze. Egyptian potters used naturally occurring iron oxide to form red and black glazes.

Fermentation processes, too—of great importance in the modern chemical industry—had their origin in the preparation of alcoholic beverages by the fermentation of sugars with yeast. Although Alex-

FIG. 124. Greek alchemical still, with three receivers

andrian alchemists were familiar with the processes of distillation (Fig. 124), it is doubtful whether apparatus was sufficiently advanced for pure, or nearly pure, alcohol to have been available before the twelfth century. In ancient Egypt it was known that the fermentation could proceed farther, resulting in the formation of vinegar: chemically, this involves oxidation of the alcohol to acetic acid.

Apart from its culinary use, vinegar was important as being the strongest acid available to the ancient world: among its uses was the making of white lead.

The needs of the kitchen called not only for chemicals but for chemical apparatus. Some of the pestles and mortars used for pounding Sumerian grain and seed, for example, are virtually indistinguishable, not only from their medieval counterparts, but from those to be found in modern chemical laboratories. The colander, a simple and convenient means of separating coarse solids from liquids, dates from at latest the third millennium B.C.; filtration through cloth as a means of separating more finely divided solids is referred to in a medical text of 2200 B.C. The sieve, too, was used by the Sumerians and is still a standard piece of chemical equipment. Industrial furnaces and ovens must certainly have derived from originals used for roasting and baking or for domestic heating

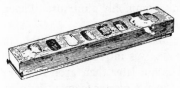

FIG. 125. Egyptian painter's palette, c. 1500 B.C.

purposes. The crucible, first of pottery and later sometimes of metal, must have derived from the cooking-pot. A possible example of this process taking place in reverse, that is to say, from the chemical industry to the kitchen, is the *bain-marie*: this, a device for maintaining the contents of a vessel for long periods at the temperature of boiling water, is attributed to Mary the Jewess, an alchemist probably of the first century A.D. though traditionally identified with Miriam, the sister of Moses.

Such, in brief outline, are some of the chemical consequences of changes in man's way of feeding himself. Others of comparable importance resulted from changes in other aspects of his way of life.

The art of painting far antedates written record, and both Europe and Africa provide numerous examples of prehistoric art. Natural pigments, mixed generally with water rather than with oil, provided a reasonably extensive palette: blacks were produced with soot or pyrolusite (manganese dioxide), red with iron oxide, and yellow with natural iron carbonate. By the time of the ancient empires, the decoration of houses, and more particularly of temples and tombs, was common practice: that most of our examples derive from Egypt is purely a consequence of its climate, which particularly favours preservation. A variety of pigments was used (Fig. 125), but, as in the cave paintings, they were still contained in an aqueous and not an oily base: the paint was commonly made viscous by addition of such substances as egg-white, gum, or honey. Pigments used included ochre, for red to yellow; red lead; orpiment (yellow arsenic sulphide) imported from Persia and elsewhere; yellow lead oxide; malachite; and chrysocolla (green copper silicate). The preparation of some of these, especially in the finely divided forms necessary for painting, would have been impossible without considerable chemical skill: thus red lead was obtained by heating lead with basic lead carbonate, itself probably made by addition of natron to a solution of a lead salt. When writing became common, an important use of pigments was in the manufacture of ink, commonly a mixture of soot, gum, and water.

The plastering of walls with lime, made by roasting limestone or chalk in kilns to expel carbon dioxide, was introduced at an early date: one Mesopotamian lime-kiln is not later than 2500 B.C. For walls that were to be decorated, a gypsum plaster (sometimes containing a little lime) was preferred: this was prepared by roasting gypsum (hydrated calcium sulphate), of which there were various natural deposits, especially in the Fayum. Wood, too, was commonly treated with gypsum plaster before painting.

With increasing sophistication there came an increasing demand for artificial illumination. Crude lamps used by Palaeolithic man consisted of an open stone container for animal fat and a wick of (presumably) twisted dried grass or moss; later, lamps of metal and pottery were apparently modelled on sea-shells used for the same purpose. The oil was probably the same as that employed for culinary purposes, although mixed with a little salt to give a yellower and more luminous flame. In Egypt olive oil was probably used; in Mesopotamia, where the olive would not flourish, the main source of oil was the seed of the sesame plant. There is evidence that the Assyrians used a hot-water process, similar to one still used in parts of India and Africa, to separate the finest quality of sesame oil. The seed was first crushed and then treated with boiling water, when the oil rose to the surface and was skimmed off; final traces of water were removed in a special vessel, later known as a *separatorium*, fitted with an outlet on the side so that the oil could be run off from the watery residue. This method of separating two immiscible liquids is still widely used in the chemical industry.

CHEMISTRY AND THE TEXTILE INDUSTRY

While the needs of housing and of preparing food had an important influence on the early development of chemical processes, it was the demands of clothing that provided the most powerful stimulus: to this day, the chemical and the textile industries are very closely related. The origin of soap (in the chemical sense of saponified fats and oils) is uncertain, but it cannot safely be put earlier than the latter part of the fourth century A.D.: long before this, however, various cleansing agents of a different chemical character were in use, both for treating new cloth and for laundering. Fuller's earth and an alkaline solution—usually made from soda or stale urine—were used in fulling mills (p. 98) until the end of the Middle Ages, even though soap-boiling had then long been common in Europe. The basic process in soap-making is to boil fats or vegetable oils with strong alkali. Hard soap is made by using soda, rendered caustic by treatment with lime, but in the textile industry soft soap was preferred, at least from the twelfth century. This was made by using caustic potash, prepared by treating wood ashes with lime, in place of soda. The effect of caustic alkali on fats and oils is to release glycerine and this, together with excess alkali, seems to have been incorporated into the final product: not until the seventeenth century was it discovered that the soap could be made to separate by adding salt to the mixture.

Although we must suppose that the earliest cloth, whether felted or woven, was made from untreated fibre, perhaps bleached in the sun, the practice of dyeing goes back to remote times, and the earliest records show that it was already a complex craft relying heavily on chemical processes. Until recently, virtually all dyes were of vegetable or animal origin, but despite this limitation a wide spectrum of colours was available, although some were elaborate and expensive to produce. Before considering the dyeing process itself, however, we must consider the preliminary preparation of the fibre. From very early times it was known to dyers that cloth would take up colours much more intensely and permanently if it was first treated with what we now know to be salts of aluminium: the most important of these so-called mordants are alums, which occur fairly widely. Because natural alums often contain iron, which seriously interferes with the dyeing, their purification early became of importance, although how, and to what extent, this was done in ancient times is uncertain. The strong presumption is, however, that it was done on a considerable scale by crystallization processes.

The Greeks and Romans used a potassium alum, obtained from certain volcanic regions, but by the thirteenth century a method of purifying natural aluminium sulphate—alum of Yemen—was described by Arabic writers. This involved treating its solution with stale urine—a convenient source of ammonia—and then concentrating it by boiling until ammonium alum would crystallize out on cooling. By the middle of the fifteenth century another mineral

(alunite) was being exploited on a large scale to meet the needs of the rapidly expanding textile industry: alunite (potassium aluminium sulphate) was purified by crystallization from water.

Up to the early fifteenth century the main sources of alum were in the Near East and the Greek islands, but the Turkish invasions, and especially the fall of Constantinople in 1453, largely cut off these supplies. It was, therefore, fortunate that enormous deposits were soon afterwards found at Tolfa in Italy,

FIG. 126. Dyeing cloth with woad, from a fifteenth-century French manuscript

which for centuries remained the most important source: attempts to make this alum a lucrative papal monopoly were unsuccessful.

Dyeing was carried out at various stages of textile manufacture. In the case of wool it was sometimes done, as in Mesopotamia, even before it was sheared or plucked from the animal. If patterned fabrics were to be woven, the thread had to be dyed in various colours before weaving: more generally, however, the woven fabric was dyed in large vats (Fig. 126). Even then, however, patterns could be obtained by painting them on with a solution of mordant: certain dyes would then fix themselves firmly to the treated parts of the cloth but could be washed out from the remainder (Fig. 127).

Dyes of vegetable and animal origin provided a wide range of colours. Of ancient dyes, perhaps the best known is indigo: this was derived from the indigo plant, extensively cultivated in India, or from woad, grown throughout Europe. The method of preparation was similar in the two cases. The plant material was crushed in water and allowed to ferment, when the characteristic blue colour appears. After a time the indigo precipitated itself as insoluble indigotin, which was collected and dried (Fig. 128). For dyeing, the indigotin was brought into solution—for example, by treatment with honey and lime—and the material was immersed in it: the blue colour, the product of oxidation, appeared when the treated fabric was exposed to the air for drying.

FIG. 127. Design on cloth obtained from painting with alum, from a thirteenth-century French manuscript

Woad is not so good a source of the dye as the indigo plant and became less popular after the sixteenth century, when trade with India was more firmly established. Although obtained from a totally different source, the famous Tyrian purple (p. 89) is chemically very closely related to indigo. It was, however, fabulously expensive and, moreover, the secret of making it was lost after the fall of Byzantium; purple was normally achieved by combining red and blue dyes.

Reds were obtained with madder—cultivated near Rome in classical times, then largely in the Low Countries, and later associated particularly with the neighbourhood of Avignon, where Colbert established the crop in 1666—or with archil, derived from lichens of the Mediterranean seaboard. The name of the fifteenth-century church of St John Maddermarket at Norwich bears witness to the importance of the madder-plant as a source of crimson and other dyes. More permanent reds were of animal origin, derived first from certain insects parasitic on European plants, and later from the cochineal insect of the New

FIG. 128. Merchants selling balls of prepared woad, represented in thirteenth-century French statuary

World. The finest scarlets had, however, to await the Dutchman Cornelius Drebbel's discovery in the early seventeenth century of the use of tin salts as mordants. The most important yellow dyes were derived from weld, safflower, or fustic. Green was obtained by combining one of these with woad or indigo. For black, a mixture of green vitriol (iron sulphate) and extract of oak galls was used: the two combine to form iron tannate, which is intensely black.

THE MANUFACTURE OF GUNPOWDER

Of the origins of the three principal acids of the modern chemical industry—sulphuric, hydrochloric, and nitric—we can say that sulphuric acid, perhaps the most important of all modern industrial chemicals, seems to have been unknown until the early sixteenth century, when it was made at Nordhausen by dry distillation of green or blue vitriol (iron or copper sulphate). It was of virtually no industrial importance until the seventeenth century, which is also when hydrochloric acid was first clearly distinguished. Nitric acid, commonly obtained by distilling nitre (potassium nitrate) with vitriol, was described by the eighth-century Arabic alchemist, Jabir. It was industrially important for separating large quantities of silver, which dissolves in it, from gold. Jabir was aware that addition of sal ammoniac (ammonium chloride, said to have been first derived from camel stables near the Egyptian temple of Jupiter Ammon) to nitric acid enables it to dissolve gold, a fact of considerable metallurgical importance.

Far more important than nitric acid, within the period with which we are now concerned, is nitre (its potassium salt), for this is—with sulphur and charcoal—an essential ingredient of gunpowder. The development of fire-arms has been considered elsewhere (p. 148), but we must here consider briefly the development of the explosives required for them. In Europe from at least 500 B.C., and in China certainly from the tenth century A.D. and probably much earlier, the use of highly inflammable mixtures was common in warfare; it became increasingly effective when catapults and similar mechanical means of discharging large projectiles came into general service. The famous 'Greek fire', which played so important a part in the defence of the Byzantine empire from the seventh century, had no precise formula, but its essential secret ingredient seems to have been naphtha (p. 514), which is highly inflammable. It appears that by the eleventh century the Chinese were aware that the incendiary proper-

ties of such mixtures could be much increased by the addition of
nitre, the reason being that when
it is heated this substance yields
oxygen. Whether or not this
knowledge inspired the recipes
for gunpowders that were later
current in the West is obscure,
but it is certain that by about
1300 mixtures of nitre, sulphur,
and charcoal were being prepared
for use in artillery and, later, in
small arms. Of these three ingredients the preparation of the
last two presented little difficulty.
Charcoal had been prepared
from ancient times as a fuel, and

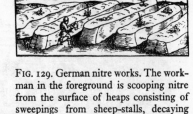

FIG. 129. German nitre works. The workman in the foreground is scooping nitre
from the surface of heaps consisting of
sweepings from sheep-stalls, decaying
vegetable matter, and rubble, 1580

sulphur occurs naturally in a fairly pure form, for example in Sicily:
if further purification of sulphur was necessary, this was done by

distillation. Sulphur, moreover,
had come to occupy a place of
exceptional mystical significance
in the operations of the alchemists, who were, therefore, very
familiar with its properties.

Nitre, however, presented
much greater difficulties, for no
pure material was readily available. The common source was
the earth from stables, pig-sties,
and so on (Fig. 129), in which
it resulted from bacterial action
on manure. Generally, all the
soluble salts were extracted from
the earth with boiling water,
sometimes with addition of potash or lime, and the resulting
solution was boiled to concen-

FIG. 130. Crystallizing nitre, Germany,
1580

trate it to the point at which ordinary salt, the most harmful impurity, separated out. The salt was removed and the solution allowed
to cool, when crystals of fairly pure nitre separated (Fig. 130).

The mixing of the three ingredients was both difficult and hazardous. It was difficult because a uniform and correctly balanced mixture was necessary for the best results, and hazardous because heat generated in the mixing process might cause explosion. At first, mixing was done by artillerymen in the field, but powder-mills were

FIG. 131. Water-driven gunpowder-mill, Germany, 1676

soon established: the earliest were manually operated, but water-power had been introduced by the seventeenth century (Fig. 131). During mixing the powder was kept damp to diminish the risk of explosion. Originally a very fine powder was used throughout, but later this was reserved for priming and the main explosive charge was prepared in granular form by passing the still-damp powder through sieves at the mills. Apart from being an essential ingredient of gunpowder, nitre served another purpose in early fire-arms. The slow-burning match, used to ignite the charge of cannon or of the matchlock fire-arm, consisted of coarse twine impregnated with nitre so that it would burn slowly and steadily and not blow out in a wind.

THE ALCHEMISTS AND THE IATROCHEMISTS

We have already referred to the work of the alchemists, which resulted in the accumulation of much empirical chemical knowledge.

Of the two principal aims of the alchemists—the transmutation of base metals into gold, and the discovery of the elixir of life—the second now demands our attention. Although the search for the elixir of life was foredoomed to failure it was by no means unfruitful, for from early days the preparation of drugs has been an important application of chemical skill. The word alchemy is of Arabic origin, possibly deriving from the name *Chem* that the ancient Egyptians gave to their country: whether this is true or not, it is certain that there was a flourishing school of alchemy in Alexandria in the second century B.C. While much of their work was highly speculative or erroneous, the extensive writings of Zosimos of Panopolis prove that they understood how to carry out a number of clearly defined operations such as the extraction of mercury from cinnabar, of arsenic from realgar, and of white lead from litharge. How far such mineral substances were used in medicine is uncertain, but Dioscorides, in his *De Materia Medica* of the first century A.D., lists several, including verdigris and copper sulphate. An eleventh-century Muslim text lists many more, but the full blossoming of medical chemistry resulted in the early sixteenth century from the work of Paracelsus of Basle, who taught that the main object of chemistry should be to produce drugs to relieve human suffering. With increasing emphasis on the prescription of drugs, inevitably came increasing demand for their manufacture. While the importance of the Paracelsian school is often over-estimated—he himself displayed an extraordinary mixture of bombast, quackery, and serious scholarship—it did lead to chemistry's becoming a recognized part of the training of medical students. Up to the nineteenth century it was virtually only the medical schools that offered formal training in chemistry: there was a chair of chemistry at Cambridge in the eighteenth century but one incumbent rarely came near the University, and an unpaid reader at Oxford. There was no systematic organization for the teaching of chemistry as a separate discipline in England until the Royal College of Chemistry was founded in 1845.

THE BEGINNING OF MODERN CHEMISTRY

Alchemy flourished particularly from the ninth to the seventeenth century—Chaucer's *Canon's Yeoman's Tale* and Jonson's comedy *The Alchemist* are interesting portrayals of alchemical activity—and provided the basis for the science on which the modern chemical industry is based. With this transition we can deal only briefly here before passing on: chemical technology during and after the industrial revolution is discussed in Chapter 18. While the change was adumbrated as early as the thirteenth century by the work of Roger Bacon, with his insistence on the importance of experiment rather than speculation, it is Robert Boyle who is properly regarded as 'the father of chemistry'. To him we owe the clear recognition of an element as the simplest form of matter—that is, one that could not be resolved into other substances. Equally fundamental was the realization, towards the end of the eighteenth century, that matter is indestructible whatever chemical changes it may undergo: the decisive statement of the law of the conservation of matter we owe to Lavoisier. Although this seemingly simple generalization needed the genius of John Dalton—who first published an account of his atomic theory in 1808—for its full significance to be realized, it was enormously important. While it is an over-simplification to say that Boyle's recognition of the true nature of elements, Lavoisier's recognition that matter is indestructible, and Dalton's recognition that every element consists of its own distinctive variety of atom and every compound of a specific combination of atoms, are the three fundamental premises of modern chemistry, the importance of the contributions of these three men of genius is difficult to over-estimate. They not only provided a logical explanation of a wealth of chemical knowledge accumulated over many centuries but, far more important, they provided the basis for the rapid and systematic exploration of vast new fields of chemistry.

For the moment, however, we are running ahead of our main task, which is to review the history of chemical technology up to the beginning of the industrial revolution. We have seen that from the earliest days chemical skill had been essential for many, indeed most, of the industries we have considered elsewhere—for example, for making metals, pottery, glass, and textiles. From the very earliest days up to almost the beginning of the industrial revolution, this knowledge had been accumulated solely by empirical methods, with little underlying theory to make understanding easier or to suggest profitable lines of experiment. During the industrial revolution, however, the situation entirely changed—during it chemistry shook off the last shackles of alchemy and emerged as a clearly defined science. While the chemical industry was slow to apply the new knowledge, it too underwent a corresponding transformation.

PART II

THE
INDUSTRIAL REVOLUTION
TO A.D. 1900

HISTORICAL SURVEY (1750–1900)

THERE has always been a strong underlying relationship between man's general history and the history of his technological progress. The Roman empire, for example, rested upon the achievements of its engineers, including the great road-makers, as truly as it did upon its more abstract concepts of law and duty. The expansion of Europe in the sixteenth century depended upon the existence of new means of crossing the oceans, as much as upon the will to do so. In the same way, the bewilderingly rapid and numerous political changes of the century and a half to which the rest of this book will be devoted, at every end and turn influence, and are influenced by, the technological revolution which is the object of our study.

Western man in 1900 looked back with complacency upon a period of both industrial and political revolution. Regarding the former, he was fully entitled to say that his relationship to natural resources had been profoundly changed, and changed for the better. He would have been equally certain of much political progress achieved, and of the promise of more to come. Today, indeed, the technological advances made up to 1900 seem by comparison a little less impressive than they once did; the political progress, on the other hand, which caused the world of 1900 to appear so vastly preferable to that of 1750, is now by many thoughtful people looked back upon with envy. Perhaps the belief that the deepest problems of politics were being solved along with the deepest problems of economics was, even in 1900, a delusion held and propagated chiefly by the possessing classes; but for our present purpose it is important to bear in mind that the industrial revolution, too often thought of in terms of the narrow field of British history, increasingly affected the politics of the whole western world, was in turn affected by them, and by 1900 shared with the political changes the credit for what was commonly identified on both counts as an age of unparalleled progress.

The age forms only an artificial unit, for the great industrial changes were beginning, as we have already seen, long before 1750 (p. 43); they are continuing, as we all of us know to our pleasure and our cost, long after 1900. Similarly, it is artificial, though extremely convenient, to attempt further subdivision of a century and a half in which events, alike in the political and the technological fields, follow upon each other in a close-woven and tangled pattern of cause and effect. We may, however, distinguish three main phases.

The first of these lasts down to the battle of Waterloo in 1815, and is marked by three great wars and two epoch-making revolutions. Out of this period of two generations that comprises what is called the industrial revolution in the narrower sense—the expansion of British industry in the time of Arkwright, Wedgwood, Boulton, and Watt—the equivalent of one whole generation is a period of war: the consequent distortion of the economy had important effects upon technology, even though these wars were not total and their physical effects were by twentieth-century standards slight. At the same time, the new revolutionary ideologies embodied in the American Declaration of Independence (1776) and the French Declaration of the Rights of Man (1789) had an enormous influence upon man's attitude to the universe in general and to his fellow-man in particular—and in the long run the evaluation of a labour-saving device is closely related to the value placed upon the labourer.

The period after 1815 begins with a deceptive lull, the political quiescence of the Age of Metternich and the slow economic recovery of Europe after the long wastage of the Napoleonic wars, trends which duly reacted upon British trade. Then from the 1840's onwards the twin and often opposed forces of nationalism and liberalism gathered strength. On the one hand there was the triumph of the North in the American Civil War, and the unification of Italy on a parliamentary basis; on the other, the establishment of the German empire by a nation in arms which owed more to militarism than to liberalism. In every case, however, the growth of the strong nation state was accompanied by the spread of the railway network, which was the most important of the technological developments pioneered by Britain in this second phase.

From 1871 to 1900 the western nations were at rest again, in the sense that their energies were diverted from internecine conflict to the exploitation of the national territories. For the United States and Canada, as also for Russia, this was the age of the 'moving frontier';

for the powers of western Europe, with their more restricted home-lands, it was the age of imperialism and the partition of Africa. An American historian, Professor Carlton Hayes, terms it 'a generation of materialism'. Certainly, a material civilization based on tremendous advances of western technology was, during these thirty years, spread over the world's surface with a rapidity unheard of before. Since technological advance brought a higher standard of living for many, perhaps most, of the countless multitudes of human beings affected by it, others besides materialists became convinced that its continuance not only could, but would, end what Winwood Reade once called 'the martyrdom of man'.

Not only does the general history of these great advances begin in Britain, but for at least 100 years British men and machines were also prominent in the more gradual extension of the 'workshop of the world' to countries outside Britain—across the Channel to France and especially to Belgium, to some of the many German states and their neighbours, such as Sweden and Switzerland, and to the eastern United States. But in the second half of the nineteenth century the general trend slowly changed, as the economic importance of Britain came to depend more and more upon the cumulative effects of her inventiveness in the past, while America, Germany, and other nations, to whom memories of the past did not give the same dangerous psychological reassurance and practical handicaps, increasingly took the lead. By 1900 the newest technological devices were for the most part not of British origin, and, what was of even greater importance, they were being more energetically developed in countries which had not a vast capital locked up in well-tried methods of production. Electric power and the internal combustion engine, for instance, were making rapid progress elsewhere while Britain, with her superb equipment based on steam-power, was slowly learning that the good is the enemy of the best.

Before turning to the start of the industrial revolution in Britain, it may be useful for us to distinguish some half-dozen influences which, in differing degrees, affected the growth of the industrial revolution in most times and places. First, there was the mysteriously rising tide of population. It is true that improved agricultural techniques increased the available supply of food, and also that higher standards of cleanliness, associated with the introduction of cotton cloth and cheap piping for water-supply and drainage, greatly assisted the work done by advancing medical knowledge in keeping more people alive for longer periods: yet the rapid growth of the population of Europe,as a whole bears no direct relation to the spread of the industrial revolution. A reasonable estimate suggests that a population of about 140 million in 1750 grew in successive half centuries to 188, 266, and 401 million, percentage increases of 36, 40, and 50 over the three periods, which do not correspond to the industrial changes: these were of small effect before 1800 and became prodigious only after 1850. Yet whatever its ultimate causes, this increase of population offered at least three incentives to industrial advance. To provide even a minimum of food, the farmer had to become industrially more efficient, and specialized means of transport were also developed to bring it from remote, often transoceanic, sources of supply. In the long run, too, the hungry mouths could be fed only if hands were employed in manufactures which, as a result of improved technology, could be exchanged somewhere in the world for adequate supplies both of raw materials and of foodstuffs. Thirdly, this growth of population gave a stimulus to the growth of town life, and most technological advances, from the steam-powered factory and gas-lighting at one end of our period to the steel-framed skyscraper and the cinematograph performance at the other, spread most rapidly in an urban environment.

The political factors are easier to disentangle. The high degree of personal and political freedom which characterized British life in the eighteenth century is generally accepted as a factor that helped the inventors. The American and French revolutions had a broadly similar effect, both in freeing the energies of the individual and in freeing trade enterprise from traditional restrictions such as internal customs barriers or trade regulations. The importance of America's freedom increased as the country filled with European immigrants. As for Europe itself, the spread of French ideas in the wake of Napoleon's armies, the upsurge of principles of liberty in the revolutions of 1848, the final disappearance of serfdom with Alexander II's decree of emancipation in Russia and Poland in 1861, and the spread of manhood suffrage from France and Germany into the smaller states during the last decades of the nineteenth century, are only some of the main stages in what was really a cumulative process. But the mention of Napoleon is a reminder that the era of growing personal freedom was also characterized, more intermittently, by international conflict. War has always given an important incentive to technological development, a fact of which there are numerous illustrations in the British industrial revolution, from the carronades, developed at the first modern Scottish ironworks (Carron) for use against the American rebels, to Bessemer steel, which was invented when improved material was in demand for ordnance at the time of the Crimean War. So also the Continent received an important stimulus from the need to circumvent the effects of the British naval blockade in the opening years of the nineteenth century, while the Civil War of 1861–5 proved to be one of the cardinal epochs in the growth of American industry.

Other factors that are common to the technological progress of Britain and the rest of the western world include the accumulation and international availability of capital, and the impetus given by the growth of international trade. Britain between 1750 and 1900 figured as the principal lender, though at the beginning of the period a considerable part of the British national debt was still held abroad, especially in Amsterdam, while towards the end of it America, Germany, and France were all playing an important part in developing the industrial revolution by loans made both to independent foreign powers, such as Russia, and to areas of open or disguised colonial exploitation. As for world trade, it has been calculated that, in a period during which total population doubled, commerce was growing ten times as fast, a growth which was due above all to improvements in transport and communications. These the technologically advanced powers were always eager to develop in the more backward regions of the world; although their object was to secure a supply of raw materials and foodstuffs, the long-term result was to provoke an industrial revolution by imitation.

Another important factor in the development of modern technologies has been the system of patent law obtaining in the different countries. The statutory English system (p. 38) was extended to Scotland by the Union of 1707, and provided the basis for the American patent law, passed in 1790 and first administered by Jefferson as secretary of state. In 1836 a Patent Office was set up in America, to provide regular means for establishing the usefulness and novelty of all claims, and in 1861 the traditional English period of fourteen years was extended to seventeen. It was of this system that Lincoln said it 'added the fuel of interest to the fire of genius': by 1857 the United States was issuing 35 per cent. more patents than Britain.

French patent law dates from 1791, when the revolutionaries, after sweeping away Crown and guild monopolies as part of the old order, asserted the principle that 'It would be attacking the rights of man if an industrial discovery were not regarded as the property of its discoverer'. One of the first patentees was Leblanc (p. 532), though the patent did not protect his factory from eventual confiscation. The principle of a patent right had, however, been clearly enunciated in France, from which it spread to some neighbouring countries, whereas in Germany there was no general validity of patents until a convention was made by the member states of the *Zollverein* (or customs union) in 1842, and protection remained incomplete there until 1877: in 1857 America granted sixty times as many patents as Prussia.

In 1883 an international convention encouraged the practice of patenting an invention in several countries by allowing the inventor a year's grace, during which time he was protected against piracy in all signatory states. Inventiveness was stimulated, inasmuch as the monopoly for a limited period, which gives the inventor the incentive to publish his discovery, was extended to a less limited area. But at the same time the growing complexity of industrial processes meant that the framing of patents and the testing of their validity according to basic legal principles that often differed very profoundly from one State to another became increasingly difficult. This helped the large concern with interests in many parts of the world, which by 1900 often used patent litigation, or the threat of it, as a convenient weapon for suppressing the development of unwanted new processes.

One other feature common to the industrial revolution of different countries is the increasingly significant part played by the growth of scientific and mathematical theory. Broadly speaking, we may say that throughout the nineteenth century the role of the scientist as a pioneer of industrial changes was becoming more evident in each of the major countries concerned, though even in 1900 his was rarely that all-important role which we associate with the research scientist of today. In general, the period in which British industries led the world coincides with that in which the empirical was preferred to the purely scientific approach to industrial problems: certainly, that leadership was already waning before the doctrine that Ludwig Mond, a naturalized German, expounded to the Society of Chemical Industry in 1889, became a commonplace even in Britain: 'The slow methodical investigation of natural phenomena is the father of industrial progress.'

THE QUICKENING TEMPO OF INDUSTRY, 1750–92

We may take first the period down to 1792, when the outbreak of the French revolutionary wars effectively halted the progress of Britain's main industrial rival, France, and at the same time introduced a period of war economy lasting until 1815, in which the trade of the whole Continent and even of the United States of America, to say nothing of Britain and France, was diverted from its normal course, causing inventors—as in the world wars of our own days— to seek new ends. The beginning of the period, that is to say, the start of the industrial revolution in Great Britain, is conventionally dated from the accession of George III in 1760, because this event was quickly followed by the key developments in textile-spinning (1764–9), by Watt's vital improvements to the steam-engine (1765– 76), by an important growth of iron-working in Scotland and South Wales, and by the first beginnings of the English canal network. Nevertheless, it is more realistic to make mid-century the starting-point. The long period of peace under Walpole had seen the initial developments in the textile industries—Kay's flying-shuttle, and the spinning inventions of John Wyatt and Lewis Paul (p. 105). The sequel to the Jacobite Rebellion of 1745 was a rapid growth of turn-pike roads, and the intellectual climate of the fifties undoubtedly prepared the way for more revolutionary industrial decades. Thus it was in 1754 that the Society for the Encouragement of Arts and Manufactures was founded, which six years later was inspired by its knowledge of Paul's work to offer prizes for further advances in spinning-machines. Meanwhile, in 1757 Josiah Tucker reported that 'In the metal industries of Birmingham and Sheffield, almost every Master Manufacturer hath a new invention of his own, and is daily improving on those of others'. Such were the beginnings: in the course of the thirty years, 1750–80, the annual number of patents was multiplied by approximately six.

The industrial revolution had been a long time in the making. It is, on the whole, less surprising that it should have come in the mid-eighteenth century, a period of stable governments, a confident middle class, wars fought by professionals with little damage to the economy and, above all, of expanding European trade, than that— for reasons already noted (p. 44)—it came first to Britain. Whereas Italy, the Low Countries, France, and the great German cities, had each in past centuries taken the lead technologically and had stood far ahead of her, it was now the turn of Britain to reap decisive advantages from her geography and her history. Starting from an island position, it was natural that her people should direct both their commercial and their military enterprises—they were of course frequently interrelated—across the oceans with their boundless possibilities, rather than, like France, towards the exploitation of the Continent. In an age when most foreign trade lay within Europe, Britain had a high proportion of oceanic commerce, while the fact that at the time of the Peace of Paris in 1763 her mercantile marine had increased sixfold in a century, suggested that she could find the transport to serve a larger transoceanic market. Within twenty years the British mercantile marine received a further stimulus when the Dutch, as a result of their rash participation in the Maritime War of 1778–83, lost their still prominent position in the carrying trade and much else.

At the same time, the industrial entrepreneur and the technologist derived a whole series of incentives from what might fairly be called the British way of life. The people described in the pages of Fielding and Smollett enjoyed a comparatively easy relationship between classes and regions that made both capital and labour more mobile than in most countries. Their government made comparatively little effort to direct and supervise production, much less to organize state manufactures—a practice as stifling to individual initiative as it was dear to the hearts of enlightened despots like Frederick the Great of Prussia. The surviving trade guilds in the main lacked the power, still common on the Continent, to restrict the activities of a self-confident middle class, whose members were not only free generally to make their fortunes as they pleased, but if successful could aspire to enter the highest ranks as measured in terms of intellectual, social, and political distinction. Arkwright, who rose to knighthood; Wedgwood, who worked at the potter's wheel before he was ten, and became an F.R.S. and the employer of Flaxman; and the calico-printer, Peel, whose father was a yeoman, and whose son was twice Prime Minister, are only three of the great pioneers whose advancement served to stimulate the ambition of their contemporaries. Goethe sums up an attitude to life as well as to patents when he writes: 'The Englishman is free to use that which he has discovered until it leads to new discovery and fresh activity. One may well ask why are they in every respect in advance of us?'

The term 'industrial revolution', as applied to the changes which affected parts of England, the Scottish lowlands, and south Wales in the later years of the eighteenth century, is historically convenient and reflects the supreme importance of the events in question as seen in retrospect. It was not, however, revolution in the sense of the American and French revolutions, that is to say, a fundamental change of which most contemporaries were in some sense aware. The agricultural improvements which helped to feed a rapidly growing population were no doubt most widely spread, but even their introduction was slow and piecemeal. The progress made at this time by the cotton industry, where the jenny, the frame, the mule, and even the power-loom were accepted more readily than in the conservative woollen industry which had been for centuries Britain's main source of wealth, was certainly revolutionary in its consequences; yet it was not until ten years after the close of the period which we are now considering that the value of cotton exports for the first time exceeded that of woollens. The expansion of the iron industry with its many new roles in peace and war was perhaps on the whole more conspicuous. As the practice of coke-smelting spread through the trade, large-scale blast furnaces came into operation near the most accessible coal seams, but it was only after 1784, when it became possible to turn pig into wrought iron by the puddling process, that the total of British iron output began to soar (p. 476). It is even more tempting to think of a revolution as deriving from Watt's steam-engine. The first two were installed in 1774, to drain a colliery and to work a blast-furnace, and by 1785 the engine in its rotative form had been applied to a cotton-spinning mill as well as to the needs of breweries and other older large-scale enterprises. Yet when Watt's patent expired in 1800 a total of rather less than 500 engines had been built, so the average output of the famous Soho works (Fig. 132) was only a score a year. Moreover, their average horsepower, so far from revolutionizing earlier industrial conditions, was not significantly greater than that of the windmill or the waterwheel (p. 312).

Since trade and the hope of trade gave the main initial impetus to inventions, one of two important factors in the developments of this period was the increasing ability of the British to finance business expansion. While Europe as a whole was receiving much benefit from a great revival of silver production in Spanish America, the gold of Brazil went chiefly to London. More far-reaching in its effects was the circumstance that, whereas most of the powers followed the example of Frederick the Great when he established

public credit banks to help to make good the damage done by the
Seven Years War, Britain was rivalled only by the Netherlands in
the number of its private banks. Of these, the country banks directly
assisted in the manufacturing districts, while the merchant banks,
particularly in London, facilitated overseas commerce and shipping.
The other important factor was the influence exercised by the wars
of 1756–63 and 1775–83. Their effect on the development of the
iron industry is clear: the inferiority of French naval cannon was
noted already in the Seven Years War, and in 1774, when the quarrel

FIG. 132. Boulton & Watt's Soho works, rebuilt 1795

with the American colonies was just coming to a head, John Wilkinson made a further improvement in British ordnance by the invention of his boring-machine—and it was the further development of
this machine-tool that made possible the perfecting of the cylinders
for Boulton & Watt's steam-engines. The wars also intensified the
recurrent trade crises which made the textile industries intensely
competitive, so that even deserving inventors of the type of Samuel
Crompton and Edmund Cartwright went quickly to the wall. Thus
brief periods of depression followed the end of both the Seven Years
War and the American War of Independence, while a third, more
serious depression was already forming at the time of the next crisis
in Anglo-French relations in 1792–3. Because the power of the
eighteenth-century state was so much less, the actual war-periods
showed fluctuations rather than any general depression of overseas
trade; it is significant that in 1780, at the height of the Maritime
War against France, English hardware was still being exported to
that country, via Hamburg.

The publication of Adam Smith's *Wealth of Nations* in 1776,
Pitt's general reductions in the tariff, and his commercial treaty with

France (1786) mark the beginning of the British free-trade movement. In the six-year period in which this affected Anglo-French relations, as in the more general free-trade era of the mid-nineteenth century, the first effect was to stimulate a superior British technology, by enhancing its profits, but the second was to stimulate technological rivalry. Yet at the outbreak of the political revolution in France, the industrial revolution was far from being that British monopoly which it appeared to be on the morrow of Waterloo. But for the long wars, it is likely that the reduction of the tariff on British textiles to 12 per cent. would have proved only a temporary discouragement to French manufacturers. Their more lasting handicap was the shortage of coal in France, which was bound to grow more important with the development of a steam economy; nevertheless, a France which had in other respects an assured position of industrial leadership might have secured the use of her neighbours' coal on favourable terms.

To return from speculation about the mid-nineteenth century to the facts of 1786, it has been claimed by an English writer that at that date, 'French industries seem to be in a brilliant position hitherto unknown'. In the course of a generation guilds had been weakened, trade monopolies revoked, and the tax on capital and profits reduced. In the great *Encylopaedia* (1751-72) and its accompanying volumes of fine plates (see Fig. 54) France possessed, among other things, the first comprehensive treatise on technology. Lavoisier's impact upon agriculture, public finance, and even measurement—he was secretary to the commission which inaugurated the metric system in 1791—shows that the French government surpassed the British at least in its awareness of the usefulness of men of science. France, moreover, had other ingenious inventors, a strong artistic tradition among her craftsmen, and many expanding trades: Marie Antoinette, for example, deserves to be remembered for her patronage of cotton fabrics.

If conditions for the development of a manufacture are equally favourable on both sides of a frontier, technical knowledge will seldom be prevented from crossing over. Since so much of the technological history related in the rest of this book is concerned with Britain because new devices were developed there first, this point requires immediate emphasis. The British laws against the emigration of artisans and the exportation of machinery were maintained, in principle more than in practice, until 1825 and 1843 respectively. It was, however, generally impossible to prevent profitable inventions from becoming known: foreign visitors could always make a pretext for seeing machinery; descriptions often found their way into technical periodicals; and machines were often smuggled abroad or exported in contravention of regulations which were difficult to enforce. Above all, skilled workmen were tempted by the prospect of high wages and promotion, often into the ranks of managers and entrepreneurs, to move to countries where they knew their skill would be at a premium.

John Kay, the inventor of the flying-shuttle, lived in France for nearly a quarter of a century before his death in 1770, and taught the use of his machine; it was, nevertheless, being retaught in 1790, a reminder that it is unsafe to argue from the availability of an invention to its prevalence. A second significant figure is that of John Holker, a Manchester calenderer and Jacobite, who served as Inspector General of Factories in France from 1755 to 1786. His interest in British progress stretched beyond the textile industries: he is known to have drawn up the instructions for a fifteen months' tour of the British coal and iron and other industries, which the French engineer Gabriel Jars made on the morrow of the Seven Years War to 'ascertain the reason why industry is pushed much further in England than it is in France'. Jars paid several other official visits to foreign countries, and had only just begun to disseminate in France what he had learnt when he died young in 1769, a year after he had tied with Lavoisier in the election to the Academy of Sciences. But half-a-dozen years later his example sent a French ironmaster, Marchant de la Houlière, to the works of John Wilkinson (p. 475), whose brother William was invited to start a royal cannon foundry on the island of Indret at the mouth of the Loire. He recommended using the Le Creusot ironworks to provide blast-furnaces to feed the foundry, and it was at Le Creusot, though not through Wilkinson's initiative, that in 1785 the coking process came into use for iron-smelting for the first time on the Continent. A still more striking example of a key invention crossing the Channel successfully though unaccompanied is that of the first steam-engine, which was imported in 1779 to help pump the Paris water-supply from the Seine. The necessary drawings and the larger metal parts were sent to the firm of Perier, who later testified that 'no Englishman ever had a hand in the setting-up of the machines'. The Danes were less fortunate. In 1788 they engaged a Scotsman to build on the spot an engine for the forge hammer in the Copenhagen dockyard: it cost more than £7,000 to erect, used three times as much coal as a Watt engine of the same power, and had to be replaced after a dozen years by the purchase of the genuine article.

Among other countries that were industrially advanced in 1750, both Russia and Sweden lost their strong position as iron-makers as the coking process spread through western Europe, but from the time of Emanuel Swedenborg—who was a metallurgist and many-sided associate of Polhem (p. 144) long before he became absorbed in religious speculation, and who died in London—the Swedes were keen observers of the industrial scene farther west; they even invited Matthew Boulton to transfer his activities to their country. Frederick the Great's conquest of Silesia, which was valuable from an economic standpoint, coupled with the existing Prussian tradition of paternal administration and the ruthless energy of the king himself, give special importance to events in Prussia. A rich find of silver-bearing lead was made at Tarnowitz shortly before his death, and in 1789 Wilkinson left England for the second time to introduce coke-smelting there at the Friedrichshütte. A couple of years later, coke-smelting was being applied also to the Upper Silesian iron-ore, and before the end of the decade Breslau had the first iron bridge on the Continent. It is characteristic of the earnestness with which the Prussian state pursued the economic development of its relatively small resources, that the career of Freiherr von Stein began in the official mining service, which sent him on a prolonged visit to England in 1786 to secure the Boulton & Watt steam-engine. The first engine was erected at Friedrichshütte in 1788 and in the following year in Westphalia, Stein's mission having secured drawings, cylinders, and some workmen. By 1800 the Prussian state had two small engine-building establishments, but by then the relationship between a more industrialized Britain and a less industrialized Continent had been considerably modified.

THE PERIOD OF THE GREAT FRENCH WARS, 1792-1815

When France declared war on Austria and Prussia (20 April 1792) and on Britain and Holland (1 February 1793) she inaugurated an age of war which lasted, with two brief interruptions, until November 1815. Thus the second phase of the industrial revolution is one which was affected by a war economy almost continuously, for the improved trade relations with France, established by Pitt in 1786, were not renewed during the fifteen months of the Peace of

Amiens (1802–3), and while Napoleon was relegated to Elba in 1814–15, Britain, except for the first two months of 1815, was still at war with America. This war régime reached a climax in the years 1806–11, when Napoleon attempted to exclude British trade from the Continent and Britain counteracted his continental system by depriving the Continent of all trade which did not pass through British ports.

Comparisons with the much shorter but far more intensive war effort of the first two world wars are, of course, misleading. Each fighting man in the field is sustained nowadays by about six times as much war work at home as was required then; moreover, the powers of government, whether by organization or by propaganda, in securing such direction of effort as was required were so much smaller then that they seem scarcely to have impinged upon the tranquil middle-class life recorded by Jane Austen. Since a food shortage, unlike a munitions shortage, requires no advertisement, the most consistent progress was probably that made in the enclosure movement and in agricultural improvement generally. By 1815 a bird's-eye view would have shown the tilled area, after long centuries of struggle against woodland, marsh, and waste, at last approaching its economic maximum. The strain was certainly felt by the munitions industries, including the building, arming, and servicing of those ships of the line on which the safety of the island was seen to depend —the block-making machinery introduced at Portsmouth dockyard is a clear illustration (p. 351)—but, in general, increased use of steam-power and machinery enabled Britain to press home the advantage which she derived from her superiority in iron production. The war also encouraged their use in the textile industries, to supply both uniforms and blankets for our own armies and the far larger forces of our allies; Isambard Brunel was even able to run an army boot factory with machine-riveting of soles—a process which reverted to hand-work when the war was over.

In comparing the situation with later war periods it is also important to remember that Britain on this occasion received no support from financial backers outside Europe and very little from accumulated overseas investments. The sum of £57,000,000, which she used to build up and sustain the five coalitions against France, required therefore a great development of the export trades. Some British goods virtually sold themselves—the re-exported colonial sugar and coffee, for example, which were smuggled from island bases on to the Continent; or the greatcoats, boots, and even regimental badges with which Napoleon, against his own rules, clandestinely equipped his soldiers. But the manufacture of cotton-cloth, which now became Britain's largest export, was part and parcel of the war effort, no less than the commercial enterprise which, within twelve months of the Navy's rescue of the king of Portugal from Napoleon's clutches, established sixty British firms in his colonial capital of Rio de Janeiro.

The sufferings of the people during the war years were probably due to the war itself rather than to any of the technological changes which accompanied it, but it is likely that the picture of the industrial revolution as mainly an oppressive force dates partly from this time. After 1799 trade unionism was, in theory at least, completely suppressed; a measure to improve the conditions under which pauper apprentices were employed in factories left the exploitation of other children completely unchecked; the legal regulation of wages and the legal enforcement of apprenticeship were both formally abandoned; and the political eclipse of both the Whigs and the Radicals left the people virtually without any means of voicing their grievances. The Luddite disturbances (p. 573) at the end of the war period, although they were a protest primarily against the abuse of an old type of machine—the knitting-frame—were no doubt symptomatic of a general malaise. Wages rose during the war years but so did prices, and if there were hand-loom weavers who on occasion walked round with five-pound notes stuck in their hat-bands, a grudgingly relieved poverty was very much more conspicuous, whenever the sudden depressions to which war-time trade was particularly liable brought the mills to a standstill. Moreover, as the steam-engine gradually replaced the water-wheel, factory work became concentrated in the towns, where war-time shortages of timber, bricks, and glass helped to establish a régime of jerry-built cottages surrounding the substantial and even gas-lit edifices which housed the machines.

Meanwhile, what was happening in France? Between 1792 and 1799 the output of textiles and trade as a whole were reduced to one-third of their former extent. The frequent changes of government, the Reign of Terror, and the Law of the Maximum, to say nothing of the enormous financial depreciation, destroyed confidence and cut short many careers full of promise for industry besides those of Lavoisier, who was made a victim of the guillotine, and Leblanc

(p. 532), who lost his property and died by his own hand in 1806. But it is evidence of the astonishing energy released by the revolutionary era that the Committee of Public Safety interested itself in Leblanc's soda-making process (even though he lost the profits), that the Polytechnique and schools of civil engineering and mining were established, and that the year 1798, when the decline of the Directory was preparing the way for Bonaparte's assumption of supreme power, was dignified by the holding of an industrial exhibition. It was, however, the age of Napoleon which left the more lasting impression on technology.

The restoration of order and the establishment of a new legal system under the Consulate and Empire gave industry a chance to revive. In 1807 the commercial code even provided a form of limited liability for sleeping partners in industry, nearly two generations ahead of British practice. Napoleon was himself interested in the industrial arts: he had the flying-shuttle demonstrated for him in a model weaving-shed at Passy; he had Jacquard (p. 570) brought from Lyons to work his loom at the Conservatoire des Arts et Métiers; and his prefects were required to encourage the use of machinery for the carding and spinning of wool which a Scotsman manufactured on an island in the Seine. By 1812 Alsace had begun to spin on a small scale by steam-power. Yet the main interest of the Napoleonic era for the present subject does not lie here but in the consequences of French military policy—the conversion of western Europe into what was virtually a single economic unit, and the attempt to make that unit viable in face of the British trade blockade.

The economic life of France was undoubtedly stimulated by a 50 per cent. increase in area and population. For example, the annexation of Belgium meant that her coal output, which was about 700,000 tons at the outbreak of the Revolution, reached 5 million tons in 1807. Yet—a significant detail—only Le Creusot sold coke-smelted iron, and that not until 1810, when the empire was drawing near to catastrophe. But it is when we examine the Napoleonic dependent states and satellites that we find ourselves at a turning-point in economic history at which European history obstinately failed to turn. As with Hitler's New Order of 1940–1, it is impossible to estimate what this unified Europe might have achieved—because it was never stabilized: the end of the beginning, when the French frontier reached Rome and Lübeck (1810), was also the beginning of the end. Beet-sugar production is an important development of the period, which reminds us of the constant factor of British pressure. The general abolition of serfdom in territories conquered by the French, which was taken up by the Prussians under Stein for their own purposes in 1807, prepared the way for all subsequent developments in European agriculture. On the west bank of the Rhine, and to a lesser extent elsewhere, the abolition of local trade restrictions liberated new industrial forces. Napoleon was an ardent advocate of canals, and as far away as the Illyrian provinces he left his mark in the road system. There were also some important spontaneous developments among the French satellites: 400,000 tons of coal raised yearly in the Ruhr; more than a quarter of a million spinning-mules in use in Saxony by 1813; the establishment of machine cotton-spinning from England at St Gall in Switzerland in February 1801; and an independent Swiss invention of crucible cast steel.

But it was only Belgium which was experiencing an actual revolution in industry, and that for exceptional reasons. Firmly joined to France since the summer of 1793, this ancient industrial region had already received a new stimulus from the French *laissez-faire* policy and the opening of the Scheldt trade, when an Englishman, William Cockerill, half a dozen years later established at Verviers a factory to make wool-carding and spinning machinery. His venture was further developed at Liège into a regular textile-machine building business, from which one-half of the output was sold to France. Liège also became the centre of an important munitions industry: iron rails were laid at a cannon foundry there in 1800, from which their use spread into the coal-mines; and in 1813 William Cockerill imported a Watt engine as a model from England. He then retired, but an enterprising Prussian, who was quartered on Cockerill's sons just before the Battle of Waterloo, found them making steam-engines and hydraulic presses on a scale that caused him to negotiate for their services at Berlin.

The trade war in Europe also had some effect on the development of the United States of America, even before the war against Great Britain which resulted from it in 1812–15. The Americans had begun to cast cannon at Springfield during their War of Independence, but it was not until after the achievement of independence that the first cotton factory was set up by Samuel Slater, who had been apprenticed to Arkwright's partner, and the wool-carding machine was brought over by Arthur and John Schofield from Yorkshire. Free America acted as a magnet to enterprising Englishmen of the type of Joseph Priestley, the Birmingham chemist, and Tom Paine (p. 450), both of whom spent their last years there. But much the most important development at that period was the planting of 'sea island' cotton from the Bahamas, which began in 1786 and was enormously expanded as a result of Eli Whitney's invention of the cotton-gin (p. 557), so that America had a readily harvested raw material to exchange for the finer qualities of manufactures of all kinds which were still the great subject of west-bound Atlantic

FIG. 133. Loading a cotton steamer, c. 1870

trade. From 1793 onwards, however, the uncertainty of European trade caused the birth of a small-scale factory system for cotton-spinning, while after the commencement of hostilities in 1812 woollen factories also became numerous, to provide military uniforms and negro clothing, and to some extent the finer qualities of cloth. The outbreak of war was due largely to the success of the American mercantile marine in reaping a golden harvest from its neutrality: tonnage registered for foreign trade had increased eight-fold between 1789 and 1810, so that Orders in Council enforced by British frigates hurt not only young America's pride but her pocket. On the water, at least, America had no need to play second fiddle to any European power: in the year preceding the outbreak of war, which necessarily reduced overseas commerce, her pioneer use of the steamboat, on the Hudson (p. 328), had already spread to the

Ohio, foreshadowing the unimpeded peaceful development of regions well provided with inland waterways (Fig. 133).

FROM WATERLOO TO THE GREAT EXHIBITION, 1815-51

For the period 1815-51 the highlights of political history offer an unreliable guide to economic development. As regards English political history, the social unrest of the immediate post-war years, the Corn Law of 1815 and the long-continued struggle for its repeal, the disclosures leading to the Factory and Coal-Mines Acts, and the Chartist agitation of 1839-48, all convey a picture of almost unrelieved gloom and oppression. This contrasts oddly with the sense of national achievement so clearly displayed at the Great Exhibition of 1851. In the same way, the history of Europe is depicted in terms of an epoch of reaction, with the Orleans monarchy in France as the exception which proves the rule, since every event from its enthronement in July 1830 onwards is seen as contributing to its overthrow in 1848. There again an enormous and seemingly inexplicable contrast appears in the sequel, when the Europe of 1848-50 resounds almost from end to end with an armed struggle for liberal rights and national unity.

In the eyes of the economic historian, at any rate, it is a period when Britain took a masterful lead, which the European nations at varying speeds endeavoured to follow: if the development of railways be used as a rough measure, Europe in the 1830's and 1840's made considerable progress (Fig. 134) and America more, but at the close of the period Britain still had the most complete and efficient network. If we measure the age in terms of trade, then we should begin with a period of European recovery about five years after the war, culminating in a Latin-American boom in 1824-5, when 250 new joint-stock companies were registered in Britain. In the same way there was an American boom in 1832-6, and in the forties a further expansion, which began with the opening-up of the China trade, continued with the railway 'mania', and culminated in the gold discoveries in California and Australia. From 1819 onwards Britain, but Britain alone, was in a position to base her currency entirely on gold, while from 1844 onwards Peel's Bank Charter Act gave the Bank of England a prestige which outlasted the century.

From the point of view of the history of technology, however, it is important to see what were the industrial processes in which Britain excelled. One was her efficient agriculture: in a single generation between 1811 and 1841, while corn laws kept out imports, the proportion of families which it employed fell from one-third of the nation to one-quarter. This meant that Britain had a much larger proportion of her population than had other nations available for other basic industrial activities, such as coal-mining, of which the output in the same period was approximately quadrupled. This was a great age of iron, with the building of railways as the main innovation, though the queen of the export trades was indisputably cotton (Fig.

FIG. 134. Railway viaduct in Saxony, constructed in 1845–51

135), which by 1851 gave employment to more than half a million workers, from the nine-year-old 'piecers' upwards. Yet from the point of view of the diffusion of advanced technologies, the most significant trend was the growth of the machine-making industry, based on the development of the machine-tool by such men as Maudslay and Nasmyth.

The spread of the industrial revolution on the continent of Europe was to some extent a result, and to some extent also a cause, of the prominence of the machine-making industry in Britain. Belgium indeed rose quickly to occupy a position which, although on a smaller scale, was similar to that of Britain herself. She possessed not only coal and iron-ore but an admirable position for transit traffic, and rulers (William I of the united Netherlands and Leopold I, first king of the Belgians) who continued the French programme of development. In 1817 the Cockerills established a great machine-works at Seraing, where, according to a British official report, all the new inventions were to be had 'ten days after they come out of England'. In the 1830's the Belgians sold machinery in Holland, Germany, and Russia, and were building their own locomotives. When the Brussels–Malines railway was opened in 1835 it carried more passengers than did all the existing lines in England.

Ten years after the close of the Napoleonic wars there are believed to have been some 15,000 English workers in France, an important

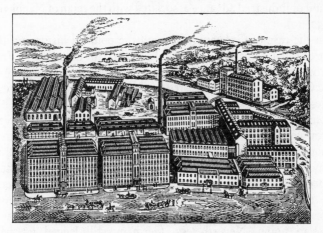

FIG. 135. Clark's Anchor Thread works, Paisley, mid-nineteenth century

contribution to her industrial growth, which, though far less rapid than that of England, began under the restored Bourbon monarchy and was the dominant feature of the reign of Louis Philippe (1830–48). In Marc Seguin, who laid the first (18-km) railway track at St-Étienne, France had one of the leaders among early railway engineers, even though the railway network, which grew rather slowly until the time of Napoleon III, owed much to British railway-builders such as Thomas Brassey: one of the most important lines, the Paris–Rouen railway completed in 1841–3, was promoted by an English diplomat with one-third English capital, employed all English drivers, and had its locomotives built by an English firm in France. By the middle of the century the use of steam-power in France, which had been quite negligible under Napoleon I, amounted to 67,000 h.p. in all—a little less than was used in Britain for cotton alone. Large-scale industry as a whole employed only a quarter as many French people as domestic manufactures, and at least half the pig iron was still smelted in charcoal furnaces scattered about the countryside; nevertheless, the French output of coal had been multiplied six times in the course of a single generation, and before 1850 the modern practice had been developed by which France imported an additional 50 per cent. to meet her needs. At about this time a slowing-up in the progress of agriculture, by making rural labour more readily available for industry, completed the preparations for the greater period of industrial advance associated with the reign of Napoleon III (1852–70).

In the case of Germany, although the political history up to the year of revolutions in 1848 is far less colourful than that of France, the outstanding development has an obvious economic significance. The Germany of 1815 consisted of thirty-eight sovereign states, the largest of which, namely Prussia, consisted of widely separated blocks of territory, including a large new acquisition in the Rhine valley; in consequence, Prussian diplomacy was soon busy establishing the famous Customs Union or *Zollverein*. By 1834 it included all Germany except an area in the north-west where British influence helped to produce a counterpoise, and by 1840 the tariff barrier, low but tending to rise, was a sufficient irritant for an English investigator (John Bowring) to be sent to examine the strength of the new Prussian union. Nevertheless, Germany still lagged far behind France. Its twelve largest towns together never showed a population more than 50 per cent. greater than that of Paris alone, and Prussia was only 2 per cent. less rural at the close of the period than at its beginning. France, indeed, had fewer railways than Germany—in 1850 about two-thirds of the mileage—but this was partly off-set by the superiority of the French roads and canals to those of Germany, where for a generation after 1815 the best network was that which the French occupation had left behind in the Rhineland and Westphalia.

The greater distance perhaps accounts for the fact that there were fewer British craftsmen seeking employment in Gemany, but despite the small number British influence was powerful. The Cockerills' machine-building works in Berlin had their counterpart at Wetten in the Ruhr, where there were two English engineers and a moulder who had been trained by Maudslay, and in Berlin (Fig. 136). The German railways, although largely built by cheap American methods, bore the imprint of George Stephenson in the adoption of the

British standard gauge, which was not particularly well suited to German needs. In 1845 the German railways employed three times as many foreign as German locomotives, and out of every three foreigners two were of English construction. Above all, the Germans were assiduous visitors to British industrial installations. P. C. W. Beuth, first director of the Industrial Institute at Berlin, which later grew into the Charlottenburg Technical High School, was the most immediately influential: he visited Maudslay's on two separate occasions and was investigating the merits of the Stockton–Darlington railway almost as soon as it was open. From the point of view of the

FIG. 136. Borsig locomotive- and machine-building works, Berlin

future, however, a student of English steel production in 1838–9 deserves special mention: this was Alfred Krupp, heir to a small ironworks in Essen.

Like the ripples of a pool the industrial revolution spread outwards into Belgium and France, into Germany, and then farther on. In 1840 one of the Cockerills died at Warsaw after an unsuccessful attempt to arrange a big railway contract with the czar Nicholas I. By 1841 thirty-five steam-engines of a total of 434 h.p. had been made in Austria, and developments in textile manufacture and machine-building were under way in Bohemia, which remained throughout the century the industrial heart of the sprawling Habsburg empire. Before the end of the decade Cavour, after studying the England of Sir Robert Peel on the spot, was preparing to transfer to the soil of north Italy the principles of free trade and expanding manufactures. But the Germany on which John Bowring reported in 1840 inevitably attracts special attention, because of the technological achievements of a later Germany. He found Germany to be already ahead of Britain in three respects—the arts of design and their application to various fabrics; a traditional skill in fine metal-work, such as the making of cutlery: and a broad-based educational system which already affected industry. 'Chemical knowledge', ran the report, 'is farther advanced than with us': Bunsen was just rising to fame, and it was in 1840 that Justus von Liebig, who had been a professor at Giessen since 1824, published his *Die Organische Chemie in ihrer Anwendung auf Agricultur und Physiologie*.

Meanwhile, the United States, though seldom regarded with ade-quate respect by European observers, approached more nearly than the European powers to the position of a technological rival to Britain. Between 1815 and 1850 the American population approxi-mately trebled; by the latter date it already exceeded the British, the final quinquennium being that in which the proportion of im-migrants to total population reached its all-time maximum. Already the opening-up of the country put America in certain respects ahead: there was, for instance, a tremendous interest in internal communica-tions. Thus, in the first decade of railway building the American mileage far exceeded that of Europe, and it is calculated that in the later 1840's the steamers on the western rivers may have had a larger tonnage than those employed by the entire British empire. On the open-sea routes the American sailing-clipper was, under favourable conditions, faster than the steamer, and the over-all growth of shipping under the Stars and Stripes enabled President Polk in 1847 to look forward to the eclipse of the British mercantile marine. Manufactures also spread in America, especially after iron-smelting with anthracite instead of charcoal became established in 1840; the use of coke followed the Civil War. If the finer qualities of manufactured goods still came from Europe—the 'fineness' can, however, be exaggerated, since Victorian Birmingham numbered among its minor exports tomahawks and even thumbscrews—that was because high-quality production commonly involved consigning each process to the hands of experts working in a special unit, where-as the Americans still preferred to carry out every process simply and under a single roof, as part of the policy of economizing in labour necessary in a country where cheap land made labour dear. Con-versely, American inventors quickly became prominent in patenting the type of labour-saving device that multiplied the efforts of one man working on his own. This was apparent at the Great Exhibition of 1851 where the Americans, who were said to 'produce for the

masses', attracted great attention with McCormick's labour-saving
reaper (p. 672), the sewing-machine (p. 575), and the Colt
revolver (p. 356).

The success of the Exhibition was perhaps as much a social as an
economic phenomenon. With the help of railway trips, six million
visitors attended from all parts of the United Kingdom and elsewhere, and the fact that such vast (and unexpectedly orderly) crowds
were both able and willing to pay an entrance fee of never less than
a shilling for a spectacle so edifying, suggested to many earnest
minds that the masses in the first great industrialized country of the
modern world found some satisfaction in the fruits of their labours.
The main reaction of William Morris, on the other hand, at the age
of seventeen, was to be appalled by the general ugliness of the exhibits. As for their technical quality, Britain succeeded in its una-
vowed aim of outclassing the work of thirteen European countries,
thirteen American countries, and the seven others participating, apart
from colonies. If Britain's neighbours were meant to learn from her
the profitableness of peace, the Exhibition was a failure, since it
ushered in two decades of war. If it was meant to mark a stage only
in the self-confident rise of British industrial technology, it was again
a failure. So far from British enterprise proceeding from strength to
strength, only sixteen years later the Paris Exhibition witnessed a
general discomfiture of British technologists by the superior inventiveness of their rivals in other lands, and when the two decades of
war in Europe and America were over, technological development
entered upon a new phase under new leaders. By the end of the
century the Crystal Palace building, re-erected at Sydenham, survived as a rather forlorn reminder of a past supremacy.

THE PERIOD OF NATIONALIST WARS, 1851-71

In the 1850's and 1860's, however, Great Britain was more than
ever the workshop of the world. Though detailed comparisons at the
Exhibition showed the workshop to be less fertile in ideas than it had
once been, the fact remained that in an age of acute political controversy resulting in a series of great wars—fought successively on
Russian, Italian, North American, Danish, Central European, and
French, but not on British, soil—Britain could sell whatever she chose
to make. In twenty years (1855-75) the value of United Kingdom
exports per head of a rapidly growing population increased from
£4 to £6. The trend towards world free trade, which reached its

maximum in these years, gave a stimulus to British exports that would not have been given if the world had not been so much in need of them.

Britain's supremacy in cotton textiles remained unchallenged. The increasing use of iron and the steam-engine in shipping gave fresh scope to the iron-founders and machine-makers, who were already developing railways in many parts of the world. In addition, the invention of cheap steel—by the Bessemer process in 1856 and by the Siemens open-hearth process ten years later (p. 484)—enabled Britain to forge and, build in a new material, though the fact that a steel rail, for example, lasted up to ten times as long as an iron one, suggested an eventual limit to the demand. Since 1851 was the moment at which census returns showed Britain to be one-half urban and one-half rural, it might be supposed that the tremendous industrial efforts of the next two decades could have been achieved only at the expense of agriculture. The additional workers did indeed come largely from agriculture, which reduced its manpower from a little under two millions to a little under a million and a half in this period. Yet the acreage under the plough and, still more significant, the acreage under wheat, reached a new maximum at the end of the 1860's: an increased efficiency in agriculture therefore clearly matched the achievements in industry.

In 1848 John Stuart Mill in his *Principles of Political Economy* had raised the doubt whether the progress of invention had done anything to diminish the toil of the worker. It may be true that the task of the iron puddler, of the early engine-driver who had no roof to his cab, and of the coal-miner—whose numbers during these two decades mounted from 200,000 to 300,000—was as exhausting physically as anything which the old rural economy demanded. But from the 1850's onwards, with sustained employment and with wages rising rather faster than prices, it became demonstrably true that the industrial worker in Britain was a gainer by the industrial revolution. He could afford to eat meat and wheaten bread produced by the improved agriculture; his clothing was of superior quality as compared with that of the homespun past; and a noteworthy use of the increased wages was a great increase in the cleanliness of his person, clothes, and home. The death-rate, which had become more severe in the towns after the Napoleonic wars, now began to fall, except among infants. The cholera epidemics, of which the third and last severe one was in 1865–6, were conquered by the main drainage which industrial progress made possible, and there was no recurrence of the London typhus epidemic of 1838, which had first attracted serious attention to the plight of the urban poor. Since neither the Crimean War, nor the Indian Mutiny which immediately followed, had any great effect upon the lives of the civilian masses at home, it is safe to picture the mid-Victorian Englishman of all classes as dimly aware of advantages conferred upon him by a heritage of superior technology which, in the main, was not shared by other peoples. It was at this time that the Saturday half-holiday, known elsewhere as the *semaine anglaise*, became a distinctive feature of life in the English factory districts.

In France the Second Empire (1852–70) was a paradise for the industrial entrepreneur, since the government was sufficiently authoritarian to keep down the demands of labour, while relying for prestige upon spectacular evidences of material progress; quick to complete the railway network, it was enlightened enough to apply the incentive of public works as well as the spur of tariff reductions. It was the age of Louis Pasteur and Pierre Martin (p. 484); the emperor himself had written on artillery, and took a keen personal interest in such projects as an experimental aluminium industry (p. 494). The Paris Exhibition of 1867, already mentioned, de Lesseps' construction of the Suez Canal, which was opened by the Empress Eugénie in the last autumn of the reign, and the quintupling of French steam-power in the course of the two Napoleonic decades suggest that the fall of the régime may be attributable less to its inherent weakness than to the mounting strength of the hereditary enemy.

In agriculture the Prussian Junker on the great eastern plains controlled a type of estate which, as compared with the peasant holdings of France, lent itself readily to the adoption of modern techniques. Industry in Germany began to profit from the relatively early development of railways (Fig. 137A), from the commercial strength of the *Zollverein*, and last, but by no means least, from Prussian ambition embodied in Bismarck. By 1860, thanks to the stimulus provided by the railways, Germany was raising 50 per cent. more coal than France. As regards pig iron, on the other hand, the position at that time was rather more than reversed in France's favour; but the decade during which Prussia fought three wars in seven years—against Denmark, against Austria, and against France—was also a decade in which Germany, under Prussian leadership, expanded her iron industry until, on the eve of the Franco-Prussian war, it already exceeded that of her western neighbour and rival. When von Moltke mobilized his forces for war in 1870 he was dependent on a vast railway network (Fig. 137B)—of iron; Krupps' iron and steelworks supplied the artillery (Fig. 138); and rail and gun together made

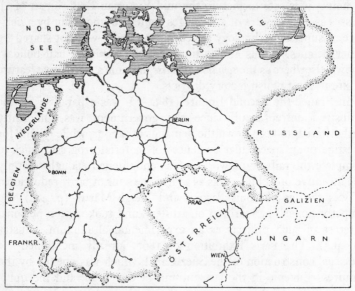

FIG. 137A. Railway network of 1850, within German frontiers of 1871

possible the sustained application of force to which Paris was eventually surrendered.

The American Civil War of 1861–5, a conflict on an altogether larger scale than any of the five European wars of the period, had also an importance in technological history more nearly approaching that of the total wars of our own century. In the decade before the war began, the development of the United States was in a sense extremely rapid. The length of the railways grew in that time from 10,000 to 30,000 miles, which was more than twice the entire network of the United Kingdom; while labour-saving inventions, patented by the thousand, became a feature of the national life, remarked upon by such a visitor as Sir Charles Lyell, the geologist. Even more striking are the words that Walt Whitman wrote in 1856: 'Colossal foundry, flaming fires . . . waste and extravagance of material, mighty castings; such is a symbol of America.' Yet until the great quarrel had been fought out, making it certain that the future of the country would be entrusted to a single government based on the principles of freedom and the abolition of the 'peculiar institution' of slavery, America remained in another sense economically backward. For one-half of the United States territory, lying between the

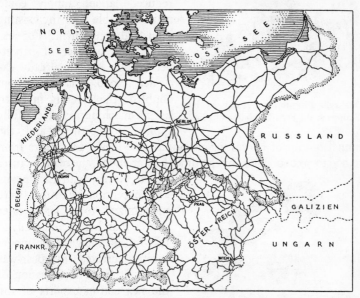

FIG. 137B. Railway network of 1880, within same frontiers as Fig. 137A

97th meridian and the Pacific coast settlements, contained only 1 per cent. of the population. In 1860 it had not even been realized that cattle could winter and find pasturage in such regions as northern Nebraska, let alone that the teeming millions of Europe required only the building of a trans-continental railway to call them to conquer the empty wilderness for the plough.

The influence of the war upon technology was many-sided. The armament industries of the North were developed with a rapidity and ingenuity (Fig. 139), that in great measure determined the issue since the Confederates were mainly dependent on such imported arms as could escape the Northern blockade—they made the first use in the field, for example, of Sir Joseph Whitworth's quick-firing gun (p. 504). Although 800,000 immigrants reached American shores during the war years, labour-saving devices of all kinds received an enormous impetus, because the unprecedented size of the armies engaged and the length of the conflict meant that the demand for food, uniform clothing, and munitions far exceeded what the reduced labour supply could make available with the existing industrial equipment. For example, the number of patents per annum, which already exceeded 2,000, was more than doubled; the recently invented sewing-machine was successfully applied to leather; and the

FIG. 138. Fifty-ton gun exhibited by Krupps at the Paris Exhibition of 1867

annual output of harvesting-machines rose in the four years from 20,000 to 70,000. Thus, by the time the war ended, the manufactures of the North, with the inevitable exception of cotton, were mechanized to a far greater degree than before and ready to take full advantage of the opportunities created by post-war immigration. The cessation of the raw-cotton exports of the Southern States, on the other hand, was accompanied by a 40 per cent. drop in the mercantile marine, most of the ships being sold abroad. While the crop rapidly regained its share of the world market, America's position as a shipping nation

FIG. 139. First 'aircraft carrier', employed for observation by Federal forces, 1861

was the one loss that was not made good after the war, for the significant reason that during the next half-century American capital was fully absorbed in the business of internal development, which reached its first great post-war peak in the early 1870's.

THE AGE OF MATERIALISM, 1871–1900

Viewed in retrospect, the last thirty years of the nineteenth century have many of the characteristics of a golden age: except in the

Balkans, Europe was free from war, and in the outer world the only considerable campaigns were those waged by Chile against Peru and Bolivia, the brief Sino-Japanese and Spanish-American conflicts, and Britain's war in South Africa. This situation was the more remarkable as almost the whole continent of Africa, considerable parts of Asia, and even the islands of the Pacific Ocean were being swiftly annexed to the empires of rival European powers. That they did not fight among themselves over the spoil may be attributed to the consideration that, broadly speaking, there was enough for all comers. That wars against resisting natives were of altogether minor importance is due chiefly to technological progress, as a single example may show. In the $4\frac{1}{2}$-hour battle at Omdurman in 1898, Kitchener was fighting a brave and desperate enemy, who had twice his number of men. Yet he won the Sudan at a cost of 48 killed, whereas over 11,000 Dervish corpses were counted: he had at his disposal 44 pieces of field artillery, 20 Maxim machine-guns, and a flotilla of gun-boats firing a high explosive (lyddite) never seen in action before. But it was also an age of peaceful penetration into regions that had hitherto been almost unoccupied. A further million Europeans a year entered the United States, other millions went to Canada, Australasia, and South America, and the 1890's witnessed the beginning of a Russian expansion into central Asia and the Far East.

This movement was in a sense the conquest of the world by a now well-established technology. The first American transcontinental railway had been completed in 1869, the year of the opening of the Suez Canal. By 1900 the railways of the world had more than quadrupled their length in a generation, so as to link up every important hinterland (except the interior of China) with a multitude of ports served by the steamships, to which the Suez Canal gave an important advantage over sailing-vessels. The world consumption of coal had increased almost as fast as the railway mileage, while the substitution of steel for iron as the basic constructional material for engines, for ships, and finally for buildings, added greatly to the durability of the heavy industrial goods which man was producing in such greatly increased quantities. But, to the reflective mind at least, the marvel of the contemporary achievement was much enhanced also by the rise of new technologies: the great developments in electricity and industrial chemistry, for example, and the pioneering of the internal combustion engine, which was to give man a new ease of transport as well as transport in a new element.

The age is remarkable, too, for a profound shift in the economic balance and relationships among the powers, a shift which was so greatly to Britain's disadvantage that it requires a distance of half a century for it to be viewed philosophically. The triumphant progress of the United States of America, with its huge natural resources, was inevitable. The successes of the Germans, which were on a much smaller scale, were facilitated at least by the very fact that Britain had long been the workshop of the world, and was therefore burdened with highly esteemed equipment and techniques which were now growing obsolete. It is also possible now to accept that in Europe the technological leadership must rest eventually with the power which most nearly matched the American resources, namely Russia. In 1900 she produced half the oil of the world and had made a great impact upon the European wheat market, but, except in the outlying regions of Poland and Finland, her factory industry was still in its infancy. For the other powers, however, the growth of the coal-mines expresses clearly the change in their relative position. In 1870 Britain mined 50 per cent. more coal than the United States, Germany, and France together; in 1900 they mined 70 per cent. more than Britain. While British output had doubled, the American had been multiplied by eight, the German by four, and even the French by two and a half.

A natural reluctance to accept British dominance of the economy for longer than necessary provided one reason for the general return to a régime of high tariffs, though continental rivalries, which promoted not only an arms-race but a cult of agricultural and industrial self-sufficiency as a precaution against eventual war, also played a part. Among European powers Germany led the way in 1879: but the others were not content merely to follow the policy of Bismarck, who established a careful balance between the conflicting interests of industrialists and landed proprietors. After a quarter of a century the average import duty on British manufactures was 25 per cent. in Germany, but 27 in Italy, 34 in France, 35 in Austria-Hungary, and 131 in Russia. The corresponding figure for America, where the tariff began to rise at the time of the Civil War, was then 73 per cent.: the transatlantic market for British wares was therefore very far from compensating for the havoc wrought among landlords and farmers by the cheap American wheat which, ever since the 1870's, had begun to flood in the opposite direction. In the new century Joseph Chamberlain's Tariff Reform campaign based its programme of retaliation upon the new sense of economic insecurity in Britain, but the strident imperialism of the period between Queen Victoria's two jubilees of 1887 and 1897 had also been due in part to an increasing awareness that only by resolute policy could the British hope to defend a position of economic advantage which had once seemed impregnable.

From about 1860 onwards British capitalists had ceased to invest to any great extent on the Continent. There was much scope for investment in India during its reorganization after the Mutiny, and it might also be supposed that other imperial interests, which were fostered by Disraeli from 1874 onwards and which continued to grow right down to the South African war of 1899, would prove a rewarding alternative. But the fact is that, after the efforts of thirty years, the proportion of British trade which was done with the Colonies had risen only from one-quarter to one-third, while of British imports less than one-quarter were of colonial origin. Thus, in a generation that saw the number of agricultural workers in England and Wales fall by one-third from its 1871 total of almost one million persons, emigration was on the whole a more hopeful remedy than the prospect of absorption in industry. Britain's share in the industrial output of the world was certainly declining at this time, and there is good reason to suppose that the annual rate of increase of the British industrial output declined as well.

For France also this was a period of disappointment, but for quite different reasons. Her defeat at the hands of Germany meant not merely a blow to the national pride and a fostering of political disunity, it meant the handicap of a war indemnity, which was bravely and quickly overcome, and a serious disorganization of industry through the loss of Alsace-Lorraine. Although many firms moved to Normandy, valuable textile and textile machine-making industries were left behind in Alsace. There was also the loss of much of the minette ore, rich in iron but very phosphoric, that lay on both sides of the new frontier in the Longwy area; from 1879 onwards the Gilchrist-Thomas process (p. 484) enabled this ore to serve the expanding German steel industry. In addition, the Germans developed important potash deposits (p. 554) in southern Alsace. Having a stationary population, France also felt more severely than Germany the burden of military conscription and armaments, which offered her the only alternative to a passive acceptance of the territorial losses. It was not until the days of the Méline tariff in the

1890's that the heavy industry of France really recovered strength; her pre-eminence in a number of luxury trades, however, kept her from technological stagnation.

Meanwhile the Germans enjoyed an immense success, seeming to justify the faith that Treitschke placed in 'the God who made iron'. In the single decade of the 1880's the German output of pig iron was practically doubled, while that of Britain remained almost stationary. At the close of that decade the United Kingdom still had a lead of more than 2 million tons in steel output: ten years later there was a lead of just under $1\frac{1}{2}$ million tons—but it was a German lead. In the electrical industry Germany had no rival except America. She was also in the forefront in the export of dyestuffs and fine chemicals, and though her exports of heavy chemicals were quite small in comparison with those of Britain, by 1900 she was able to supply the chemicals for her own industries and to feed her soil on a gigantic scale. Hence the remarkable fact that in the last twenty years of the century, without relaxing her efforts in industry, Germany was able to place an additional 2 million acres under food crops, of which 10 per cent. was wheat. Among the roots of this striking technological progress were the close relations maintained between the universities and industry and the large provision of technological education of all kinds, from the twenty-eight agricultural schools existing in 1900 to Charlottenburg with its world-wide reputation. Soon after the end of the century a British journalist was noticing with surprise that in Saxony one technical school was provided for every 10,000 of population, and that the average chemical manufacturer had one chemist with university qualifications to every forty workers.

The tempo of American life at this period may perhaps be illustrated by the fact that the completion of the first transcontinental railway, which in 1869 ushered in the modern era, was achieved by a labour force of 20,000 men who laid two miles of track a day. That tempo, which was related both to the pioneering spirit and to the high cost of labour, helps to explain the swift advance of the Americans in technology. Down to 1880 agriculture was still their main source of wealth, but it was an agriculture that depended upon efficient harvesting-machinery to overcome the shortness of the harvest season in the Middle West, upon a new type of metal windmill to raise a water supply on the plains, and upon the new device of barbed-wire to control cattle. Twenty years later, industrial products were already twice those of agriculture in terms of prices and the

American output of manufactures was approximately three times the British; the value of goods exported had nearly trebled in a single decade. Moreover, the export of wheat was then reaching its climax with a yield per acre which was no more than half that obtained in Britain, Germany, or Holland. Although land-grant colleges, pledged to promote 'agriculture and the mechanic arts', date from 1862 and the Massachusetts Institute of Technology from 1865, the scientific approach to problems of agricultural and industrial exploitation was only just beginning: yet America had already seized the lead by developing techniques which helped her to exploit prodigal natural resources with the minimum of human labour.

Throughout the world the period 1873–96 had been one of decline in prices, which meant that, in countries like Britain, where there was in any case relatively little opportunity for new large-scale development, the period was mainly one of trade depression. The situation was, of course, made worse by the agricultural collapse already referred to. Investment stagnated, and there were attempts to find remedy or amelioration in financial changes (such as American bimetallism) and the organization of trusts and cartels, of which the Nobel dynamite trust of 1886 and the Coates sewing-cotton monopoly are early British examples. But the fall in prices outstripped the fall in wages, while the increased regard shown by the state for the welfare of the worker—for example, in the insurance schemes in Bismarckian Germany and in the long-overdue reforms of local government in Britain—also meant some improvements in health and amenities. Any prolonged spell of unemployment still wrought havoc with the worker's standard of living, and it is estimated that in Britain there were still about as many very poorly paid persons as there had been in the 1840's: but since the total population had doubled in the meantime, the proportion of very poor had in fact been halved.

The average of real wages in Britain is believed to have risen by 100 per cent. in the second half of the nineteenth century: if this estimate is even approximately correct, the technological disappointments of the later years pale into insignificance by comparison with the magnitude of the Victorian achievement. Britain had pioneered the technology and organized the accompanying social changes, which for the first time in human experience made the rank and file of men to some extent the masters rather than the slaves of their physical environment, so that at Queen Victoria's death

37 million persons were living, most of them with some degree of comfort and leisure, on a small and not particularly fertile island. Others might better her example. In America, with its huge natural resources, the standard of life was already rather higher than in Britain; in most parts of the European continent lower, but not so far below as it had been in 1870. The various technologies, of which we are now to trace the separate histories, still offered great prizes to individuals and nations through the more efficient exploitation of nature made possible by the experience—including the mistakes—of a century and a half of rapid change.

11

THE STEAM-ENGINE

INTRODUCTION

As we saw in Chapter 8, the industrial revolution was well under way before the steam-engine came into general use for driving machinery. Only two prime-movers—the water-wheel and the windmill—were widely available, and with very few exceptions these yielded no more than 10 h.p. and often less. The biggest water-wheel installation ever constructed was the 'Machine of Marly', built for Louis XIV in 1682 to supply the fountains at Versailles (p. 41). At its best it probably generated as much as 75 h.p., but its performance fell rapidly through neglect. In the late eighteenth and in the nineteenth century the efficiency of the water-wheel was considerably improved by theoretical and practical studies made by John Smeaton, investigations which earned him the Copley Medal of the Royal Society, its highest award. He showed that the overshot wheel was theoretically capable of a much higher efficiency (63 per cent.) than the undershot (22 per cent.), and he defined the operating conditions most favourable for achieving good results. Smeaton did not test, although he often made, breast-wheels—in which the water strikes the wheel roughly half-way up—but he showed that the same principle must apply to them as to undershot and overshot wheels.

Smeaton himself designed many water-wheels, none of which now survive because wood was the main constructional material used, but a tide-mill constructed in 1776 at the confluence of the Lea and the Thames was still at work after 160 years. One of Smeaton's undershot wheels, which was installed in an arch of London Bridge in 1768, was 32 ft in diameter, 15 ft wide, and had 24 floats; in 1817 it was replaced by an iron wheel, an example of the general change towards iron for constructional purposes in the nineteenth century. Smeaton himself experimented with the use of iron for certain parts of water-wheels, including the shaft and later the rim, and in this was assisted by the circumstance that he was consulting engineer to the Carron Company's ironworks near Falkirk. Among the numerous

engineers influenced by his work was Joseph Glynn, who constructed many large water-wheels in Britain in the nineteenth century.

Up to 1800 there were no steam-engines developing more than
about 50 h.p., and although the high-pressure engines built in the
following decade by Trevithick in Britain and by Evans in the
United States generated up to 100 h.p., as late as 1835 the average
power of steam-engines in Britain was only about 15 h.p. A giant
of 2,500 h.p. was exhibited in America in 1876; by the end of the
century, however, 10,000-h.p. engines were in use for the new electric
power-stations (p. 616). The growth of industrial use of steam-
power is reflected in the consumption of coal. Indeed, coal and steam
were intimately related, for one of the most important early uses for
the steam-engine was to pump water from mines, while later, the hauling of coal was one of the main tasks of the steam-locomotive. In
1700, two years before Savery's 'Miner's Friend' was first advertised
for sale, some 3 million tons of coal was mined in Britain annually.
By 1800 output had risen to about 10 million tons, but by 1850 it was
60 million tons, the increase being mainly due to the demands of
steam-engines. Thus, although the water-wheel and windmill remained important well into the nineteenth century, that century
can fairly be described as the Age of Steam. As early as 1824 the
French pioneer in thermodynamics, Sadi Carnot, summarized the
position in Britain in the following words: 'To rob Britain of her
steam-engines would be to rob her of her coal and iron, to deprive
her of her sources of wealth, to ruin her prosperity, to annihilate that
colossal power.' Even more striking were the words which Hus-
kisson uttered the same year: 'If the steam-engine be the most
powerful instrument in the hands of man to alter the face of the
physical world, it operates at the same time as a powerful moral lever
in forwarding the great cause of civilization.'

PIONEERS OF THE STEAM-ENGINE

The early history of the steam-engine requires some preliminary
discussion of the principles on which it is based, and, in particular,
of the development of ideas concerning the pressure of the atmosphere.

Until as late as the eighteenth century, ideas about the nature of
gases were far from clear, even among natural philosophers, and they
were looked upon as mysterious, intangible substances. Greek philosophers as early as the sixth century B.C. had postulated Air as being
one of four 'elements' of which they supposed all material bodies to

be composed, the others being Fire, Earth, and Water. Fire, according
to Anaximenes, was a rarefied form of Air, and when condensed
formed first Water, and then Earth. Such Air was not, however,
necessarily the same as the air of which the atmosphere is formed,
but rather an idealized philosophical conception of it. The corporeal
nature of ordinary air must surely have been understood even by
primitive people, however, for they could witness its destructive
force in gales, and sailors had visible evidence of it when the wind
literally filled the sails of their ships. Anaxagoras and Empedocles
gave more direct experimental evidence of this by showing that
water can enter a vessel only when air escapes from it, and demonstrated that air is distinct from both a vacuum and a vapour, such as
steam, the latter being readily condensed to re-form the liquid from
which it is derived. Heron of Alexandria's 'Sphere of Aeolus', in
which a jet of steam impinging upon a wheel made it rotate, gave
further practical demonstration of the tangible effects that could be
produced by vapour.

But even in the seventeenth century A.D. ideas about the physical
nature of the atmosphere were qualitative rather than quantitative.
That water or other liquids rush into a vacuous space was attributed
to the fact that 'nature abhors a vacuum'. Although mining engineers were aware that a suction-pump could not draw water above
about 30 ft, there was no explanation of why there should be this
limit; it was, indeed, the urgent problem of mine-drainage that
finally led to an understanding of the true nature of atmospheric
pressure, and this, in turn, inspired the earliest steam-engines.

When the engineers of Cosimo de' Medici II failed in an attempt
—foredoomed to failure—to build a suction-pump capable of lifting
water from a depth of 50 ft, the problem was referred to Galileo,
and finally solved by his brilliant pupil, Torricelli. In 1644 Torricelli
announced that the pressure of the atmosphere was equal to that of
a column of mercury about 30 inches in height: this corresponds to a
column of water rather over 30 ft in height. He predicted that the
pressure of the atmosphere would fall with increasing altitude, a
truth which was confirmed experimentally in 1647: when a baro-
meter was carried to the top of a 4,800-ft mountain in the Auvergne,
the height of the mercury in it fell by 3 in. during the ascent. In 1654
von Guericke, in the famous experiment at Magdeburg, gave a
spectacular demonstration of the immense force that the atmosphere
could exert (Fig. 140). He showed that when two close-fitting

hemispheres, about 20 inches in diameter, were placed together to form a sphere and the space within was evacuated, two teams of eight powerful horses could not pull them apart. In fact, as the atmosphere exerts a pressure of about 14 lb a sq. in. we know that a force of several tons would have been required. In another experiment, more immediately related to the history of the steam-engine, he showed that, when a partial vacuum was created below a large piston working in a cylinder, the combined force of fifty men could not prevent atmospheric pressure driving the piston into the cylinder.

FIG. 140. Von Guericke's demonstration to show that sixteen horses could not pull apart the two halves of an evacuated sphere, 1654

Such experiments suggested that if some simple means could be found of repeatedly creating a vacuum, atmospheric pressure could be used as a useful source of power. First thoughts on the subject were, however, by no means all directed to steam as a means of creating the vacuum. Although this was later recognized as the most practical solution, the first steam-engines were often quite properly called atmospheric engines, for it was the pressure of the atmosphere that provided the driving force. Some early inventors turned their attention to the possibility of using gunpowder. In 1680 Huygens, the versatile Dutch scientist, suggested an engine in which gunpowder was exploded in a cylinder closed by a piston. When the gunpowder was fired, most of the hot gases into which it was converted, together with some of the air originally present, which expanded on heating, were to be expelled through relief valves. On cooling, the valves would close, and a partial vacuum would be created within the cylinder; when cold, the gas would occupy a much smaller volume than when hot, and in consequence the pressure of the atmosphere would drive the piston into the cylinder. Such an arrangement had two fundamental disadvantages, however. The first was that the residue of gas within the cylinder would be considerable, so that only a partial vacuum could be achieved; the second was that recharging with gunpowder, essential for continuous action, would be both difficult and dangerous. For these reasons Huygens's assistant, Denis Papin, turned his attention to steam. In 1690 he put forward this idea in the following historic words, which are an admirable description of the mode of action of the earliest steam-engines:

Since it is a property of water that a small quantity of it turned into vapour by heat has an elastic force like that of air, but upon cold supervening is again resolved into water, so that no trace of the said elastic force remains, I concluded that machines could be constructed wherein water, by the help of no very intense heat, and at little cost, could produce that perfect vacuum which could by no means be obtained by gunpowder.

Although the quantitative relationship was not known to Papin, one volume of water in fact yields 1,300 volumes of steam at its boiling-point, so that a very high vacuum could potentially be achieved by completely converting the steam back into water by condensation.

Papin put his ideas into practical effect in an engine that consisted of a vertical tube about $2\frac{1}{2}$ inches in diameter, closed at the lower end, and fitted with a piston and rod (Fig. 141). A little water was put into the bottom of the tube, the piston was inserted, and the water was boiled by heating the lower part of the tube. The steam generated raised the piston, which at the top of its stroke was held by a catch. The apparatus was then allowed to cool, so that the steam condensed to form water again, creating a vacuum beneath the piston; when the catch was released, the piston was driven back into the cylinder by the pressure of the atmosphere. This device was of no practical importance, but it established the vitally important principle that steam could be used to move a piston up and down in a cylinder. This principle was soon turned to practical account by Savery, Newcomen, and Smeaton, whose work we must now consider.

Of Thomas Savery, who made the first useful steam-engine, we know disappointingly little—it is even uncertain whether his title of 'Captain' denotes the military engineer, a status acquired in the Cornish tin-mines, or a career at sea. He certainly had some influence at court, was a prolific inventor, and wrote a number of pamphlets, including one with the significant title, *The Miner's Friend*, descriptive of his 'engine to raise water by fire': hence the use of the name 'fire-engine'. His machine (Fig. 142) was demonstrated to William III at Hampton Court in the summer of 1698, in which year he took out his master patent, and to the Royal Society a year later. It was energetically advertised from his workshop in Salisbury Court, off Fleet Street, and was used in the first few years of the eighteenth century to pump water for large buildings and water-wheels. Its maximum lift, however, was inadequate for the needs of mine drainage.

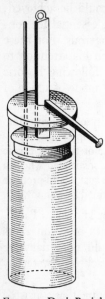

FIG. 141. Denis Papin's atmospheric steam-engine, 1690

In Savery's steam-pump, steam from a boiler resembling an old-fashioned kitchen copper was conducted through a pipe, fitted with a valve, into an oval vessel full of water, expelling the water upwards through a second pipe. When the oval vessel was full of steam, the steam was condensed by pouring cold water on the outside. This created a partial vacuum, so that when the vessel was connected, through another pipe, with water at a lower level, atmospheric pressure forced this water upwards into the oval vessel. There were two vessels, filled and emptied alternately, the whole cycle of operations being controlled by suitably located valves.

In an attempt to increase the height to which his engine would pump water, Savery used high-pressure steam, but this presented constructional problems which could not at that time be satisfactorily solved. Nearly a century was to pass before high-pressure steam-engines came into common use. To understand the working of high-pressure engines something more must be said of the relationship between steam and water. When water is heated, the pressure of its vapour rises and it boils when the vapour pressure equals the external pressure: in a vessel open to the atmosphere at sea-level boiling takes place at 100° C. If the pressure above the water is reduced it will boil at a lower temperature: a practical consequence of this is that an egg cannot satisfactorily be boiled at high altitudes, since the water does not get hot enough to coagulate the white. Conversely, if the pressure above the water is increased, for example by restricting the escape of the vapour by means of a loaded valve, boiling takes place at a higher temperature. This is the principle of the familiar pressure-cooker, invented by Papin; the same principle is used in the sterilization of surgical instruments, where a controlled temperature rather above 100° C. is required. Great pressure can be generated by superheating water in this way. Thus at 200° C. the pressure of steam is fifteen times greater than at 100° C. Steam generated at 100° C. has, as we have noted, a pressure equal to that of atmosphere at sea-level and therefore can raise water to a maximum height of only 30 ft. Generated at 200° C., however, it could potentially raise water to a height fifteen times greater, that is to 450 ft. It was for this

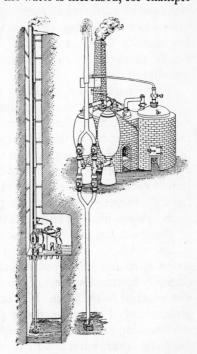

FIG. 142. Savery's 'Miner's Friend', 1699

reason that Savery tried to use steam at about 8 to 10 atmospheres pressure in his engine, this giving a potential lift of about 300 ft.

It would be tempting to suppose that Thomas Newcomen, ironmonger and smith of Dartford, a contemporary of Savery and a fellow Devonian, based his engine, which was at work in 1712, upon the work which Savery had done a decade or so before. The available evidence, however, indicates that Newcomen made his invention quite independently of Savery, and that the reason why he eventually entered into an association with him was because Savery's patent was drawn in such wide terms as to block the way to the use of almost any new invention in this field. Newcomen in fact adopted the cylinder and piston proposed by Papin, of whose work he may possibly have had knowledge, whereas this feature was absent from the 'Miner's Friend'. Unlike Savery, Newcomen did not attempt to make use of high-pressure steam, and his employment of atmospheric pressure made his engine far easier to construct. Newcomen's success may be attributed to many factors, among them his direct experience of the drainage problem in Cornish tin-mines; the skill of his assistant Calley, a plumber; and his constructional methods which, although very clumsy, were well within the limits of craftsmanship of his time.

Newcomen's boiler produced steam at atmospheric pressure. When this was introduced to the bottom of the cylinder, it was mainly the weight of the pump-rod, hanging from the other end of the beam, that caused the piston to rise. When the cylinder was full of steam and closed by a valve at the bottom, a jet of cold water to condense the steam was introduced into the cylinder through an injection-cock—a device that J. T. Desaguliers had used to improve Savery's engine—with the result that the piston was forced down again by atmospheric pressure. As the piston-rod drew down one end of the beam, the other end rose, carrying with it the pump-rod, which sucked up water. To maintain the cycle of operations, the steam-valve and the injection-cock were opened and closed automatically by the movement of the rod of the injection-pump, which was attached to the beam. It is evidence alike of Newcomen's ingenuity and of the impossibility at this date of securing accurate workmanship for machinery of such size, that his method of sealing the piston was to cover it with a flexible leather disk which was kept airtight by covering it with a layer of water.

Such was the engine which Newcomen, in association with Savery, erected for the colliery at Dudley Castle, Worcestershire, in 1712 (Fig. 143). The beam made twelve strokes a minute, in each of which it lifted 10 gallons of water 153 ft through tiers of pumps, which is equivalent to about 5½ h.p., as compared with the 1 h.p. of the original 'Miner's Friend'. Efficiency was limited, however, by the fact that in the early eighteenth century it was not possible to bore accurate cylinders, such as were needed for the barrels of cannon and pumps, greater than 7 inches in diameter. Newcomen engines required much larger dimensions than this: thus the cylinder of an engine erected at Edmonston, Midlothian, in 1725 had a diameter of 29 in. and a stroke of 9 ft, and one in use at Newcastle in 1765 had a diameter of 74 in. and a length of 126 in. Nevertheless, the invention

spread to eight countries in the first four years, and before the death
of its inventor in 1729 it was in use in Hungary, France, Belgium,
Germany, Austria, and Sweden. In a further quarter-century it
had reached even to the American colonies, the first being sent out
with spare parts in duplicate, and some even in triplicate, to serve in

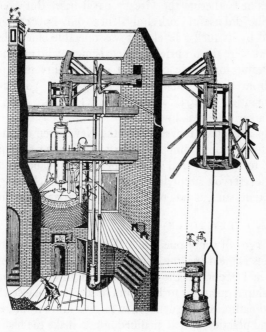

FIG. 143. Newcomen's steam-engine at Dudley Castle, 1712

a copper-mine at Newark, New Jersey. Its main impact, however,
was in Britain, where at least two a year are known to have been
built for two-thirds of a century. It met the pressing needs of Newcomen's neighbours in the Cornish tin industry; revived the fortunes
of the deep coal-mines in the north of England, which had been
seriously impaired by flooding; pumped water-supplies for towns;
and fed water-wheels in the flat areas of the industrial Midlands.

In 1767 Smeaton began a scientific study of the 'duty' of a steam-
engine, calculated in terms of the quantity of water which it could
raise 1 ft for each bushel of coal burned. This made it possible to
compare the efficiency of one engine with another and to measure the
effects of modifications. He found that the average duty was then

about 6 million ft-lb, and with the help of a special cylinder-boring mill, built at the Carron ironworks, he proceeded to devise a number of far more efficient engines with very large cylinders. By 1774 he had succeeded in doubling the duty, and one of his large engines was sent as far afield as Kronstadt in Russia, where it served to empty the docks at Catherine the Great's naval base. But even then the 'fire-engine' did useful work equivalent to only 1 per cent. of the heat generated by its fuel, a level that was tolerable chiefly because the main users were the proprietors of coal-mines who ran their engines on unsaleable low-grade coal. But its reliability may perhaps be judged from the last survivor, at Parkgate in Yorkshire, which was dismantled in 1934 after running for more than a century without a serious breakdown.

The up-and-down movement of the Newcomen engine was very suitable for working pumps. If rotary movement was required—for example, to hoist material from mines—it could be used to pump water to a reservoir supplying a water-wheel. The latter gave a uniform motion, such as was required for cotton-spinning machinery.

WATT AND TREVITHICK

At the age of twenty-one James Watt brought the craft of mathematical instrument-making, which he had left his native Greenock to learn in London, to the service of Glasgow University, for apprenticeship regulations forbade him to set up shop elsewhere in the city. The natural consequence was to give him an interest in both theory and practice, which qualified him to make the historic transition from the atmospheric engine to the steam-engine. The unsatisfactory performance of a model Newcomen engine, which the university had previously sent without any success to a London instrument-maker for repair, gave Watt his starting-point. He quickly realized that the main reason for the unsatisfactory running of the engine was the cooling of the cylinder, in order to condense the steam, between each stroke: if the cylinder could be kept hot continuously, a great improvement could be expected. Despite this, months of pondering preceded his historic Sunday walk on Glasgow Green, when the idea came to him, as he told in later life, 'that, as steam was an elastic body, it would rush into a vacuum, and if a communication was made between the Cylinder and the exhausted vessel, it would rush into it and might be there condensed, without cooling the Cylinder'.

It was in May 1765 that Watt formulated the idea of a separate condenser, and the patent for this 'new Method of Lessening the Consumption of Steam and Fuel in Fire Engines' dates from January 1769. Yet it was not until 1776—the year of the American Declaration of Independence and of the publication of Adam Smith's *Wealth of Nations*—that Watt's first two engines were actually set to work. An engine built in the following year is shown in Fig. 144. The

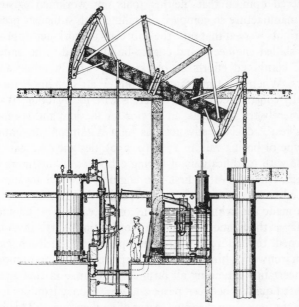

FIG. 144. Early Boulton & Watt pumping engine; built in 1777, this engine is known to have worked for over 125 years

length of the delay does not indicate the absence of demand. Most of the Newcomen engines then in use were as inefficient as their proto-type had been two generations earlier: the Cornish tin-mines would not have been able to afford them at all but for the remission of a duty on coal. Moreover, the rapidly expanding iron industry was only one of many in which late eighteenth-century conditions were obviously favourable to the introduction of a new prime-mover if a suitable one could be found. But Watt had to contend with enormous difficulties as regards the supply of skilled labour, the material and tools to execute his designs, and the financial support necessary to make his invention a commercial success.

On the constructional side the greatest difficulty, already alluded to, was in boring a really accurate cylinder, so that there would be no escape of steam between its walls and the piston. Newcomen's device of sealing the piston with cold water did not suit Watt's purpose, which was to keep the cylinder as hot as possible. The extent of the constructional difficulty is indicated by the fact that Smeaton, as experienced and progressive as any engineer of his day, gave his considered opinion that 'neither tools nor workmen existed that could manufacture so complex a machine with sufficient precision'. Millwrights were at that time the only class of workmen approximating to skilled engineers, and engine-building had to be undertaken by the combined efforts of blacksmiths, wheelwrights, and carpenters. When the time came to build Watt's engines, they were normally constructed of local materials with local labour; Watt supplied merely the drawings, an erector for the job, and special parts like valves. A decisive advance was John Wilkinson's invention of a new type of boring-mill in 1774 (p. 350), designed for cannon but capable with modifications of boring cylinders to fine limits for any purpose. One of Watt's first two engines, referred to above, was designed to supply air to one of Wilkinson's blast-furnaces; he in return made the cylinders for many of the early Watt engines.

So far as the financial problems of exploiting Watt's invention are concerned, the failure of Watt's first partner, John Roebuck of the Carron ironworks, himself a very enterprising inventor, reminds us of the uncertainty attending all business enterprise in that age which fluctuated quickly between peace and war. Money troubles led Watt to take up for a time the safer career of civil engineer. This brought him to London, where friends gave him an introduction to Matthew Boulton, a leading manufacturer with works at Soho, near Birmingham. The classic partnership of Boulton and Watt which followed, bringing the skill and prestige of the Soho works to the service of the new invention, perhaps gained by the delay. When Watt brought his experimental engine to Birmingham in 1774, his patent had only eight more years to run, which Boulton realized was too short for profitable manufacture. Accordingly, Watt petitioned Parliament for an extension, which was granted in 1775; this gave him protection until 1800, so the immensely important partnership of Boulton and Watt spanned the last quarter of the eighteenth century.

The firm constructed 496 engines in all, of which 164 supplemented the work of the Newcomen engines as pumps, 24 served blast-furnaces, and the remaining 308 functioned directly as prime-movers for machinery, although it was not until 1795 that Lancashire with its factories began to take a larger share of the output than Staffordshire. This last application involved designing a device to obtain uniform rotary motion; this will be described later.

The separate condenser was the most important novel feature of Watt's engine, but as he introduced various other improvements it will be most satisfactory to describe here the machine in its more fully developed form, as used from about 1788. First and foremost, the cylinder was steam-jacketed to keep it hot, and there was a separate condenser, evacuated by an air-pump. As the piston reached the top of its stroke, the exhaust-valve opened and simultaneously steam was admitted through an inlet valve into the space above the piston; steam pressure and atmospheric pressure combined then drove the piston downwards. At the bottom of the stroke, both inlet- and exhaust-valves closed and an equilibrium valve opened; this equalized the pressure on the two sides of the piston, which was then pulled up again to the top of its stroke by the weight of the pump-rod.

The device of making the engine double-acting, and thus roughly twice as powerful, by admitting steam alternately to each side of the piston, led Watt in 1782 to the invention of what he regarded as his most elegant device, the 'parallel motion' mechanism. The problem to be solved was that of transferring the thrust of the piston-rod, on its upward stroke, to the end of the beam: for this purpose the chain, which dragged the beam down in the single-acting engine, was useless, since a rigid connexion was essential, while direct connexion was impossible because whereas the piston-rod travelled in a straight line the end of the beam described an arc. The parallel motion device, used for more than a century, entirely overcame this difficulty. Watt's second major improvement was to use the steam expansively, cutting off the supply early in the stroke and leaving the rest of the work to be done by its expansion.

These and other improvements, such as a governor to regulate the inflow of steam and so keep the engine running at a steady speed, trebled the duty of pumping-engines compared with those of Smeaton. But it was as a rotative engine that Watt's invention slowly conquered the field of industry in general. Debarred from using a crank by a patent taken out by a rival, Watt developed the sun-and-planet gear, so called because the planet-wheel, which was rigidly attached to the connecting rod, moved round the perimeter of the sun-wheel, which was keyed to the shaft. A 10-h.p. engine of this type was built by Boulton & Watt for varying uses from 1784 onwards.

One of the great advantages of the beam-engine was that its construction and assembly presented little difficulty. There were very few plane surfaces, which until the invention of the planing machine in 1820 had to be laboriously worked by hand, and the engine would function satisfactorily even if there were considerable misalignment in assembly. Compared with these, the disadvantages of its size and clumsiness were then relatively unimportant.

FIG. 145. Trevithick's high-pressure engine, 1803

Nevertheless, the expiry of Watt's condenser patent in 1800, when he retired from business, opened the way to development by others, especially through the use of high-pressure steam, which Watt had considered both too dangerous and too difficult, although Jacob Leupold of Leipzig had published a description of a high-pressure engine as early as 1725. It is significant that a Delaware wheelwright, Oliver Evans, introduced the idea in the New World—where even as late as 1803 there were no more than half a dozen steam-engines—simultaneously with the better-known English experiments. By 1804 Evans was grinding plaster of Paris and sawing marble at Philadelphia with a very small engine—the stroke was only 8 in.—that worked at a steam-pressure of 50 lb a sq. in. Two years earlier the Cornish mine-engineer Richard Trevithick had had built at Coalbrookdale a pumping-engine of small size but great power, with a cast-iron boiler 1½-in. thick, developing a steam pressure of 145 lb a sq. in., i.e. ten times the pressure of the atmosphere (Fig. 145). A remarkable feature of this was that in spite of its power the cylinder was only 7 inches in diameter with a stroke of 3 ft. In 1800 he had built a double-acting high-pressure engine for winding duties in Cornwall, and he had also built a steam road-carriage that would carry several people.

A Trevithick high-pressure stationary engine of 1802 is seen in Fig. 146. In 1804 he built the first successful railway locomotive, which will be described later. His interest in steam locomotion did not, however, interfere with his development of stationary engines, of which he had built nearly fifty by 1804. Very soon his 'Cornish' engine had no rival and it continued in use until the end of the century, not only for pumping but for a variety of industrial purposes, including iron-rolling, corn-grinding, and sugar-milling. An important factor in its development was that, from 1811 onwards, the Cornish mine-owners published regular reports of the performances of their engines, to promote efficiency. By 1844 the average duty was 68 million ft-lb a bushel of coal, compared with 6 million ft-lb for a Newcomen engine in 1767.

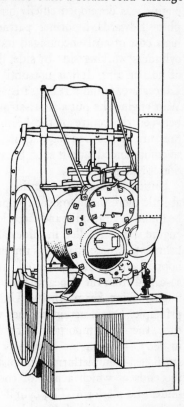

Fig. 146. Trevithick's high-pressure direct-acting engine, patented 1802

Another line of development was the 'compounding' of engines—though this term for the addition of a high-pressure cylinder to the original Watt engine was not used until well into the nineteenth century. A compound engine of only 11·5 h.p., which Jonathan Hornblower built at a Radstock colliery in 1780, was declared an infringement of Watt's patent. After its expiry a more ambitious attempt was made in 1803 by Arthur Woolf, working for a London brewery, but owing to a miscalculation his first high-pressure cylinder proved to be too small in proportion to the low-pressure cylinder. He was more successful when he returned to Cornwall, where he had had previous experience, though his compound engine was too expensive there and he made none after 1824. This type of engine was developed chiefly on the Continent—notably by Humphrey Edwards, a former partner of Woolf—where the relatively high cost of coal encouraged its use: on a beam-engine with two cylinders working side by side, the saving in fuel was of the order of 50 per cent. It was not until 1845 that McNaught, of Bury in Lancashire, found a really satisfactory method of compounding the Watt engine: he put a short-stroke high-pressure cylinder half-way between the centre of the beam and the connecting-rod, using a pressure of 120–150 lb. a sq. in. Many existing Watt engines were so compounded, and it soon became the standard form of construction for new engines.

Until McNaught's invention, Watt's beam-engine, using steam at little more than atmospheric pressure, was the one most likely to be found in large mills and factories, while the high-pressure Cornish engine was unrivalled in mines and water-works. In smaller establishments, where space was important, resort was had to the 'grasshopper' engine, first patented in 1803 by William Freemantle and so-called from the appearance of the link used in it to eliminate the huge rocking beam. In the United States, Evans used the same principle. Direct-action engines were developed at about the same time, the most important being Maudslay's table engine, patented in 1807. This was an extremely compact machine, mounted on a small cast-iron platform. The piston-rod carried a cross-head, from the ends of which a pair of connecting-rods drove a crank-shaft under the platform. The cylinder, however, was placed vertically, in the mistaken belief that this would prevent uneven wear from the weight of the piston: the more convenient horizontal engine did not come into general use before 1825, when it was introduced by Taylor and Martineau in London.

THE STEAM-ENGINE APPLIED TO TRANSPORT

In the opening years of the nineteenth century the growth in the use of the stationary steam-engine, which was steady rather than spectacular, was accompanied by the first successful applications of steam-power to the development of modern forms of transportation. Mankind's first great step in the conquest of distance since the development of the sail required a new prime-mover that would be self-contained, reliable, and powerful—in a word, the steam-engine.

The bulk and weight of early steam-engines led to the first application of steam to transport being made in ships, though even here practical difficulties taxed the ingenuity of designers. In stationary engines used for pumping and similar applications the disadvantages of great size, weight, and heavy fuel consumption were more than counterbalanced by ease and cheapness of construction, erection, and maintenance. In ships, however, the disadvantages were far more serious. To transport an enormous deadweight of machinery and fuel was clearly uneconomic. Moreover, not only the total weight but the distribution had to be considered, because in ships a low centre of gravity is necessary for stability: the massive beam of early steam-engines was placed high up, so a modification of design was required that placed the beam lower. The question of fuel supply was relatively unimportant as long as steamships were thought of only in connexion with rivers, lakes, canals, and coastal trips, because frequent refuelling presented no great problem. The situation radically changed, however, when ocean-going ships began to be considered: the unhappy history of the *Great Eastern* is a reminder that half-way through the nineteenth century the problems of fuel supply had not been satisfactorily solved, for the failure of this remarkable ship was due primarily to a serious underestimate of her coal consumption. For naval vessels the problem was even greater, because from the nature of their duties they had to be ready to go at short notice into regions where coaling facilities were limited or non-existent.

Such considerations had a powerful influence on the design of marine steam-engines. The need was for more compact, more efficient, and more reliable engines: smaller engine-rooms and bunkers meant more capacity for cargo and passengers. Boiler design came in for close scrutiny, for wasteful use of fuel was as serious as inefficient use of steam.

The pioneers of steamships were the French, who tried an engine with an 8-in. cylinder in a boat on the Seine in 1775, but the power was insufficient. In 1783 the Marquis Jouffroy d'Abbans, after several earlier attempts, successfully ascended a reach of the river Saône near Lyons in a 182-ton paddle-wheel steamer, the *Pyroscaphe*. In 1787 one of several American experiments in steam propulsion employed a pump to draw in water at the bows of a boat and to drive it out at the stern, an early example of jet-propulsion. In the next year, in Britain, an atmospheric steam-engine, constructed by William Symington, was used to propel a small boat on a lake near Dumfries; by chance, the party on board for a trip that proved to be of some significance in Scottish national history included the poet Burns. In 1801 Symington, at the instance of the Secretary of State for War— an interesting hint of the direction in which thoughts about steam-propulsion were then turning—constructed an engine that had a horizontal double-acting cylinder 22 inches in diameter, with a connecting-rod that drove the crankshaft of the paddle-wheel. Its use in the tug-boat *Charlotte Dundas* on the Forth and Clyde canal was

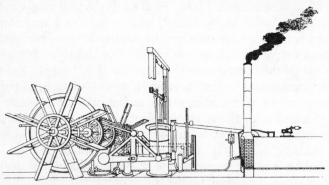

FIG. 147. Machinery of the p.s. *Clermont*, 1807

not followed up, despite successful trials, for fear of damage to the banks by excessive wash; but it is remarkable that the direct-action method, dispensing with the use of the cumbersome beam, was not adopted by Symington's immediate successors.

The American Robert Fulton, who had seen the trials of the *Charlotte Dundas*, conducted further experiments on the Seine, and in 1807 achieved the first commercial success with a Boulton & Watt engine, which drove the paddle-steamer *Clermont* (Fig. 147) between New York and Albany; within two years it had a successor on Lake Champlain. The low-pressure engine built in Glasgow for the *Comet* (Fig. 148), the first commercially successful steamboat in Europe, which came into service on the Clyde in 1812, resembled Fulton's engine in having a pair of beams placed low down on either side of the vertical cylinder.

The conventional engine with a massive overhead beam proved suitable for shallow-draught river-steamers, which were soon much in vogue in America, because from the nature of that design the bulk of the weight had to be above the water-level. But when paddle-steamers began to be developed for the ocean routes, British practice favoured side-lever engines, in which the two beams were brought low down near the foundation plates, so as to lower the centre of gravity and improve stability. In the early 1830's the so-called 'steeple' engine was introduced, in which the guides for the cross-head on the connecting-rod towered above the decks: hence the name. The object of this device was again to overcome problems resulting from the limited vertical distance between the paddle shaft and the bottom of the vessel. After direct-acting vertical engines were introduced in 1837, the necessary length for the connecting-rods was obtained by various devices, including the elimination of the piston-rod altogether by attaching the connecting-rods direct to the upper face of the piston. Alternatively, the connecting-rod might be eliminated: this was done in the oscillating engine, which

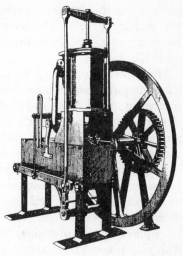

Fig. 148. Engine of p.s. *Comet*, 1812

eventually became the most popular form for paddle-steamers, the piston-rod being connected directly to the crank. This device was used in 1822 in the first iron paddle-steamer, the *Aaron Manby*, built in England to ply on the Seine. Huge oscillating engines were constructed in 1858 for the paddle- and screw-steamer *Great Eastern*, whose four 74-in. cylinders drove both a screw and paddle-wheels of 56 ft diameter.

The steamship underwent a decisive change with the substitution of screws for paddles. Since the Archimedean screw was a water-moving device of classical antiquity, it is at first sight surprising that forty years of experiment—which included trials by John Fitch in New York in 1796—preceded the construction in Britain of the first successful screw-steamer, the *Archimedes* of 237 tons, in 1838. The invention was made simultaneously by (Sir) Francis Pettit Smith and

the Swede, John Ericsson, who terminated his thirteen-year residence in Britain to sell the idea in the United States. A relatively
high speed of rotation was necessary for the new method of propulsion, so that in the first screw-steamers the drive to the propeller shaft had to be geared. Fears that the ordinary piston-engine
could not achieve a sufficient speed to be coupled direct to the propeller proved ultimately to be unfounded, and various engines were
designed for this purpose. In 1842 the United States Navy introduced, in the *Princeton*, a special screw-engine designed to keep
the machinery below the water-line for protection, and in the
following year the *Great Britain* was the first screw-steamer to
cross the Atlantic.

Horizontal direct-acting engines were widely used, though the
connecting-rods had to be inconveniently short because of the limited
transverse space in the ships of the day. In 1784 Watt had patented
a 'trunk-engine', in which the connecting-rod was linked direct to
the piston; although it had several inherent disadvantages, it was
used extensively in the middle of the nineteenth century because of
its important saving of transverse space. When the *Great Eastern*
began her first voyage in 1859, designers were already turning to the
use of an inverted vertical engine, which could be satisfactorily
accommodated even when the development of the twin-screw vessel required two sets of engines. When warships began to be equipped
with side armour, the inverted vertical engine became standard in
naval vessels.

Compound-expansion engines were first fitted to a sea-going vessel, the S.S. *Brandon*, in 1854. Triple-expansion engines came into
use in the 1870's, working at a steam pressure of 150 lb to a sq. in.,
while for the most economical use of fuel with pressures above
180 lb, quadruple-expansion engines were by 1900 deemed essential.

Changes in the design of steam-engines, and particularly the use
of higher pressures, resulted in corresponding changes in the boilers
that supplied them. The rate of progress is illustrated by the fact
that, whereas the *Comet* of 1812 had a simple boiler, set in brickwork,
generating steam at only a little above atmospheric pressure, by 1900
the Babcock & Wilcox water-tube boiler, standard in the Royal
Navy, provided steam at 250 lb a sq. in. The basic problems were
how to increase the efficiency of boilers and how to obtain sufficient
steam at increasingly high pressures to keep pace with the development of steam-engines. The water-tube boiler, a feature of Stephen-

son's *Rocket* locomotive of 1829 that was first adopted for marine engines in 1842, was a major step forward because it very greatly increased the surface area of the water exposed to the heat of the furnace. Corrosion difficulties experienced in the early days were much reduced when mild-steel tubes replaced iron ones. At sea, corrosion difficulties were particularly acute as long as sea-water was used to feed the boilers: frequent emptying and scraping were necessary to remove deposits of salt. Replacement of iron tubes by copper ones mitigated the difficulty, but there was no really satisfactory solution until 1834, when Samuel Hall introduced the surface-condenser that provided distilled water for boiler feed.

Throughout the period with which we are here concerned, coal was the principal fuel of steamships. But from the 1860's onwards the possibility of using oil was seriously explored, the incentive being the accumulation by the rapidly growing petroleum industry of large quantities of heavy oil, for which there was then little demand. Despite much experimentation, however, fuel-oil found only very limited application until after the turn of the century.

LOCOMOTIVES AND STATIONARY STEAM-ENGINES

The problem of accommodating steam-engines within the hulls of the relatively small ships of the early nineteenth century taxed the ingenuity of designers. To fit the steam-engine within the even narrower confines of road and railway locomotives was even more difficult. It is a measure of the inventiveness of engineers of the age that the basic problems were solved in Stephenson's *Rocket* (Fig. 149) as early as 1829.

FIG. 149. Stephenson's *Rocket*

In the first year of the nineteenth century, when Symington was designing his tug-boat, Trevithick made his first steam road-carriage: earlier experiments had been conducted by Nicolas Cugnot (Fig. 150) in France (1769) and by Murdock in Cornwall (1785). To keep the vertical cylinder hot, Trevithick partly enclosed it in the boiler; the drive was by connecting-rod from the piston-rod to the rear wheels. The engine included Trevithick's special device of sending the exhaust-steam up the chimney to increase the draught; if patented, this invention might have given him a hold upon locomotive development comparable to that which Watt achieved for the stationary engine through his condenser. His first steam-carriage satisfactorily carried its passengers, but was allowed to boil dry during the subsequent celebrations. In 1803 he ran a similar steam-carriage through the streets of London between Holborn and Paddington, but this attracted less public attention than the explosion of the boiler of one of his high-pressure stationary engines. Following this explosion Trevithick introduced a steam-gauge, and a safety-plug to the boiler.

It was Trevithick who effectively joined the steam-locomotive to the rail-way, demonstrating the suitability of their combination for

FIG. 150. Cugnot's steam-carriage, 1769

the conveyance not only of heavy goods but of passengers. The latter was a discovery of the utmost importance, for whereas steam transport by road never grew to any big dimensions, the development of the railway passenger service was one of the great formative factors in nineteenth-century history.

In 1804 Trevithick designed a locomotive to pull a load of 10 tons on a cast-iron tramway running for 9¾ miles between Penydarran ironworks and the Glamorganshire canal. This proved capable of pulling five vehicles and seventy men as well as the load specified, moving under one man's control at a speed of 5 m.p.h. This demonstration effectively controverted the argument that the friction between an iron wheel and an iron rail was insufficient to permit the use of steam traction on tramways, and in the following year a similar engine was built at Gateshead for a Tyneside colliery by one of Trevithick's mechanics. This was an event of more significance than the five-shilling trips by locomotive which he offered to the London public in 1808 on a circular track near Euston Square. For this was in the great northern industrial area where George Stephenson, who was aware of the importance of Boulton & Watt's inventions before he even learned to read, ran his 'travelling engine' *Blucher* for an identical purpose eleven months before Waterloo. The link with Napoleon is closer than might be supposed, since Stephenson and others owed their chance of experimenting with steam locomotives, in part at least, to the rising wartime cost of horse-fodder. The success of 1814 led, by way of *Locomotion No. 1* of 1825, to the decisive triumph of Stephenson's *Rocket*, which his son Robert helped to design, in October 1829. The steam-pressure of the *Rocket* was only 40 lb, but this famous locomotive set the pattern for the future with its tubular boiler and direct drive between piston and driving-wheels.

There were now twenty-six locomotives at work in Britain, including eighteen in collieries; two had been exported to France, and four to America. Despite the rapid establishment of railway systems in both America and Europe, locomotive design, to which we shall return later, continued for a long time to be primarily, though by no means exclusively, a British domain: Marc Seguin, for example, patented the multi-tubular boiler ahead of Stephenson, and another French engineer, Henri Giffard, was responsible for the first injectors. Before the latter invention, which very surprisingly was resisted by some conservative British designers, there was no means of introducing feed-water into the boiler if the engine remained stationary for any length of time, a great inconvenience. Few changes took place in the design of the frame or chassis: Gooch's 'colossal' locomotive of 1846 (Fig. 151) represents one of the largest of its day. At mid-century locomotive engineers all over the world were basing their work either on the plate-framed type, characteristic of British steam locomotives as long as they continued to be built, or on the bar-framed type, which was elaborated in the United States. Speeds of over 60 m.p.h. had then become commonplace.

By the 1860's British locomotive engine design was being affected by the substitution of coal for coke, the latter, though more expensive, being then used in order to comply with the legal requirement in Britain that railway engines 'must effectively consume their own smoke'. Complex fire-boxes were devised to achieve complete combustion of coal; these were very economical, and one of them proved able to drive a loaded express train, under far from favourable conditions, using only 23 lb of coal to the mile. Fire-box design varied greatly, however, according to the fuel: in many countries wood was commonly burnt and in Russia experiments were being made in burning oil.

British engine designs continued to be widely used on the Continent, and in some cases proved better suited to continental than to British permanent ways. English engineers were to be found in German and Austrian railway firms, but the Russian locomotive industry was started mainly by Americans. An exception to the general Anglo-American predominance at this period was that Belgium,

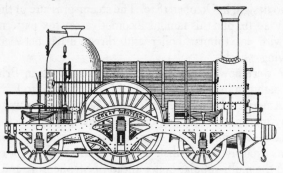

FIG. 151. Gooch's 'colossal' locomotive, built for the Great Western Railway, 1846

which had the earliest of the continental railway systems, produced the Walschaerts valve-gear, employed on British railways and many others today.

To economize fuel by using compound engines was an obvious goal for locomotive designers, for non-stop range was limited by the amount of fuel and water that could be carried and reduction in the ratio of weight to power was a constant aim. In the later years of the nineteenth century compounding was widely practised: in England the commonest type of improved engine was that designed by Francis Webb, having two high-pressure cylinders outside, which drove the trailing-axle, and a large low-pressure cylinder between the frames, which drove the middle axle (Fig. 152). A German locomotive of two-cylinder compound design was employed to some extent in England and worked well in countries, such as Germany itself, Sweden, and Ireland, where scheduled speeds were lower. But for a long time the main home of the compound locomotive was France, where A. G. de Glehn from the 1880's onwards devised immensely successful four-cylinder engines.

In the last half of the century, a major change in locomotives was a great increase in size—the first 6-coupled bogie express locomotives appeared in Italy in 1884. Coupled driving wheels, giving better grip on the rails, had been introduced to Britain in 1859, and the use of the modern long-based four-wheeled bogie with laterally sliding pivot likewise encouraged the building of bigger and more powerful locomotives, as did the Westinghouse brake (p. 385), first employed on American passenger trains in 1868. Nevertheless, there were no radical changes of design; the influence of earlier British models

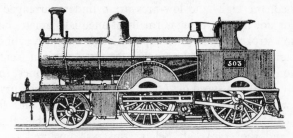

FIG. 152. Francis Webb's three-cylinder compound express engine, built for the London & North Western Railway, 1884

remained very evident on the continent of Europe, and in the enterprising America of the 1890's the New York Central locomotives were still recognizable descendants of those which had helped Sherman's advance from Chattanooga to Atlanta in the war of thirty years before.

LATER DEVELOPMENT OF THE STEAM-ENGINE

In the second half of the nineteenth century the steam-engine captured the civilized world. Between 1840 and 1880 the steam-power of the world rose from 2 to 28 million h.p. Every year it was applied in new countries, new industries, and new services—in the 1860's, for example, it transformed the fire-engine—while the network of communications, established by steamship and railway, at once extended and unified the civilized areas. But there were no fundamental changes—save for the introduction of the steam-turbine at the end of the century, to which we shall refer later—in the steam-engine as such: it was, however, much improved in detail. There were better designs, materials, and methods of manufacture, resulting in a better power/weight ratio and more economical use of fuel, while the development of the machine-tool industry (Ch. 12) also had a profound effect. Progress lay at least as much in the increased efficiency of the machinery to which the now supreme prime-mover was harnessed, as in the case of the substitution of screws for paddle-wheels in steamships.

One important trend from 1826 onwards was the increasing use of horizontal engines, with one double-acting cylinder held between cast-iron side-frames, and a governor automatically regulating expansion in accordance with load. An improved valve-gear was invented by G. H. Corliss in America. Compounding became widely established, the high- and low-pressure cylinders, arranged either tandem or side by side, being normally of unequal diameter but with a common stroke: a famous example, though one with cylinders of equal diameter, was built by Corliss for the American Centennial Exhibition at Philadelphia in 1876, where it drove machinery through a 30-ft flywheel at a speed of 360 r.p.m. Another mid-century innovation, which became standard practice for pumps and for the blowers of blast-furnaces, was a vertical engine with the cylinder at the top and the crankshaft below; this was invented by James Nasmyth, and resembled his famous steam-hammer.

In the last quarter of the century high-speed engines were needed increasingly to drive dynamos. One successful vertical type was devised in the United States by George Westinghouse, but the most important advance was made in England by P. W. Willans, whose main patents were taken out in 1884 and 1885. He developed a compound engine with the high-pressure cylinders on top, single-acting and very smooth-running, the steam being distributed by a novel system of vertical piston-valves, that worked up and down inside the hollow piston-rod, which had ports cut in it. They were built as single, double, or triple expansion engines. Willans was a pioneer in standardization, machining parts to within 0·001 in., and arranging that the high-pressure cylinder of one size of engine corresponded exactly to the low-pressure cylinder of another; pistons, rings, valves, and so on were also interchangeable. Many engines of this type were built for driving electric generators between 1890 and 1900, and by the end of the century the maximum power had risen to 2,400 h.p.

Double-acting vertical engines were, however, commoner, and after the development of forced lubrication in 1890 there was less fear of the consequences of their not running smoothly. The largest triple-expansion condensing-engines using superheated steam could develop up to 2,900 h.p. by 1900, but by then the steam-turbine was established and the decline of the large reciprocating steam-engine had begun.

STEAM-TURBINES

The coming of the quadruple-expansion engine (p. 330) completes the story of a century's development from the steam-engine as it was known to Watt and Trevithick. The prime-mover was still essentially the same at the end of the period as at its beginning, though incomparably more efficient. But in the development of the steam-turbine, nineteenth-century inventors provided the world with a new prime-mover springing from much earlier studies of the use of steam and based upon different principles.

Heron's 'Sphere of Aeolus' of the first century A.D. can be described as a sort of reaction turbine, since it made direct use of the pressure exerted by a jet of steam. In the seventeenth century, again, there was not only a fanciful scheme for a wind-turbine, which we have already mentioned (p. 247), but projects for a rolling-mill to be worked by hot air from a chimney, and for a stamp-mill to be driven by a jet of steam. In 1784 the Hungarian Baron Kempelen temporarily roused Watt to fear competition from his project for a steam-turbine, which was taken up more seriously by Trevithick thirty years later. Trevithick's 'whirling-engine' consisted essentially of a pair of hollow arms mounted on a shaft: steam at a pressure of 100 lb a sq. in. escaped at a tangent from a small hole at the end of each arm, causing them to whirl round. The weakness was that the rotational speed of 250 r.p.m., which was the maximum attainable, represented only about one-fifth of the power potentially available from the steam.

The modern steam-turbine was developed out of the water-turbine (which we shall briefly consider later in relation to the generation of electric power) by C. A. Parsons, youngest son of the Earl of Rosse and an engineer of exceptional skill and ingenuity. The immediate incentive was the urgent need for an engine to drive a dynamo directly, for which purpose a speed beyond the apparent range of the reciprocating steam-engine was desirable. He succeeded in getting high efficiency, combined with a satisfactory speed of revolution, by passing the steam through a series of small elemental turbines. In this way the total drop of pressure as the steam expanded was divided into a number of small stages, which theoretical considerations indicated to be necessary for efficient working. The outside of each turbine consisted of a fixed circular casing known as the stator, with rows of stationary blades on the inner surface; a shaft in the centre, the rotor, held a ring of similar blades. Steam flowing through the stator in a direction parallel with the shaft passed alternately between the two sets of blades, causing the shaft to rotate. The first patents were taken out in 1884, and in the same year the first turbo-generator ran at a speed of 18,000 r.p.m. Three years later Parsons made a compound reaction-turbine with high- and low-pressure stages, and in 1891 he built the first condensing turbine,

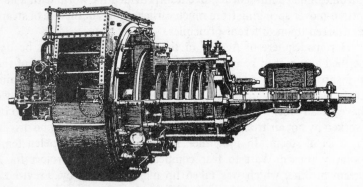

FIG. 153. Radial-flow turbine from the *Turbinia*, 1894

which proved to have a smaller steam consumption than a conventional steam-engine of equal capacity; it also had advantages in space-saving, reliability, and freedom from vibration. But meanwhile Parsons had suffered a serious setback through loss of control of his patents, so that he had to abandon the axial-flow type of turbine (that is, one where the direction of flow is parallel with the shaft) for a less efficient radial- or outward-flow turbine. In December 1893 he regained control of the patents, however, and in the last year of the century he made the first tandem-cylinder turbines—turbo-alternators generating 1,000 kw each—for the German town of Elberfeld.

Parsons crowned his achievement of providing a prime-mover suitable for the rapidly growing electrical industry by making the first successful application of the steam-turbine to ship propulsion. His first attempt, in 1894, with a radial-flow turbine (Fig. 153) failed, as the design of the propeller was such that at the high speed of rotation it could not provide the necessary thrust. In 1896 he devised a system with three shafts, each of which carried three screws, driven by a connected series of turbines, those for high and intermediate pressure at the sides, with a low-pressure turbine in the centre; there was a separate turbine, driving the central shaft, for reversing. The difficulty in the design of the propeller was overcome by increasing its surface area. The three turbines together developed about 2,000 h.p., and the *Turbinia* (Fig. 154), when it made its first appearance at the Jubilee Naval Review in 1897, startled 'the captains and the kings' by its hitherto unheard-of speed of $34\frac{1}{2}$ knots.

FIG. 154. The *Turbinia* at speed, 1897

It was found, however, that the turbines ran most efficiently at higher speeds than were suitable for the screws. As the turbine came into wider use for ship propulsion, therefore, reduction-gearing was introduced, together with double-reduction gearing for slow merchant ships in which the propellers were required to turn at fewer than 100 r.p.m. As an indication of the subsequent speed of development of the marine turbine, it may be remarked that within a decade Cunard liners were being fitted with turbine-machinery developing 70,000 h.p. and it had been adopted for the British Navy.

Contemporaneously with Parsons, Gustav de Laval had developed a turbine of different design in Sweden. De Laval's turbine, perfected in 1887, was essentially a steam 'windmill', in which jets of steam impinge on vanes set round the rim of a wheel. This comparatively simple device achieved considerable success for engines of relatively small power, especially after Curtis, in the United States, introduced the device of velocity compounding, in which a second, and occasionally a third, row of vanes was introduced to utilize the energy remaining in the steam after it had passed through the first row. A basic limitation of the single turbine is that the fall in steam pressure takes place in one stage, as it leaves the nozzles; the advantage of Parson's method was, as we have seen, that the reduction in pressure took place in a series of stages.

THE THEORETICAL BACKGROUND

The development of the steam-engine from Savery's 'Miner's Friend' of 1698 to Parson's fast turbine of 1884 corresponded, though by no means exactly, with an immense increase of understanding of the underlying scientific principles, and this chapter would be incomplete without some reference to these. Fundamentally the steam-engine is a device for converting heat energy into mechanical energy, and its performance is governed by the laws of thermodynamics. These laws were, however, not established until the middle of the nineteenth century, nor, indeed, was the nature of heat at all generally understood until that time: this circumstance is a further reminder that technology is by no means synonymous with applied science.

The steam-engine is a heat-engine, and it is remarkable that its development proceeded as far as it did without any clear idea of the nature of heat itself. Heat was long looked upon as a fluid, possessing neither weight nor substance, that could flow from a hot body to a cold one. Although erroneous, this belief was a useful one, for it led Joseph Black, whose ideas greatly influenced Watt, to carry out quantitative experiments that led to the formulation of the concepts of latent and specific heats. As his unit of measurement Black used the quantity of heat required to raise the temperature of a given weight of water by a given amount: substances vary in the amount of heat— their 'specific' heat—required to raise their temperature by a given extent. He showed that a definite quantity of heat is required to convert water into steam at the same temperature: this 'latent' heat is released when the steam condenses again. On this basis Watt could assess the relative efficiency of steam-engines in terms of the heat put into them and the mechanical power they developed. As we have already seen, comparable measurements had been made by Smeaton in 1767, when the 'duty' of pumping engines was measured in terms of work done per bushel of coal consumed, but this type of measurement was less satisfactory as it contained an unknown factor, namely, the amount of heat released from the fuel that was in fact utilized by the engine.

The nature of the relationship between heat and work was examined more closely by Benjamin Thompson, Count Rumford, who founded the Royal Institution in London in 1799. While Minister of War in the Bavarian service he made a study of the heat developed during the boring of brass cannon. This well-known phenomenon had been explained on the assumption that solid brass contains more 'caloric' than does the same weight of brass turnings: the difference would thus be expected to appear as heat when solid brass was converted into a finely divided form. Rumford found, however, that the specific heat of the turnings was the same as that of the original metal. He concluded that heat is a form of motion, and that in this instance it derived from the work done in the process of boring. Although a quantitative measure of the mechanical equivalent of heat can be derived from Rumford's published work he did not in fact make the necessary computation: this was left to J. P. Joule, whose value, substantially the same as that accepted today, was published in 1847 in *The Philosophical Magazine*. The establishment of a precise relationship between heat and work was an event of the first importance—though only gradually recognized as such—to the design of every kind of heat-engine. It established quite unequivocally that, regardless of the type of heat-engine, there must be a limit—further defined by the Second Law of Thermodynamics (see below)—to the amount of work that it could perform for a given amount of heat supplied to it.

Joule's work was fundamental to one of the most important physical generalizations of the nineteenth century—the theory of the conservation of energy. Briefly, this states that if energy of a particular kind disappears then an exactly equivalent quantity of energy of other kinds appears in its place. This is the First Law of Thermodynamics: it states, in effect, that energy, like matter, can be neither created nor destroyed. The two basic principles of the conservation of matter (p. 272) and of energy dominated nineteenth-century science: in the twentieth century they have had to be united in the light of discoveries in atomic physics, but for all practical purposes they apply rigidly over almost all fields of science and technology.

From the First Law of Thermodynamics followed the Second, enunciated in 1851 by William Thomson (Lord Kelvin) and by R. J. E. Clausius: briefly, it states that there is a theoretical maximum to the efficiency of any heat-engine. The Second Law of Thermodynamics governs virtually all processes involving the transformation of heat, and thus is applicable to a very wide range of technological processes and not merely to the steam-engine and other heat-engines.

MACHINE-TOOLS AND THEIR PRODUCTS

INTRODUCTION

THE development of the steam-engine by Watt and Trevithick made possible the creation of a civilization based on power-driven machinery, but did not of itself create such a civilization. In fact, as we have seen, the steam-engine took something like half a century to establish itself as the principal source of power for industry. For this, two main reasons can be seen. One was the trade conditions existing during and after the great French wars; the other, no less important, was the purely technical difficulty of constructing steam-engines and the machinery they were to drive. In this con-nexion we have already noted that long after better steam-engines were available the ponderous beam-engine continued to be built, simply because it was well within the capacity of the materials and craftsmen of the day. The making by hand of parts of machinery to precise standards could prove not merely prohibitively expensive but even a practical impossibility. The rate at which standards changed is forcibly illustrated by the fact that in 1776 Boulton was delighted that Wilkinson had bored for him a 50-in. cylinder that 'doth not err the thickness of an old shilling in no part', whereas by 1856 (Sir) Joseph Whitworth was regularly using in his workshops a machine capable of measuring to one-millionth part of an inch. Whitworth roundly condemned the old method of working to such meaning-less limits as 'a bare sixteenth' or 'a full thirty-second' with which many, though not all, engineers were then satisfied: he claimed that it was easier to work to one ten-thousandth of an inch by his methods than to one-hundredth of an inch by the old ones. The general intro-duction of these new standards of precision not only made possible the practical realization of new inventions and designs, but led the way to the mass-production methods that are an essential feature of modern industry. No longer was it necessary to build each machine separately: instead, individual parts could be manufactured in large numbers, and the final machine assembled by drawing the necessary components from a stock of interchangeable parts. This mode of operation, which originated in France but was developed mainly in the United States, profoundly affected the role of the individual: craftsmen became less and less concerned with complete projects and more and more with limited parts of them, perhaps never even seeing the final product.

While the need for greater precision was the most important factor that led engineers to turn to machine-tools, the frequent need to

FIG. 155. Foot-operated lathe, 1395

work very large and heavy pieces of metal also inevitably led in the same direction. The machine-tool industry thus became a very important feature of the later phases of the industrial revolution: it has indeed been said that the making of machines to make machines was its most important single aspect. While there is much truth in this assertion, it is misleading to the extent that it gives the impression that the making of machine-tools was wholly a development of the nineteenth century, whereas its beginnings can be traced back for a great many years before this. In the eighteenth century, for example, the makers of clocks and scientific instruments used extremely accurate lathes, screw-cutting machines, and dividing-engines, a further reminder that when great precision was required mechanical methods were not merely cheaper and more convenient than working by hand but often essential. Wood-turning lathes had been in use long before this, and are illustrated in medieval works (Fig. 155): they may indeed be regarded as an offspring of the potter's wheel, which was a very early device. Nevertheless, the widespread use of machine-tools is certainly a nineteenth-century development. William Fairbairn recorded, in his inaugural address as President of the British Association in 1861, that when he first went to Birmingham in 1814 all machinery was made by hand; by the time of his address, however, 'everything is done by machine tools with a degree of accuracy which the unaided hand could never accomplish'. Less than half a century had seen a revolution in manufacturing methods in one of Britain's chief manufacturing centres.

Before considering individual machine-tools, it is perhaps useful to consider the principles of their operation. Generally speaking, there are only two forms of movement, rectilinear and circular, that can be easily and accurately obtained with relatively simple mechanisms, and most machine-tools achieved their results by applying one or other of these movements or a combination of both, either the tool or the work being firmly fixed. Clay is shaped on the wheel, for example, by its rotary movement combined with the upward and the sideways movement of the potter's hand, the role of which is strictly comparable with the cutting-tool of a lathe. Spiral movement, such as is necessary for making an accurate screw-thread, can be achieved by simultaneous rotary movement and rectilinear movement at right angles to it: the pitch of the spiral can be controlled by varying the relative speeds of the two motions. Drilling also is achieved by a combination of rectilinear and circular movements, the drill moving forward as it rotates. Planing, by contrast, depends upon rectilinear motion alone.

Many machine-tools represent the mechanization of the traditional methods of the artisan to give greater precision and, as metal

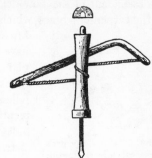

FIG. 156. Egyptian bow-drill with copper bit, *c.* 1200 B.C.

FIG. 157. Carpenter's brace, part of an altar-piece by Meister Francke, 1424

replaced wood, greater power. The machine-drill, for example, is a descendant of the bow-drill of the Egyptian joiner (Fig. 156) and the carpenter's brace, which, though not certainly known before the

fifteenth century A.D. (Fig. 157), may possibly have been in use among the Assyrians. The plane was established as a hand-tool in Roman times (Fig. 158): although it seems to have fallen into disuse afterwards until the fourteenth century, it is substantially the same today save that the frame is usually iron instead of wooden. Because continuous rotary movement is mechanically more suitable for high-speed continuous work than reciprocat-

FIG. 158. Carpenter's planes: (*above*) Roman; (*below*) modern

ing movement, there was a tendency for the to-and-fro motion of some hand-tools to be turned into circular motion. Thus circular saws came into use in the third quarter of the eighteenth century, and band-saws in the middle of the nineteenth, especially in America, where there was a great demand for wood-working machinery of all kinds; but their principle—that of cutting by means of continuous friction by a sharp serrated edge—was still the same as that of the flint saws which date from Upper Palaeolithic times, or of the Iron Age saws in which raked teeth first occur.

GROWTH OF PRECISION WORK

The lathe, the oldest machine-tool, is of unknown antiquity, but it was not until about 1700 that it became really useful for accurate work. The clock-makers, inspired by the work of such men as Hooke and Huygens, then developed the first precision lathes (Fig. 159) which were also of much use to the makers of scientific instruments. These were built on a square iron bar, which usually had one movable and one fixed headstock, through which passed rods to secure the work; between the headstocks was a sliding bracket to hold the working tool. The work was turned by a bow, so that rotation was first in one direction and then in the other. Although this intermittent rotation was a disadvantage, satisfactory cylindrical parts and arbors for clocks could be produced in this way. By 1750 the Frenchman Antoine Thiout made the very important innovation of equipping a lathe with a tool-holding carriage moved longitudinally by a screw-drive. As a result accuracy was no longer wholly dependent upon the eye and skill of the operator. Some time between 1768 and 1780 another French inventor, Jacques de Vaucanson, an expert in the field of textile machinery, devised both a lathe and a drill, each of which was fitted with a tool-holding carriage moved by a threaded screw. He also began the practice, which was later applied to all machine-tools, of making the carriage for the tool move along a prismatic metal bench. This was part of a general move towards greater strength and rigidity, which among other things resulted in the replacement of wood by metal as the material of construction.

Precision mechanics and the making of machine-tools overlap to

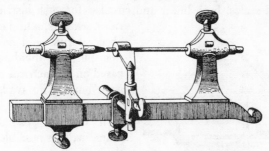

FIG. 159. Clock-maker's lathe, eighteenth century

a great extent in the case of screw-cutting lathes. Accurately threaded screws were important for a variety of purposes, as, for example, the moving of the tool-holder—since each turn of the screw must correspond to a precisely determined linear movement forward. Screws of relatively large pitch could be made satisfactorily by the use of stocks and dies, but for long, finely pitched screws—such as were required for the fine adjustment of micrometers—a lathe was essential. The first satisfactory screw-cutting lathes were made by the English instrument-maker Jesse Ramsden in 1770. The more elaborate of his two machines (Fig. 160) had the rod to be threaded placed parallel to the guide-bench, and rotated through gearing by the driving-crank of the lead-screw. Long screws could be made from a small original, carefully cut by hand with a file from a geometrically drawn pattern; the accuracy of the result was largely dependent upon the care and skill of the operator. Screw-cutting was a highly skilled craft, but by the end of the eighteenth century a number of workshops doing work of high quality had been established, most of them in France or Britain. No great accuracy was, of course, necessary for screws and nuts used merely for holding together the various parts of machines.

Ramsden's work had far-reaching consequences. In 1797, for

example, Maudslay designed a large screw-cutting lathe, widely used by engineers, that was probably inspired by Ramsden's model, descriptions of which had been published. Two years earlier Senot, in France, had also built a lathe for cutting screws with precision, but this seems to have attracted little attention. Also in France, Jean Fortin developed an accurate method of screw-cutting, but little is known about this, save that he worked by a method of successive approximations.

With increasing precision, there was a growing need for accurately graduated scales, both linear and circular, for such instruments as

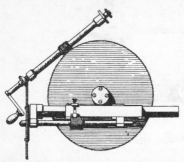

rules, sextants, mural circles for observatories, and so on. For this purpose dividing-engines based on geometrical principles were built. The availability of accurately cut screws, engaging with equally accurately cut gears, made it possible to effect the controlled movement of the scriber that cut the graduations of the scale. In this field the Duc de Chaulnes did much pioneer work, introducing the use of

FIG. 160. Ramsden's screw-cutting lathe, 1770

microscopes, with cross-hairs in the field of view, for the precise location of the graduations of the master plate; he also used the tangent-screw drive. In the experienced hands of Ramsden these methods proved very valuable, and he built the first dividing-engine suitable for work on an industrial scale. His machines excited great interest, and early in the nineteenth century many of a similar type were built. On the Continent, Lenoir produced work of exceptional accuracy, but perhaps the most successful precision instrument-maker of that time was Henry Gambey. His dividing-engine was more exact than any that had preceded it: in 1840 he used it to graduate a great 2-metre mural circle for the Paris Observatory that remained in use until 1920. Among his refinements was the use of remote control, so that expansion of metal by the body-heat of the operator was avoided.

The rapid development of methods for constructing precision instruments of all kinds in the second half of the eighteenth century and the early part of the nineteenth had far-reaching practical consequences. Clock-making, which had given the original impetus, achieved a great triumph in 1759, when John Harrison completed his chronometer No. 4, which was of watch size. This enabled longitude to be determined within an accuracy of half a degree and ultimately won for its designer the £20,000 prize—the size of the prize is a clear indication of the enormous importance of an accurate chronometer to navigators—that the Board of Longitude had since 1714 offered to the inventor of a marine chronometer capable of attaining this degree of accuracy at sea. Harrison, however, made only five chronometers in all, and the man who created the modern marine chronometer was a Swiss, Ferdinand Berthoud. Under Berthoud's nephew, the manufacture of marine chronometers became industrialized in France in the first half of the nineteenth century. In England the best models were those of Mudge, Arnold, and Earnshaw. By the end of the Napoleonic wars both British and French navigators were satisfactorily provided with a means of determining longitude at sea. The sextant, too, had come into use from 1757 as an aid to navigation, and the requirements of its manufacture had in fact given an additional impetus to the invention of the dividing-engine. Large reflecting telescopes charted the heavens, and much greater accuracy was being introduced into terrestrial survey. When the French and English triangulation surveys were connected across the Straits of Dover in 1787 the French were achieving great accuracy by means of the repeating-circle, first manufactured by Lenoir. In England at that time the most precise surveying instruments were two very large theodolites, constructed by Ramsden, which had an accuracy of 1 second at 10 miles or 2 seconds at 70 miles. Smaller theodolites of similar type were used throughout the nineteenth century.

Thus the development of precise machine-tools for the construction of suitable scientific instruments profoundly affected both the art of navigation and the construction of charts and maps just at the time of the great voyages of discovery of the eighteenth and nineteenth centuries. No less important, they paved the way for the industrial machine-tools essential for the construction of the later types of steam-engine and of the machines they had to drive. Accurate surveying instruments were necessary, too, for the building of canals, roads, and railways. The importance of these connexions between science and technology, through the instrument-makers, is not always appreciated.

THE SUCCESSION OF PIONEERS

In view of its profound effect on the development of Watt's steam-engine, it is sad that the only relic of the original boring-mill built in 1775 by John Wilkinson, at what had been his father's ironworks in Denbighshire, is a 15-ft boring-bar. The hollow boring-bar was, however, the essential feature. It was keyed to the large driving-wheel at one end and supported in a bearing at the other; the cutter-head was mounted on the bar, with which it rotated, and was fed forward by a rod inside the bar, while the cylinder itself was held rigidly in

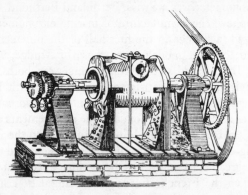

FIG. 161. Borer for locomotive cylinders at the Swindon works of the Great Western Railway, 1851

a cradle. Although his horizontal boring machine was originally designed to make cannon, Wilkinson had for about twenty years a virtual monopoly of the manufacture of cylinders for Boulton & Watt. Even by the middle of the nineteenth century few modifications of his design had been made (Fig. 161).

The next main figure in the development of machine-tools for industry was Joseph Bramah, a Yorkshire farmer's son who became a versatile inventor. Among his eighteen patents, which included an improved water-closet (p. 425), a hydraulic press, a wood-planing machine, the suction beer-engine, and a device for printing the serial numbers on banknotes, was a type of lock that is still manufactured; a specimen remained unpicked, despite a standing challenge prize of 200 guineas, from 1784 until 1851, when the success of a light-fingered American visitor—who took fifty-one hours spread over sixteen days to complete his task—was hailed by *Punch* as 'the Pick of the Exhibition'. Such a lock was necessarily complicated, and machines had to be devised to cut grooves in the barrel of the lock, notches in the keys, and unlocking notches in the steel sliders. In addition, Bramah had a spring-winding machine, in which a geared lead-screw made it possible to manufacture springs of varying pitch. This was the forerunner of the screw-cutting machine made by Maudslay, a young blacksmith from Woolwich Arsenal, where he had started life as a powder-monkey at the age of twelve, whom Bramah employed as his foreman. Finding his ingenuity rewarded with a wage that did not rise above 30s. a week, in 1797 Maudslay founded his own firm, important alike for the machines it made and the minds it trained.

Maudslay set a new standard of accuracy, partly by using metal alone as the material of construction (the machine-tools he had made for Bramah had wooden frames), and partly by causing his workmen to test every important plane surface—especially those of slide-valves for steam-engines—against accurate standards. He was the first to popularize among engineers the use of a slide-rest, already familiar to instrument-makers, as we have seen, to hold a traversing tool. Then in 1800 he produced his famous screw-cutting lathe. This used a lead-screw, as in the fusee-engine, linked with the headstock through gear-wheels fixed on three spindles; the slide-rest travelled on prismatic bars. Similar lathes had in fact been devised in France and in America a few years earlier, but the invention is commonly attributed to Maudslay, partly no doubt because of his exceptional interest in the formation and reproduction of accurate screw-threads. His screw micrometer for bench work was accurate to 0·0001 in.

The firm of Maudslay, Sons & Field became important builders of steam table-engines and marine engines, but Maudslay's first major order was for machine-tools for Portsmouth dockyard. Sir Samuel Bentham, younger brother of Jeremy Bentham, the political philosopher, had taken out a patent in 1793 for all kinds of wood-working machinery, with which he proposed to reduce costs in the Royal Dockyards consigned to his charge as Inspector-General of Naval Works. For mechanizing the manufacture of pulley-blocks, required by the Admiralty at the rate of 100,000 a year, Bentham was supplied with a design of machinery superior to his own by M. I. Brunel, a royalist refugee from the French Navy. The scheme, which was officially adopted in February 1802, took five and a half years to complete. As the blocks were required in three size-ranges, some of the machines for sawing, boring, mortising, and scoring had to be supplied in more than one size; altogether, there were forty-three machines, which did everything except the final fitting and polishing in the whole of the long business of turning elm logs into finished pulley-blocks. Driven by a 30 h.p. steam-engine, the machines made 130,000 blocks a year, cut the labour force from 110 skilled men to 10 unskilled men, and saved the Admiralty almost a third of the capital outlay in a year. This example of mass-production methods, which were also extended to Chatham and to the government yard in Spain, was far in advance of its time, and some of the machines that Maudslay built for Portsmouth remained in use for more than a century after his death in 1831.

Maudslay had a lasting influence on the British machine-tool industry. Of the three great British machine-tool makers of the next generation, both Richard Roberts and Joseph Whitworth had worked for a short time under him, while James Nasmyth, the greatest of the three, had been his personal assistant in his old age and did not open his own workshop until after Maudslay's death. Roberts, who had also worked for Wilkinson at the Bradley ironworks, in 1817 made a lathe with a back-geared headstock, and in the same year made the first planing machine for metal, which is still in existence. When a larger type came into use a few years later, its maker was another employee of Maudslay, Joseph Clement. For ten years Clement's machine was the only one in the world capable of taking work up to 6 ft square: such was the demand for it that it was his main source of income, capable of earning up to £20 a day. Roberts is best known for his self-acting spinning-mule, but he also invented a number of machine-tools, including a punching-machine specially designed in 1847 for making the rivet-holes in the railway bridge over the Menai Straits.

Nasmyth, the son of a Scottish landscape-painter, became Maudslay's personal assistant when he was only twenty-one. His inventions included a milling-machine and a planing-machine or shaper, quite distinct from the shaping engine used by Brunel for block-making; the shaper could produce any small surface that can be formed of rectilinear elements. But Nasmyth is best known for his steam-hammer, which could be raised higher than the old tilt-hammer and lowered with great force but yet under perfect control. It was designed in 1839 to solve the practical problem created by the proposal, not subsequently carried out, to equip the steamship *Great Britain* with a paddle-shaft of 30-in. diameter. In the steam-hammer the piston of an overhead cylinder is connected with the hammer-head by a rod, the head being raised prior to the blow by the admission of steam to the cylinder. Increased power was obtained later by admitting the steam above the piston for the downward stroke to make the hammer double-acting (Fig. 162). Iron beams and plates could now be forged of larger size than ever before. The great hammer could, nevertheless, descend—as the Exhibition catalogue of 1851 pointed out—'with power only sufficient to break an egg shell'. Pile-driving, as required for Robert Stephenson's Newcastle bridge in 1849, for example, came to be carried out at the rate of a blow a second instead of a blow every few minutes as by earlier methods.

FIG. 162. Nasmyth's steam-hammer

Whitworth, a schoolmaster's son, set up as a tool-maker in Manchester in 1833 with the intention of making machine-tools for sale. In this respect he stands in marked contrast to those whom we have been discussing, since they made machine-tools primarily as a necessary step in some other manufacture in which they were interested. As a tool purveyor he stood far ahead of all rivals at the Exhibitions of 1851 and 1862. His twenty-three exhibits at the Crystal Palace included various forms of planing-machine, one of which was not only power-driven and self-acting but was equipped with guide-pulleys which reversed the tool-holder at the end of each stroke, so that it cut in both directions. He also made a number of improvements to the lathe, including the hollow-box design for its bed, which provided much greater rigidity for a given weight, as well as providing the all-important lead-screw with satisfactory protection from dust and shavings. One of his earliest devices, already mentioned, was a measuring-machine that could measure to an accuracy of one-millionth of an inch (Fig. 163): this contrasted with the general standard of the day, although we have already noted that Maudslay's bench micrometer had an accuracy of 0·0001 in.

Yet another way in which Whitworth sought to improve engineering methods was through the standardization of screw-threads. Since 1760 the increasing demand for screws had been met by factory production, first patented by J. and W. Wyatt. Whitworth, after collecting sample screws from as many British workshops as possible, put forward his two proposals—that the angle between the sides of the threads should be 55°, and that the number of threads

FIG. 163. Whitworth's machine for measuring to one-millionth of an inch, 1856

to the inch should be specified for various diameters. His recommendations became standard practice in Britain in the 1860's, but on the Continent the firm establishment of the metric system prevented their general acceptance and the American government officially adopted the rival Sellers system in 1868.

In tracing the great dynasty of British machine-tool makers through Maudslay to Whitworth, the main emphasis has been laid on tools that were used for the working of iron and other metals, but there were also some important new machines for working both wood and stone. The Americans of log-cabin days had a very great interest in wood-working machinery of all kinds, but it was nevertheless for Woolwich Arsenal that the first rotary wood-planing machine was devised, by Bramah, in 1802; it remained in use for half a century. In this machine the wood was moved backwards and forwards on carriages by means of an endless chain and 40-ft rails; above hung a disk fitted with gouges and planing-irons, which was turned by a steam-engine at 90 r.p.m. A machine which converted planks into tongued and grooved floorboards was made in 1827 by a former employee of Maudslay.

Machines for the reproduction of irregular forms began with the eighteenth-century medallion-lathe. In the original machines the feeler caused the cutter to make a reverse copy of the matrix, but about 1800 the feeler and the cutter were placed on a bar pivoted at one end, so that a positive copy of the matrix could be made; the scale of the reproduction could be adjusted by varying the position of the two instruments on the bar. James Watt, after his retirement from active business, made an improvement by adding a pivoted arm to the bar and rotating the cutters, so that it was possible to undercut and to copy objects in the round in the original or a different size. He neither patented nor publicized these inventions, made between 1804 and 1819, and an independent invention was made in the following decade by Benjamin Cheverton.

One practical application was a machine built in France and used at the Paris Mint from 1824 onwards to convert medallion designs into master punches. Another was a machine that could copy carved panels in wood and soft stone; invented in 1845, it was used extensively for ornamental stonework and in particular for the panelling of the new Houses of Parliament, built to replace those destroyed by fire in 1834. But perhaps the most significant type of copying lathe was that developed in 1818 by the American inventor Thomas Blanchard. This was for mass-producing gun-stocks, and was introduced into England shortly after the 1851 Exhibition as part of the 'American system'.

THE 'AMERICAN SYSTEM'

The spread of the so-called 'American system'—that is, the improvement of the economy of manufacture by producing fully interchangeable parts—is one of the most striking technological developments of the second half of the nineteenth century. At the Great Exhibition of 1851 British engineering reigned supreme; the space allocated to the Americans was not even filled. Nevertheless, the American exhibits included half a dozen army rifles manufactured on the system of interchangeable parts, and within two years the system was being studied by a British committee, including both Nasmyth and Whitworth. The latter pointed to the root cause of the extraordinarily rapid rise of American technology when he reported: 'The labouring classes [there] are comparatively few in number, but this is counterbalanced by, and indeed may be regarded as one of the chief causes of, the eagerness with which they call in the aid of machinery. . . . wherever it can be introduced, it is universally and willingly resorted to.'

Although known as the 'American system' after the country in which it was most fully exploited, its starting-point was in fact in Europe, where it was first used for the manufacture of muskets, of which eighteenth-century governments were large-scale purchasers and manufacturers with a special interest in uniformity and facility of repair. In 1785 Thomas Jefferson reported from Paris, where he had succeeded Benjamin Franklin as American Minister, that a gunsmith there made locks of fully interchangeable parts and expected to be able to cheapen the musket in consequence. Later correspondence shows that the system was extended to the whole gun. Something similar appears to have been attempted in the Black Forest in 1806—the year in which Napoleon completed his subjugation of Germany. But it was in America that Eli Whitney, unable to secure the profits from the cotton gin which he had patented in 1794, began interchangeable manufacture of muskets for the United States government on what he mistakenly claimed to be 'a plan which is unknown in Europe'. That America, with its few gunsmiths, provided ideal ground for such a development is shown by the fact that his proposed method was imitated almost immediately by Simeon North in the manufacture of pistols. From 1819 onwards the system was adopted in the two main arsenals of the United States. In the same period it was introduced into the American clock trade for a shelf-clock produced by Eli Terry in large quantities, the wheels of which were accurately stamped with dies from sheets of brass. From 1828 onwards a rotary pump was also made in this way.

The most striking developments of the system, however, continued to be in the manufacture of small arms, particularly after the Mexican war of 1846–8 had shown the remarkable value of the revolver, invented by Samuel Colt (p. 502) a decade before. In 1853 he developed an armoury using 1,400 machine-tools. At the same time rifles were being mass-produced by the firm of Robbins & Lawrence, and it was their exhibit in London in 1851 that brought the American system to England, where they equipped the Royal Small Arms Factory at Enfield with 150 machine-tools and the necessary ancillary equipment. By 1857 Enfield was producing 1,000 rifles a week, later 2,000, each requiring more than 700 separate operations; all parts of all rifles were completely interchangeable, a military advantage whose immense importance needs no emphasis.

In the second half of the nineteenth century the further development of the interchangeable system of manufacture (Fig. 164), in which America continued to take the lead, was one of the main factors that resulted in complicated and efficient machinery being placed in the hands of the many for purposes of peace as well as of war. Harvesters, sewing-machines, typewriters, and many other

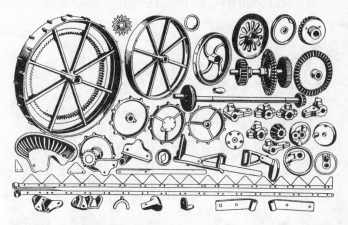

FIG. 164. Interchangeable reaper parts as used at the middle of the nineteenth century

machines spread from under-populated America to lighten the physical toil—and temporarily to complicate the economies—of other continents.

FURTHER DEVELOPMENTS, 1850–1900

In the first half of the nineteenth century a handful of men, whose industrial experience made them aware of the great need for machine-tools, made and exploited a series of inventions of cardinal importance. In the second half of the century the demand for new machines called for the development of some new machine-tools. Progress resulted also from the availability of new materials for tools and new sources of power with which to operate them. For the most part, however, technical progress came from the improvement in detail of the tools already in existence. But whether the tools were of an old or new type, the period witnessed a decline in the proportion of heavy manual labour used in industry and a higher regard for the safety and convenience of those operating the machines. The conditions in which even so enterprising and enlightened a firm as Chubb, the London lock- and safe-makers, worked in 1868 would have seemed old fashioned by the end of the century (Fig. 165).

The working life of a cutting tool depends upon the speed at which it is driven; for the carbon-steel tools of 1850 this meant a maximum speed of about 40 ft a minute. The steel invented by Robert Mushet about 1865, in which tungsten and vanadium were

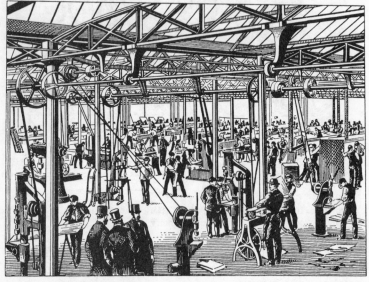

FIG. 165. Chubb & Son's London factory for making locks and safes, 1868

incorporated and the proportion of manganese increased, enabled the cutting speed to be increased by a half. This in turn gave place, at the very end of the century, to high-speed steel, containing chromium, which raised the cutting speed to 120 ft a minute. This change had two effects on the machine-tools used. Increased strength, better design, and improved bearings were needed to take the strain; at the same time, with the possibility of employing very high speeds, it became desirable to have a better method of changing speed than that of simply slipping the driving-belt on to a pulley of different diameter. In 1892, accordingly, a gear-box for machine-tools was introduced in America, enabling speeds to be selected by a hand-lever. The use of the gear-box spread rapidly, and by 1900 a friction-drive also had been developed, enabling the spindle-speed to be varied at will. New materials—silicon carbide (carborundum) and aluminium oxide—also came in during the 1890's to revolutionize the grinding-machines, which played an important part, for instance, in the manufacture of sewing-machine components.

In the long run, however, the most important basic change was the introduction of electricity as a prime-mover. Its application to machine-tools was publicly demonstrated at the Vienna Exhibition

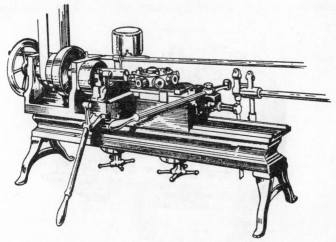

Fig. 166. Turret-lathe built by the Robbins & Lawrence Company, Vermont, 1855

of 1873, and at about that time it began to replace steam-power for driving the network of overhead belts characteristic of most factories at that time. By the close of the century, however, individual electric motors might occasionally be found incorporated in the structure of machine-tools, as is now general practice.

Important developments in the lathe began in America in the 1840's. By 1855 Robbins & Lawrence's guns were being manufactured with the help of a fully developed turret lathe (Fig. 166). Although it has been claimed that there was a British patent for a capstan-lathe with vertical turret before 1840, and that American developments in the following decade are to be attributed to immigrants from Britain, the turret-lathe was not to be found in British engineering practice, or even listed in the International Exhibition catalogue, as late as 1862. Eight tools could be locked into the lathe's octagonal turret, which could be rotated to bring each to bear in turn for its appropriate process: eight machining operations could thus be conducted by a single operator. By the time of the outbreak of the American Civil War in 1861, a ratchet-and-pawl mechanism had been developed to rotate the turret automatically, as well as a device for feeding-in the bars to be worked on without stopping the rotation of the spindle.

The war years in America greatly stimulated the demand for still further economy of labour. Automatic screw-making lathes were

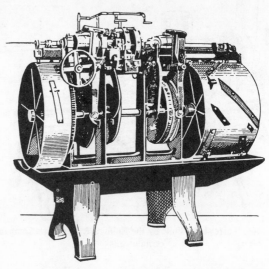

Fig. 167. Spencer's automatic lathe with cylindrical cams

built in war-time, and were soon followed by a remarkable American lathe with cylindrical cams, known as 'brain wheels' (Fig. 167). The cams were adjustable, and controlled both the cutting tools and the turret: if continuously fed with raw material, this machine would continue to manufacture screws or other small components as long as the cutting tools endured. A British automatic screw-making machine followed in 1879, turning out screws of $\frac{1}{8}$-in. diameter at from 80 to 150 an hour according to their length; it incorporated a roller device to feed in the material. By the end of the century machines of this kind had increased in size and power and were in common use: they are early examples of what is now called automation.

In 1895 the needs of the American sewing-machine industry caused the principle of the automatic lathe to be carried a step farther. By placing four or more spindles in a single lathe, and arranging for them to rotate periodically to new positions, it became possible to machine all components simultaneously, though the total time required would be determined by the longest of the four processes. By 1900 such machines were available in Sweden as well as in America.

The same principle had been applied earlier in the multiple-spindle drilling machine (Fig. 168). A machine designed on this principle was used in 1860 to drill the holes in the ⅝-in. thick plate used for the side girders of Charing Cross railway bridge, London.

FIG. 168. Multiple-spindle drilling machine, 1851

But there was no major advance in the type of drill, except for the introduction of the twist-drill, which made higher speeds possible in the sixties. Nasmyth's slot-drilling machine of 1862 was a valuable innovation: until this became available, slots, such as were necessary in piston- and connecting-rods, could be made only by the laborious process of drilling a series of holes, chipping out the metal between them, and filing the slot to shape. Nasmyth called it 'one of the most tedious and irksome jobs that an engineer could be set to' and one, moreover, with which only the very best men could be entrusted.

In boring machines, apart from an increase in size and accuracy, the chief change was a growing use of the vertical boring machine (Fig. 169), because with a large component it was easier to work with the part clamped on a horizontal rotating table. Such vertical boring machines had, however, been known since the days of Boulton and Watt.

A more important development was in the milling machine, first built for sale in 1848. In contrast to shaper, planer, or lathe, its large number of cutting edges enabled it to move relatively fast without over-heating, and it had an obvious advantage in its ability to cut special shapes in a single operation. Its use, however, was for a long time held back, particularly in Britain, because of the difficulty of making the cutters and keeping them sharp. In 1862 the American firm of Brown & Sharpe achieved what has since been recognized as the first true universal milling machine (Fig. 170). This machine was originally designed to mill helical grooves for the new twist-drills, but Joseph Brown, who designed it, soon saw that it could be used to replace a large number of difficult hand operations. The machine won immediate wide acceptance in America, but milling machines did not come into general use in Britain until after the turn of the century.

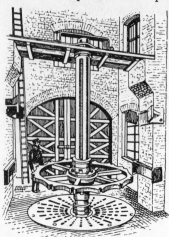

FIG. 169. Early vertical boring machine, installed in Boulton & Watt's Soho foundry

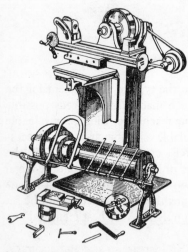

FIG. 170. First universal milling machine, made by the Brown & Sharpe Company, United States, in 1862

With an increase in the rotational speeds of all kinds of machinery, and the need to transmit much greater power, there developed a pressing demand for methods of manufacturing gears from very tough metals to exacting standards. They continued to be produced mainly in milling machines by means of formed cutters, although automatic gear-cutters were employed in America in 1877. In 1856 an alternative method had been conceived, known as 'hobbing', in which the gear-blank was rotated synchronously with the cutter. But the first hobbing-machine patent was not applied for, in America, until about 1887, and another ten years passed before the machines came at all widely into use; it is significant that one of the first British hobbing machines was that built by the motor-car manufacturer F. W. Lanchester in 1896 to machine worm-gears.

In the twentieth century the rapid development of the motor-car, and subsequently of the aeroplane, industry opened immense new fields for the application of machine-tools. Although never a large industry in terms of the number of people employed, the machine-tool industry has long been of the most fundamental importance to technological progress of every kind.

MODERN TRANSPORT

TRANSPORT improvements occupy a key position in the history of the industrial revolution, operating both as a cause and as an effect of countless other changes. They are an effect because the steam-engine and other new prime-movers both suggested and made possible the new modes of transport by sea, land, and air. But the new means of transport were also a cause of industrial change. Without them bulky and heavy raw materials—in the first phase, coal and iron, and later, steel, petroleum, Malayan tin, and rubber—could never have been concentrated for manufacture, nor could the food have been found for the manufacturing populations. They made possible the two great new social phenomena of the age—widespread urbanization and mass emigration. By enabling men to envisage the whole world as a single economic unit, in which every area could supply something to the needs of industrial manufacture and was consequently a potential market for its products, modern transport provided a compelling incentive to technological development.

Transport must therefore be treated as a whole, since its importance as a technological instrument is distinct from the history of the steam-engine, already related, or those of the coal and iron industry, the internal combustion engine, and electricity, which are to follow. Building construction for transport will likewise be treated as a whole (Ch. 15), but in the case of the railway everything except the road-bed is included here because—unlike the canal and road—the making of the railway was substantially a novel, perhaps the novel, achievement of nineteenth-century transport engineering. We will, however, consider first the progress of sea communications. The sailing-ship was perhaps the finest technological achievement of the pre-industrial era: yet it was the network of steam-ship services which, as much as any other single factor, created the western world and western civilization as they stood in 1900.

THE LAST ERA OF SAIL

The wooden sailing-ship of the eighteenth century, its size limited by the mechanical qualities of the timber from which it was built, its shape and gear determined by long and arduous experience, was not commonly regarded as capable of substantial further development. This does not appear surprising when we reflect upon the

FIG. 171. The *Endeavour*, dispatched by the British Admiralty in 1768 to chart the South Pacific Ocean and observe the transit of Venus

achievements even of tiny colliers such as Cook's *Endeavour* (Fig. 171) and *Resolution*. It was the flat bottom, designed to allow unloading of coal into carts on beaches at low tide, which made it possible to run *Endeavour* ashore for repair after she was holed on the Great Barrier Reef of Australia. Less than 100 ft long on the lower deck, a ship like this was seaworthy enough to ride out the storms of the Roaring Forties, and could be sailed close enough to the wind for Cook to perform his astonishing surveys of Newfoundland and Australasia. The bluff-bowed East Indiaman, on the other hand, with its full-bodied hull, designed to carry the maximum amount of cargo, was slow but safe; it would complete three voyages in six years, was then overhauled, and might be re-employed by the Company.

As for displacement, at the end of the century the largest vessels belonging to the East India Company in London had an official rating of 1,200 tons, while a first-rate ship of the line—there were three rates—might well be considerably heavier than this. Such a fighting-vessel needed to be fast as well as strong, and might carry upwards of a hundred guns, that is to say about three times the defensive armament of the East Indiaman. A distinctive feature of the man-of-war was the 'tumble-home', a pinching-in of the top-sides which reduced deck space and was a disadvantage when heeling, but which gave increased stability by bringing the weight of the guns well inside the beam of the vessel as expanded at the water-line. This feature was imitated by the British Navy from captured French warships, the lines of which were always faithfully recorded, for progress still depended not upon applying scientific principles but upon following a successful design with appropriate modifications. At the same time, Britain accepted the position that foreign warships of a given rating were normally built a little larger than her own because she had great difficulty in finding the money and material to maintain a line of battle numerically superior to her nearest rival. As for the fitness of the man-of-war for the purposes it served, it must suffice to quote the example of the *Victory*, which was involved in eight major actions over a period of thirty-four years, flew the flags of fourteen admirals, and carried Nelson through the storm-tossed years of the great blockade and to his death at Trafalgar. She still survives.

Success breeds conservatism. As late as 1850 fundamental changes in the Royal Navy were few. Six small steamships took part in the bombardment of Acre in 1840, but in the Crimean war the British flagship in the Black Sea was a wooden three-decker, which was towed into action by a tug, and was set on fire by Russian shells. One important change in dockyard methods was the introduction of block-making machinery by Bentham, already mentioned (p. 351). Of more direct value to the working of the ship at sea was the introduction of copper to sheath ships' bottoms, which became established during the American War of Independence. The copper was found to resist the ship-worm, which infests tropical waters, so that it was no longer necessary to career ships on West Indian islands and elsewhere in order to burn off the encrustation (*see* Fig. 87). At about the same time an increased use of iron in the structure was called for, both to economize in timber and for strength: knees, standards, and diagonal braces of iron were slowly introduced. Although great improvements in rope-making had been recently devised by Edmund Cartwright and others, in 1808 (Sir) Samuel Brown, naval officer and engineer, urged the introduction also of iron cables and rigging. Chain cable had the obvious advantage that it could not readily be shot away—a factor in the success of the Anglo-Dutch bombardment of the pirates' nest at Algiers in 1816—as well as being less affected by climate, less easily cut by jagged rock, and handier to stow than the old hempen cables, which tended to kink. By 1840 chains were also commonly used in rigging. Yet, despite this considerable use of iron, the building of iron-clad warships was long delayed, even though the risk of shell-filling in the magazines of wooden ships was helping to prevent the abandonment of the old-fashioned solid shot: one reason was anxiety about the hazards of missiles ricochetting from ironwork.

With the exception of a brief period of intensive frigate building during the American war of 1812, in the half-century that followed Trafalgar the field of international rivalry was not so much the warship as the mercantile marine, with the steamship, for reasons already noticed (p. 327), playing a rather minor part. In the year of Queen Victoria's accession her subjects in the United Kingdom disposed of only 668 steamships, averaging no more than 120 tons apiece. Yet the freeing of the Far Eastern trade from the East India Company's monopoly in 1833 was followed by intense competition in the delivery of opium to China and the carriage of tea from China to the West. In 1849 the repeal of the remaining Navigation Acts opened British trade to all comers, and in the same year the gold rush round Cape Horn to California placed a new emphasis on speed, as did the Australian gold rush which quickly followed. Hence the great age of the clipper, with its sharp long bow, hollow lines, and raked masts. Where the old-fashioned traders to the Far East were commonly 'snugged down' by reducing sail for the night, clippers crammed on all sail in their much-advertised tea races with the first of the new crop, in which they might make London from Shanghai in ninety days or less.

The clipper design seems to have originated from the eighteenth-century Yankee schooner, a two-master which skimmed over the water, as further developed at Baltimore for privateering against Britain in the war of 1812. Something rather similar was being developed by Aberdeen shipbuilders in the 1840's with the incentive of the east-coast passenger and cargo run to London, but their main interest lies in the part they played after 1849 in the upsurge of the American mercantile marine, whose cheaper, though shorter-lived, soft-wood ships threatened to capture the carrying trade from the hard-wood products of British shipyards.

Some of the emigrant clippers exceeded 2,000 tons, with a tall sail-plan and the power of being driven through any weather; they were the only sailing-ships known to have run 400 sea miles in a day.

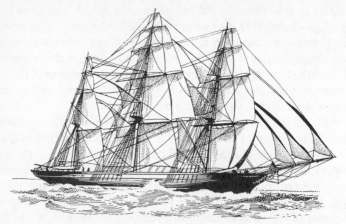

FIG. 172. The *Ariel*, one of the last of the tea-clippers

The tea-clippers were commonly less than half their size, but had to be built with greater skill so as to gain the utmost advantage from the light winds of the China seas. American competition came to an end with the outbreak of the Civil War in 1861, while in 1869 the opening of the Suez Canal (passable only by steamships) marked the beginning of the end for all sailing-ships in fast trade with the East. The millennia-old design of the sailing-ship may therefore be said to have reached its climax with such vessels as the Greenock-built *Ariel* (length 197 ft, beam 33 ft 9 in.), which as a new ship (Fig. 172) raced the *Taeping* up the English Channel in 1866 at 14 knots: both vessels docked in the Thames on the same tide ninety-nine days out from the Pagoda anchorage. But by this time wood construction was going out as well as sail propulsion; it was only the fact that an iron hull was considered injurious to tea that delayed its adoption in the tea trade. *Taeping* and *Ariel* are examples of a temporary compromise, known as composite construction: they were

built of teak planking laid over iron frames. Iron lower masts and
wire rigging had also been introduced to support the tremendous
pressure on their sails.

The achievement of the sailing-ship is all the more impressive
when measured against man's continuing ignorance of the seas over
which he sailed. In 1702 Halley had published a world chart of
magnetic declination, which proved extremely valuable to navigators, but much still remained to be learned about the vagaries of
the magnetic compass. The 'deviation' of the compass resulting
from the ship's own ironwork was not scientifically investigated
before the opening years of the nineteenth century, when Captain
Matthew Flinders, sent by the newly formed Hydrographic Department of the British Admiralty to make a further survey of the coast
of Australia, used his enforced leisure as a Napoleonic prisoner of
war in Mauritius to write a paper on this subject for the Royal
Society; hence the invention of the 'Flinders bar' to correct the effect
of the soft iron of the ship. Dead-reckoning of a ship's course continued to be based upon the literal hourly heaving of the log. Sound-
ings also were made in primitive fashion with lead and line, the lead
a weight of 14 lb and the line a length of hemp marked in fathoms.
Until the days of steamships, it was impossible to sound more than
10 fathoms without stopping the survey vessel, and the hollow in the
bottom of the lead (which was filled with tallow to make it sticky)
brought up a specimen of no more than 4 sq. in. of the sea bottom.
Though Captain C. J. Phipps, returning from Spitzbergen in 1773
(with midshipman Horatio Nelson on board), made the first deep-sea
sounding on record, and Benjamin Franklin about the same date
was using the thermometer to fix the limits of the Gulf Stream by
temperature observation, systematic oceanography dates only from
the middle of the nineteenth century.

The number of positions accurately fixed in terms of latitude and
longitude increased from 109 in 1706 to more than 6,000 in 1817;
by 1849 the British Admiralty had issued 1,748 navigational charts.
M. F. Maurey, who had been made head of the U.S. chart depot in
1841, charted the north Atlantic and inspired a conference at Brussels
to secure international co-operation. His *Physical Geography of the
Sea* (1853) became a standard textbook, and the use of his wind
and current charts was said to have reduced by a quarter the average
duration of the passage from New York to California round the
Horn, and by one-fifth that from England to Australia via the

Cape. The differences are of the order of forty-eight and twenty-seven days respectively—a striking illustration of the routine hazards to which sailing-ships had been exposed.

THE ERA OF IRON AND STEEL STEAMSHIPS

The change from wood to iron, and later steel, and the roughly parallel change from sail to steam, ended much of the romance of sea-faring; from the point of view of the historian of technology, however, the prime importance of the change is the lead which it gave to the British shipbuilding industry. It is computed that in the 1840's 90 per cent. of the world's merchant shipping was built of wood. At that date, the United States, with its huge lake and river traffic, owned a larger tonnage than Britain and half the shipbuilding of the world was conducted on the American and Canadian seaboard, where timber prices made British competition impossible. We may contrast the position in 1892–4, when Britain's share of a very much larger total construction of merchant shipping reached 81·6 per cent. But the new material did more to produce this result than the new prime mover, for the statistics of the Clyde shipyards in Scotland clearly show that the construction of iron sailing-ships, economical for long hauls with wool or grain (which in the less watertight wooden ships had always to be sacked), was at that very time reaching its final peak.

With all allowances made for aesthetic considerations and for the conservative traditions of a well-established trade embodying much of the most skilled craftsmanship of the woodworker, the shift to iron in British shipbuilding seems surprisingly slow. In 1787 John Wilkinson launched on the Severn a 70-ft barge of bolted cast-iron plates, and there were others on the canals around Birmingham in 1802. In Scotland the first iron barge was designed in 1816 by an enterprising military officer returned from the service of the Nizam of Hyderabad; built by a carpenter and two blacksmiths, it was used successfully for half a century to carry coal on the Firth of Clyde. In 1822 the first iron steamship to cross the Channel was assembled on the Thames from parts prefabricated at a Staffordshire ironworks. On two early occasions (1834 and 1844) iron ships advertised their strength by their survival after being driven ashore in exposed conditions. The great shipbuilding firm later known as Cammell Laird began to work in iron at Birkenhead in 1829, and the engineer William Fairbairn on the Thames in 1836. Nevertheless, Clydeside did not begin to produce its staple commodity of iron ships until

1839, and when the newly formed Cunard Line tendered to carry transatlantic mails by paddle-steamer in 1840, the first four ships in service all had wooden hulls.

Against the easily exploded fallacy that a vessel of iron would not float, there were to be set the solid advantages of strength and economy of production; potentially, too, iron ships could be made much longer than wooden ones. The maximum length of a wooden ship was considered to be about 300 ft, a restriction imposed by the limited strength of wood. The importance of the ship's ability to withstand bending of its long axis, especially in relation to the distance separating waves, had been made clearer by theoretical studies which Pierre Bouguer published in Paris in 1746. He showed that the combined effect of the weight of the ship and its buoyancy in the water was to create strains in the hull as it moved through the waves, the centre portion of the vessel being alternately pressed upwards (hogged) or pressed downwards (sagged) in relation to its two extremities. Bouguer's analysis was improved upon by the savant Thomas Laing in 1811, but a further half-century elapsed before this fundamentally important problem was rigorously analysed by Fairbairn and by the Glasgow professor W. J. M. Rankine. An iron hull could then be designed to meet the calculated strain.

An iron ship could be made strong enough to dispense with a keel, and built to any desired length from iron plates or slabs. With the development of the rolling-mill, it became possible to build up the transverse frames with single bars of iron reaching from centre-line to gunwale. Nevertheless, some of the early builders of iron ships, practising a conservatism not uncommon in the history of technology, assiduously built their assemblages out of short pieces of iron, just as the builders of wooden ships had of necessity used short pieces of wood. The well-known Victorian naval architect John Scott Russell was among those who preferred to dispense with the frames, and to rely for strength on transverse partitions or bulkheads joined by longitudinal stiffeners, which would also provide a series of watertight compartments. The transverse frame served during construction as a convenient scaffolding to hold the hammered and (later) rolled iron plates, already being made for boilers, which gave the iron ship its almost indestructible shell. The plates ran fore and aft in series as in a wooden ship, and to begin with were laid in clinker fashion; but after about 1850 they were fastened together end-on with rivets through the frame. Joints between the plates were made watertight by hammering. There were liners, and later other devices, so that the outer plates could be riveted to the frame without any risk of a 'spring' between the parts.

It was soon realized that in any given ship great economies could be achieved by standardizing the thickness of the plates, the size of the rivets, and the type of angle-iron used in the construction of the frame. But until near the end of the century—when hydraulic riveters began to appear in shipyards—the rivets, which might run to millions in a large vessel, were driven home by hand. Each was heated in a portable hearth by a boy, who passed (or threw) it to the holder-on; he hammered it through its hole, and held it in place for two riveters, who flattened the point with alternate blows.

In December 1853 Isambard Kingdom Brunel signed the contract for 'the great iron ship'. This famous railway and bridge engineer had already designed two highly successful steamships for the transatlantic service—the *Great Western*, the first steamship ever designed to make that crossing, and the *Great Britain*, an iron steamship which did service for thirty years after spending its first winter aground off the west coast of Ireland. The *Great Eastern*, however, was intended to show the full potentialities of the iron steamship by carrying enough fuel for a voyage to Australia and back, out by the Cape and home via the Horn. This was a bold attempt to overcome the great obstacle to the development of the steamship, namely the fact that the coal took up so much space that there was no room for any other commodities less profitable than passengers and mail; for coaling-stations hardly existed yet along the long ocean routes. As an advertisement of the structural possibilities of iron, the *Great Eastern* was a great success: as a demonstration of the economic use of coal she was a dismal failure.

The ship had a double skin of plates to the waterline with the frames between, supporting the machinery and huge coal bunkers: above this there were bulkheads placed lengthwise, designed like two Britannia Bridge tubes (p. 454). A feature of the design was the standardization of the sizes of plates, angle-irons, rivets, etc. Accommodation for 4,000 passengers was arranged on a total of five decks; even her coir-fibre rope, 47 inches in circumference, was of record size. The fact that her total tonnage of 18,918 tons was not equalled until the nineteenth century had closed may well argue that the basic conception was unsound, as events proved, but the hull, with an approximate weight of 6,250 tons, made up of 30,000 plates held together by some 3 million rivets, proved to be in excellent condition when the ship was broken up in 1888—thirty years after the difficulties of her launching, which involved an unforeseen expense of £120,000, had driven the original company to virtual bankruptcy. The *Great Eastern* was never employed on the long passenger runs for which she had been designed, and *faute de mieux* did her best service as a cable-layer. The fatal defect lay in an underestimation of the quantity of coal which her combined paddle- and screw-engines—developing 6,600 h.p.—required to drive this huge

FIG. 173. Intermediate paddle-engine shaft of the *Great Eastern*

ship at the designed speed of 14 knots (Fig. 173). The steaming-time required for the round voyage to Australia was about seventy-five days; the bunkers held 12,000 tons of coal, but the difference between the coal consumption that had been provided for and what was in practice required was of the order of 75 per cent.

It is now easily seen why the final triumph of the steamship, though accelerated by the opening of the Suez Canal, was a much slower and more complicated process than, for example, the supersession of the coach by the railway. For the carrying of cargoes of imperishable commodities, in particular, sail was only slowly replaced in the second half of the nineteenth century, as engines became more economical of fuel: the first great success was that of Alfred Holt, an engineer turned shipowner, who in 1865 equipped a ship with compound engines (p. 326) enabling it to carry 3,000 tons of cargo on a non-stop voyage of 8,500 miles, from Liverpool to Mauritius. The spread of coaling-stations over the world, on the other hand, was a result as well as a cause of the growth of steamship traffic, since the building up of stocks at suitable points was mainly the work of tramp-steamers.

Warships contemporary with the *Great Eastern* provide an interesting illustration of the changes that were going on. Armour, 4¾ in. thick, was first employed by the French to encase a wooden frigate built in 1859. To this the British replied two years later with the all-iron H.M.S. *Warrior*, whose length of 380 ft was made possible only by the use of an iron frame. But although she had a powerful screw-engine, she was also fully rigged for sail, and there was lifting-gear, operated by 600 men, for hoisting the screw into a trunk while the ship was hove-to. Warships carried large crews, and were not concerned to economize manpower by abandoning sailcraft; moreover, it was desirable for them to remain at sea for long periods at minimum cost, and often in areas remote from coaling-stations. As the turret (p. 503) replaced the broadside, masts and rigging became a serious hindrance; yet down to 1900, in spite of the more intense naval rivalry which began in 1888, the British Navy still maintained some sailing-ships on foreign stations.

In the later nineteenth century the most conspicuous change was the replacement of iron by steel as a shipbuilding material. Some of the earliest examples of its use were in the building of fast blockade-runners by the Confederates during the American Civil War to elude the *Monitor* and its consorts: the lighter construction that this material made possible meant a gain in speed. But the launching of a steel dispatch-vessel for the British Navy in 1877 marks the moment at which a rapid change began, such that by the end of the century iron had been almost completely superseded. The methods of constructing in steel were similar to those for iron, but there was a regular saving of one-fifth in the thickness of the material. The steel Cunard liners *Campania* and *Lucania* of 1893, with steam-engines developing 30,000 h.p., represent the climax of nineteenth-century ship construction. They had more than four times the power of the ill-fated *Great Eastern*, though designed to carry less than half as many passengers less than half as far. Whereas most of the shell-plates of the *Great Eastern* were each 10 ft by 33 in. and weighed 825 lb, those of the two Cunard liners were commonly 25 ft by 6 ft., and weighed 2 tons; some were even larger. Significantly, there was no provision for setting sails.

The other main change in shipbuilding generally was the increase of specialization. The early steamers had been built to carry both passengers and cargo, even though on the north Atlantic route concern with speed kept the cargo-carrying to a minimum. But Britain, as the chief shipbuilding power, was in the happy position of being able to sell obsolescent types of shipping to less fortunate countries, like Norway, which found the management and manning of tramps sufficiently profitable; moreover, the Merchant Shipping Act of 1894 enforced more stringent regulations for all British ships designed to carry passengers. Hence the emergence of the cargo liner, with its steel decks, numerous derricks and winches, and immensely strong fore-and-aft steel-tube girders. The longitudinal girders made it possible to construct holds without the rows of closely spaced pillars which in earlier ships had held up the decks to the serious detriment of stowage capacity. But increasingly important cargoes were appearing for which the size of the hold was not the only consideration. The provision of cold storage (p. 699) for meat and other quickly perishable foodstuffs is one obvious example. Another, which in the twentieth century was to prove a vital factor in both peace and war, was the development of the oil-tanker.

FIG. 174.   Late Roman tank-wagon for the conveyance of wine

When oil was carried in casks or drums, as was usual at first, although tank vehicles had long been in use for liquids such as wine (Fig. 174), its stowage required nearly twice the volume of the oil itself; if it was carried in bulk, there were dangerous possibilities of an uncontrollable surge causing the vessel to capsize. Hence the development from the 1870's onwards of a special type of steamship for the purpose. It had the machinery arranged aft so as to reduce the risk of fire; elaborate division by bulkheads to hold the oil in separate tanks; and expansion-trunks, providing space above the tanks, to prevent leakage or contraction of the oil leaving room at the top of the tank for movement. In addition, a tanker required a superior quality of riveting. In an ordinary ship minor leakages of water are usually quickly sealed by corrosion, but as oil prevents corrosion of the metal, leakages in tankers were not self-sealing. But tanker transport of oil developed rather slowly up to the end of the nineteenth century because, until the needs of the motor-car built up an insistent demand for the commodity, authorities were reluctant—on account of the risk of fire—to allow the necessary large storage-tanks at the ports of arrival.

The enormous increase of maritime traffic of all kinds was accompanied by an important growth in devices for guiding and guarding it. Although international co-operation in this field had been established in 1853 (p. 369) and the use of steamships eventually facilitated the work of the surveyor, the science of oceanography derived its first great impetus from the world voyage of the *Challenger* in 1872–6, and the 50-volume report which followed. During the second half of the century the number of British Admiralty charts approximately doubled, reaching 3,413 in 1900. A great increase in accuracy and speed of observation resulted from the introduction in 1878 of sounding-machines, developed by Sir William Thomson (later Lord Kelvin) from earlier inventions. He used thin piano wire instead of a hemp line; a 'feeler' on the wire showed when it had hit the bottom; and there were tables that related the length of the wire paid out to the speed of the ship. This device was suitable for depths up to about 20 fathoms. Thomson was responsible also, at about the same period, for the dry-card compass, which is still standard equipment on merchant vessels. Patent logs were another innovation, enabling the distance run to be read from dials without hauling the log on board: Massey's was in general use by 1840, Walker's by the last two decades of the century. Meanwhile, the extension of the electric telegraph made accurate time for longitude determination available to mariners at the world's principal ports. But perhaps the biggest advance of all was in the increased availability of one of the oldest of all aids to navigation. In 1850 the number of lighthouses and lightships in the whole world known to the British Admiralty was 1,570; by 1900 it was 9,424. The latter total has been more than trebled by the present day.

It is estimated that the mercantile marines of the world in 1800 totalled about 4 million net tons, which is twice the figure calculated by Sir William Petty for 1666. The growth of commerce during the nineteenth century may be measured by the fact that the total tonnage was more than doubled by 1840 and doubled again by 1860; in 1886, the earliest year of precise returns, it was 17,910,000 tons; and 20,531,000 tons in 1900. The final figure is all the more impressive because fully two-thirds of it was steam tonnage, reckoned on an average to perform an annual stint four times that of the same weight in sailing-ships, which were generally slower and far less punctual and reliable in their movements. As for the share of the British mercantile marine in this huge development, for two decades after Waterloo the tonnage remained stationary at about 2,500,000 tons. At mid-century Britain was believed to possess about 60 per cent. of the total of ocean-going ships owned by the powers, though she was then and up to the Civil War fast being overhauled by the United States. In 1900, however, the shipping fleet of the United Kingdom, with 9,304,108 tons, was more than twice the size of the two next largest fleets, the American and German, combined. What then appeared to be a long-term preponderance was further secured by the fact that more than three-quarters of the British ships were steamers.

THE GROWTH OF RAILWAYS

The development of inland communications to meet the needs of the industrial revolution was above all the work of civil engineers, for

FIG. 175. Horse-drawn coal-tram, Newcastle upon Tyne, 1773

neither the narrow boat (70 × 7 ft) nor the mail coach involved any striking new departure in methods of construction. Nor were there any important new branches of technology that arose immediately out of the actual working of the canal system or the macadamized turnpikes. It was otherwise with the railway train and track.

The rail-way or wagon-way, as we have seen (p. 212), is very much older than the locomotive. By the late eighteenth century it was used as an occasional convenience for many purposes—rails to help a drainage scheme had been laid across Chat Moss, for example, a whole generation before the Liverpool–Manchester railway came there—but still assisted mainly in the transport of coal (Fig. 175). The introduction of canals in Britain enhanced its usefulness as an inexpensive link with the busy pit-head; in 1800 it was brought to the Ruhr as 'the English coal-road'. Long before the permanent ways of modern parlance, which will be considered as a part of building construction (p. 446), were driven across the country, development was beginning in the rail itself, which we will therefore make our starting-point.

Iron replaced timber as a rail-making material at Whitehaven as early as 1738, but its more extensive use may be dated from the casting of rails at Coalbrookdale in 1767. As for shape, a broad plate-rail with a vertical flange on the inner side to hold plain wagon-wheels in position was the most usual, having the advantage that it did not

debar the wagons which ran on it from running along the public highway as well. But edge-rails used in conjunction with a flanged wheel (Fig. 176) were also a device dating from a very early period, at least in the north of England, and were becoming more widespread at the time of their employment in Trevithick's experiments with locomotives, already mentioned (p. 332), in South Wales and London (Fig. 177). Further advance was delayed by the brittleness of the cast-iron material, but in 1820 experiments with the more expensive wrought iron culminated in a patent for rolling wrought-iron bars into edge-rails, the durability of which caused their adoption for the Liverpool and Manchester Railway in 1830; their use then became standard practice. By mid-century the British railways generally employed double-headed iron rails not very different from the modern 'bull' rail, keyed into chairs on transverse wooden sleepers. An alternative was the inverted-T rail, designed by the American R. L. Stevens in 1830; this had a flat foot resting directly on the sleepers, to which it was secured with a spike, and with the addition of a tie-plate was eventually adopted generally, except in Britain.

FIG. 176. Coal-wagon with flanged wheel, 1783

As regards the gauge, early British practice has had great influence. The Surrey Iron Railway, opened from Croydon to Wandsworth in 1805, which was the first public railway, had a gauge of only 4 ft; but the experiments which led to the supersession of horse traction by the steam locomotive in the course of the 1820's (p. 333) took place mainly on Tyneside, where 4 ft $8\frac{1}{2}$ in. was the traditional width between the wheels of the coal wagon, a tradition which may derive from the ancient rut-road. The gauge which was therefore adopted for the Stockton–Darlington railway in 1824 was imitated by other early British railways, and was in fact well suited to the low centre of gravity of the early locomotives. The versatile inventor Richard Roberts proposed a gauge of 5 ft 3 in., but in practice the chief exception was I. K. Brunel's Great Western Railway; its gauge of 7 ft 0¼ in. was more expensive in land and construction costs, but it

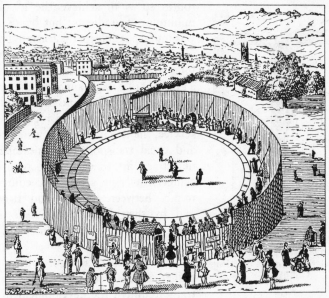

FIG. 177. Trevithick's 'Catch-me-who-can', the world's first passenger railway, 1808

provided a smoother journey for more comfortable rolling-stock drawn by more powerful locomotives. In 1846 the narrower gauge was given legal status, though the Great Western Railway did not remove the last of its broad-gauge track until 1892. British engineers abroad generally adopted the gauge to which they were accustomed at home, while in America 4 ft 8½ in. was approved by President Lincoln for the Union Pacific line and became the standard, as in Britain, in 1885. But broad gauges were established in Ireland, the Iberian Peninsula, and Finland, as well as for the great distances of Russia and India. Narrow gauges, ranging down to 2 ft, were used where expense of construction, rather than capacity or comfort, was the main consideration.

In the 1840's the British railway network increased at an amazing rate, and the traffic became denser. Although the speculative railway mania of the middle years of the decade provided the immediate occasion for this mushroom growth, it should be noticed that it was made possible by technological advance, particularly the increased tractive power of the locomotives. The first main lines (London–Birmingham, London–Bristol) depended upon the planning of their routes so as to achieve the absolute minimum of gradients; but by 1840 it was found possible for the Birmingham–Gloucester railway to operate a two-mile stretch over the Lickey hills with a gradient of 1 in 38, and even the prospective routes to Scotland then lost their terrors. As for speed and regularity of service, the two qualities in which road and canal transport were inescapably defective, in 1849 five locomotives achieved average speeds exceeding 50 m.p.h. between London and Bristol, and by then Bradshaw's *Guide* had been advertising precise train-times for ten years.

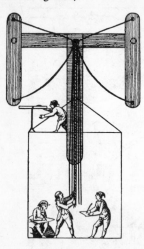

FIG. 178. Chappe's semaphore for relaying messages over long distances

The multiplication of junctions, higher speeds, and intensification of traffic required the development of an elaborate system of signals. In the earliest years it had been deemed sufficient to place a signal at 'danger' for some agreed period after the passage of any particular train, and the casualness of the system was made worse by each company's having its own style of signals. But after an experiment on the London–Croydon line in 1840 it was realized that the semaphore, which Chappe had invented to signal the orders of the French revolutionary government in 1793 (Fig. 178), was particularly suited to the peaceful needs of the railway. By this time the electric telegraph in its most primitive form was coming into use to transmit information between stations: the first such installation was between Paddington and West Drayton (1839). This made it possible gradually to introduce the block system, the line being divided into 'blocks' by signal-boxes (Fig. 179); no new train was admitted into a block until the emergence of its predecessor had been reported by the signalman at the farther end. Later in the century this became the standard practice enforced on all British and most other European main lines. The interlocking of points and signals began at important London junctions—first on the Hampstead Junction railway in 1859—and was patented, but countries where distances were longer were mostly content with single lines and a much simpler system of signalling. In America telegraphic train-orders were largely used for a long time to control

FIG. 179. Early signal-box, Victoria, London

a vast single-track network, although as early as 1860 the London and North Western Railway had devised the train-staff system, by which the passing of a token to and fro made it impossible for two trains to be brought into the same single-track section from opposite ends by mistake.

The second half of the century saw great improvements in the track itself. As with shipping, the biggest change was the replacement of iron by steel, which proved to be about fifteen times as durable. The pioneer work as far as railways are concerned was done at Crewe, where Bessemer steel was both made and rolled into rails, the first successful trials being conducted in 1862. Steel rails for the rapidly expanding American railways were being made in Pennsylvania in 1867, and in 1869 contracts for importation were placed with a Sheffield firm. Although steel rails could be lighter than equivalent iron ones, rails increased in weight to meet the requirements of heavier and faster trains. There was also an improvement in rail-joints. Before the fifties the rail-ends were merely keyed into a common chair, but R. L. Stevens in America then introduced fish-plates—narrow plates bolted to the web of each pair of rail-ends at both sides.

From the point of view of the travelling public, however, the most noticeable feature of any railway was its stations. To begin with, they served for carriage sheds as well as to shelter passengers, and even

FIG. 180. Baker Street station, London, 1863

when the great city termini began to blossom forth in huge arched roofs of iron and steel (p. 411), their splendid spaciousness was necessitated largely by technical considerations of lighting and ventilation, arising from the need to move crowds of people and innumerable packages in a confined space while locomotives waited with steam up. Fan-shaped metropolitan termini; the layout of platforms as islands by-passed by through-lines on either side; and the complete separation of goods and passenger stations, were three Victorian solutions of the difficult technical problem of making a large railway station accessible for both the railway and its would-be users.

Towards the end of the century, resort was had in some urban areas to the immensely costly expedient of taking the railway below ground. This began in 1863 with the Metropolitan railway, which passed through central London in a built-over cutting just below street level (Fig. 180). One of its chief functions was to link up the principal railway stations north of the river, and it was worked by steam-locomotives provided with surface-condensers, which were intended—but not infrequently failed—to keep the air in the tunnels from becoming quite intolerable. The first 'tube' in the modern sense was the City and South London railway, passing under the bed of the Thames and built in true tunnel fashion, which was operated by electric locomotives of 150 h.p. This was opened in 1890, and by the end of the century the completion of two more London 'tubes', the Waterloo and City and the Central London lines, showed that an acceptable solution had been found for the traffic problem of the capital, while a subway with cable traction had also been intro-duced in Glasgow. Even more important for the future was the opening of the first main-line electrification in America in 1895; this

FIG. 181. Stephenson's passenger coach as it appeared in the
opening procession of the Stockton–Darlington railway

was in a 4-mile tunnel under Baltimore. The first electric railway, which was 300 yards long and conducted the current to its 3 h.p. engine along a centre-rail, had been seen at an exhibition in Berlin in 1879, but down to the end of the century the chief use of electricity in local transport was for the tramway.

The material progress of the Victorian age is well epitomized in the development of railway passenger rolling-stock from the single horse-drawn coach, designed by Stephenson, and owned by the Stockton and Darlington Company in 1825 (Fig. 181). While railway travel was a novelty, and speed alone could attract custom, it was sufficient for the appearance of the first-class coach to resemble the vehicle from which it had its name, except that what would have made up three or even four horse-drawn vehicles was now mounted on a single frame (Fig. 182). As for the third-class, it resembled the open wagon in which its occupants a few years earlier might have expected to travel—at a walking pace: the exposure and discomfort of the new accommodation was at first overlooked in the exhilaration of its conquest of distance. These early coaches were four-wheeled or, exceptionally, six-wheeled; the first eight-wheeled coach was introduced into the broad-gauged Great Western in 1852, but such carriages continued to be a rarity for twenty years. Though the bogie-truck was patented by an Englishman, William Chapman, in 1812, the regular provision of bogies at each end of a long passenger-coach to facilitate the taking of curves was an American innovation, a valuable precaution against derailment on imperfectly laid tracks.

In passenger-coach design America led the way, not only because the long distances made the introduction of such amenities as sleep-

FIG. 182. First-class carriage, Great Western Railway, 1839

ing-cars, dining-cars, and lavatory facilities a virtual necessity, but for the more interesting reason that the most obvious model in American eyes was not any horse-drawn vehicle, but the long cabin of the canal- or riverboat. Russia was a close imitator of American practice. A higher standard of comfort for those who would pay for it entered the British railway system with the first imported American Pullman cars in 1874. In the very next year, however, the Midland Railway set a standard, which few foreign countries even attempted to match, by the introduction of upholstered seats for all classes of passengers. What is now the regular type of British side-corridored coach, made up of small compartments with lavatories at either end, first came to Britain in 1882 as a small version of an Austrian vehicle. Electric lighting from a dynamo beneath the coach was not patented until 1896, though an electrically lit Pullman car, imported from America, was running between London and Brighton in 1881: in this, the electricity was derived from storage batteries.

In two other important matters of railway practice, America with its long distances led the way. At an early date, America adopted huge freight-cars with double bogies and an automatic central coupler. Europe, however, continued to make do with small four-wheeled wagons, such as a team of horses might have drawn, and to use the screw-couplings and side-buffers, which had been invented in the 1830's; many such trucks are still in use. Even more remarkable was European indifference to the need for improved braking systems. A steam-brake was invented by Robert Stephenson in 1833, but anything more than a hand-brake on tender and van was long regarded as a luxury. In 1875 in a test at Newark the American Westinghouse brake—worked by compressed air, continuous, and automatic in the event of the train dividing—proved its ability to stop a 200-ton train at 50 m.p.h. in less than 1,000 ft. An effective British vacuum brake was patented by J. A. F. Aspinall in 1879, thirty-five years after the earliest patent had been taken out by Nasmyth. Yet it was not until eighty people were killed in a collision near Armagh in 1889 that automatic continuous power-brakes were made compulsory for British passenger trains. The result was not only to avert many possible disasters and to reassure the anxious traveller, but to improve the timing of express trains by enabling them to pull up more quickly.

Although railways, as we have seen, originated in the needs of heavy goods traffic, especially coal, their development in Britain in the early years of the locomotive received an unexpectedly large stimulus from passenger traffic, which at the time of the boom in the middle 1840's provided almost two-thirds of the earnings. During the second half of the century the railway mileage of the United Kingdom grew from 6,621 to 21,855 miles, and the number of passengers carried (exclusive of season-ticket holders, a class of passenger indicative of social change) from 73 millions to 1,142 millions a year. The weight of the goods carried also increased enormously, from 90 million tons in 1860 to 235 million tons in 1880 and 425 million tons in 1900, but their share of the total earnings, though larger than before, never reached 60 per cent. In the same period the railways of the United States grew from a length of less than 10,000 miles in 1850 and 30,626 on the eve of the Civil War to 93,261 miles in 1880 and 198,964 in 1900—the last figure being nearly 23,000 miles greater than the railway mileage of the whole of Europe. Their functions were correspondingly important: whereas in Britain and other long-settled European countries the railway for the most part stimulated the social life and developed the trade of existing communities, in vast areas of America it created the community and the trade. On American railways, accordingly, with forty freight cars to every passenger car, more than 75 per cent. of earnings came from goods traffic.

Mention has already been made of the electric tramway (p. 383). When the steam locomotive replaced horse traction for long-distance rail transport, the horse omnibus—brought from Paris to London in 1829—was just coming into use as a popular street conveyance. Rails had obvious advantages for a heavy vehicle pulled along rough stone surfaces, so the first tramway car, with a 30-seater omnibus body mounted on four flanged wheels, ran along the Bowery, New York, as early as 1832. The system spread to some other American cities, in 1855 to Paris, and in 1860–1 to Birkenhead and London. But

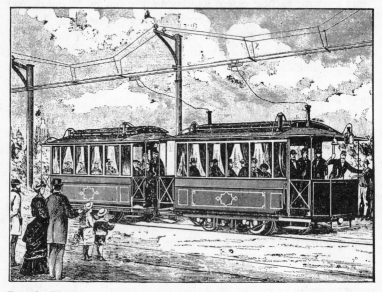

FIG. 183. Electric tram on the Frankfurt-am-Main and Offenbach service, with overhead supply, 1884

neither a rail with a deep wide groove, which was first adopted, nor a 5-in. flat rail with a $\frac{7}{8}$-in. high step at one side, introduced in Philadelphia and the type first laid in England, was free from danger to other traffic. The first London tramway was taken up again in consequence, but the modern flat-grooved rail was produced in time to save the situation in the provinces, and the Tramways Act (1870) was passed to encourage local development. Traction methods also began to be improved towards the end of the decade, when the introduction of girder-rails provided a stronger track. As horses or mules, up to four in number, maintained an average speed of only 6–7 m.p.h., use was made of steam-power, sometimes by means of an underground wire cable attached to a stationary engine, more commonly in the form of an enclosed locomotive coupled to the car. The steam tram, however, was noisy and dirty. In Britain it was popular only in the industrial districts—there are many references to it in Arnold Bennett's descriptions of The Potteries; elsewhere, horse-traction held its own until the last decade of the century.

Electric trams, deriving their power from overhead lines and bearing a strong resemblance to those still used in many continental cities, were in use in Germany by 1884 (Fig. 183), and the first extensive overhead trolley system in the United States was built at Richmond, Virginia, in 1888. In Britain, electric traction was successfully installed at Leeds in 1891; other large towns followed, but ten years later London had no more than 16 track miles converted. The golden age of tramways then quickly followed, though in Britain their value to the community was always restricted by their parochial systems of management: Leeds and Bradford, for example, though near neighbours, clung to their respective tramway gauges of 4 ft 8½ in. and 4 ft.

THE ROAD-STEAMER AND THE BICYCLE

The railway conferred enormous social as well as economic advantages, not only by reducing the physical barrier of distance, but by lowering the no less frustrating barrier of class. Travel, unaccompanied by privation, was made available indeed to all except the very poor, but it was a disciplined form of travel, and as the high-roads became empty and silent the individual seemed to lose something of the freedom of self-expression which we find in British travellers of the pre-railway age as depicted by Borrow, Surtees, or Dickens. The development of mechanical road-vehicles, culminating in the last quarter of the century, therefore has an interest far beyond the modest place which it occupied in the economic life of an age when the motor-car was still a curiosity, while bicycles, though numerous, had scarcely descended to the practical uses even of the errand-boy.

It is at first sight rather remarkable that neither steam nor electricity should as yet have powered a generally satisfactory all-purpose road-carriage. The first pioneer was N. J. Cugnot in France, who made a steam-driven three-wheeler move at walking-pace in 1769 (see Fig. 150). The idea had also attracted the attention of the American inventor Oliver Evans, and of Boulton & Watt's employee William Murdock, before Trevithick built his steam road-carriages (p. 332). He was followed by a fellow Cornishman, Sir Goldsworthy Gurney, who in 1831 perfected a steam-carriage that provided a regular service between Gloucester and Cheltenham—9 miles in 45 minutes; within the next three years there was a steam-driven omnibus in London, covering an 8-mile route in less than one hour on one sack of coke, and similar enterprises in the neighbourhood of Glasgow and other large towns. Church's steam-carriage (Fig. 184) is of approximately the same date. But stage-coach proprietors and others whose interests were threatened drove the new vehicles off the roads by heavy tolls: the Liverpool–Prescot Turnpike Trust, for example,

FIG. 184. Church's steam-driven road carriage, 1833

charged 4s. for an ordinary coach but 48s. for a steam-coach. The triumph of the railway locomotive in the next two decades had a double effect. On the one hand, its success suggested that a road locomotive must also be fully practicable; on the other, a powerful new interest had been created which naturally sought to keep traffic off the roads. In Britain, the so-called Red Flag Act of 1865, as amended in 1878, restricted all mechanical road vehicles to a speed of 4 m.p.h. and required them to carry a crew of two, with a third man going ahead to give warning.

The road-steamer invented by Thomas Rickett in 1858 resembled a curious cross between a railway-engine and an invalid-carriage. It seated three behind the tiller, carried a stoker standing on the platform at the back, and was normally driven from the rear offside wheel alone. Other models followed, ranging from a fully enclosed steam-coach (Fig. 185), which might weigh as much as $4\frac{1}{2}$ tons, to the steam-tricycle (Fig. 186), developed in France in the 1880's. One of the makers of steam-tricycles, Léon Serpollet, invented an instantaneous steam-generator, which worked by pumping a small quantity of water through red-hot coils of nickel-steel tubing. He adapted this to a four-cylinder engine for a steam-carriage in 1894, and with American financial support this vehicle became well known in Britain and France. In America, too, success came at the very end of the century, when a twin-cylinder engine—fitted, like some of Serpollet's later models, with a petroleum burner—was used by the brothers Stanley to drive a wooden two-seater vehicle with

FIG. 185. Randolph's steam-carriage, 1872

a total weight of only 7 cwt. Their steam-cars enjoyed a considerable vogue—until the new era in which the Model 'T' Ford swept the market.

Only the steam traction-engine, however, had a long-term future. As early as 1871 there was a type of road-steamer with solid rubber tyres, manufactured in Aberdeen, which was exported as far afield as India, where it drew two-wheeled omnibuses. But the main line of development was through the steam-plough, first introduced about 1850 as a portable engine placed at the end of a field to draw a plough along it by a wire rope. Half a dozen years later it was judged more convenient for the engine itself to move to and fro across the field. By 1870 the steam traction-engine, with the cylinder at the front of the boiler,

FIG. 186. Serpollet's steam-tricycle, 1887

gear transmission, and wheel-steering from the driving position, had reached its modern form. Their tractive power was very great, so that it was a long time before the heavy petrol-lorry and trailer could compete with them effectively, especially in the industrial north; as the showman's engine, which could also be used to turn the contraptions it pulled from fair to fair, they lasted even longer. But at the present day virtually the only steamer still to be met with on the roads is an occasional example of the heavy and almost imperishable road-roller (*see* Fig. 217), first propelled by steam in 1867.

The road-steamer was practicable but cumbrous; the self-sufficient electric carriage an ideal mode of conveyance, but impracticable. Its history begins when suitable storage batteries (p. 612) became obtainable, about 1880, and a tricycle, a cab, and a dogcart were

FIG. 187. The hobby-horse, *c.* 1818

all produced experimentally in quick succession. In 1899 a cigar-shaped machine built for a Belgian established a world speed record on land of nearly 66 m.p.h., but in the same year the London Electric Cab Company, with thirty-six cabs in use and more than this number under construction, was wound up after only two years' operation. These cabs are described as having been heavy, slow, and jerky—but the contemporary hansom cab and the 'growler' had their limitations, too. The design was neat, and although the battery restricted the range to 50 miles on a single charge, arrangements were made for its rapid replacement. Nevertheless, it was the limitation imposed by the need to carry and recharge heavy storage batteries that prevented electric carriages becoming popular and gave the future to the petrol-driven motorcar.

Meanwhile the bicycle, which brought new life to the roads, romance to the young, and emancipation to the weaker sex, was a technological development which in the 1880's and 1890's did much to transform the leisure hours of civilized man. The idea of propelling oneself along by the feet while seated astride a two-wheeled machine goes back beyond the nineteenth century, but it was in 1818 that a German, Freiherr Drais, patented his 'Draisine' ·(Fig. 187). A pad was provided on the front of the frame, so that the rider might lean forward to get the maximum impetus out of his kick; the primitive steering-bar derived additional importance from the fact that there was no brake. Treadles linked to the rear-wheel—which we think of as the essential feature of the bicycle—

were added by a Scotsman, K. Macmillan, about twenty years later, and he also introduced a brake; but it was a Frenchman, Pierre Michaux, who, in the 1860's, put cranks and pedals directly on to the front wheel and formed a company to manufacture his 'velocipedes'. The bicycle industry (like its concomitant, bicycle racing) thus began in France, whence it spread to Coventry in 1869. Fifteen years later there were more than 200 varieties on the market, if we include tandems (Fig. 188) as well as dicycles with two parallel wheels,

FIG. 188. Design for a tandem, 1869

tricycles, and even four-wheelers. For a long time the predominant type, the 'ordinary' bicycle or 'penny-farthing', was that in which the rider was precariously balanced over the front wheel, which was made as large as possible to maximize the distance covered by the wheel for each revolution of the pedals (Fig. 189). It was the use of geared-up chain-drive to the rear wheel which made possible the model originally known as the 'safety' bicycle, in which a more satisfactory balance and better steering and braking were achieved by returning the rider to a position between two wheels of equal dimension, though with the bulk of his weight apportioned to the back wheel. Such a machine was first adumbrated in 1876, but commercial success was not achieved until the Rover bicycle of 1885 (Fig. 190). Apart from the introduction of the motor-cycle (to be considered in the next section) two other important innovations were made by the end of the century which brought the bicycle substantially to its present stage of development. One was the free-wheel; the other was the improvement of the steering by curving the front fork so as to place the steering column in line with the point of contact of the wheel with the ground.

In 1888 a Belfast veterinary surgeon, J. B. Dunlop, invented the pneumatic tyre (p. 529) for the benefit of his ten-year-old son. This

FIG. 189. Rudge 'ordinary' bicycle, 1884   FIG. 190. Rover safety bicycle, 1885

device had been patented as early as 1845, but at that time the demand for more smoothly running horse-drawn carriages was not sufficient for commercial success. But whereas in a carriage much of the road-shock was absorbed by the suspension, the cyclist's contact with the ground was far more direct, so the pneumatic tyre rapidly became standard equipment. The same device also proved applicable to the needs of the newly arrived motor-car.

THE EARLY MOTOR-CAR

Although petrol-driven vehicles in essentially their modern form had been developed by the end of the century, they differ from the mechanically propelled vehicles we have so far considered in that their social impact came later. Steam-driven vehicles had, as we have seen, a modest success, especially for heavy-duty work, but they had disadvantages which limited their appeal to the private user. Not only were they slow and cumbersome, hot and dirty—for passengers had necessarily to sit close to the boiler—but they needed considerable preparation before a journey could be made and also frequent attention while on the road. Many of these drawbacks might have been reduced in time, had not the advent of the petrol-car offered such immediate advantages that there was little incentive to proceed with attempts to improve steam-cars.

The evolution of the internal combustion engine itself is described elsewhere (Ch. 21): here we are concerned only with its application to transport. An Austrian inventor, Siegfried Markus, is reported to have mounted such an engine upon a handcart about the year 1864, and the Technical Museum in Vienna still preserves a vehicle built by him about ten years later. This is a heavy, clumsy object with a horizontal single-cylinder four-stroke engine, giving a maximum speed of only 5 m.p.h., and is steered by a hand-wheel swivelling

FIG. 191. Benz motor-car, 1888

the entire fore-carriage, as in a cart. Nothing came of Markus's inventions, however, and Karl Benz of Mannheim may properly be regarded as the father of the automobile. The single-cylindered light vehicle, first constructed by him in 1885 and in the following year driven through the streets of Munich, had a vertical crankshaft at the rear of the car, and a belt-drive which could be moved from a fixed to a loose pulley, thus acting as a clutch to allow the engine to be run in neutral (Fig. 191). A small tiller controlled the single front wheel; the speed was about 8 m.p.h. Eight years later Benz elaborated his design into a four-wheeled car with horizontal crankshaft, as in all modern cars, and two-speed belt-drive, and this $3\frac{1}{2}$ h.p. machine was built in hundreds by the end of the century.

The launching of Benz's first design was followed immediately by the first high-speed engine, the achievement of a fellow-German, Gottlieb Daimler of Württemberg. His compact, vertical, single-cylinder engine (p. 605), rotating much faster than Benz's, was tried out on a motor-cycle in 1886, and in 1887 at the rear of an experimental carriage. He then produced various designs of four-wheeled motor-carriages, all of them employing belt transmission. These were produced at the Cannstatt works near Stuttgart, and are the ancestors of the Mercédès cars.

The earliest English pioneer was Edward Butler, whose 'petrol cycle' was designed in 1884, but was not built and tested until four years later. This had a horizontal, twin-cylinder engine driving a single rear wheel, which could be lifted clear of the ground by a foot-lever for starting. There was promise in Butler's use of electric ignition, but he gave up his experiments because of the restrictions of the Red Flag Law, which effectively handicapped British inventors until its repeal in 1896. Another pioneer vehicle was one built in Denmark in 1886; it was steered with a wheel instead of a tiller, had a leather-lined cone-clutch for the driving of each rear wheel, so that there could be some slipping at curves (a problem eventually solved by the rear-axle differential gear), and made provision for taking the drive from the camshaft so as to go into reverse. The French began with Daimler engines built under licence in Paris, but they quickly developed a layout of their own, initiated in 1891 by Panhard and Levassor, which, with modifications in detail, rapidly became standard practice for nearly all other makers. The twin-cylinder engine at the front was connected through a friction clutch to a three-speed gear-box, whence there was a central chain drive to the rear axle, which included a differential gear.

From 1895 onwards, English and American designers become increasingly important. The first three-wheeled Wolseley was designed by Herbert Austin while he was still in the employment of the Wolseley Sheep Shearing Machine Company. This had a balanced, horizontally-opposed, twin-cylinder engine, mounted on a steel tubular frame; a roller chain linked the gear-box with the single rear wheel; the 2-h.p. engine was air-cooled. But technologically a more striking figure is that of F. W. Lanchester, who was already an engineer of distinction before he set out to design a motor-vehicle. He was the first to study the new vehicle from first principles: earlier designers had been very much influenced by the design and construction of horse-drawn carriages—the early name of 'horseless carriage' is an indication of this preoccupation with the past. Several features which Lanchester introduced in 1895-6 (Fig. 192) are to be found in every modern car. The single-cylinder air-cooled engine of his first 5-h.p. machine is described elsewhere (p. 606); it also had an epicyclic gear-box, giving low and reverse speeds as well as direct drive on high gear, together with tangentially spoked wire wheels (already in use for bicycles) and Dunlop pneumatic tyres.

In the new century, however, all other companies faded into insignificance, so far as scale of operation was concerned, by comparison with the Ford Motor Company, founded in 1903. Henry Ford had his first car running as early as 1896, and had been developing his ideas for it since 1890. It had a twin-cylinder water-cooled engine, placed in the rear, and belt transmission, but it was tiller-steered and the wire wheels had solid rubber tyres; nevertheless, its maximum speed of 25 m.p.h. compared favourably with that of most European models of the same date. Ford improved upon this in his second model, and by 1908 was ready to make the world motor-minded with the mass-production of his Model

Fig. 192. First Lanchester car (converted to wheel-steering), 1896

'T', which was sold for nineteen years, without any major change of design, to a total of 15 million customers.

Like the mass-produced tourer, the heavy lorry and the motor omnibus were important developments from nineteenth-century technology which it was left for the twentieth century to experience. Mention must, however, be made of the development of the motorcycle, which was the subject of Daimler's first patent application for his high-speed petrol-engine in 1885. The engine was mounted vertically between the wheels, the drive being to the rear wheel by a leather band, which could be tightened or slackened at will by the rider, but it is doubtful whether the trials of this machine were successful. A second motor-bicycle, driven through cranks and connecting-rods, was built in Germany in 1893, and was manufactured from 1895 onwards in an improved form in France. Finally, the brothers Werner, Russians who settled in France, experimented with putting a small motor on a safety bicycle. Their first patent was for a system of front-wheel drive, with the engine placed above the wheel, but in 1900 they brought the engine back to the midway position between the wheels, where Daimler had had it. This was the prototype of the modern motor-cycle, which leapt into popularity in the years immediately preceding the First World War.

INITIATION OF THE CONQUEST OF THE AIR

We have seen how new inventions enormously reduced the difficulties of transporting persons and goods by land and by sea. During the same period the problem of sending messages was solved by the introduction of telegraphy, telephony, and wireless (p. 621–9), so that ultimately a message could pass round the world in a matter of seconds. There remained the conquest of the air. The main history of the lighter-than-air machine falls just within our period, for the

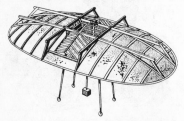

FIG. 193. Swedenborg's design for a flying-machine, *c.* 1716

first Zeppelin, virtually the end of this line of evolution, was launched in 1900. But the heavier-than-air machine, with which the future lay, depended upon the development of the internal combustion engine to provide a sufficiently light and powerful prime-mover, and did not achieve its first successful flight until December 1903. Its impact upon mankind being purely a twentieth-century phenomenon, only a few threads of its early history can be examined here.

Man has always wanted to fly, as witness the myth of Daedalus and Icarus. The flight of the bird has always symbolized for him unimpeded transportation by a route of unparalleled directness and apparent ease. The Chinese flew kites, possibly including man-lifting kites, in the first millennium B.C., while Leonardo da Vinci's inquiries and speculations about the problems of flight represent only a Renaissance intensification of an interest which can be traced back through the Middle Ages into the world of Greece and Rome. In the eighteenth century Emanuel Swedenborg produced a detailed design (Fig. 193) for a light-weight flying machine of the ornithopter type. The wings, which were to expand on the downward stroke and fold on the upward, were to be worked by springs controlled by the aviator, and stability was to be achieved by means of a weight suspended below the centre of gravity. Interesting though it is, there is no evidence that any serious attempt was made to translate Swedenborg's design into practice. That buoyancy in air is governed by the same Archimedean principle as governs the floating of solid objects in liquids, seems first to have been clearly understood by a seventeenth-century Jesuit, Francesco de Lana-Terzi.

But successful balloon ascents began in France in the age of Lavoisier and the Encylopaedists. Though hot air was employed on the very first occasion, it was only a matter of days before knowledge of the properties of hydrogen, discovered in 1766, was used to make a more efficient lifting device. These first two flights were made from Paris, in late November and early December 1783 respectively, by two pairs of adventurous Frenchmen, including on the second occasion the famous physicist J. A. C. Charles, who had suggested the use of hydrogen and who afterwards went on alone to reach a height of 9,000 ft.

Hardly more than a year passed before the first crossing of the English Channel (Fig. 194). In the course of the nineteenth century balloons were used for meteorology and the examination of the upper atmosphere to a height of 25,000 ft; for occasional air photographs and emergency transport (as during the siege of Paris in

FIG. 194. First aerial crossing of the English Channel, by Blanchard and Jefferies, 1785

1870); and even for an ill-fated attempt to reach the North Pole (1897). Captive balloons were used for military observation as early as the battle of Fleurus in 1794, by the Federal Army in the American Civil War (see Fig. 139), and by the British in South Africa—to say nothing of imaginative proposals, such as one for their participation in a Napoleonic invasion of England (Fig. 195). Yet the chief use of the balloon was at fairs and fêtes—as early as 1810 the installation of a new chancellor of Oxford university was celebrated by a balloon ascent from Merton Fields—often as an evening spectacle illuminated by fireworks, or dramatized by parachute jumps: so long as the

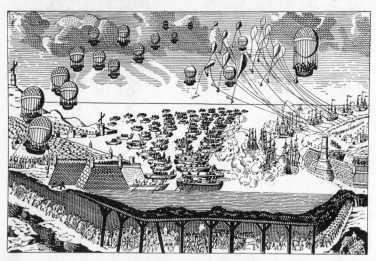

FIG. 195. Imaginary concept for French invasion of England by balloon and tunnel, 1805; the English forces fly single-seater kites in defence

balloon remained at the mercy of the wind, its practical usefulness was limited.

The problem of propulsion was a difficult one, even after the obvious preliminary step had been taken of giving an elongated shape to the envelope: the light but powerful engine required was not available pending the development of the petrol engine. In 1852 the French engineer Henri Giffard experimented with a 3-h.p. steam-engine driving a three-bladed propeller (Fig. 196); this achieved steerage-way, but little more. In 1884 a balloon fitted with a 9-h.p. electric motor driven by especially light batteries attained a speed of 14 m.p.h. on a circular flight of about 5 miles, and at the very end of the century France—where both these experiments had been conducted—was building both large and small airships, which were flown with considerable success, especially by the Brazilian aviator Santos-Dumont. These were all pressure-airships, in which the gas maintained the shape of the envelope.

The Germans adopted the alternative plan of building a rigid airship, of which the streamlined hull enclosed a series of self-contained gas-bags; nacelles, carrying the engine and crew, were suspended below. Rigid airships were made much bigger than the pressure type, and the first attempt to fly one, in 1897, proved a failure. But they were enthusiastically promoted by Count F. von Zeppelin, who launched, in the summer of 1900, the first of the long series to which his name became attached. They played such a spectacular, though largely ineffective, part in the early years of the First World

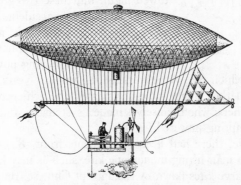

FIG. 196. Giffard's steam-driven airship, 1852

War that the virtual extinction of the airship in the 1930's could hardly have been anticipated. One major problem, never satisfactorily solved, was that of obtaining the necessary lift with safety. Hydrogen is by far the lightest gas known, but in admixture with air is violently explosive, and this was the cause of many disasters. Helium, discovered in 1895 but not commercially available until much later, and then only in limited quantities, is completely inert but has only a quarter of the lifting power of hydrogen.

The apparent promise of airships and the plausibility of attempting direct imitation of bird-flight distracted many inventors from making a correct approach to the problem of flight, which lay through the kite and the glider. The father of modern aerial navigation was Sir George Cayley, who not only saw, as a few other pioneers had seen, that fixed wings were essential, but in 1804 began a series of experiments in the flying of model gliders from hilltops. He continued his tests for almost half a century, in the course of which he is believed twice to have achieved success—to the extent, that is, of flying a glider for a short distance with a human occupant (Fig. 197). Experiments with gliders, aimed at securing stability and control with a full-sized machine, continued after Cayley's death, and it

FIG. 197. Caley's design for a man-carrying glider, 1799

was on his principles that success was finally achieved by the German, Otto Lilienthal, and his English follower, P. S. Pilcher. In the 1890's Lilienthal made more than a thousand glides in his so-called 'hanging glider' (Fig. 198). Pilcher also achieved towed flight, but these two great pioneers were killed in gliding accidents in 1896 and 1899 respectively, so that it is impossible to tell how much they might have achieved with the ideas for applying power to their gliders, on which they were working in their last years. It is quite possible that they might have anticipated the achievement of the Wright brothers, who themselves made a systematic study of gliding before attempting powered flight.

Meanwhile, there had been experiments from 1827 onwards in developing a man-lifting monoplane kite, such as may have figured among the large kites flown by the ancient Chinese. But there were no practical results until the more efficient box-kite with biplane lifting-surfaces was invented by L. Hargrave in Australia in 1893; this was influencing the ideas of Pilcher at the time of his death. Among others who saw the significance of the box-kite was the French engineer and gliding pioneer Octave Chanute, who passed on the notion of the trussed-biplane structure to the Wrights and encouraged them in other ways.

Although the glider was of paramount importance, it would be wrong to ignore other nineteenth-century developments which pre-

FIG. 198. Lilienthal's glider, 1895

pared the way for the final achievement of the Wright brothers. For example, there was a Chard lace-maker, John Stringfellow, who in the year of revolutions, 1848, succeeded in flying a fixed-wing model aircraft on a wire. From the 1850's onwards there were model aeroplanes which took off from the ground and made flights under various forms of power—twisted rubber, clockwork, steam, or compressed air. The French were the most prominent pioneers in this, though

Hargrave also played a considerable part. There was even a dart-shaped design which it was proposed to propel by a steam jet; this, like the development of the fin-stabilized Hale rocket for military purposes, anticipated by nearly a hundred years the line of mid-twentieth-century man's most spectacular advance in aeronautics. In 1896 the use of models culminated in the achievement of an American professor of astronomy, S. P. Langley, whose steam-powered monoplane with a 16-ft wing-span flew three-quarters of a mile.

Yet it is the event of 17 December 1903 that truly marks the end of the nineteenth century. The tailless pusher biplane, powered by

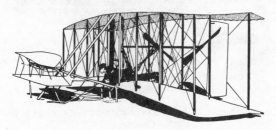

FIG. 199. The Wright brothers' original flying-machine, 1903

a 12 h.p. petrol engine, which the young American bicycle manu-facturer Orville Wright flew that day, was home-built by himself and his brother Wilbur (Fig. 199). The first flight covered no more than 40 yards and lasted 12 seconds, but what had been triumphantly demonstrated was man's capacity to convey himself through the air by the use of heavier-than-air machinery, with adequate control of speed, height, and direction. The American press, nevertheless, en-tirely ignored the event, and it was not until 1908 that the Wrights' invention, improved in successive years, was taken up in America and Europe. Before that, the Brazilian aviator Alberto Santos-Dumont had made the first flight in Europe in an independently conceived but inferior biplane; the Voisin brothers at their French factory had designed a superior box-kite biplane, from which the modern tractor biplane was evolved; and their associate, Louis Blériot, was design-ing the monoplane in which he next year flew the English Channel (Fig. 200). The essential technical evolution was thereby completed, for with the growth of the theory of aerodynamics—to which the nineteenth century made virtually no contribution save that of Cayley—the monoplane design became supreme. It was also the dramatic beginning of a new period of political history, in which man's new mastery of a third element intervened to complicate and perhaps eventually to obliterate the age-long rivalries between land power and sea power.

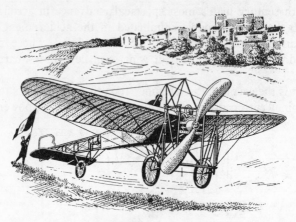

FIG. 200. Blériot landing at Dover after the first crossing of the English Channel, 1909

BUILDING CONSTRUCTION: REQUIREMENTS OF URBAN COMMUNITIES

THE CIVIL ENGINEER

THE growth of population and rapid industrial changes of the period 1750–1900 called for an immense amount of building construction. Some of this, like the permanent way for the steam locomotive to travel on, was wholly new. Other elements, such as the water-supply and drainage systems of large towns, were very largely new in technique and scale if not in inception. Domestic housing, though it followed on the whole traditional forms, made use of new materials and new techniques of mass production. The many new requirements of modern factories, workshops, and office blocks presented novel problems of architectural contrivance. Space is lacking, therefore, to consider the subject in any detail in terms of changes in architectural style or the growth of structural theory. Instead, it will be treated in the present chapter primarily from the point of view of materials, which conditioned all the work of the civil engineer, and of two branches of engineering, namely water-supply and drainage, which made an essential contribution to the growth of modern urban life. The following chapter will mainly describe the wide range of constructional work required in connexion with modern transportation, though the division, made for convenience, is subject to exceptions.

It was at the start of this period that the profession of civil engineer first clearly emerged; just as military engineering had been separated from civil engineering in France in the days of Colbert and Vauban (p. 184), so the later eighteenth century witnessed the establishment of a clear distinction between the civil engineer and the architect. France again led the way, for its official staff in charge of bridges and roads (p. 188) were the first recognized civil engineers. The French Revolution for a short time submerged their school in a larger organization, but when it resumed its independent existence its position had in fact been enormously strengthened by the institution of the great Polytechnic School, where the civil engineer and others obtained a preliminary training before admission to the specialist schools. It is not surprising, therefore, that France also led the way in the field of engineering literature, so much so that the French language was deemed an essential accomplishment by practical engineers like Rennie and Telford, while in 1816–23 a Napoleonic veteran was professor of engineering at the U.S. Military Academy, West Point. J. R. Perronet, the first head of the École des Ponts et Chaussées, wrote on bridge-building, while *La Science des Ingénieurs* by B. F. de Belidor was reissued as late as 1830, 101 years after publication, with mere footnotes recording subsequent advances. In 1826 a standard textbook of constructional theory was published for French students by C. L. M. H. Navier, a service which was not performed for British students until Rankine became professor of engineering at Glasgow University in 1855.

The growth of the engineering profession in Britain, though slower, was marked by the formation of a society of engineers, later known as the Smeatonian Club, in 1771, and of the Institution of Civil Engineers in 1818. The Mechanics' Institutes which sprang up in the industrial areas in the 1820's operated at an altogether humbler level, trying (to quote the aims stated at Manchester in 1827) 'to teach the workman those principles of science on which his work depends'. Even at this level, their efforts were largely frustrated by the absence of the necessary basis of primary education; nevertheless, the institutes contrived occasionally to sow the seeds of intellectual curiosity from which a self-made career in civil engineering might spring. It was only with the establishment of the first engineering chair at the University of Glasgow in 1840 and of the second at University College, London, in the following year, that the British engineer, who had meantime transformed the face of the country, fully established his claim to professional recognition. Major works were increasingly entrusted to trained architects and engineers, though most of the house-building and small-scale construction of all kinds continued to be undertaken largely by small firms employing traditional rule-of-thumb methods.

BUILDING MATERIALS, 1750–1850

In the eighteenth century, timber for house-building became scarce in coastal areas because of the demands of the shipyards, in good agricultural areas because of the advance of the plough, and even in some woodland areas, where it paid to grow coppice for charcoal-burning rather than trees for timber. The general use of stone as a building material—the circumstance which still delights the eye of the visitor to the Cotswolds or to Bath—likewise became confined to the areas where it was most easily quarried, though its superior dignity, and in most cases superior durability, caused it still to be preferred for buildings of exceptional luxury or importance. But in general the first effect of the industrial revolution on building was to extend the use of brick. Clay deposits were far more widespread than stone for quarrying, while the rapid growth of coal-mining and improved transportation for coal, first by canal and later by railway, made it easier almost everywhere to feed the brick kilns. The use of brick was indeed even more extensive than appeared, for the Regency architect John Nash popularized the practice of covering inferior brickwork with stucco. When painted and indented, this mixture of lime and sand gave a superficial resemblance to a massive stone wall. In the same way, repetitive ornamental stonework which it would be expensive to carve by hand was replaced by clay that had been moulded to shape before firing. What was really a terracotta based on kaolin (china clay) had a considerable vogue in London, under the name of Coade stone, from 1769 until the disappearance of the originating firm, Coade & Seely of Lambeth, about 1840.

The composition of plaster for wall-finishing, of mortar for joining stone or brickwork, and of concrete for foundations, all underwent an important development as a result of studies that began when John Smeaton was planning the third Eddystone lighthouse (p. 462) in 1759. It was then well known that pure lime from marble made the best plaster (whence a holocaust of ancient statuary), and that hydraulic qualities could be imparted to lime by the addition of Italian *pozzolana* or other substances. But Smeaton, by analysing lime from all over the country, discovered that this hydraulic quality—essential for his building, which would be partly submerged by every tide—depends upon the presence of clay in the limestone from which the lime is made. The best natural mixture was found to occur in the London clay at Harwich and Sheppey and the use of this was patented in 1796 under the name of Roman cement, an allusion to the durability of work still surviving from the Roman occupation of Britain. In America natural raw materials for cement were located and developed after 1818 as a direct result of canal building, and were used in larger quantities than artificial mixtures until the last years of the century. Yet the theory of mixing lime and clay to form cement was stated in 1839 by the Frenchman L. J. Vicat, who made a successful cement for Cherbourg harbour and introduced the special use of the word 'hydraulic' for this essential quality of hardening and becoming impervious under water.

Meanwhile, empirical cement mixtures had been made with great success in Britain. In north Kent, where the London clay and the chalk of the North Downs occur together, coal was brought in by sea for the lime kilns and a satisfactory cement carried away by river to London and other building-sites. Northfleet, near Gravesend, was also one of the first places of manufacture of the so-called Portland cement, though it was actually invented at Wakefield in 1824. Joseph Aspdin was a bricklayer turned builder, who—whether by accident or design is uncertain—calcined his mixture of chalk and clay at a temperature high enough to sinter it, that is to say, to cause the particles to coalesce without actually melting. The name given to the product represents Aspdin's optimistic belief that the concrete made from it would be accepted as a substitute for Portland stone. Its dull-grey colour made this unlikely, but superior strength and consistency ensured its adoption for many purposes. Portland-cement concrete was used by M. I. Brunel in 1828 for filling-in the river bed over his Thames tunnel (p. 458), and came into large-scale use a generation later, when 70,000 tons of it went into the making of the London main-drainage system.

Although the use of reinforced concrete still lay in the future, the eighteenth century had seen an increasing use of wrought iron to strengthen both timber and masonry. By this time the timber in use for roofs, sash-windows, and doors consisted of imported softwood instead of the axe-dressed hardwood of the Middle Ages, and roofing work had been substantially improved by the use of systematically designed trusses such as had been employed by Wren. An interesting illustration of economy in timber resulting from better design is provided by the rebuilding of the roof of St Paul's church, Covent Garden, after the original structure, planned by Inigo Jones in the reign of Charles I, had been gutted by fire: when rebuilt on the same scale in 1796, the timber-content of the roof was reduced by almost exactly one-third. The usefulness of the wooden beam was frequently increased by the introduction of forged straps and improved bolting. But English builders were deterred from employing iron inside masonry by the fact that masonry joints let in damp, which causes iron to rust; the increased volume of the rust, as compared with that of the original metal, forced apart the structure. In France, however, wrought iron was used more ambitiously by such architects as J. G. Soufflot, both as a frame for roofwork and as a built-in reinforcement for masonry. In the well-known case of the reconstruction of the Paris church which later became the Panthéon, he strengthened the masonry with iron bars where it might be expected to crack under the pressure of the dome. The severe cracks which appeared subsequently led to an extended controversy—for Soufflot's proposals had already scandalized conventional architects—but they proved to be due only to faults in the masons' work and not in the placing of the iron, even though the latter was not wholly protected from corrosion.

Cast iron, which had been employed for bridge-building as early as 1779 (p. 450), was increasingly substituted for masonry. It shares with wrought iron the defect that intense heat, though unable to consume it, may cause it to collapse, though it could be regarded as fire-proof in comparison with existing structural materials. For example, the multi-storey mill-buildings that were springing up in the north of England at the turn of the century had solid plank floors supported by heavy wooden beams; these, too, if the distance from wall to wall was too great, were held up by intermediate rows of wooden posts. The fire risk was very serious, for textile materials, too, were readily inflammable; much work was done at night with naked lights; and overworked humanity could not be expected to be superhumanly careful. Premiums for fire insurance were correspondingly high for such buildings, and there was therefore a strong incentive to develop fireproof methods of construction. William Strutt, a mill-owner who interested himself in this problem, made some use of hollow earthenware pots embedded in plaster, which had earlier been used in Paris to protect iron beams against heat. He also put in brick arches spanning the space between the beams, and these eventually carried stone-flagged floors. But the big change was the far wider use of cast iron, first for the supporting columns, then to replace the wooden beams, and finally even in the window-frames. Not only did this become the standard practice for factory buildings, but in the first half of the nineteenth century both shops and offices often had a similar mode of construction. As developed by James Bogardus in New York office buildings (Fig. 201), the use of the cast-iron frame, which sometimes reached a height of 70 ft, fore-shadowed the modern type of structure in which no part of the weight is borne by the walls.

Cast iron, as the early history of the fire-back shows, lends itself readily to the reproduction of ornament. This fact was seized upon by an enterprising Merseyside founder named John Cragg, who

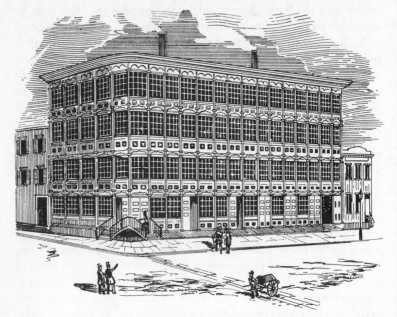

FIG. 201. Building with cast-iron frame, New York, 1851

with the co-operation of the architect Thomas Redman—a Gothic-style architect who later repented of the experiment—in five years endowed Liverpool with three churches of which every feature down to the window-mullions and tracery was of cast iron; roofs and walls of slate slabs held between iron castings did nothing to relieve the grim effect. Such Gothic ironmongery happily did not become gener-ally popular with church-builders, though cast iron provided the material for the gigantic open-work spire of Rouen Cathedral; never-theless, ornamental detail became a common feature of cast-iron columns and was even applied to the frames of steam-engines and industrial machinery. The use of cast iron as a structural material for important buildings reached its climax in London in the Houses of Parliament, where it provided the main material for the roof, and in Joseph Paxton's Crystal Palace (Fig. 202), where the epoch-making speed and simplicity of erection depended mainly on the use of some 3,500 tons of uniform cast-iron girders, which were tested for size and strength in less than four minutes apiece as they arrived

Fig. 202. Raising the first ribs of the transept roof of the
Crystal Palace, 1850

on the site from the three ironfounding firms that shared the huge contract. In Paris the counterpart of Paxton's work was one of the earliest improvements made by Haussmann for Napoleon III, namely the Halles Centrales or wholesale provision market, which he rebuilt in glass and iron according to the emperor's prescription of 'vast umbrellas' (Fig. 203). But although the Crystal Palace is an influential example of a long-continuing practice in which wrought and cast iron were used together in the same building, 1851 marks approximately the transition to an era of new building materials, of which wrought iron is one: Paxton used only wrought iron for members under tension.

Meanwhile, the earlier nineteenth century had also brought with it some developments in the use of wood. One new demand of the 1830's was for quickly erected houses in new American settlements, where wood was plentiful but carpenters few. The result was a type of house-construction first developed in Chicago, which by the time of the Great Fire of 1871 had grown to a city of 300,000 inhabitants, with two-thirds of its buildings of timber. The type was nicknamed the 'balloon frame' (Fig. 204) by its critics because heavy frame timbers were completely omitted. Instead, roof and floor were supported by uniform lengths of timber known as studs, which were

Fig. 203. The Halles Centrales, Paris, 1860

placed about 18 in. apart; three plates of wood were nailed across, supporting the two floors and the rafters of the roof; and all the remaining timbers, numbered at the mill to facilitate assembly by amateurs, were joined by nailing, a bag of machine-made nails being supplied to the would-be home-builder along with all the weatherboarding and ready-made doors and windows.

While this type of structure was beginning a long career of usefulness in the fast-growing settlements of the American pioneers, in Britain timber enjoyed a more temporary revival in the building of the early railway stations; these required a roof of considerable span to cover not only the passenger platforms, as at the present day, but engines not in use, and in some cases goods wagons as well. The first Liverpool station at Crown Hill had a span of only 35 ft; but within ten years I. K. Brunel gave Bristol's Temple Meads station what was ostensibly a hammer-beam roof, with a span 4 ft wider than that of

Westminster Hall, though the tied, pointed arch was actually employed. The climax of wooden construction in this field, however, was the two barrel-vaults of King's Cross station, London, built in 1852, which for seventeen years were borne on semicircular arches with a span of 105 ft; the shoes for the arches were of cast iron, resting on brick piers. Wood was found to resist smoke well, but as it tended to hold the moisture from the steam the iron fastenings rapidly corroded. Other railways, therefore, eventually followed the practice of all-iron construction for roofs which the London–Birmingham railway had used from the beginning.

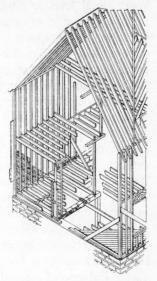

FIG. 204. 'Balloon frame' house, as developed in Chicago in the 1830's

FURNITURE

Since wood long continued to be the chief material employed in furnishing buildings of all kinds—station waiting-rooms and business offices as well as domestic interiors—we may interpolate here a brief reference to the changes in the character and mode of construction of furniture. In the early eighteenth century the introduction to Europe of seasoned mahogany from San Domingo and the Bahamas, so hard that it could be worked only with steel tools of the highest quality, led to remarkable achievements in carving in the rococo style of the French *ébénistes* and their more restrained English counterparts. Fine cabinet-making at last became clearly distinct from superior joinery: *The Gentleman and Cabinet Maker's Director*, published by Thomas Chippendale in 1754, was the first English book of its kind. Hepplewhite and Sheraton, whose *Guide* and *Drawing Book* appeared respectively in 1788 and 1791, are the most famous of a number of other cabinet-makers and designers who wrote for the practical use of the trade. In the case of the chair, for instance, where Hepplewhite popularized both the shield-backed and the winged variety, eighteenth-century design has never been surpassed. But the taste served by these great designers was that of a very limited upper class, formed—if we take the English 'milord' as our example

—by the Grand Tour undertaken in youth or by consultation with a much travelled and expensive architect like Robert Adam. At a lower social level furniture continued to be sparse and simple, traditional in style, and local in origin, except where a special supply of material encouraged manufacture for a wider market: this was the period when the Windsor chair first emerged from the Chiltern beech-woods, with its seat shaped from a clay mould and the simple stick-back raked for greater ease.

The French Revolution came when Louis XVI furniture was giving Europe a graceful lead towards simpler, classical forms, but in the following decades the prestige of Napoleon carried his empire style, with its imitations of Egypt as well as of Greece and Rome, all through Europe and even across the Channel, where it influenced Regency design. At a humbler level we may notice that plywood, made by glueing successive sheets at right angles, was popularized in Britain through the work done by French prisoners of war. But the most important effect of the French Revolution was the shock which it everywhere inflicted upon age-old distinctions of rank, so that quality and quantity of furniture were increasingly valued as visible emblems of a social elevation which could now be attained merely through money. The result was to be seen most clearly in Britain as the Regency style gave place to Early Victorian, for the dominant influence was that of a middle class increasing rapidly in wealth, numbers, and self-confidence, home-loving and house-proud, and eager to carry into its domestic surroundings the sense of value for money and the productive 'know-how' which served British business interests so well. The result was the sort of furniture shown at the Exhibition of 1851, commonly said to represent the nadir of British taste.

The workmanship was usually good, since solidity of construction had a moral appeal; mahogany was still a favourite wood; and the availability of furniture-springs (first patented in Britain in 1826) and a rich variety of textiles encouraged the art of the upholsterer. But this was also the golden age of japanned papier-mâché chairs and beds, shown by French and German as well as by British exhibitors, the material being built up into boards by 'stoving' successive layers of paper which were subsequently varnished and inlaid in Japanese fashion. Ornament was admired in proportion to its elaboration, ranging from the chiffonier, with naturalistic carving of every visible surface, to the occasional table, enriched by such feats of ingenuity as the marquetry picture, in one instance containing 110,000 pieces of wood. Machine-carving (p. 355), too, had arrived just in time to meet a huge demand for intricate reproductions of medieval and Renaissance pieces.

In the following half-century furniture in general became less heavy and elaborate, though the influence of William Morris, attempting to restore the craftsmanship of the Middle Ages, and of more practical pioneers like (Sir) Ambrose Heal, affected only a very small part of the total output; there was likewise only a limited European vogue for American patent furniture, such as the adjustable chair and the equipment of the railway sleeping-car. But the growth of wood-working machinery, which from its humble beginnings in the dockyard (p. 351) advanced until it could imitate each of the standard processes of handicraft furniture-making, now transformed the methods, though not the end-products, of the industry. At the same time the economy of large-scale manufacture was helped by the growth of urban communities, transport, and the advertising arts, which taught the consumer gracious living—with period furniture in suites. Measured in sales, the American furniture industry in 1900 was seven times as large as half a century before, and from the 1870's onwards most of its products were factory-made. Where labour was cheaper than in the United States, hand work was less easily ousted: within living memory the pole lathe (p. 102) was still used to turn chair-legs by isolated craftsmen in the Chiltern hills. In the long run, however, Europe succumbed no less completely to the vogue of standard types, not very carefully constructed, often ugly, and sometimes—as when the kind of wood is disguised by graining—faked. But the social loss involved in the decline of a fine trade must be weighed against the social gain in the increased availability of furniture for the masses. The metal bedstead, exhibited in 1851 and commercially developed soon afterwards, is an instance of the way in which new standards of comfort and hygiene penetrated as a result of mass production into the homes of the poor: cast iron did not harbour parasites, and if broken the bed was easily replaced.

NEW USES OF WROUGHT IRON, STEEL, AND CONCRETE

An increasing use of wrought iron, which in earlier periods had figured mainly as a supplement to work of wood or cast iron, was one important development of the 1850's and 1860's. In 1847 the first very small wrought-iron beam for use in floors was made for a Paris engineer, and within ten years its value as a constructional material was being advocated by (Sir) William Fairbairn. Meanwhile, the manufacture of long beams of heavy section had been made possible by the invention of the 'universal mill'. Their use was, however, restricted for many years by the fact that a puddler could provide only one small bloom at a time, and a massive beam could be produced only after a number of blooms had been hammered together into a suitably sized billet. What became common, therefore, was the construction of large beams by riveting together plates, angle tees, and other sections. Wrought-iron roof trusses for railway stations began in London with one of 40-ft span for Euston in 1839 and culminated in a span six times as great at St Pancras, but a complete load-bearing frame of wrought iron continued to be very rare. One of the best early examples is the Menier chocolate works (1871–2) at Noisiel-sur-Marne, which required a light skeleton-frame because it was built over the river on masonry piers in order to use power supplied by water-wheels. The construction of the British Museum Reading Room (1854–7) is perhaps more typical: wrought-iron ribs and beams for the 100-ft dome were combined with cast-iron columns made in three sections, which were bolted together; they were then cemented at the gaps between the castings, which did not join quite precisely because they were not machined, by a special cement supposed to have been invented by William Murdock for the early steam-engine frames. The tallest of all wrought-iron buildings dates from as late as 1889, when the exhibition to mark the centenary of the French Revolution occasioned the erection of the 984-ft Eiffel Tower, which was intended to remain for five years but is still the most striking of Paris landmarks (Fig. 205). The superstructure,

FIG. 205. The Eiffel Tower

standing on a massive base of reinforced concrete, consists of 7,300 tons of wrought iron, chosen by Eiffel in preference to steel on the grounds of its greater rigidity. As with the Crystal Palace, the 12,000 principal iron members were prefabricated.

The employment of cheap steel as a structural material became possible with inventions of the 1850's and 1860's, but much of the supply was absorbed in rails, because steel tracks were known to last much longer than those of iron (p. 381), whereas for other purposes wrought iron was often preferred as more homogeneous and familiar: it was not until 1877 that the British Board of Trade authorized the use of steel in bridge-building. The Bessemer and Siemens processes made large billets available, which could be rolled into the long-desired I-beam of substantial section. In 1882–9, 50,000 tons of steel were employed in building the Forth Bridge, and the manufacture and sale of

Fig. 206. Elisha Otis demonstrating his safety elevator, 1854

rolled-steel beams became firmly established in Britain by Dorman Long and other firms.

Meanwhile, however, America not only took the lead in the output of cheap steel, but developed its use for a new type of building: steel begat the skyscraper. The main incentive was the rapid rise of site values in the congested central areas of booming cities like New York and Chicago. The way had been prepared by the vogue of the 'elevator building', after E. G. Otis in 1854 made the hydraulic lift safe for passenger use by providing the cage with pawls, which were forced by springs to engage ratchets at the sides of the lift-shaft the moment the rope failed (Fig. 206). Without the elevator neither these buildings, nor the still taller ones that followed, would have attracted a sufficient clientèle of indefatigable stair-climbers. To begin with, the new type of structure had wrought-iron floors and cast-iron fronts—the parts being prefabricated—but carried upon masonry walls, requiring increased thickness at the base in proportion to the height. Up to fourteen storeys could be erected, as in the case of the Pulitzer building completed for the *New York World* in 1890, but at the ground floor—where space was most highly valued—the walls were 9 ft thick. An all-steel frame had no such limitations. Steel columns could be raised to virtually any height, and could be given a secure footing without any increase in the size at the base. Tied together at each floor-level by steel girders, they would support the entire weight of the building, so that the function of the walls was merely to give shelter and privacy.

Steel beams were used in the upper storeys of an iron-framed Chicago office block in 1884; the first complete steel frame followed, also in Chicago, in 1890; and its twenty-one-storey Masonic Temple of 1892, described both as the biggest building in the world and as one of its seven wonders, set the pace for the new era. The erection of New York's first skyscraper two years later illustrated two great difficulties of this type of building: the foundations had to be carried 50 ft below ground by the use of caissons, subsequently filled with concrete, and the frame had to be braced with extra metal members to withstand winds at gale-force. But by the end of the century New York had eclipsed Chicago, with twenty-nine skyscrapers to sixteen and a maximum height of 386 ft to Chicago's 300 ft. The cities of Europe had no such skylines, no such waterfronts. Britain in the 1890's applied steel only to industrial construction, and sparingly at that. A furniture warehouse at West Hartlepool, built in 1896, is the first British example of a complete steel frame; but more than another decade passed before the London Building Act acknowledged that the thickness of the external walls might safely be reduced when they could be inserted piecemeal into a frame that bears all the load.

In the same period yet another structural material of great importance had been developed from the widespread use of Portland cement, which until the 1890's, when America developed the rotary kiln for sintering the raw material, was an important British export to the New World as well as to the Continent. For building work of all kinds its value was limited by the fact that, unlike lime concrete, concrete made with Portland cement begins to set so quickly that only very large works used big enough batches to warrant the employment of a steam-driven mixer. For foundations to give adequate strength to tall buildings concrete was invaluable, but for other uses in building it was found that neither concrete walls, cast on the site between shuttering, nor factory-made concrete blocks had any great appeal. What remained to be exploited was the embedding of iron or steel in a concrete so completely impervious that there was no risk of corrosion: this would provide a structural material which combined the tensile strength of iron with the virtual incompressibility of concrete.

Reinforced concrete began humbly enough with the making of concrete tubs for orange-trees, in which the Frenchman, Joseph Monier, embedded a mesh of iron rods. This was in 1849; only five years later W. B. Wilkinson, a builder in Newcastle upon Tyne, patented a much more elaborate system both for embedding iron rods in plaster and concrete ceiling work and for reinforcing concrete beams with worn-out mining cable. But no lasting results followed from his enterprise, whereas Monier took out a series of patents, including one for beams in 1877, and from 1885 onwards had his patents developed under licence in Germany. Pioneer work was done by Wayss & Freitag of Frankfurt-am-Main, who also commissioned Mathias Koenen's study of *Das System Monier*, which discussed the theory of the combination of resistance to tensile and to compressive stresses. In the 1890's, moreover, important work was being done by two other Frenchmen. Edmond Coignet—whose father a generation earlier had taken out a patent for concrete floors and had visualized, though he did not attempt to design, most forms which reinforced concrete structures would later take—showed in sewer construction in Paris that a $3\frac{1}{8}$-in. shell of the new material could safely carry 15 ft of earth. His rival was François Hennibique, who in the same year (1892) introduced into reinforced concrete beams a system of vertical hoop-iron stirrups to resist change of shape by shearing.

Five years passed before Hennebique's system was introduced into Britain, who in this matter lagged far behind Continental practice. This is remarkable because not only had early pioneer work been done by Wilkinson, but also it was a British immigrant to America, Thaddeus Hyatt, who had in 1877 successfully outlined the theory of reinforced concrete on the basis of tests made for him at a laboratory in London. It was also an Englishman, E. L. Ransome, sent to San Francisco as sales agent for an Ipswich ironworks, who began the embedding in concrete of the iron beams of factory structures. Ransome erected his first important building with reinforced concrete beams in 1888, and at the end of the century was developing a system of unit-construction, including floors based on reinforced concrete beams carrying spirals of wire, so that the beams would bind together with a reinforced concrete floor-slab cast on the site. But in bridge-building with the new material the Continent out-distanced America, not to mention Britain. When the first American road-bridge of reinforced concrete was opened in 1894, with a span of 30 ft, there had been concrete bridges of the Monier type in Europe for almost twenty years, three in Switzerland having 128-ft spans. Hennibique was also a bridge-builder, and in 1898 he completed a 172-ft arch spanning the river Vienne at Châtellerault.

In the long run the main use of reinforced concrete, either in sheet or pillar form, was to help in the production of high buildings, towards which the general rise in site values accompanying urbanization caused technological development to be directed. It may therefore be appropriate to notice briefly that the later nineteenth century had already tackled some of the main ancillary problems. The hydraulic lift had been so far improved that the three which served the Eiffel Tower (one by Otis, two of French construction) carried the visitor to the top by three stages in seven minutes. Moreover, in 1889 the much faster electric lift was about to take its place. There were also acute problems of fire prevention, arising chiefly from the increased height of buildings, but also from increased window-space —the blank walls of the past were far better preventives of the spread of fire—and from the substitution of light sections of wrought iron or steel for the more massive, and therefore less vulnerable, cast iron.

Part of the solution was to protect high buildings by the installation of water-tanks at heights above 80–100 ft, the maximum to which hoses could play from the ground under the pressures normally available. At the same time, the search for fire-resisting floor systems was intensified. Solid concrete slabs were often used in key positions, but by 1875 machine-made hollow terracotta blocks became available in America for floor-units. Within ten years A. D. Gilman in Iowa had produced a porous block, which could be sawn into shape, by mixing sawdust with the clay before firing; this was much used in the tall buildings of the 1890's. Another later practice was to protect steel beams by surrounding them with 3 in. of concrete closely bound with gauze: intense heat would dehydrate the outer layer of the concrete, its insulating properties being thereby increased.

IMPROVEMENT OF WATER-SUPPLY

The fire hydrant represents only one special use of the continuous water-supply to which modern town-dwellers look to satisfy their

needs for drinking and washing, for many industrial processes, and
to assist sewage disposal. During 1801–51 the population of Great
Britain almost exactly doubled, but this does not show the full extent of the problem, since the growth was most rapid in the great
cities. The population of Glasgow, for example, grew twice as fast
as the national average, and in a single decade the demand for water
there approximately doubled.

In such circumstances the methods of the past could not possibly
suffice. London, for instance, at the end of the eighteenth century

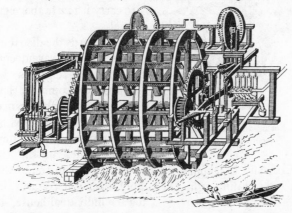

FIG. 207. Water-wheels driving pumps, London Bridge, 1749

had at least three of its water companies deriving their supply from
the Thames. The oldest raised it by water-wheels at London Bridge
(Fig. 207); a second, which had once employed Thomas Savery's
'fire engine', pumped the water out near the Strand; and a third
brought it from the river at Chelsea to fill two reservoirs in Green
Park. Since the early seventeenth century this supply from the
Thames had been supplemented by the New River, a 38-mile aqueduct that brought water from some springs in Hertfordshire and
from the river Lea. A third source comprised wells (Fig. 208), local
springs, and deep bore-holes constructed to reach supplies below the
London clay, methods which proved increasingly ineffectual as London grew, though elsewhere the progress of geology led to greater
success in tapping water underground. When a well was sunk in
1845 to provide water for the fountains in Trafalgar Square, the
water-level was 112 ft below ground; by 1911 this had sunk to 236 ft,
and the well was then abandoned. New wells were, indeed, sunk—

for example, at the bottom of Hampstead Heath and in Kentish Town—but in the London area there was no such success as that which rewarded seven years of boring at Grenelle, Paris (Fig. 209), where water was struck at a depth of 1,800 ft, having a yield of 800,000 gallons a day and a pressure sufficient to carry it 122 ft above ground-level.

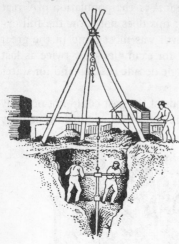

FIG. 208. Boring an artesian well, nineteenth century

As regards the distribution of water, in the seventeenth and eighteenth centuries wooden mains were common, especially of elm, though France had made a beginning with cast-iron pipes for the waterworks at Versailles in the time of Louis XIV, and by about 1750 they were used to some extent in London and in Edinburgh. The supply was not necessarily directed to each individual house, still less to different parts of it, nor was it by any means continuous; itinerant water-vendors were still a common sight in London, Paris, and many other large cities. At the beginning of the nineteenth century the denizens of a working-class street would consider themselves well served by a single stand-pipe where the water was running for stated periods—often only one hour—each day, though the well-to-do could normally expect a supply piped into the basements of their houses (Fig. 210), whence domestics must carry it upstairs.

FIG. 209. The artesian well at Grenelle, Paris, mid-nineteenth century

Progress in the first half of the nineteenth century came as a direct result of the great industrial changes. Thus the Cornish engine

(p. 325) made it possible to pump water through the mains at much greater pressure; James Nasmyth produced the first adequate sluice valve; and cast-iron pipes, which became generally available, were not only strong and very long-lived but relatively easy to install inside houses. The industrial needs of Lancashire dyers and bleachers likewise prompted attempts even before 1800 to use gravel and sand beds for the purification of water; in London the first slow sand-filters (p. 424) were built by James Simpson in 1827. Lancashire had also to face the special problem of safeguarding the interests of the still-numerous water-driven mills: if a water-works diverted a supply from springs or river sources, it was usually required to provide a compensation supply for riparian mill-owners. Accordingly, the damming of the Pennine valleys to provide a secure source of supply began in the Bolton area in the 1820's, and in 1848 Manchester Corporation began work on five embankments for a series of reservoirs in the Longdendale valley 10 miles east of the town, two of which were intended solely for storing 'compensation water'.

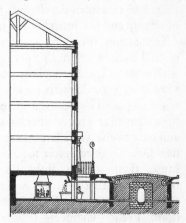

FIG. 210. Section of house and road, Piccadilly, London, showing systems of water-supply and sewage removal, early nineteenth century

The yield proved to be 19 million gallons a day, which compares with 46 million for all nine London water companies in 1848–9; yet within a single generation Manchester needed more.

In the second half of the nineteenth century it was not merely the continued growth of population and industry (including agriculture with its special requirements for irrigation), but important changes in social habit—cleanliness coming next to godliness in what was still an eminently God-fearing population—that caused the demand for more, and better, water to be widely expressed. Moreover, the political atmosphere in Britain and elsewhere was now favourable to the growth of municipal services, which took over the provision of water-supply from profit-earning companies, could raise big loans for capital expenditure, and need not show a profit. In London, indeed, the private companies survived until 1902 and—although they never matched the vigour with which the Paris municipal authority acted under Napoleon III to substitute spring water for the polluted Seine—they were supplying five times as much water at the end of the century as in 1848. A striking example of municipal enterprise was Bradford, where soft water was essential for the expansion of the woollen industry: in 1855–73 the supply was increased almost eighteenfold. Since the local water sources available in industrial areas did not become larger or less tainted with the passage of the years, the two main developments were the resort to distant sources of supply and the introduction of better methods of purification.

Great dams, therefore, were among the most striking achievements of civil engineering in this period. The early dams in the Pennines, where the valleys are shallow and there is no firm rock foundation, were mostly made with puddled clay in the centre and with flat outer slopes. They proved generally adequate, though the Holmfirth dam near Huddersfield was undermined by leakage in 1852 and only twelve years later there was a sensational disaster when the new Dale Dyke reservoir for Sheffield collapsed on being filled and caused the loss of 244 lives. The reason for the collapse of the embankment in that case was never fully determined, but it has been supposed that its weight fractured the cast-iron outlet pipes underneath. French engineers believed that earth dams were unsafe if their height exceeded 60 ft, and soon after 1850 they produced the first dam designs based on scientific principles.

De Sazilly and Delocre realized that dam-building was not merely a matter of blocking a valley with material that could reasonably be expected not to slide or overturn; the internal stresses had also to be considered. Its strength must be sufficient to stand the maximum strain at the upstream face of the dam when the reservoir was empty and at the downstream face when the reservoir was full. Delocre also favoured the principle of making the face of the dam slightly convex, so that part of the thrust of the water would be conveyed to the land on either side in the same way as the weight of an arch is conveyed to its piers. The 184-ft Furens dam, completed in 1866 to supply St Etienne from a tributary of the Loire, was the first to be built on these principles and was for a time the tallest dam in the world. The first high masonry dam in Britain was not completed until 1891, when the river Vyrnwy, the chief Welsh tributary of the Severn, was blocked by works lower than those at Furens, but more massive, one-third of the stones weighing 4–10 tons each (Fig. 211).

This Liverpool enterprise was followed in 1894 by the completion of the Thirlmere dam for Manchester, and the Elan valley dams which serve Birmingham were also under construction before the end of the century. In regions where the valleys are narrower and have steeper sides than at the sites in Wales and the Lake District, resort was had not merely to a slightly convex upper face, as proposed by Delocre, but to the design of a true horizontal arch. The Zola dam, built in 1843 near Aix-en-Provence, was the first of this type; another was the Bear valley irrigation dam in California, built

FIG. 211. Vyrnwy dam, completed 1891. It is approximately one-fifth of a mile in length and can impound over 12,000 million gallons of water

in 1884 with a radius of curvature of 335 ft. Arch dams did not, however, become common until the twentieth century.

The conveyance of water from distant catchment areas involved the building of aqueducts comparable with the great works of the Romans: indeed, the 51-mile canal aqueduct, built in 1839–47 to serve Marseilles, crosses a river at a height of nearly 300 ft on a three-tiered stone bridge 1,300 ft long which recalls and even excels the splendour of the not-far-distant Pont du Gard (p. 170). At New York in 1885–93 a 30-mile tunnel was bored straight through the rock from Croton Lake to Central Park from thirty shafts with an average depth of 117 ft; the brick lining is up to 24 in. thick. Its horseshoe cross-section of 160 sq. ft far exceeds that of European aqueducts, but the aqueduct from Thirlmere to Manchester is 96 miles long and those serving Liverpool and Birmingham are each of about three-quarters that length. The mains required to hold water under high pressure could be made satisfactorily from cast iron, but large pipes were also built up from wrought-iron plates riveted together. From 1860 onwards steel was preferred, especially in America, but distribution from the mains to consumers continued to be through cast-iron pipes. The first recording meters were introduced in 1873 to check waste; the public, however, soon became educated into the habit of turning off taps when by doing so they no longer risked missing an intermittent supply.

It was not until the later nineteenth century that the quality of drinking water could be judged otherwise than by clarity, the absence of taste and smell, and freedom from detectable ill-effects. The London Water Act of 1852, which forbade the numerous water companies of the metropolis to take any supply from the tidal reaches of the Thames or to distribute water without filtering it, is an important landmark, but it was not until two years later that the famous anaesthetist, John Snow, was able to show conclusively that an outbreak of cholera in Soho must be connected with the pollution by human excreta of one particular pump in Broad Street. From the 1860's onwards the development of bacteriology by Pasteur, Koch, and others gave a scientific basis to water purification, and by 1885 the London water-supply was subjected to systematic analysis. Results showed that, when kept in proper condition, sand-filters, originally designed to remove suspended inanimate solids, also took away as much as 98 per cent. of the bacterial content.

The early sand-filter worked by gravity alone, the water sinking through layers of sand and gravel at the rate of about 3 gallons per sq. ft per hour. It suffered from the three defects that it was slow, required laborious attention, and took up much space, especially when preliminary settling basins were added to trap the heavier solids before they passed into the filter proper: by the end of the century London alone had nearly 150 acres of such filters. Hence the development of pressure filters, especially in France, some of which worked as much as a hundred times as fast as the original slow sand-filter; but they were not medically very safe, and were approved chiefly for the clarification of water for industrial use. A better type of rapid sand-filter was patented in Britain in 1880; this replaced the laborious hand-cleaning of the sand by agitating the surface with powerful jets of air blown from underneath, so that the dirt was loosened and carried away. The Americans, however, finding the existing sand-filters unsuitable for the treatment of their frequently silt-laden river water, developed another type of rapid sand-filter, which had a mechanical agitator embedded in the sand.

From 1857 use was made in Europe of gelatinous iron hydroxide to collect and precipitate suspended impurities, but the employment of aluminium hydroxide for this purpose, though eventually adopted to some extent in Europe, began on a large scale in America in the 1880's. These methods proved as effective as filtration and much faster. Chlorination, which in the twentieth century became a standard safeguard for all major water-supplying organizations, first came into use as an emergency measure to deal with typhoid epidemics at Pola in Italy and at Maidstone in England, in 1896 and 1897 respectively. It had, however, been applied much earlier to the treatment of sewage.

DRAINAGE AND SANITATION

By 1900 the civil engineer was winning the long battle for communal cleanliness, a battle which in 1800, and even in 1850, might still have seemed a losing one. There were really three problems: disposing of the rain-water which might flood the towns, of the miscellaneous rubbish which in the course of time would make the streets impassable, and of the decomposing organic matter which, as nineteenth-century sanitary experts slowly established, was not merely an offensive nuisance but a grave danger to health. For a small, scattered, and unsqueamish population, these problems presented no serious difficulties, but by the end of the eighteenth century a town like London, with more than a million inhabitants, was driven to attempt a number of solutions, all of which proved increasingly inadequate. Since the Great Fire of 1666, dumping-places for rubbish had been officially provided in the streets of the City, from which the refuse was removed by a paid staff of 'rakers'. The contents of privies were removed by night-soil men at times when the streets were deserted—the service was once in twenty-four hours in the best districts, less frequent and less regular in the poorer ones. Both rakers and night-soil men made considerable profits from selling much of what they collected for agricultural or other uses; the rest was burnt, dumped, or tipped into the sea.

But at this juncture the water-closet, described by Sir John Harington 200 years before, was beginning to be introduced into better-class houses where the water-supply permitted (Fig. 212). As patented with two valves in 1778 by Joseph Bramah, the closet when flushed discharged its contents directly to a cesspool in the basement or under the garden. A trap containing a water-seal was first patented in 1782; but even when this became a regular part of the closet equipment, the existence of the cesspool, which was emptied at something like annual intervals, constituted a double danger to health, from the

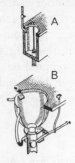

effluvia which commonly entered the house and from the leakages which tainted wells, rivers, and even the imperfectly jointed water-pipes of that period. It was strictly, but not always successfully, forbidden to any London householder to allow a water-closet to discharge into a sewer, for the sewers then were merely bricked-over watercourses intended to drain the ordinary surface water into the Thames.

The remedy found for this situation was to build a new type of sewer, which was flushed by a more regular supply of water than rain provided and could be used to carry suspended refuse by underground routes for eventual disposal at points well clear of the urban area; this was a characteristic achievement of great urban authorities in the second half of the century. Hamburg, rebuilding after a big fire in 1843, was perhaps the first important town to construct such a complete sewer system, which was flushed thoroughly with river water every week. The drains of Paris were almost five times as long in 1863 as in 1837, and in constructing new sewers the city took the opportunity to make its roadways convex instead of concave,

FIG. 212. Evolution of the water-closet: (A) Sir John Harington's original design, 1596; (B) Bramah's closet, 1778; (C) nineteenth-century closet with water-seal

with drainage gutters at each side and headroom for the sewer under the centre: the principal collector, however, upon which the sewers converged under the Place de la Concorde, emptied into the Seine at a distance of only 3 miles. Some extension of the London sewer system was made in the 1840's (Fig. 213). But the work done by Sir Joseph Bazalgette, as engineer to the Metropolitan Board of Works, set up in 1855 after 20,000 Londoners had died in two cholera epidemics, provided a more drastic remedy for the particularly horrible situation in London, where evil-smelling mudbanks proclaimed the fact that the river Fleet (Fig. 214) and the other rainwater sewers were discharging vast quantities of household effluent into the Thames, to be carried to and fro on the tide even in the heart of the capital.

Bazalgette built five main sewers running parallel to the course of the Thames, three on the north bank and two on the south, which would be capable of dealing with all household sewage, together with the normal flow of rain-water. Only in the event of abnormal rainfall was it necessary for the excess storm-water—carrying with it some diluted sewage—to flow over weirs into the old main-line sewers connected with the river. The Thames Embankment, replacing the ancient mudbank, marks part of the course of one of the new sewers. As they discharged at a point about 12 miles below London Bridge, three pumping stations were required to lift their contents, so that the sewage should flow throughout by gravity and maintain an average speed of $1\frac{1}{2}$ m.p.h. with the sewer half full. The large brick sewers were fed by a network of smaller ones, having an approximately oval section but narrower

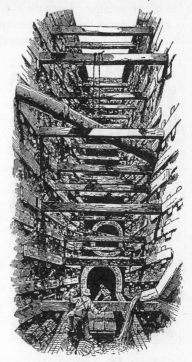

FIG. 213. Deepening a sewer under Fleet Street, 1845

at the bottom; this shape provides the maximum rate of flow when there is little liquid moving through. Built of brick jointed with Portland cement, Bazalgette's sewers, protected by their position underground from the effects of temperature changes, have proved to be very long-lived; nevertheless, the wearing away of the bottom, and risk of obstruction, made it necessary to provide means of access and ventilation shafts for maintenance men. The best method proved to be the construction of ventilators as frequently as possible in the centre of roadways: one of Bazalgette's less successful experiments was when he tried to destroy foetid air from the sewers by drawing it into a furnace built in the Clock Tower of the Houses of Parliament.

It remained to dispose of the sewage. At first it was all discharged into the Thames, but this was obnoxious to the local population living by the river banks below London. To apply it to the land was impracticable with such large quantities, though this was done with success in smaller places such as Salisbury. A system of chemical clarification was therefore developed at the outfall works both north and south of the river. The sewage normally contained only about

FIG. 214. The river Fleet, 1844

0·1 per cent. of solid matter, and about half of that was innocuous sand or grit: thus the problem narrowed down to the treatment of the remaining organic matter, so as to prevent it from absorbing oxygen as it decomposed, releasing offensive gases and so destroying fish and plant life in the river. No fewer than 500 patents for chemical precipitants had been taken out by 1894, but the London outfall-works continued to use a mixture of lime and ferrous sulphate, the process being similar to that used to purify drinking-water (p. 425): the sewage was screened to remove the larger solids and then treated twice with the precipitant. The final product was a sludge containing 7 per cent. of solid matter, to be poured from ships into the sea.

London because of its size, and Great Britain because of the general density of its population, presented problems of sewage disposal in their most acute form. In other parts of the world, such as Germany and the United States of America, often only the screening for larger solids was carried out, the rest of the sewage being discharged directly into large rivers or lakes. The ampler space available in some countries also encouraged experiments in drying the sludge for eventual use as manure on the land, just as the miscellaneous rubbish accumulated in urban communities was turned to profit by the incinerator, introduced for this purpose at Nottingham in 1876. By the end of the century these had been adapted to provide a part of the heat for the new electric power-stations.

BUILDING CONSTRUCTION:
REQUIREMENTS FOR TRANSPORT

ROAD-MAKING

THE all-weather road, the canal, and the railway are three characteristic features of modern industrial society which it was the function of the civil engineer to imprint upon the face of the land. He left no such mark upon the sea, but the increased speed and efficiency of shipping presupposed the improvement of harbours and docks and the girdling of the world by lighthouses. Road-building may be considered first, as representing the oldest form of communication: in western Europe, at any rate, old highways were improved rather than wholly new ones laid out along new routes. Nevertheless, down to 1900 the road in most countries played only a minor part in the bulk interchange of food and raw materials for manufactured products which was the characteristic feature of industrial progress.

The French roads, as we have seen (p. 188), were for a long time admired, and to some extent imitated, by the rest of Europe. The French were also ahead of others in the mapping of their country (p. 231), on which the logical development of a road system partly depended. In 1787 William Roy, with the help of Ramsden's theodolite, made a triangulation which linked up London with the measurements already established along the north coast of France. But although the Ordnance Survey was set up only four years later, the triangulation of Great Britain was not finished until 1852, by which date many European countries had national surveys producing maps comparable to the British one-inch series. In the United States, where there was no triangulation before the 1830's, the mapping of inland regions became a Federal concern in 1879, one year after the second complete survey of France had been finished.

Two decades before Arthur Young, the last great observer of provincial life under the Ancien Régime, rode across France to the Pyrenees and recorded some of the roads as 'truly noble', a new three-layer system of road-making was introduced by P. M. J. Trésaguet. He improved upon the earlier work of the École des Ponts et Chaussées by laying the stones for the foundation evenly and on edge, hammering this layer into a contour which ran parallel with the intended camber of the surface, and employing the hardest and smallest stones for the top layer. This top layer was to be 3 in. thick and the two lower ones together were to be between 6 and 7 in. This saved nearly half the materials as compared with the standard stone causeway preceding it, which was 18 in. thick at the middle and 12 in. at the sides. But the debt which later road-makers owed to Trésaguet derives especially from his injunction regarding the material for the topmost layer, 'The last bed to be of pieces broken to about the size of a small walnut'. His roads also had the advantage that they avoided excessive camber, which was often dangerous. He claimed that in Limoges—the district where Young made the comment quoted above—they lasted for ten years when properly maintained, although maintenance was an uncertain quantity as long as the *corvée* system existed, since this compulsory labour was performed only during spring and autumn: its final abolition in France in 1789, however, removed the last excuse for the older, thicker section.

The new method was adopted by most French road engineers and it spread to central Europe, Switzerland, and even Sweden. Some enterprise in road-making was characteristic of the enlightened despots of the late eighteenth century: Joseph II of Austria, for example, continued the work of his two Habsburg predecessors by making a road through the Arlberg Pass; Catherine the Great started the great Siberian highway in 1781, and in the following reign a modern road-surface of an English type was laid at the 'Tsar's village' (Tsarskoe Selo) south of St Petersburg. But the main impetus was given by Napoleon, whose policy was to establish fourteen imperial highways radiating from Paris in order to expedite the movement of troops and trade to the frontiers of his dominions, and who organized both the military engineers and a central body of road commissioners to carry out his wishes. In Switzerland, for instance, where native engineers had made plans before the French conquest, two brigades of French pioneers worked on a 48-mile stretch of the Simplon road, opened in 1805; the Mont Cenis road was completely reconstructed by 1810, in which year 17,000 vehicles went through the pass from Savoy to Italy; and French forces of occupation worked on other key-roads as far afield as Hamburg and the Illyrian provinces.

In Britain, on the other hand, the ancient system, so productive of inertia, by which the upkeep of the roads was a purely local responsibility to be discharged by the parish, gave place not to any enlightened centralization but to the *ad hoc* statutory authorities known as Turnpike Trusts. The Great North Road was first turnpiked in 1663, but it was not until the Duke of Cumberland's lumbering pursuit of the Jacobites to Culloden in 1746 that better roads came to be regarded as an urgent national interest. The result was that new Turnpike Trusts were already being created at the rate of about thirty a year in the period immediately preceding the commencement of George III's reign, when the economic incentives were so dramatically increased. Turnpike Trusts, each operating its toll-gate-enclosed sections of road, were obviously an imperfect way of getting things done, and only about half the money they collected was spent on actual road work. Nevertheless, down to the middle of the nineteenth century, the piecemeal-maintained turnpike was the characteristic English highway. In their heyday the Trusts spent as much as £2 million a year (the figure for 1809) on road repairs, provided the tracks over which the mail coaches and the post-chaises ran and competed, and attracted both Telford and McAdam into their service.

Thomas Telford enjoyed great fame as a builder of bridges, canals, and harbours, but his original occupation, that of a journeyman stonemason, is the one most directly linked up with his work as a road-maker. His early services in this connexion were rendered to the Turnpike Trusts of Shropshire, but he was employed by the government to improve the Carlisle–Glasgow road and the roads of the Scottish Highlands, originally built by Marshal Wade for military purposes, and in his most famous work, which was to render the whole route from London to Holyhead worthy of the position it then held as the main link between two capitals of the recently expanded United Kingdom. When the Holyhead road was finished in 1830, Telford prepared a similar survey for the Great North road, so as to reduce the journey to the Scottish capital by 20 miles; but the fact that his earlier venture, including the Menai bridge (p. 452) and harbour improvements at Holyhead, had cost £733,000, made Parliament reluctant to act. There is a broad resemblance between Telford's methods of road-construction and those employed by Trésaguet. The main difference lay in Telford's provision of a flat foundation or pavement, such as would naturally commend itself to a former stonemason: he had it made of stones set on their broadest edges lengthways across the road and formed into a regular surface by breaking off projections and filling-in the interstices with stone chips. The centre of the road was then built up to a width of 18 ft—the camber being only 1 in 60—by the use of stones, of roughly cubic shape, small enough to pass through a 2½-in. ring. This building-up was to be done in two stages, so as to allow the first 4 inches to be worked in by the traffic before the last two were added. Nearer the edges of the road the covering would naturally be thinner, because of the camber, but the whole surface was finally to be spread with 1½ inches of clean gravel. Both the first and the last features were heavily criticized—the foundation of big stones for its cost, the gravel because it sank between the stones, so that water and frost got in. The stones themselves, it was held, were not sufficiently compacted to withstand heavy traffic.

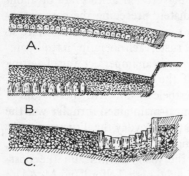

FIG. 215. Sections of roads, showing methods of: (A) Trésaguet, 1764; (B) Telford, 1824; and (C) McAdam, c. 1820

John Loudon McAdam was a Scot, like Telford, but unlike Telford he had already made his fortune in America and was Deputy Lieutenant of his native Ayrshire when he first experimented in road-making, as a road trustee and amateur inventor. In 1815 he became Surveyor-General of the Bristol roads, and after publishing a series of road-making manuals held a similar office under the government from 1827 until he died, internationally renowned, in 1836. McAdam's novel principle was not the use of small stones, in which he had many predecessors (Fig. 215), but the conclusions that he drew from his basic proposition 'that it is the native soil which really supports the weight of traffic; that while it is preserved in a dry state it will carry any weight without sinking'. He dispensed altogether with the stone foundation, content to use for this purpose the soil already on the site, provided it could be kept sufficiently dry either by constructing drains to lower ground or by raising the soil some inches above the water-level. He also reasoned that 'the thickness of a road is immaterial': what was material was the construction of an impervious and indestructible cover over the soil to which the road transmits the weight of the traffic; drains at the side of the road could then fulfil their proper function, provided the road was not too hilly and the camber kept it free from puddles. As for the stone for road-making, McAdam proposed to test for size with a 2-in. ring ($\frac{1}{2}$ in. smaller than Telford's), and to allow a maximum weight of 6 oz. each. It was to be applied in three stages, with the camber carefully shaped each time, so that traffic might have the maximum opportunity of compacting the surface; there was to be no addition of gravel.

In the course of the nineteenth century 'metalled' and 'macadamized' became almost synonymous in descriptions of roads. To Britain the new surface came in time for the heyday of coaching: by 1832 speeds on all the main routes averaged 10 m.p.h., and Edinburgh, which in 1776 was still four days' journey from London, could be reached in $42\frac{1}{2}$ hours. The coach and four gave place to the railway more rapidly in Britain than in most other countries, but both at home and abroad its coming actually effected an increase in the total of horse-drawn traffic, made up of shorter hauls to and from the line. The new roads, on which a horse could haul three times as much as on an unmetalled track, continued to serve this need. McAdam's books were translated into several languages; American engineers came over to study his methods, with the result that the Cumberland Road, the first national road in the United States, was given a macadamized surface east of the Ohio river in 1832; and by the end of the century some 90 per cent. of the principal European highways had been macadamized. His faith in a soil foundation would not nowadays be accepted as good practice, but it had the enormous advantage of cheapness. His system was at its best in the repair and reconstruction of existing roads; a macadamized surface was not infrequently combined with a Telford base. The position at the end of the 1860's shows a significant lead established by the road-makers of the United Kingdom, where the length of metalled roads per thousand of population was rather more than 5 miles, as compared with less than 3 in France, $2\frac{1}{8}$ in Prussia, and only $\frac{3}{4}$ in Spain.

The surfacing of streets in towns presented a separate problem, which greatly affected the lives of the masses in days before the tram-car and the cheap early-morning train had reduced the burden of the labourer's walk to work. Paved raised footpaths bounded by curb-stones were introduced in Westminster in 1765 and in the City of

London a little later. An American traveller, however, found no 'side-walks' in Paris as late as 1811. In districts where heavy traffic precluded the use of a macadamized base, resort was had to a recommendation made by Telford in 1824: a 12-in. deep foundation of broken stones was to be covered by rectangular paving of granite (Fig. 216), the stones for first-class streets measuring about 12 in. long by 6 in. wide by 10 in. deep, and being fitted together like masonry blocks. These granite setts, as they were later called, proved to be very durable and in general well suited to urban traffic, except that they were almost as noisy as the cheap cobbles of the past, and

FIG. 216. Paving a London street with setts of Scottish granite

setts, like cobbles, when heavily worn created dust. Wood-blocks were an alternative introduced into London experimentally from Russia in 1838: they had been used in New York three years earlier than in London, and a creosoted type appears to have originated in America in 1867. But stone-paving, though with a narrower form of block and—after 1870—an increasing use of a concrete base, continued to predominate wherever the density of city traffic justified the expense of special surfacing to ensure smooth running; it was in 1870 that Disraeli described the fully sprung hansom cab, then one generation old, as 'the gondola of London'.

Concrete was one of two new materials which came gradually into use for road-making during the century of the triumph of McAdam. Though there are one or two earlier examples of the use of concrete foundations for roads and of a system of filling-in the interstices in a macadam surface with lime-mortar, the concrete road proper appeared with the increasing availability of Portland cement (p. 406) in the 1850's. Some concrete roads were built in Austria in that decade, the first in England in 1865, and various continental countries followed suit; the earliest American example is one laid round an Ohio courthouse as late as 1892. Machinery for their construction was invented in Germany in 1879, after which their widespread development awaited only the demands of the motoring age.

The history of the asphalt road is somewhat similar, except that its development from 1832 onwards by de Sassenay in France rested upon work done in the eighteenth century. A mastic made near Seyssel, from powdered rock-asphalt and bitumen from natural oil seepages, was being used in 1835 at the rate of 1,000 tons a year, which later became the monthly rate, though its first introduction into London was not until 1869. Meanwhile, alternative sources of asphalt were being developed, including the Trinidad Lake product which competed with native material in the United States. Even more important was the development of two additional processes. One was the use of compressed rock-asphalt rolled into the road base in powdered form. This was introduced in Paris in 1854 and proved to wear very well. A rather later improvement was the use of sand-asphalt, a mixture which in fact included powdered limestone and even fair-sized stones as well as sand; it was applied at a temperature of 150–200° C. and was spread and rolled while still hot. This provided a watertight road surface and was introduced into America in the 1870's by the Belgian engineer, E. J. De Smedt. A somewhat parallel development was the use of the heavy tar which was available as a by-product of the gas industry. Tar and stones were mixed hot, spread on the road, and consolidated after cooling, with a final coat of sand on the top. What we call 'tarmac' was first made in Nottinghamshire in the 1830's, first introduced in America in 1873, and used in a three-layer system at Melbourne in the nineties. But although asphalt pavements had a considerable vogue—De Smedt laid one in front of the Capitol in Washington in 1876—the true importance of asphalt and tar as road-making materials belongs to a later period, when suction from the rubber-tyred wheels of fast motor-vehicles began to break up macadamized roads in clouds of fine dust, and a new type of surface became essential.

While the use of these new materials clearly required the development of improved road-rolling machinery, machinery was already making the laying of the macadamized surface easier. The first stone-crusher was constructed in 1858 for the roadways of Central Park, New York; this labour-saving device was more urgently needed in America than in Britain, where the breaking-up of stone by the roadside continued down to the twentieth century to be the regular and ill-paid employment of destitute old age. Various types of horse-drawn iron roller had been proposed during the eighteenth century, but their use was not advocated by either Telford or

FIG. 217. Aveling & Porter's steam road-roller, 1867

McAdam and they were not in much demand before the 1830's, when the practice grew up of compacting the road surface by stages, using lighter rollers first. The steam-roller, the use of which appears in retrospect to have been so obvious, was introduced belatedly and slowly. It was first invented in France in 1859 and in a more successful form (a $17\frac{1}{2}$-ton roller driven by a 5-h.p. engine) by another French inventor in 1862. A Paris firm produced this and two other smaller models from 1864 onwards, but it is claimed that the English steam-rollers made by Aveling & Porter from 1866 onwards (Fig. 217) were the first that were fully effective.

CANALS AND RIVER-IMPROVEMENTS

The canals of Great Britain were the contribution in the main of only two generations of canal engineers, among whom Brindley, John Rennie, and Telford are the most famous. The earliest of them, the Sankey Navigation from the St Helens coalfield to the Mersey, a 10-mile cut with nine locks, dates from 1757, while the last of the series, the Caledonian canal, was begun by Telford in 1804, though he did not live to see its completion in the 1840's. By that time they

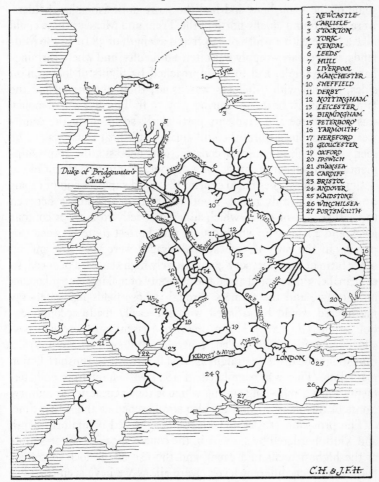

FIG. 218. Inland waterways of England and Wales, 1858

were beginning to be superseded by the railway network, and after 1850 the Manchester ship canal, promoted by local enthusiasm for the establishment of a port at Manchester, was the only important new construction. But at their greatest extent (in 1858) the inland waterways had a length of about 4,250 miles (Fig. 218), as compared with 1,000 miles, consisting of river improvements only, just over a century before.

There were three principal types of canal. The widest, which were some of the main lines and had the more optimistic shareholders, were to be found chiefly north of the Trent and Mersey; these could take a barge with a width of $13\frac{1}{2}$ ft and a length of 58 ft. In the Midlands, where water-supply was often a difficulty, and where Birmingham, for example, had to be approached by flights of locks on all sides, a canal with 7-ft locks was usual; these accommodated the familiar 'narrow boats' measuring 7 by 70 ft. Thirdly, where money was very scarce and gradients particularly steep, as in the south-west and in Shropshire, the still smaller tub-boat canal was to be seen. This lack of uniform construction, necessitating trans-shipment of long-distance cargoes and discouraging improvement in the design of barges, goes far to explain the rapid supersession of canals by railways, already noted. Another broad distinction is between the earlier type of canal, which adhered strictly to a given contour level, and a later type which sought the shortest route between two points. In the early days boatmen's wages were very low and no other form of transport set a competitively high standard of speed, so the canal engineer could avoid the necessity of making embankments or cuttings, and the farmers through whose fields his water-way meandered would be satisfied with the easily made accommodation bridge (Fig. 219). When wages had risen and there was possible competition with fast coach services and even with railways, a canal might be made as straight as what is now the Shropshire Union main line. This was completed in 1835 with numerous embankments and a 2-mile-long cutting which is the deepest in the country. Some of the older canals were also straightened at about that time.

The provision of a reasonably watertight bed of uniform depth and width bordered by a towpath, the contrivance of a water-supply at the highest point in a canal, and the use of the lock to convey barges between different levels, were all, as we have seen (p. 187), well-established practices on the Continent before the middle of the eighteenth century. Nor was there any particular novelty about 45 miles of tunnels—the final total for Great Britain—constructed usually to avoid a more expensive cutting, and made for the most part by sinking a series of shafts, excavating from shaft to shaft, and drawing up the spoil by horse-gins. To reduce the span, the earliest tunnels had no towpath at all, so that the boatman must lie on his back in the darkness to propel his barge by kicking against the roof; the 3-mile-long Standedge tunnel through the Pennines, constructed in 1811, was still worked in this fashion in 1928. Later canal tunnels had timber (or iron) stretchers built out at a suitable height above the water to support a makeshift path, while some of the largest, such as the Strood tunnel on the Thames and Medway canal, which was 26 ft 6 in. from wall to wall, provided a towpath proper. Embankments usually presented no special difficulties, but the aqueducts, of

FIG. 219. Counterbalanced accommodation bridge for a canal, *c*. 1780

which Brindley built the first to carry the Worsley canal over the river Irwell, attracted great attention to the marvel of water crossing water and boat moving above boat (Fig. 220). Their structure was that of a viaduct, but stronger because of the great weight of water, either stone or brick being used, and the waterway, of minimum dimensions, carried at first in a bed of clay that had been thoroughly kneaded to render it waterproof; but by the end of the eighteenth century an iron trough was used instead. The largest of this latter type was constructed by Telford in 1805 to carry the Ellesmere canal for a distance of over 1,000 ft, at a height of 126 ft above the river Dee; the trough was just under 12 ft wide, including the towpath, which was built out over it on iron supports, as in some canal tunnels.

Locks, with a counterbalancing beam to the gate, were mostly of a well-established type. The first double locks, placed side by side, were opened in 1820 for the Regent's canal in London, and there were also staircase locks having gates in common, the biggest being a five-lock staircase on the Yorkshire side of the Pennines. Some special interest attaches to the inclined planes, of which there eventually were a couple of dozen in Britain—slopes up which boats, generally the small tubs, were hauled, often on some form of wheeled carriage and usually by water-power. The Bude canal in Cornwall employed this system to raise the boats a total height of 225 ft, but this was quite exceptional. Lastly, there was a single example in Britain, worked on a canal near Bridgwater from 1838 to 1867, of a

FIG. 220. Brindley's original aqueduct over the Irwell

successful perpendicular lift, the barges being raised to a new level by means of a crane, a tub of water providing a counterbalance. But the twentieth century was well advanced before vertical lifts, based on the use of electrical power or of the internal combustion engine, became important features of great canal systems in many parts of the world.

As for the craft using the canals, a single boat loading up to 20 tons and drawn by one horse or a pair of donkeys at not more than 2 m.p.h., was the normal unit; on rivers they were quite often hauled by men, and some early canal boats carried sails. There was also a specialized type of express boat, which employed relays of horses and carried about half as heavy a load of goods—or passengers—at nearly twice the speed. But the early canal experiments with steamboats, such as the *Charlotte Dundas* (p. 328), bore little fruit apart from the use of tugs in tunnels, a system employed in the Islington tunnel on the

Regent's canal as early as 1826. Both at home and abroad the success of the small steam-driven vessel on estuaries and river improvements was not repeated on canals for many years, both because the wash tended to destroy the banks and because paddle-wheels were easily damaged in narrow waters. The screw propeller, introduced in 1844 on a Belgian canal, also proved to be too destructive at first, and for a time it was even found worth while to lay along the canal-bed a chain that passed round a steam capstan on a tug. This very roundabout way of using steam propulsion, as employed in Belgium in the 1870's, is described by R. L. Stevenson in his *Inland Voyage*.

Whereas in Britain the main river improvements were completed before the era of canal-building, on the Continent and in America river improvement schemes were especially characteristic of the first half of the nineteenth century. Thus the Hungarian soldier and statesman, Count Istvan Szechenyi, a veteran of the Napoleonic wars, organized a survey of the whole of the lower course of the Danube and tried to build a lock to by-pass the gorge at the Iron Gates. This particular project failed, but many cuttings were made past rapids, and the upper part of the river was regulated for a distance of 144 miles. Much was also attempted on other rivers, including the Rhine, the Oder, the Rhône, and even the Guadalquivir, either by laborious straightening and embanking work with pick and shovel, or by preparing a rough course for a new cut and then turning in the full force of the river at flood time to complete the task—a process which often had results different from those intended. A general difficulty was that cuts increased the speed of the current, often making it impracticable to haul any load upstream. Even the great Mississippi could be ascended, apart from the use of steam-power, only by keeled boats that were poled and warped upstream by a crew of as many as ten for a 40-ton cargo.

The improvements of the St Lawrence river are a great New World task that has only just been completed. The first successful cut was made in 1821, by-passing the 46-ft Lachine rapids at a depth of 5 ft, which had to be increased to 9 ft within twenty years. Four other sets of rapids had been overcome earlier by a canal which rose more than 80 ft in 14 miles, but four more short canals were required to complete the route from Montreal to Lake Ontario. When this task was successfully accomplished in 1847, the Welland canal round the Niagara Falls had already been in existence for nearly two decades and the Americans were about to build a canal to by-pass the 'leap' at Sault Sainte Marie—a fall of 20 ft in one mile of river which alone barred the way through from Lake Ontario to Lake Superior.

The three rapids on the Ottawa river were similarly by-passed in order to connect Ottawa with Montreal, but a more striking venture, which the Canadian government began in 1826, was a waterway with military protection running inland from Ottawa, requiring forty-seven locks to carry it over the watershed and bring it down to Lake Ontario. This provided for the contingency of war with the United States, which controlled the far side of the St Lawrence: it was not forgotten that the lock of an earlier canal on the Canadian side of Sault Sainte Marie, the first lock on the American continent, had been in existence for only sixteen years when it was destroyed by American troops in the war of 1812. Of happier omen was the improvement of the Richelieu river between 1830 and 1850, which eventually provided a through-traffic route to New York along the line by which Burgoyne had marched to disaster at Saratoga in 1777.

Since the American continent was virgin soil for canals as well as for river improvements, canals might be expected to have played a larger part in her nineteenth-century history than in that of Europe, but it was not so. The 364-mile Erie canal, built between 1817 and 1824, was indeed of outstanding importance, because it enabled the grain from the Great Lakes to be brought down to New York, and by linking that city to a hinterland of enormous potentialities first made it the financial and economic metropolis of the Union. The canal crossed two watersheds and had seventy-two locks, but a two-horse barge could complete the round trip, except in the months in which the canal was frozen up, in about four weeks; within a quarter of a century double locks were required to cope with the increase in traffic. Another major canal, completed in 1831 with the help of Dutch capital, was the Morris canal, which carried coal 102 miles through the hinterland of New York. This had a remarkable system of twenty-three inclined planes to cope with the rise of more than 900 ft. On entering a lock, a barge, built in two parts and hinged at the middle for easier handling, came to rest on a trolley which ran on rails, the total weight of 110 tons being carried down by gravity and hauled up—a 50 ft rise in $3\frac{1}{2}$ mins.—by a drum and cable worked by water-wheel (Fig. 221). The Pennsylvania canal, another construction of the 1820's, which had a length of nearly 400 miles and rose to a height of well over 2,000 ft, was the only other successful attempt to link the Atlantic states with the Ohio river area, where by 1850 the State of Ohio alone had over 1,000 miles of canals out of a total of 3,700 in the Union. Despite such exceptional enterprises, American canals as a whole remained local in their commercial significance, rapidly giving place to the railways after canal construction had suffered an early check in the commercial crisis of 1837.

On the continent of Europe, by contrast, the interest and importance of canals was well-nigh universal. In Russia, for instance, the large number of navigable rivers had attracted attention to the possibility of canal links in the time of Peter the Great. By 1760,

FIG. 221. Inclined plane for the Morris canal

3,000 80-ton craft a year were travelling by canal between the Neva and the Volga, and no less than three other important canal links were opened in the period 1805–11, when Alexander I's minister Speranski organized a transport department. By mid-century the total inland waterway system of Russia reached a length of 50,000 miles and the average barge haul there was nearly twenty times as long as in Britain. Something comparable to a Russian waterway was, however, constructed in Sweden in 1810–32 under the direction of Telford, to link Stockholm with Gothenburg via the great central lakes; only 54 miles had to be excavated in a total distance of 360 miles, but 58 locks were required, cut mainly in solid rock.

Farther south a great impetus was given to canal-building by Napoleon. He set de Prony, director of the revived École des Ponts et Chaussées, tasks which ranged from the building of the Ourcq canal to the draining of the Pontine marshes. Then there was the Pavia canal, which served for irrigation as well as navigation, and much activity in the Low Countries: in 1810 the great St Quentin canal, involving two tunnels, was opened to link that region with the rivers Somme, Oise, and Seine, giving access both to Paris and to Channel ports as far away as Le Havre. The work of the Napoleonic régime was continued by its two successors, reaching a climax in the reign of Louis Philippe (1830–48), during which the length of the French canals was virtually doubled: both the Marne and the Rhône were linked with the Rhine, and a number of lateral canals were constructed to run parallel with rivers that were difficult for navigation. In the second half of the century France did much more than Britain to standardize the dimensions of her canals, which retained much of their importance, especially near the coal-fields and the Belgian frontier.

The Low Countries, too, continued to be one of the great canal areas of the world long after the time of Napoleon, as they had been long before it. In the period immediately after 1815, a whole series of canals was constructed east and west from the coal-fields of the Mons and Charleroi area. A second important series linked inland ports with the sea, so that a river-route originally canalized in 1722 continued in the mid-nineteenth century to be the way by which 200-ton British schooners carried Mersey salt from Ostend up to Bruges, while Ghent in 1827 built a new ship canal along the line of a sixteenth-century predecessor to the Scheldt estuary. A third ship-canal 50 miles long, with a minimum depth of 18 ft, was constructed to give better access to Amsterdam by by-passing the shallow waters of the Zuider Zee. Later in the century the ancient connexion between transport canals and works of drainage and irrigation was revived in the building of the North Sea ship canal, for this was an important step in the reclamation of the Zuider Zee, first planned about 1840 and finally completed in our own generation.

The length of the German canals at no time amounted to much more than half that of the French, their main purpose being to provide connexions with the Rhine and Elbe, the two rivers which between them carried the major part of the water-borne trade of the country. But the German canals were given dimensions to correspond with the river improvements. The Ems, for example, in 1877 could float no cargo in excess of 80 tons: by the end of the century 600-ton cargoes could not only pass along the river, canalized for 55 miles, but along the 94 miles of the new Dortmund–Ems canal; this had a 46-ft lift in a 223×28-ft tank holding 8 ft of water. The German empire also built the first modern ship-canal of international importance, the Kiel canal, which by 1914 carried 10 million tons a year of Baltic shipping. It had a small-scale predecessor in the Eider canal, by which Christian VII of Denmark in 1784 linked the south-west corner of the Baltic at Kiel in Schleswig with the upper waters of the Eider river, which flows out into the North Sea just north of the Heligoland Bight. Óne hundred and ten years later, after Schleswig-Holstein had passed from Danish into Prussian hands, the much wider and deeper Kiel canal was made, with a course of 59 miles to the estuary of the Elbe. Both these canals saved shipping a long and rather dangerous passage round the Skaw; their construction was made relatively easy by the flatness of the country and the availability of water from the Eider.

The Suez canal was an enterprise on an altogether larger scale, 92 miles long, 26 ft deep—this was later increased—and 72 ft wide, and equipped with docks, sidings, and a signal system. Although the benefits that such a canal offered to European trade with the Far East and Australasia now appear indisputable—its influence in promoting the use of steamships has already been mentioned (p. 373)—its construction was greatly hampered by British opposition, since it would create difficulties for naval strategy. It was begun by a French company under Ferdinand de Lesseps in 1859, but it was not until 1866 that his pertinacity was rewarded with the Turkish sultan's final approval of the cutting of the canal as 'one of the most desirable events in this age of science and of progress'. Apart from extensive harbour works at Port Said and the removal of some banks of rock, one of which, at Shaluf, required the special employment of 1,500 Piedmontese labourers, the main task was excavation of earth. In all, about 2,650 million cu. ft were removed, much of it by the hands of the fellahin—though forced labour was forbidden by the sultan in 1863—but most by the introduction of dredgers. The French contractor Lavalley devised a type of trough-dredger, which deposited silt by long shutes reaching well beyond the canal banks; a floating sand-pump was invented, to deepen the bed of the canal by ploughing and suction (Fig. 222); and chisel-pointed rams were introduced, so that rock or other hard material could be broken up to a manageable size for steam-driven chains of buckets to handle. By 1867 sixty dredgers, including twenty-two long trough-dredgers, were shifting 56 million cu. ft a month, which was four times what was done by a force of 7,500 labourers.

The Suez canal prospered from the time of its opening in November 1869; by 1879, 3 million tons of shipping already used the new route annually, and by 1901 it took nearly 11 million tons. De Lesseps was therefore encouraged to attempt what seemed to be the equally feasible project of a sea-level canal through the Panama isthmus. He failed, and died in disgrace; the American lock-canal, built under quite different conditions of politics, finance, and hygiene, was completed in 1914.

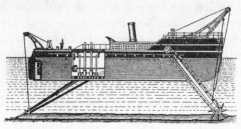

FIG. 222. French steam-driven sand-pump, from a model, *c.* 1865

RAILWAYS: THE PERMANENT WAY

As regards the construction of the permanent way, the problems of the railway engineers were in some respects the same as those that had already been tackled for the canals. In each case the shifting of enormous quantities of earth by a vast expenditure of the then cheap manual labour was the key process (Fig. 223). The earliest railways resembled the earliest English canals in being planned to follow as flat a route as possible, for the early locomotives could not be relied upon to take severe gradients (p. 380). Thus the London–Birmingham route, opened in 1838, and the London–Swindon section of the Great Western route to Bristol which Brunel had surveyed in 1833 in less than a month, were very nearly level. But the later railways in all parts of the world drove straight courses rather than deviate around any but the most unmanageable obstacles. As speeds increased, safety required curves to be less severe: in Britain the minimum approved radius was one mile, even with a gentler transitional curve at either end. When the railways did resort to such devices as zig-zagging and corkscrewing, it was in order to overcome barriers like the Alps—first passed by the Vienna–Trieste line in 1853—where canal work was never even contemplated. The result, therefore, was an altogether greater expenditure on bridges and tunnels (pp. 452, 457).

Even on level ground it might sometimes be difficult to provide a base firm enough to bear the weight of a fully loaded train. The

Liverpool and Manchester Railway, for instance, was able to cross Chat Moss only by the expedient of sinking huge bundles of faggots, on to which loads of stone and earth were tipped. In some similar cases later, it was found necessary to use huge piles of timber or concrete. In many wet areas special drainage works were needed to preserve the line, and in particularly exposed situations it might require to be protected from snow-drifts or landslides by screens and tunnelling.

FIG. 223. Building of retaining wall at Camden Town station, London, 1837

In general, however, apart from bridging and tunnelling the main task of construction was to make cuttings and embankments, the latter as far as possible built up from the spoil of the former. The width of the work was determined in the first place by the number of tracks and their gauge; even main lines were often single-track only, either because they traversed vast, sparsely populated areas, as did the Trans-Siberian Railway, which was begun in the 1890's, or because natural difficulties inevitably made the track expensive, as was the case with one of its smaller contemporaries, the Bergen Railway, which rises to 4,000 ft in the Norwegian mountains. This was also one factor in the so-called 'battle of the gauges' in English railway history; if Brunel's 7-ft gauge rather than the present standard gauge of 4 ft 8½ in. had been approved by Parliament in 1848, the capital cost of the British main lines would have been substantially increased. But the over-all width of cutting or embankment depended upon a further factor, the angle of repose, that is to say the slope at which the ground above or below the railway would remain firm. For embankments, structural rules were worked out that took account of the type of material. In a cutting, a rock face could normally be left very steep, but not a face of earth and stones, unless it was found worth while to add a retaining wall of stone or brick.

Precise figures are available for the work involved in building the last of the British main lines, the Great Central Railway, an alternative route from the north, which opened its London terminus at St Marylebone in 1899. To construct 105 miles of double track required the excavation of 13·82 million cu. yds of earth and rock. About 660,000 cu. yds of brickwork were laid, together with 220,000 cu. yds of concrete and 9,000 cu. yds of ashlar masonry. The amount of ballast laid was just over a million cu. yds. This work was done mainly in the Midland plain: comparison may therefore be made with the first stage of the Bergen Railway in Norway, a 67-mile single line completed to Voss in 1883, for which more than a million cu. yds of rock had to be removed by blasting.

The steam-excavator was brought into use during the construction of the first Pacific railway in America in the 1830's, the stone-crusher in America in 1858, where it was first used for roads (p. 436); track-laying machinery and cranes to lower the rails from the front of construction trains that advanced with the railhead were introduced there a decade or so later. But a great part of the work still had to be done with pick, shovel, and wheelbarrow. The base must be arranged with a slight camber and provided with occasional drainage-channels for rain-water, so as to prepare a suitable surface for the ballast; the ballast of broken stone or iron slag was then deposited in two layers, arranged to give maximum drainage as well as stability; and finally each wooden sleeper—the 'dormant timber' in earlier parlance—required to be carefully embedded. On the whole, the chief reduction in manual labour came through increasing use of a temporary rail layout for tip-wagons to operate between the cuttings and embankments, enabling the spoil from one to be conveyed by rail almost into its final position in the other. But the final task of laying the track became more exacting as the growing weight and speed of the traffic necessitated the use of heavier rails (p. 382).

BRIDGES

The erection of great bridges is less repetitive than most forms of building, since the problems presented by the interrelationship of land and water on the site are almost infinitely variable. It also provides a more critical testing of the builders' work, as we are reminded by the still-familiar story of the Tay railway bridge disaster of December 1879, when seventy-three persons were drowned through the failure of the longest bridge in the world within eighteen months of its erection. Moreover, great bridges played a special part in the development of both Europe and America during this period—in the embellishment of large cities old and new, in making new road routes possible, and still more in enabling the railway to keep a straight course across valleys and rivers, and even the narrower arms of the sea. The bridge-builders therefore deserve our attention.

The first great name in eighteenth-century bridge-building is that of Perronet (p. 404), whose engineers were taught to flatten their arches—the low gradient being of great assistance to wheeled vehicles—so that the crown rose as little as one-twelfth of the span above the springing, and to thin the piers until they were only one-tenth of the span. Such bridges were elegant and convenient while remaining within the limit of safety. The last of Perronet's works was a bridge in Paris, originally designated the Pont Louis XVI, of which the road ran level from the quays while its slender piers reduced the obstruction of the waterway to one-third, as compared with two-thirds in some of the great Roman bridges. Begun two years before the Revolution, it was finished with stone from the ruins of the Bastille and had among its earliest users the mob assembling for Louis XVI's execution in the near-by Place de la Concorde, from which the bridge now takes its name. The temporary timber centres on which Perronet built up his arches were made of bolted pieces carrying the thrust to the permanent piers, and when the bolts had been removed the whole temporary structure was made to collapse into the river by pulling at ropes. An improved centring which used multiple wedges, so that it could be lowered bit by bit while testing the permanent structure, thereby diminishing the risk of catastrophe if weakness became apparent, was introduced by a Scotsman, Robert Mylne—the last important British architect to be also a civil engineer—when he began the construction of Blackfriars bridge, London, in 1760 (Fig. 224). This was the first British bridge with an elliptical arch; other interesting features were the resting of the caissons on piles and the employment of a rather crude inverted arch for transmitting the thrust of the nine spans, the largest of which was 100 ft.

Three famous masonry bridges for London were planned by John Rennie—who together with Telford established in Britain the system of over-all contracts for all trades required in an engineering project—in the period following the Napoleonic wars. The first Waterloo bridge, which introduced granite for bridge-building to London and of which the sculptor Canova said that 'it was worth a journey from Rome to see', was completed by him in 1817, the new London Bridge (since widened) by his sons in 1831, ten years after the designer's death. Its longest span (152 ft 6 in.) was the first in Britain to exceed, though only by 12 ft 6 in., that of the Pont-y-ty-Pridd over the swift-flowing Taff in Glamorganshire, which a local stonemason had built by the light of nature at his fourth attempt in 1756. Rennie took over Mylne's system of bridge-centring and his use of the inverted arch, but in place of caissons he founded his bridges on piles built inside coffer dams: by this time the steam-engine had been adapted to wind up the pile-driving hammer as well as for haulage gear. But it was Rennie's third and most famous bridge at Southwark which introduced cast iron as a new structural material to London.

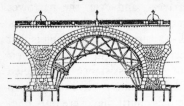

FIG. 224. Mylne's bridge over the Thames at Blackfriars, showing centring still in position

In 1779 Abraham Darby of Coalbrookdale, the third-generation owner of the famous ironworks (p. 147), designed, cast, erected, and largely paid for an almost semicircular iron bridge which gave his workpeople and vehicles access to the farther bank of the Severn (Fig. 225). The 70-ft-long main ribs were cast in open sand-moulds direct from a blast-furnace; the parts—weighing in all $378\frac{1}{2}$ tons— were hoisted up, fitted together, and secured by wedges without a single bolt or rivet. Although cast iron had never been used structurally on this scale before, the ironwork (though not the approaches of masonry) has stood the test of time: the bridge is still used by pedestrians.

The achievement aroused widespread interest. Tom Paine, for instance, celebrated the triumph of the American Revolution by designing an iron bridge with thirteen ribs, one for each state in the new republic, to be cast in England for erection in Pennsylvania: a casting was made, and exhibited in London in 1791, but the bridge was never erected. The second iron bridge was built by Telford a little higher up the Severn to replace one that had been carried away by flood in 1795, and at about the same time a much more ambitious one, with a span of 236 ft, crossed the river Wear at Sunderland. In the latter structure, however, the use of solid iron ribs meeting at the crown of the bridge was superseded by ribs built up over timber centring from openwork cast-iron voussoirs and wrought-iron straps.

Rowland Burdon, Member of Parliament for Sunderland and director of the Rotherham iron-foundry that built the bridge, took out a patent for this type of construction. But when Telford two years later proposed to build a cast-iron London Bridge (Fig. 226) with a span of 600 ft, a House of Commons committee, unable to extract a reliable figure for the strength of cast iron from a host of conflicting expert witnesses, turned down the scheme. Rennie, however, produced a

FIG. 225. The iron bridge over the Severn at Coalbrookdale, from a trade token

test figure while he was building Southwark bridge. This was completed in 1819 and had a life of just over a century; the central span was of 240 ft, with shorter side spans; and the Rotherham firm referred to above made both the segmental iron ribs and the thirteen voussoirs forming each arch.

A pioneer suspension-bridge, hung from iron chains by vertical rods, was built by James Finley in Pennsylvania in 1800, and the

FIG. 226. Telford's ambitious but unrealized plan for a new London Bridge, 1797

difficulty of making big iron castings in America during the earlier part of the century gave iron suspension-bridges a considerable vogue. In Britain the earliest were built for tempestuous Scottish rivers. In order to dispense with masonry piers supporting arches in midstream, which were liable to be undermined by flood, wrought-iron suspension chains consisting of flat links were patented by (Sir)

Samuel Brown, the designer of two important suspension bridges over the Tweed, though one at Berwick, with a 449-ft span, was blown down within six months. His links were nevertheless adopted by Telford for the great bridge which carried the Holyhead Road across the Menai Straits on chains 580 ft long. The original timber deck proved too light, and was wrecked in a storm in 1839 only thirteen years after completion, but although it sometimes heaved as much as 16 ft the bridge itself, with its original iron chains, carried the road traffic to and from Anglesey without rebuilding until 1939. Wire-suspension was first used for a road-bridge by Marc Seguin near Lyons in 1825. Within ten years a span of 870 ft had been achieved by an associate of Seguin in Switzerland, who employed a cable made up of 1,000 wires bound with wire wrapping; but this in turn was exceeded by Charles Ellet, the 'Brunel of America', whose cable-bridge over the Ohio in 1848 was the first in the world to span more than a thousand feet. But the fact that it was seriously damaged by a tornado only six years afterwards, and that Ellet lost at least two other bridges through uncounteracted swaying, were reminders of the dangerous weakness of this form of bridge unless girders were used to stiffen it, thus depriving the structure of the lightness and cheapness which were among its merits. Robert Stephenson accordingly rejected the suspension bridge for railway work, and when I. K. Brunel used it in 1852 at Chepstow, where special allowance had to be made both for the needs of navigation and for the 40-ft tidal range of the Wye, he put in wrought-iron tubular top-booms 9 ft in diameter and supported each of the two railway tracks on a pair of wrought-iron girders.

Meanwhile, truss bridges, for which Palladio had published the first known designs in 1570, had made great headway in America, where the architect Ithiel Town in 1820 secured a patent for a type constructed in diamond pattern with wooden planks and wooden piers, roofed and weather-boarded; since this could be erected by carpenters from local material, royalties at not less than a dollar per lineal foot yielded him a considerable fortune. The earliest American railway bridges were of this kind, to be compared with the inexpensive wooden trestle viaducts long employed in English railway-building in districts like Cornwall, where traffic was light. In the 1840's T. W. Pratt and other American engineers designed improved composite trusses, using wood and wrought iron, and as late as 1873 Pratt patented a truss of wood and steel.

But Britain, where timber was relatively scarce and cast iron plentiful, for a time built railway-bridges of cast iron, of which the most notable—though it includes some wrought iron—was that erected by Robert Stephenson in 1849 at Newcastle upon Tyne. The railway is carried just above the level of the crown of the six tied arches, and there is a roadway at the level of the tie; at both levels the bridge still copes with modern traffic. Such solid construction was helped by the fact that by the close of the cast-iron age, as we may call it, the making of the foundations of bridges had been greatly improved. Stephenson was able to drive in the piles with a Nasmyth steam-hammer delivering a blow a second; Brunel at Chepstow could build a cast-iron tower upon the river-bed, to carry one end of his suspension chains, by the use of compressed-air caissons.

Such caissons were first introduced for constructing foundations on marshy ground by the versatile Sir Thomas Cochrane (later tenth Earl of Dundonald) in 1830. The essence of the system was the pumping of compressed air into a working-chamber at the bottom of a caisson, the pressure being raised to correspond with that of the water outside as the cutting-edge of iron or steel reached greater depths. The workers themselves, and the spoil which they were removing from the river bed, were brought out through an air-lock in the roof of the working-chamber. As the caisson sank the side walls were extended upwards, section by section, so keeping the top always above water-level: in effect, the foundations were built from the top downwards. Although Brunel used caissons on a considerable scale for the Royal Albert bridge (p. 454), it was the bridging of the Rhine at Kehl by Fleur Saint-Denis in the same year (1859) which fully established the system, in the sense that the final masonry was placed direct on the top of the caisson. One grave complication was the fact that the use of compressed air gave rise to the painful and often fatal caisson disease or 'bends'. If the decompression process for men emerging through the air-lock from great depths was not sufficiently gradual, bubbles of nitrogen became liberated in the tissues—a physiological condition, encountered also by deep-sea divers, that was not fully understood and effectively guarded against until after the end of the century.

Robert Stephenson's Britannia bridge, which carries the railway across the Menai Straits at a point a few hundred yards south-west of that chosen by Telford, where the water is much wider but divided by the Britannia rock, was much more remarkable than its neighbour. The main feature was the use of pairs of huge rectangular wrought-iron tubes designed after careful testing in association with Fairbairn, the shipbuilder, and Eaton Hodgkinson, a Fellow of the Royal Society who had made a special study of the strength of materials. Their span over the water was 459 ft—and there was no precedent for a wrought-iron span exceeding 31 ft 6 in. The tubes were made up of the riveted wrought-iron plates developed for boilers and iron shipbuilding: the solid tube form, which was un-

FIG. 227. One of the 459-ft tubes of the Britannia bridge being floated into position, prior to raising, 1849

necessarily heavy and harboured noxious fumes, was soon dispensed with for later bridges, but the material was adopted for innumerable girder-bridges. The Britannia bridge also provided a dramatic novelty in its mode of completion. Heavy towers reminiscent of the massive architecture of ancient Egypt had been erected to carry suspension chains, but Stephenson found the cost of the latter excessive, and in the end the tubes were floated out on pontoons (Fig. 227) and lifted into position by hydraulic jacks installed near the tops of the towers.

In spite of Stephenson's triumph and the successful use of oval tubes, 17 ft by 12 ft in diameter, for I. K. Brunel's Royal Albert bridge over the Tamar (1859), which carries the railway into Cornwall at the same height above high water (100 ft) as Stephenson's, the future of long-span bridging lay with the suspension system. This is the more remarkable because it was not until the twentieth century was well advanced that a fully satisfactory theoretical explanation was found for the way in which continued vibrations from wind or even traffic may build up potentially destructive oscillations. The present-day engineer can contemplate spans of as much as 10,000 ft; but Britain with her small distances had relatively little need for them, and the climax of her nineteenth-century suspension-bridge construction was reached with the bridge over the Avon gorge at Clifton in 1862. This was a design by I. K. Brunel, though completed after his death, using the huge wrought-iron chains made twenty years earlier for his Hungerford bridge over the Thames in London, which had been dismantled to make room for Charing Cross station.

But the most important advances in technique were made by John A. Roebling, an early German immigrant to America, with a form of wire cable that he patented in 1841: unlike the stranded wire ropes of earlier practice (p. 452), where the wire was weakened by twisting, this was made up of parallel wires laid separately and then wire-bound. It was first used on a large scale in 1855 for the Grand Trunk bridge at Niagara, which carried a single-track rail-way above a road and—what was more important—sustained the rail load with unprecedented success. Stiffening girders were placed between the decks (a device which was also used to steady the Clifton bridge), and it was further strengthened against the action of the wind by wire-rope stays above and below the deck. The weight was carried on four main cables, which had a 10 in. diameter after binding. The same method was employed by Roebling for the Brooklyn bridge, New York—which was completed in 1883 by his son, W. A. Roebling, although he had been rendered a permanent invalid at thirty-five by caisson disease—and became standard practice for all the great American suspension bridges that followed. Suspension was by galvanized steel wire (p. 498), of which the standard thickness was one-fifth of an inch, placed in huge reels at the two ends of the bridge. Loops of wire were then hauled across in both directions by pulley-wheels on endless ropes carried over the towers; they were adjusted by men on the cat-walks to secure the correct level and uniform sag; and the wires were finally bunched and bound together (Fig. 228).

At the close of the nineteenth century steel was replacing iron as a bridge-building material, and at Châtellerault, north-east of Poitiers,

Hennibique had even introduced the use of reinforced concrete (p. 418). J. B. Eads, who had built armoured gun-boats during the American Civil War, used steel for the three 500-ft arches of his great bridge at St Louis, which was designed to give a height clearance of 90 ft, allowing 40 ft for a maximum Mississippi flood and 50 ft for the great smoke-stacks of the river steamers. To secure adequate foundations in the sandy river-bed, he introduced from Europe the use of compressed-air caissons, but there was also the

FIG. 228. Compacting and binding cables on Brooklyn bridge

problem of the erection of the huge arches, for which it would be extremely expensive, if not entirely impracticable, to erect staging over the water. To overcome this, temporary towers were built on the piers, over which cables were passed to tie back the halves of each arch during construction.

Within a few years of the successful completion of the St Louis bridge in 1874, the cantilever principle was more fully employed for the steel railway bridge over the Firth of Forth (Fig. 229), designed with the Tay bridge disaster freshly in mind, yet with spans so great that they were nowhere exceeded until 1917. To preserve the balance, the work was built out simultaneously on both sides of the three immensely strong main piers, which were made nearly four times as wide at the base as at the top to resist gales— a device that its designer, John Fowler, picturesquely described as 'the straddle of Henry VIII'. Two of the piers had shorter members linking them with the shore, but the main spans, which linked them with the centre pier on the island of Inchgarvie, required a total reach of 1,710 ft. The cantilever arms left gaps of 350 ft, across which the plates were built out from the cantilevers. The precision of the assembly, using hydraulic cranes and riveting machines, was such that, when the work from the two sides was to be joined up, it required only hastily improvised fires of wood-shavings and waste to expand it by $\frac{1}{4}$ in. for the final bolts to be inserted. Steel plates 16 ft long, 4 ft 6 in. wide, and up to $1\frac{1}{4}$ in. thick were fabricated on the spot and bent into shape in a 2,000-ton hydraulic press. The use of

FIG. 229. Building of the Forth bridge, *c*. 1890

54,000 tons of open-hearth cast steel in a single structure, the organization of temporary shops and yards covering an area of 50 acres, and the final success of the vast enterprise, which on its completion in 1890 reduced railway travel-time to the north of Scotland by an hour, make a fitting climax to the story of British bridge-building in the Victorian era.

TUNNELS

The most important British railway tunnel, that which passes under the Severn, was completed three years before the Forth bridge but a few years later than the historic Mont Cenis and St Gotthard tunnels under the Alps. The development of new tunnelling techniques to serve transportation was little needed before the nineteenth century, for there were no important road tunnels and the earlier canal tunnels, whether in seventeenth-century France or eighteenth-century Britain, were carried through the solid rock by the methods long employed in mining (p. 248). One of the two

tunnels on the Napoleonic St Quentin canal in France is said to
have been the first wide tunnel driven through pressure-exerting
material, in this case sand, by means of timbering and arching. But
in 1830 the railway had to enter Liverpool by tunnelling through
soft blue clay as well as wet sand, and
from that time the construction of
tunnels under all conditions became an
accepted part of the railway engineer's
duties.

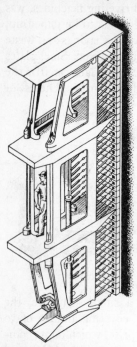

One of the several modes of excavation was to protect the roof of the immediate working-area by timbers drawn
forward from a space above the finished
lining, their front ends being supported
upon posts which rested on a short
sill at the bottom of the heading. As
the work advanced, the spaces above
the finished lining were successively
packed and filled. This timber shoring
was quite inadequate, however, for
tunnelling through such ground as
exists under the Thames at London,
a feat that Trevithick attempted but
had to abandon after cutting a heading 3 ft wide by 5 ft high for nearly
1,000 ft, while M. I. Brunel with his
improved shield and immense determination was able to accomplish it only

FIG. 230. Part of Brunel's shield
for the Thames tunnel

after he had faced two inundations and three minor floodings.
Brunel's shield (Fig. 230) enabled thirty-six men to attack the face
simultaneously, each of them working at a rectangular area approximately 7 ft 6 in. by 3 ft; there were two intermediate platforms, so
that they could work at three levels inside the main cast-iron frame.
The top and foot of the shield were hinged and were pressed forward
by jacks working against the completed masonry, while smaller jacks
held boards against the face, except at the points where it was actually being cut. The shield was moved forward 18 inches at a time, and
was followed up by a double arch of masonry set in Roman cement.
When six men were drowned by the second inundation, work stopped
for seven years, but resort to a heavier shield and the plugging of

holes in the river bed with Portland-cement concrete enabled it to be completed: the tunnel, which was opened to foot passengers in 1843, is still in use for the underground railway between Wapping and Rotherhithe. The next tunnel under the Thames was the 7-ft-diameter Tower subway, built in a single year, 1869; this was lined with permanent cast-iron rings and for a time accommodated diminutive 12-seater cable-cars.

The lengths of the great Alpine railway tunnels—the Mont Cenis nearly 8 miles, the St Gotthard 9⅓ miles, and the Simplon (begun in 1898) 12¼ miles—presented special problems of boring, ventilation, and survey. Work on the Mont Cenis tunnel to link the Paris–Lyons railway with Turin and north Italy was begun in August 1857, three years before its northern end became French territory through the cession of Savoy to Napoleon III; its construction was an all-Italian project, of which France shared the cost. The preliminary triangulation required the establishment of twenty-one survey points in a difficult mountain terrain; the correct alignment for the tunnel was then marked on posts at the two entrances; and a telescope sighted along that line checked the position of a lamp at the working-face. The tunnel was to be driven through solid rock, without intermediate shafts, and at a maximum depth of about 1 mile below the summit of Mount Fréjus. Excavation proceeded from both ends simultaneously, working by stages outwards from an advanced gallery about 10 ft square, until the brick walls enclosed a space 26 ft wide and 25 ft high to the crown of the arched roof. The blasting was done with gunpowder, and pneumatic drills operated by water-powered compressors came into use during the progress of the work, speeding it up more than threefold. The compressed air from the drills ventilated the advanced galleries; farther back the tunnel was divided by a horizontal brattice, so that a current of air could be drawn in through the lower half and expelled through the upper, a technique which was known to medieval miners. There were long delays in the early years, but the two ends were successfully joined on Christmas Day, 1870, and the tunnel was opened the following year (Fig. 231). The St Gotthard tunnel was constructed at the rate of a mile a year, as compared with half a mile for the Mont Cenis, a fact that may be accounted for by greater experience, by the availability of rock-drilling machinery from the start, and by the use of dynamite (p. 547) for blasting. But it cost over 300 lives from among the workmen, mainly Italians. The existence of seven spiral-turns in the approaches made the alignment extraordinarily difficult, but when the advanced galleries met in the middle of the mountain, the difference in height was only 4 in., and horizontally between 6 and 8 in.—a striking example of the precision that surveying instruments had then achieved. Altogether, the St Gotthard route required 28½ miles of tunnelling in 105½ miles, but its completion in 1882 (the year of the Triple Alliance) reduced travelling-time between Germany and Italy by 36 hours.

The 1880's were also a decade associated with three great underwater enterprises in Britain: namely, the proposed Channel tunnel,

FIG. 231. The first train traverses the Mont Cenis tunnel, 1871

of which a mile or more was excavated at the Dover end in 1882 and 1887 in the face of much military and political opposition that only now seems to be abating; the mile-long railway tunnel connecting Liverpool and Birkenhead (1886); and the more ambitious Severn tunnel, also opened in 1886. The last, over 4·3 miles long, took thirteen years to build, chiefly because of a disaster in 1879, when the Big Spring was encountered (Fig. 232) and flooded all the works, which by that time extended under nearly the whole width of the estuary. Additional pumping plant had to be provided and extra shafts sunk on the landward side of the Big Spring. Certain precautionary measures had been neglected in the panic, and these were later carried out by a diver equipped with compressed oxygen who penetrated 1,000 ft through the flooded tunnels. In the circumstances it is understandable that the tunnel was eventually provided with a pumping power that could deal with more than twice the maximum water-intake experienced, which was 30 million gallons a day. Another striking feature is the size of the ventilating fans needed at the ends of the tunnel to cope with the effects of heavy traffic drawn by steam locomotives, the one in the main shaft on the Monmouthshire side being 40 ft in diameter. The lining is of $2\frac{1}{2}$–3-ft-thick vitrified brick set in cement.

Newer methods and materials appear in the construction of the Hudson river tunnel, New York, which was begun in 1874 but as a

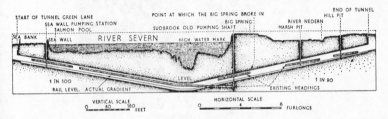

FIG. 232. Section of the Severn tunnel as in October 1879, when the Big Spring flooded the works

result of financial difficulties was not completed until 1908. The project involved the driving of two tubes, 16 ft wide and 18 ft high, mainly through underwater silt; the river is a mile wide. The excavating was done in a compressed-air chamber at a pressure of 35 lb per sq. in., requiring for medical reasons the use of an airlock at ground level, in which the air pressure could be slowly reduced, to prevent caisson disease among the workmen. At a later stage three British consulting engineers, including J. H. Greathead who had made the Tower subway, introduced a steel shield (Fig. 233), which was jacked forward by hydraulic rams while compressed air kept out the silt and water. At the tail of the shield, providing the butt against which the jacks worked, rings of cast iron formed the tunnel lining: such rings are both durable and readily handled. A speed of as much as 72 ft in a week was being achieved when financial difficulties intervened a second time. Greathead, however, successfully demonstrated the value both of his cast-iron rings and of what came to be known as the 'Greathead shield' in 1890, when he completed the first $3\frac{1}{2}$-mile 'tube' for the City and South London railway (p. 383). His methods continued in use as the new type of transport spread under London, but compressed air was employed only where the line came out of the clay into water-bearing gravel.

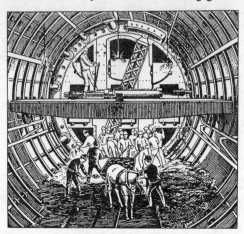

FIG. 233. Steel shield used in construction of the Hudson river tunnel

LAND WORKS FACILITATING SEA TRAFFIC

The improved road, the canal, and the railway were among the most important of the many influences that stimulated the growth of sea-borne trade. Thus the annual tonnage of shipping entering the Thames was 1¾ million in 1800 and 13 million in 1891. Such a development could not have occurred without a corresponding increase in harbour facilities of all kinds. In the late eighteenth century John Smeaton recorded a depth of less than 4 ft in the part of the Clyde where the *Queen Mary* was later launched. But even before a ship entered an estuary, building construction had a major part to play through the development of lighthouses: it is significant that the building of the best known British example was almost exactly contemporary with the beginning of the great industrial changes in the reign of George III.

Lighthouses on the Eddystone rock, built chiefly of timber, had been destroyed by gale in 1703 and by fire in 1755; Smeaton therefore rebuilt the lighthouse as the first of the great wave-swept towers constructed in stone (Fig. 234). Since the Eddystone Rock faces straight into the Atlantic storms in a position to which single blocks of great mass could not in those days be transported, Smeaton built his stones into the solid rock as far as he could; shaped each stone to dovetail into its neighbour; and pegged each course to the one above and below it with trenails of oak. As he was also at pains to find a strong hydraulic mortar (p. 405), the final result was exceptionally solid. It ultimately became unsafe, not because of failure of the structure but because there was some erosion of the rock under the foundations. After riding out the storms of 120 years, Smeaton's lighthouse was re-erected on Plymouth Hoe, looking out across the water to its modern successor, one-third higher but four and a half times as heavy, which was built with the help of a coffer-dam. The Bell Rock tower of 1811 (Fig. 235) and the lighthouse on the Skerryvore Rocks in Argyllshire, built by Robert and Alan Stevenson (respectively grandfather and uncle of the author), are stone towers which still stand, but an iron-work structure on the Bishop Rock in the Scillies, said to be the most exposed situation in the world, was swept away by a storm in 1850 when ready to receive its lantern. The cast-iron tower built a few years later on the Fastnet Rock, marking the southern extremity of Ireland, was likewise eventually replaced by granite. In general, stone light-houses were preferred, except when the foundations had to be of iron and steel, until the days of reinforced concrete con-struction.

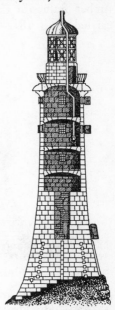

FIG. 234. Smeaton's Eddy-
stone lighthouse, 1759

In 1780, at the height of the American War of Independence, the French began the development of an artificial harbour at Cherbourg, a breakwater surmounted by batteries to keep both the weather and the British at bay. In the course of eight years, eighteen cone-shaped timber structures, 70 ft high with a diameter tapering from 150 to 60 ft, were towed out to sea, filled with stone, and sunk. But they broke up and the stone heaps, which stood at a slope of 1 in 3 in deep water, were flattened out to a slope of 1 in 10 higher up by the action of the tide. A bed of blocks weighing 3 or 4 tons apiece was eventually superimposed and crowned by forts, but storms destroyed them. This vast work was not finally completed until 1850, when Vicat's hydraulic lime made it possible to build up a concrete causeway with masonry, reaching from low-tide level to a height of 3 yards above high water. Something similar, but on a less ambitious scale, was undertaken by John Rennie in front of the harbour at Plymouth. He found the same difficulty in getting his material to settle at a satisfactorily steep slope, and his great bank of limestone rubble assumed much the same shape as the stones that burst out from the timber frames at Cherbourg. But the English design, which was carried out in 1812–41, used 10-ton blocks for the exterior, because

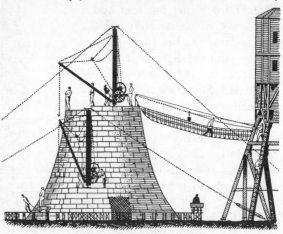

FIG. 235. Building the Bell Rock lighthouse, 1811

these would stand at a slope of 1 in 5, and secured the top by paving it with granite blocks set in cement.

The harbour works at Ramsgate, which were completed by Smeaton, are a good example of an entirely artificial commercial port; it was badly needed as a protection for ships caught in northerly gales near the Goodwin Sands. The problem which faced Smeaton in 1774 was the silting-up of the outer basin at a rate with which the available labour could not cope. He dealt with this by enclosing an inner basin, from which the water could be suddenly released at low tide through one of six sluices. A barge manœuvred in its path helped the rush of water to scour a wide channel; because of the rapid flow the suspended material was deposited well away from the harbour entrance. The same principle of making the water do the work was applied later at the mouths both of the Mersey and the Ribble, stone being dumped in quantity in order to direct the current into particular channels.

Dredging equipment, needed from early times to keep water channels open for drainage as well as for navigation, began with the use of a scoop or bag on the end of a pole, worked from a boat by hand along the bottom of the water. The Dutch, as we might expect (p. 72), took the lead in developing more effective devices, such as ladle-dredgers, which cut a wide channel; grab-dredgers, employing a pair of tongs suspended between pontoons; and the mud-mill, which raised soft mud on flat boards rotated by a chain. About 1750 a more efficient chain-dredger began to come into use, which brought up its load in buckets, but the first big step in modernization was the introduction of steam-power. A 4-h.p. Boulton & Watt engine was harnessed to a ladle-dredger at Sunderland as early as 1796; in 1804 a steam-dredger with a bucket-chain was developed independently by Oliver Evans for the Philadelphia docks and by Rennie at Hull, whence it spread to the Clyde in 1824 and to the Ribble in 1839. Further improvements were made, as we have seen (p. 445), during the construction of the Suez canal. The use of a centrifugal pump with a dredger was begun in America in 1871, and by the end of the century the Liverpool bar was being cleared by a pump of which the impeller could deal with much coarser solids than sand, could work at a depth of 70 ft, and which discharged at a rate of over 200,000 cu. ft an hour. Yet another late nineteenth-century dredging device was the pumping of water through tubes laid in a mud deposit, so that the mud might flow out in suspension on the ebb tide—an elaboration of the methods of washing away silt practised by Smeaton very much earlier.

But the characteristic feature of the modern industrial port was the provision of docks, to make the loading and unloading of ships independent of the tide and of the cumbrous and expensive services of lighters. Docks were not altogether unknown in the eighteenth century—the Howland Great Wet Dock at Rotherhithe was completed in 1700 and a dock was begun at Liverpool in 1709, the year when that city first engaged in the slave trade—yet even London found one to be sufficient until the notorious depredations of river thieves aroused commercial interests to concerted action, which began with the institution of the Thames Police in 1798. The West India Docks, the first on the north side of the river, were constructed in 1802 by William Jessop, a pupil of Smeaton; they were followed almost immediately by the London Docks lying nearer the City, where Rennie introduced cast-iron columns and roofs for dockside

buildings and the use of steam-cranes on the quayside. The opening
of the East India Docks followed in 1808, and from that time the
growth of docks continued throughout the nineteenth century as
both an effect and a cause of the concentration of shipping in particular ports. For repair purposes, where a dry dock might not
otherwise be available, there was invented the floating dock, which
could be towed to any part of the world and would remain afloat with
a vessel inside it after the water had been pumped out. An iron
dry dock for use by the Royal Navy was launched at North Woolwich
in 1868 and successfully towed to Bermuda.

COAL AND THE METALS

COAL-MINING

IN the latter part of the eighteenth century coal was a well-established industry of long standing in certain parts of western Europe, especially near the north-east coast of England (Fig. 236), where the coal-mines were, significantly enough, the first main scene of operation of the Newcomen pumping-engine. It was from this

FIG. 236. Conveyance of coal from mine to barge, as shown on plan of Tyne and Wear collieries, 1788

engine that the new prime mover sprang, and it was by this industry of coal-mining that the new prime mover was fuelled and kept in action. By 1900 coal was being mined in every continent, and the output of the United States already exceeded that of Britain: nevertheless, coal enjoys pride of place during this century and a half, as the raw material whose abundance above all else enabled Britain to benefit from the lead which she had established in the manufacture of the steam-engine and the new machine-tools and in the development of the new means of transport. The mechanical inventions and the production of coal reacted, of course, upon each other; together, their history provides a succinct summary of how Britain became, and for a time remained, the 'workshop of the world'. In 1770, when Watt was at work on his steam-engine, British coal output was a little over 6 million tons. In 1856, when Bessemer

steel began, it stood at 65 million tons. By the end of the century it was nearing its all-time maximum (reached in 1913) and stood at the gigantic figure of 220 million tons.

For a long time the increase of output depended mainly upon the availability of almost unlimited supplies of cheap labour—the pit-men's families, and the Irish im-migrants to the western seaboard of Britain—which was readily ex-pendable. The steam-engine, for which the fuel was so cheaply available, made its appearance first on the surface, increasingly in the form of the high-pressure Cornish engine of Trevithick (p. 325), without which deep mines could not be freed from water: but its employment for hoisting the coal and its hewers from the depths below came much more slowly. In the early nineteenth century Scots-women still carried the coal in wicker baskets 100 ft or more up ladders (Fig. 237). Hand-wind-lasses were used in the West Riding of Yorkshire as late as the 1840's, and the degree of dependence upon horse-whims may be judged from the fact that they were then also thought to be adequate for hoisting the earth out of railway-tunnel ex-cavations. The horizontal rope-

FIG. 237. Women coal-bearers, Scot-land, early nineteenth century

drum, 12-16 ft in diameter, round which horses paced, was only gradually replaced by a winch driven, as a rule, by a low-pressure, single-cylinder, vertical steam-engine. About 1840, also, increased efficiency was achieved by the introduction of wire ropes, which were not only stronger, but less liable to spin and sway than those of hemp. But winding by engine continued to be slow and wasteful of steam, and it was difficult to devise any satisfactory counterbalance for the varying weight of hanging rope as the load went up or down the shaft.

Meanwhile, mines of increasing depth were being worked by hand-pick and crowbar, in successive areas hazardously opened up by blasting with ordinary black powder; the safety-fuse was not invented until 1831. The commonest mode of extraction was that traditionally known as 'bord-and-pillar', the bords being the first excavations made at right angles throughout the seam or some smaller area which it was desired to keep separate for safety or better ventilation. These divided the rest of the coal into pillars from 22 to 60 yds sq., which were then removed by cutting slices about 6 yds wide off one side at a time. The roof was supported by timbers during the cutting of the slice, and was then allowed to cave in, a plan which worked satisfactorily so long as an angle of about 45° was maintained between the line of debris and the natural slips or breaks in the roof, and provided also that the overlying rock was not more than about 900 ft thick: with any greater thickness there was grave risk of collapse. In the very deep mines common in the second half of the century, it became necessary to avoid the risk of crushed pillars by taking out the coal in a single operation known as 'longwall' working. By this method a wall of coal about 100 yds long is taken out in line, and as the wall or face advances, stone packs are built up at right angles to the advance so as to support the roof when the coal has been withdrawn.

Haulage of coal from face to shaft was done at first by loading wicker baskets on to wooden sleds. As the distances increased, wheeled trams came into use, and at the very end of the eighteenth century Thomas Wilson, the collier poet of Tyneside, was celebrating the man 'that first invented metal plates'—that is, light iron rails which greatly relieved the work of the haulier. The fact that trucks were commonly dragged along by roughly harnessed women and children is a horrifying circumstance but in the eighteenth century they normally performed the ancillary tasks, however unhealthy and exacting, which related to the employment of their menfolk; moreover, they could haul in passages which were too low even for the pit pony (Fig. 238), introduced about 1763. The layout of some mines facilitated the use of inclines down which the loaded trucks could run, but there were many others where the route to the shaft involved the negotiation of dips. In 1812 George Stephenson was engaged in altering a pumping-engine for the haulage of coal on a dip-road, and by 1840 stationary engines were commonly positioned underground for this purpose. In 1844 the mining engineer, John Buddle, introduced a system of endless-rope haulage at Wallsend, and the provision of steam haulage gradually became common for important main roads, even on the level. But every

FIG. 238. Winning coal in the Bradley mine, Staffordshire, early nineteenth century

large mine contained miles of subsidiary roads, which fed the main roads with coal, and these continued to be operated by animal power, by manpower, and—even after Lord Shaftesbury's Mines Act of 1842—by boys, once they had reached the manly age of ten.

The increase in the depth at which coal was worked, that inevitable concomitant of the huge increase in the quantity of coal brought up, created a third problem, besides the pumping of water from the workings and the hoisting-up of the products of the work and the workers themselves. This problem was the presence of gas in the mines. As long as they remained shallow, only black-damp was encountered—air deficient in oxygen, the danger of which the miner could generally recognize in time, because the light he carried gradually dimmed. But as the use of explosives increased, there was far greater danger from the presence of after-damp—that is, the product of incomplete combustion left after the explosion, with a high content of carbon monoxide—which renders its victims unconscious without their becoming aware of its presence. Thirdly, the greater depths held the unexpected dangers of fire-damp. This was the explosive mixture formed with air when methane gas was liberated from the coal seams or their surroundings, often in very large quantities. The modern mining official called a fireman was originally a miner who safeguarded his fellows by going ahead of them into the

FIG. 239. Ignition of fire-damp

workings, where he lay covered in wet sacks holding up a lighted candle on a long pole to ignite the gas (Fig. 239). But in spite of this risky form of precaution there was a series of disastrous explosions in the deep mines of north-east England, which led to the formation in 1813 of the Sunderland Society for preventing accidents in coal mines.

The Davy lamp, because it was invented by the leading chemist of the day, is something of a landmark in the relations between science and technology, as also in the use of technology to serve humanitarian rather than purely economic purposes. But it was not the first safety-machine, nor was it the only lamp resulting from the Society's appeal, nor was it the perfect solution of the problem. Before the middle of the eighteenth century a Whitehaven man had invented a flint-and-steel mill which enabled a continuous stream of sparks to be struck, bright enough to work by but becoming warningly larger and more luminous in the presence of explosive gas. The device spread to the Continent, but it could be a cause as well as a fore-warner of explosions. In local competition with Sir Humphry Davy were George Stephenson and an Irish doctor, W. R. Clanny, each of whom made a series of increasingly successful lamps, though it

was Davy's third lamp which, when taken underground in January 1816, caused the colliery manager and engineer, John Buddle, to exclaim with optimistic enthusiasm, 'We have at last subdued this monster'. In a matter of months Davy had discovered the conditions under which fire-damp explodes, and had considered how to make a naked flame safe in them. He concluded that a flame passing through a fine wire-gauze cylinder lost so much of its heat as to become incapable of igniting the gases. Moreover, the lamp (Fig. 240) would reveal the presence of fire-damp by the elongation of the flame and the growth of a blue cap upon it. To begin with, Davy's gauze suffered from the defect that when it became red-hot, as it was particularly liable to do in a draught, the flame passed through it. To remedy this, a second gauze was added and a sheltering bonnet,

FIG. 240. Davy lamp, as used in 1816

while its value as a lamp to work by was improved by the provision of a cylinder of glass, with the gauze admitting the air either below or above the flame. Further improvements were made by Meuseler in Belgium and Marsaut in France.

While the safety-lamp was being developed to minimize the risk of explosion, improved ventilation was the obvious means of striking at the cause of the risk: mixtures of methane and air do not explode if the methane content is less than 5·4 per cent. The shaft which gave access to the mine was also its natural means of ventilation, and an obvious safety precaution was to have two shafts, so as to provide a continuous flow of air through the workings. This was not, however, made compulsory until after an accident to a one-shaft mine at Hartley, Northumberland, in 1862, when the collapse of a cast-iron beam supporting the large pump blocked the only means of access, with the result that 202 men and boys were buried alive. A furnace was commonly installed at the foot of the up-cast shaft, so that the rising current of hot air might ensure a steady ventilation of the workings, though careful design was needed to avoid pockets of gas accumulating away from the main flow; at some mines extracted fire-damp might be seen burning at the surface. The first air-pump for ventilation, introduced by Buddle in 1807, was a wooden piston working in a wood-lined chamber, and it exhausted 6,000 cu. ft of air a minute: this compares with 160,000 cu. ft a minute displaced by Nixon's ventilator towards the end of the century. About 1830, steam-driven fans were brought in. At the same time it came to be realized that the roads which gave access to the coal-face must also serve systematically for ventilation. It became regular practice to drive parallel roads connected only at the far end, so as to compel the air to travel right round. Traffic requirements, however, often made it necessary for additional routes to be used, to which the air current must be diverted as little as possible: hence the frequency of hinged wooden doors, which were opened and shut for the passage of the coal trams by small children who waited in silence and often in darkness, until Lord Shaftesbury rescued them.

In the second half of the nineteenth century conditions of work in the coal-mines did not change fundamentally: in 1900 boys still went underground at the age of twelve. Though the perils of damp had been greatly reduced, disastrous explosions continued, partly because the danger of the ignition of fine coal-dust was not yet appreciated, and partly because existing safety regulations were often ignored. By 1900 nearly all coal was loaded on to wheeled trams, the rails being laid as near as possible to the coal-face, so that the tubs could be filled without the hewer having to cast his coal back more than once or at the most twice. This meant the construction of very numerous roads, and the physical toil of tub-filling remained; no satisfactory coal-face conveyor was invented until 1902. As for the hewing itself, the first practical mechanical coal-cutter was a device like a circular saw, driven by compressed air. Other pneumatic machines followed, in which the cutters were placed on the links of a chain or throughout the length of a rotating bar. All suffered, however, from the fact that compressed air, while safe for underground use, was uneconomical because of the often considerable transmission losses between the compressor and the machine; the electric coal-cutter, which eliminated this defect, was a much later development.

In general, the winning of coal—essential for virtually every industry—continued to depend upon arduous handling, performed in peculiarly exhausting conditions; blasting, made safer by improved explosives and easier by the use of the pneumatic drill to prepare the shot-holes, could only prepare the way. The hewer at the coal-face, cramped for space and often unbearably hot and sometimes working in very wet conditions, cut his groove as close to the floor as possible and as far in as 4 ft, preparatory to breaking the mass down with pick, crowbar, or wedge. Neither the work with the shovel or fork which loaded the trams, nor that involved in installing numerous pit-props of pine or fir to secure the roof for the excavation, nor the daily journey along low, rough, and often wet passages between shaft and face allowed much respite from exhausting physical exertion.

CAST AND WROUGHT IRON

In the first half of the eighteenth century, as we have already seen (p. 147), a new use for coal had been developed by the Darbys of Coalbrookdale. By using coal with a low sulphur content, they contrived to substitute coke for charcoal in smelting, from carefully selected ores, an iron of great liquidity, from which they cast pots and similar ironware of exceptionally light and delicate design. But the pig iron produced in this way was made brittle by impurities, especially phosphorus, which found their way into it because of the fusion resulting from the high working temperature. The pigs were therefore at first inacceptable for further manufacture, except for cheap nails (p. 477). But from about 1760 the adoption of a number of improvements brought coke-fired furnaces steadily to the fore. In that year they numbered no more than seventeen; in 1775 there were thirty-one; and in 1790, eighty-one—which was practically four-fifths of all British blast-furnaces. Moreover, their location, which was predominantly in Staffordshire, South Wales, and parts of the Scottish Lowlands—and not in traditional homes of British iron-founding, such as the Sussex Weald—emphasized the new dependence of iron upon coal, which was transforming the geographical distribution of heavy industry throughout Britain.

The first change was the making of coke in closed ovens, like brick beehives, instead of in open piles, imitated from the burning of charcoal. A much more important change, however, was the improvement of the iron obtained from the coke blast-furnace by remelting it in foundry furnaces. These had previously been used on a small scale both in Britain and France to provide iron for such purposes as bullet-making, and the name of cupola for a kind of furnace used in remelting lead dates from 1701. The remelting made the iron more homogeneous and purer, and as the foundry furnace employed the reverberatory principle, there was no risk that the impurities in its coal fuel would be transferred to the iron, since only the incandescent gases passed from the grate into the top of the furnace. One result of these changes was an astonishing improvement in the quality of the cast-iron cannon of the British Navy, which—according to the envious French—did not experience a single burst gun in twenty years: hence, no doubt, their invitation to William Wilkinson to set up a cannon-foundry in France, which was completed in 1785 (p. 286). But the use of a foundry furnace, though desirable, was not absolutely essential: in 1777 Abraham Darby made preparations for casting the first iron bridge by deepening the hearth of his blast-furnace (p. 450), from which he cast the bridge-members direct.

The other main obstacle to the use of coke in the blast-furnace was the fact that it burned less easily than charcoal. The first attempt to meet the difficulty was by increasing the water-power which drove the bellows, until some ironworks had wheels with diameters of 30–40 ft. The second was the use of water-powered blowing-cylinders, introduced by John Smeaton to secure more complete combustion. But the vital change came in 1776, when John Wilkinson employed a steam-engine with a 38-in. cylinder to produce the blast for one of his Shropshire furnaces. Within four years he had four engines at this work, and by the end of the century the British iron industry was producing blast air with twenty-four, almost exactly 5 per cent. of Boulton & Watt's total output. Not only did the steam-engine enormously enhance the strength of the blast, but the work of the furnace could be continued without intermission wherever coal and iron ore were available, instead of being dependent upon the access to a water-supply, with its seasonal variations.

British cast-iron production thus came to stand far in advance of that of the Continent or the United States. As we have already seen, the coke furnace was introduced tentatively into France in 1785 and six years later into Silesia (pp. 286, 287), but its use remained unknown in Belgium until 1823, in the Austrian empire until 1828, and in the Ruhr until about 1850. Meanwhile, Britain extended the use of cast iron from utensils to building (as with the bridge at Coalbrookdale) and to machinery. Cast iron was used, for instance, for gear-wheels and for the first steam-driven forge-hammers, and in 1784 a London flour-mill was designed with plant consisting entirely of cast iron. Nevertheless, the form of the metal principally in use was still wrought iron, and it was the application of coal to the manufacture of this that chiefly

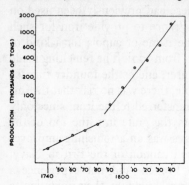

FIG. 241. Graph of English pig-iron production, 1740–1839

explains the astonishing growth in Britain's pig-iron production from the 1790's onwards (Fig. 241).

There was still a grave obstacle to the full exploitation of coal by the iron industry. Coke-made pigs were, as has already been pointed

FIG. 242. Running molten iron into pigs, c. 1850

out, generally rendered too brittle by the impurities they contained to serve as the raw material for wrought iron. Moreover, as compared with pig iron (Fig. 242), the making of wrought iron used 50 per cent. more fuel per ton of the product—and the cost of the fuel, the charcoal which had always hitherto been used for this purpose, was constantly increasing. According to a letter written by his widow, the second Abraham Darby, in about 1750, invented an (unspecified) method 'to make bar from pit coal pigs'; but the first definite progress was made in 1766 by two brothers named Cranage, one of whom was a founder in the works at Coalbrookdale (Fig. 243). The details of their patent were deliberately vague, but it seems clear that they produced in a coal-fed reverberatory furnace a bar iron which was sufficiently workable to satisfy the requirements of at least the nail-makers. It is also quite possible that the Cranages anticipated the process later known as 'puddling', which was certainly

FIG. 243. Upper works at Coalbrookdale, showing transport of cylinder for Newcomen engine

devised independently by a Welsh ironworks foreman, Peter Onions, only a few months before it was launched upon the world as one feature of the combined new process always associated with the name of Henry Cort.

Cort was the owner of a forge and slitting-mill at Fareham, near Portsmouth, which did work for the Admiralty, then a large consumer of Swedish wrought iron. He had experimented for years, and was known to both Boulton and Watt, the latter of whom called him 'a brother projector'. The essential feature of the puddling process which he established in 1784 was the 'raking, separating, stirring, and spreading about in the [reverberatory] furnace', which gave the air full and fairly rapid access to the melted pig iron, so that it was decarburized to the point at which it became malleable. As in all reverberatory furnaces, the coal used as fuel made no contact with the metal. It was Cort who made the puddler, plying his stirring-bar at the furnace door, one of the key industrial workers for the next hundred years (Fig. 244); the weight of the metal and the temperature at which it was manipulated perhaps justify the view that this was the heaviest regular task ever accepted by man. Cort's success was enhanced by the fact that he combined puddling with the use of grooved rollers, in which he had been anticipated by C. Polhem in Sweden in 1745: the combination resulted in great economies. As soon as the lump of malleable iron had been brought to the proper temperature in the furnace and formed into half-blooms under the hammer, they were made into bars by means of grooved rollers; previously a plate had to be stamped and then slit or the bars produced by hammering. The rollers dealt with fifteen tons of iron in

FIG. 244. Iron puddlers at work, mid-nineteenth century

the time a hammer took for one, so that puddled iron made up in cheapness for its inferiority to charcoal-iron in quality.

The manufacture of wrought iron, which was thus in the ascendant at the end of the eighteenth century, suffered a temporary depression with the cessation of demands for war material in 1815, but there followed a new period of prosperity, and by 1850 Britain was producing an annual output of about 2½ million tons of iron, including cast iron. One important improvement was the introduction of Neilson's hot blast into the Clyde Ironworks, in Glasgow, in 1829. This quickly came into general use when it was shown that a preheated blast, which gave a substantially higher temperature, was twice as effective as a cold blast; applied to stoves working at 600° F. it produced three times as much iron for the same quantity of fuel. The blast was passed through an oven, whence it entered the furnace through a tuyère or nozzle, wrapped in a water-cooled coil to prevent its melting: this coil was also a Scottish invention. The higher temperature made it possible to use raw coal instead of coke, a matter of particular importance to Neilson's fellow-countrymen because most Scottish coal did not coke well; Scotland also profited from the fact that it became possible for the first time satisfactorily to smelt the Scottish black-band ironstone. Farther afield, the hot blast brought in the use of anthracite for iron-smelting; this was patented in America in 1833, practised independently in South Wales in 1837, and effectively introduced by David Thomas, a Welsh immigrant to Pennsylvania, three years later. Not until 1850 was coke-smelting generally introduced into the United States.

Meanwhile, furnaces also became larger and more efficient (Fig. 245). The outer casing was made round instead of square and was raised upon cast-iron pillars, so that tuyères could be inserted all round; the traditional rectangular shape of the hearth area in which the molten metal collected was likewise rounded, which resulted in quicker smelting with less fuel. For greater economy, even the waste gases which had been allowed to blaze at furnace-

FIG. 245. British blast-furnace, showing preheater and moulds in which the pig iron is cast, c. 1850

mouths, lighting up industrial regions by night with the glare of an inferno, were captured—first in Württemberg in 1831—and employed to preheat the blast.

The same period saw two important improvements to the puddling process. One of these met a special difficulty encountered in the processing of pig iron made from phosphoric ores, namely, corrosion of the sand-bed that formed the bottom of the puddling-furnace, because the sand and the iron oxide made a slag too acid to combine with the phosphorus. A Monmouthshire ironmaster found a solution as early as 1816, but he was ridiculed as 'Mr. Iron Bottom' for a long time before the advantage of a cast-iron bottom plate was acknowledged. Another weakness in the existing Cort process was the slowness of the hand-stirring of the metal. This was remedied from 1839 onwards by coating the furnace floor with small pieces of slag or 'bull dog', which had been removed from it after a previous operation, calcined, and cooled. In this way iron oxide in the 'bull dog' combined with the carbon in the charge to produce carbon monoxide under the surface of the molten metal, which in consequence was stirred up and appeared to be boiling. This so-called 'wet' puddling processed the iron rapidly in a single stage.

In the second quarter of the nineteenth century puddlers from South Wales played an important part in introducing British manufacturing methods in France, Belgium, Germany, and Sweden. In the last-named country, where wood was still cheap and plentiful, they helped to make charcoal plate, and introduced a special type of refining-hearth, known as the Swedish Lancashire hearth, though it actually originated at Pontypool and not in the north of England. It spread into Germany, and was eventually reintroduced into Britain under that misleading name.

THE COMING OF CHEAP STEEL

As we are now approaching the period at which the age of iron, which had been so long in growth and had come to so great a culmination, gave place to the age of cheap steel, which stretched far into the twentieth century, it will be convenient to return to the beginning of the industrial revolution. The part which steel then played was remarkably small: this fact is the more surprising because the influence of carbon-content on the hardness of steel was realized by the Swedish metallurgist, T. O. Bergmann, as early as 1750. In the case of steel, British eighteenth-century inventiveness did not produce any cheap or large-scale manufacture to sweep the Continent.

In the early part of the century, steel was still produced in Britain by the cementation process from Swedish bar iron of superior quality, imported chiefly through Newcastle upon Tyne and amounting by 1737 to about 1,000 tons a year. The primary product, known as blister steel, was obtained by covering the bar iron with fragments of charcoal and subjecting it to intense and prolonged heat from a charcoal fire. This blister steel was then converted into the tough shear steel required for cutlery by further heat treatment and forging. Even so, it did not reach the absolutely uniform quality which was increasingly needed for clock-making and instrument-making—the crafts which Benjamin Huntsman of Doncaster practised. He succeeded in making a purer steel—at first from the existing blister and shear steel, later from Swedish bar iron of his own refining—by subjecting it to a more intense heat. For this he used a melting-chamber lined with fire-brick, placed on top of a coke furnace. Inside the melting-chamber there were crucibles 9–11 inches in height, made of a special heat-resisting clay, the production of which gave Huntsman great trouble. Five hours' intense heating, with the addition to the steel of a secret flux, produced a cast steel completely free from particles of silica or slag. The cost of production was less than by the older methods; the only difficulty was that the product could not be welded, since it could not stand being heated to more than about 900° C.

Huntsman had moved about 1744 to Sheffield, where he developed his invention (p. 145), but the cutlery-makers at first considered his cast steel too hard, though the French metallurgist, Gabriel Jars, who visited the works in 1765, found that it was already being used for edged tools and for clock-makers' requirements. A factor which helped to bring it to the fore was the competition on the home market of cutlery made in France from imported supplies of Huntsman's steel. By 1787 at least half a dozen Sheffield firms were employing his crucible process, the secret of which is said to have been first penetrated by a rival disguised as a beggar. With the export trade reaching across Europe as far as St Petersburg, it is not surprising that a Swiss industrialist, J. C. Fischer of Schaffhausen, was able to reinvent Huntsman's method. Fischer, who also invented copper-steel and nickel-steel alloys, eventually had steelworks in both Austria and France.

Nevertheless, by comparison with wrought or cast iron, the making of cast steel was still a laborious and costly small-scale process, in which no notable improvement was made during the first half of the nineteenth century: in 1850 the entire British output was only about 60,000 tons. Moreover, even this expensive material was still not completely faultless. Krupps won their fame as specialists in the making of cast steel, yet their first gun, a 3-pounder with a cast-steel lining, burst under testing at Berlin in 1849, and Prussian artillery experts had great doubts about the feasibility of constructing heavy ordnance from steel. Yet at that very moment the problem was being solved for them in far-off Kentucky.

Although William Kelly enjoyed no commercial success, his name deserves to be better remembered than it is, for his career illustrates two marked features of the second half of the nineteenth century—

the rise of American inventors and the growth of the American steel industry. Kelly manufactured sugar-kettles for farmers from pig iron refined in a charcoal furnace, but the cost of charcoal was rising fast even in Kentucky. He made the chance observation that an air blast playing on the molten pig iron generated the most heat when the iron was not covered with charcoal, and so learned empirically that the carbon in the pig iron could be blown out by air alone, the carbon itself acting as a fuel. If a higher proportion of carbon was retained in the metal than was needed for wrought iron, this same 'air-boiling' process could be used to make steel. Steel-making without fuel was thought by other ironmasters to be an absurdity, but from 1851 onwards Kelly built a series of converters, and his American patent of June 1857 officially recognized him as the first inventor of the new steel. But he went bankrupt in the same year, and his claims were eventually made over to Bessemer, from whom this type of steel still takes its name.

Bessemer's object was the same, as is shown by the title of the paper that he read on 13 August 1856 to the British Association for the Advancement of Science—'On the Manufacture of Malleable Iron and Steel without Fuel'. That high hopes were already entertained of his work is clear from the fact that it was fully reported next day in *The Times* and had reached *The Illustrated London News* before the end of the month. Unlike Kelly, Bessemer aimed at keeping the metal completely liquid by using a very high temperature. His first experiments, in 1855, had been conducted with a fixed vertical converter, but in 1860 he patented the tilting converter that has been used ever since (Fig. 246). This was designed to avoid loss of heat by placing the conical fireclay tuyères at the top, so that they were out of action while the molten metal was being run in and out of the converter: but during the actual process of conversion it was turned to bring them to the bottom, thus enabling the blast to be forced upwards right through the molten metal. The method worked quickly—today 25 tons of iron can be converted into steel in as many minutes—though some of the iron was carried away with the blast; a drawback of a different kind was the intense heat to which the workmen were exposed in tapping the metal, a point that was raised rather belatedly at a Home Office inquiry near the close of the century. Meanwhile, within ten years of its first invention Bessemer steel was being blown in Britain, the United States, and three or more countries on the European mainland.

But to begin with there were serious teething-troubles. Bessemer's early experiments were conducted with a non-phosphoric pig iron, and it was not at first realized that the common phosphoric ores could not be employed. A further difficulty was that the excess oxygen introduced blow-holes in the steel, but R. F. Mushet, the son of an ironmaster in the Forest of Dean, discovered that spiegel, an alloy of manganese and iron, could be added to remove the excess of

FIG. 246. Bessemer tilting converter in operation

oxygen and to adjust the carbon-content of the steel, provided that the carbon-content required was a relatively high one. A notable advance was made, in 1858, by the Swedish steel-maker, G. F. Göransson, who had the advantage of the availability of a very pure non-phosphoric ore from the Bergslagen district of central Sweden. He proved the possibility of making all grades of steel by stopping the blowing at the instant when any given carbon-content had been reached.

Meanwhile, from 1856 onwards an alternative process was being developed, the open-hearth process, which by 1900 was drawing level with the Bessemer process in the quantity of steel produced, and shortly afterwards surpassed it. This process derived from an invention not originally intended for steel-making at all, but to improve the efficiency of steam-engines by introducing a heat-exchanger.

In 1856 Frederick Siemens obtained an English patent for a process of heat-regeneration, in which hot waste gases were used to pre-heat incoming fuel and air. In iron-making the principle was first applied in the Cowper stove of 1857, invented by an associate of Siemens, in which the waste gases of the blast furnace were used to preheat the blast. In 1861 Siemens invented a gas-producer which made it possible to use as fuel gas derived from low-grade coal: the patent stated the possibility of applying the invention to melting steel in an open-hearth furnace, but its first application was in a Birmingham glass-works.

In 1863 Pierre and Émile Martin, in France, used a regenerative furnace built by Siemens's engineers to melt steel bars and scrap. More important, they used the method to obtain steel of a given carbon-content by melting a suitable mixture of cast iron, made from Elba iron-ore, and malleable iron: this is the Siemens-Martin process. Shortly afterwards, the Siemens brothers, first at Birmingham and then in South Wales, made steel by decarburizing cast iron with iron-ore: this is the Siemens process. The open-hearth process has three notable advantages: firstly, it enables a very high working temperature (about 1650° C.) to be attained; secondly, it is economic because scrap iron and low-grade coal can be used; thirdly, it is a relatively slow process, so that strict control can be applied.

The open-hearth process was further developed in the United States, where in 1899 Benjamin Talbot of Leeds built at Philadelphia the first furnaces for continuous operation, which gave still greater fuel economy; the earliest employment of his method in Europe was in Lincolnshire in 1902. The size of furnace was also greatly increased and a means of tilting it was introduced. In 1870, out of a total British steel production of 220,000 tons all but 5,000 tons was made by the converter process; thirty years later the total had risen to 4,900,000 tons, of which 3,156,000 tons was made by the open-hearth process. About two-thirds of the American steel output, which totalled 10 million tons in 1900, was Bessemer steel, but in that year Carnegie declared that the open-hearth process was the method of the future.

The inventions of both Bessemer and Siemens required the use of non-phosphoric iron ores. The means of eliminating phosphorus was discovered in 1875 by a scientific amateur, S. G. Thomas, and his cousin, Percy Gilchrist. They introduced limestone in the firebricks (p. 590) of the converter and in the charge, with which the phosphorus combined to form basic slag. As the basic slag when pulverized provided a valuable fertilizer, it is the more surprising that Thomas's invention was not an immediate commercial success. In Britain, however, the use of the so-called 'Bessemer ore' of Cumberland and other high-grade ores imported from Sweden and Spain was preferred until towards the end of the century. But Belgium, France, the United States, and Germany all had large quantities of phosphoric ores, which this method made available for steel-making, including the *minette* ore of Alsace-Lorraine which had changed hands

FIG. 247. Rolling steel rails, 1876

in 1871. The Gilchrist-Thomas process in effect doubled the potential steel production of the world; by 1895 basic steel already totalled nearly 3 million tons.

The availability of cheap steel, which from the 1870's onwards met an expanding world-wide demand for rails (Fig. 247), was closely related to improvements in the production of the pig iron from which it was made, as also in the finishing processes and in the development of steel alloys. Furnaces rising to an average height of 75 ft began to be built in north-east England in the 1860's and 1870's, but it was the Americans who introduced 'rapid driving' by increasing the size of the hearth itself. In 1880 one with an 11-ft diameter was built for Carnegie at Pittsburgh, which had room for eight tuyères and made 1,200 tons of iron a week.

In the finishing processes the chief improvement was in the technique of rolling. Reversing-mills were introduced, which passed the metal to and fro, so as to obviate the time-consuming task of passing the billets back; three-high mills, in which the third roller passed the metal back without reversing the machinery; and continuous mills, with roller-stands arranged in a series of decreasing size and power. Each of these three devices was coming into use in England in the 1860's, and later underwent important development at the hands of American engineers.

Alloy steels were first produced accidentally in the smelting of mixed ores, but both chromium and nickel steel were prepared experimentally by Faraday as early as 1819. Commercial development, however, came only with the needs of a new age of steel. In 1868 Mushet began the manufacture of a high-carbon tungsten-manganese steel, which required no quenching yet gave tools with five or six times the normal length of life; his invention of tungsten steel had, however, been anticipated by an Austrian, F. Köller, more than ten years earlier. Chromium steel for armour-plate and shells began to be developed commercially in France in 1877. Manganese steel, hardened by quenching it in water from a temperature of $1,000°$ C., was discovered by (Sir) Robert Hadfield of Sheffield in 1882, and nickel steel was marketed from Le Creusot in 1888. Finally, F. W. Taylor in Philadelphia prepared a high-speed steel, which became harder the faster it cut.

The total world output of steel grew from 500,000 tons in 1870 to 28 million tons in the last year of the century. The lion's share in this tremendous growth fell to the United States, which began the period producing about a quarter as much as Britain and ended it producing twice as much (p. 484). Almost equally striking was the growth of the German steel-making industry, which ended the century making 8 million tons a year—nearer to the American total than to the British.

EXPLOITATION OF NON-FERROUS METALS, 1750–1900

The meteoric growth in the use of steel in the last quarter of the nineteenth century, with its enormous social consequences, is paralleled to some extent by the growth in the world production of non-ferrous metals. For example, the output of the six principal base metals increased in that period from 268,000 to 1,955,000 metric tons. But between 1750 and 1850 their growth had been slow, and there are comparatively few technological changes to be recorded. The bulk of the mining activity continued to be in the traditional areas of Britain, Sweden, Bohemia, and Spain, so prospecting did not play a very important part. Conversely, the availability of steam-pumps of increasing efficiency often made it possible to reopen workings that had been drowned, as in the case of the Cornish copper-mines; by 1798 forty-five of Boulton & Watt's engines were

FIG. 248. Working by descending levels, early nineteenth century

in use in Cornwall, though the old rag-and-chain pump turned by hand had not even then wholly disappeared.

The general method of mining for metals was much the same as for coal, with the same dividing-up of a given area into rectangular blocks; but as the veins generally run vertically rather than horizontally, the usual method of extraction was to work downwards or upwards in a series of steps (Fig. 248). In comparison with a coal-mine the distance from face to shaft was usually short, and poisonous and explosive gases were extremely rare. Miners in the Harz practised the ancient custom of leaving fires burning over the week-end preparatory to shattering the rock-face by pouring water on it when the week's work began again (Fig. 249).

The extraction of metals from their ores, too, continued to be conducted largely by traditional means. Gold was still simply washed from the sand or gravel containing it, and silver was parted from copper and lead after smelting. In 1833, however, H. L. Pattinson of Newcastle upon Tyne patented a new process for extracting silver from lead by skimming the crystals of pure lead from the surface of a succession of cast-iron pots of molten argentiferous lead, which was stirred as it cooled, until one pot finally provided a metal containing 300 oz. of silver to the ton. This gave a much greater recovery of silver. Copper, lead, zinc, tin, and mercury were all produced by smelting the ores with charcoal or coal, and there were various

adaptations of blast and reverberatory furnaces, as in the case of iron. Copper may be taken as an example, since Britain at this time played an important part both in its mining—in the 1780's Anglesey had at Parys mountain the largest copper-mine in the world—and in its smelting, which centred on South Wales and Lancashire, while the British

FIG. 249. Heating rocks preparatory to splitting them by throwing on water

Navy was among its principal users; the first copper pennies, struck in 1797, weighed a full ounce.

There were six major operations. The ore was first roasted for 12–24 hours, and cooled with water. It was then melted with slag from a later stage, granulated in a water-tank, calcined at a gradually rising temperature, melted again with further quantities of slag, and run out of the furnace to form pigs (Fig. 250). The heating of these pigs with free access of air in a melting-furnace produced 'blister' copper. But to obtain 'tough pitch' copper suitable for manufacture, the blister copper had to be melted again, so as to remove slag that had escaped previous removal, and the final product was toughened by throwing charcoal or anthracite on to it, the reducing action being enhanced by stirring the molten metal with a green-wood pole.

Copper was used in many forms. There was, for instance, Sheffield plate, which Thomas Bolsover, the Sheffield cutler, first developed about 1742 for making buttons. This was manufactured by fusing or soldering thin sheets of silver on to each side of a thick sheet of copper, and then rolling the combination into a thin sheet. Since it gave a similar appearance for a lower price than pure silver, its use spread rapidly to such items as tea- and coffee-services and candlesticks, especially when Matthew Boulton and others introduced a technique for soldering-on silver thread to cover the copper exposed at the edges. A Birmingham invention was Muntz's metal (three parts of copper to two of zinc), which after 1832 replaced copper sheathing for the bottoms of ships in the merchant navy. Most kinds of brass, however, contained a higher proportion of copper, since it was prized for its handsome colour, resembling gold. Here, too,

FIG. 250. Making copper pigs, Lancashire, nineteenth century

Birmingham took the lead, and by 1795 was using a thousand tons a year. Gilt objects such as buttons were produced from what was called calamine brass, which was not a direct alloy of copper and zinc, but was obtained by heating copper together with calamine and charcoal. There was also much use of acids, dragon's blood (a kind of resin), and lacquer to vary or disguise the surface appearance of the many imitative wares for which Birmingham was becoming famous.

Chemical research was revealing the existence of new metals, but manufacturers on the whole were not very interested in developing their use, especially as extraction and working were often difficult: as late as 1828 S. F. Gray in *The Operative Chemist* contemptuously dismissed a number of them as mere hypothetical assumptions, adding his own opinion that 'nothing but the rage of the day for the invention of new metals could have prompted their insertion in the list'. The platinum metals as well as cobalt and nickel, however, were effectively studied in the eighteenth century and became available commercially.

The platinum in the South American mines had been ignored for generations as unusable, until the Spanish navigator, Antonio d'Ulloa, who accompanied a French expedition to Peru, described it in Europe in 1736. Chemists devised a process based on solution in *aqua regia* for separating the platinum from the metals occurring with it and from other impurities; a black powder resulted, which could with difficulty be pressed and beaten into sheets and forged. From 1824 onwards an ore was obtained from the west side of the Urals, which provided the basis for manufacture at St Petersburg. Other sources were found in Europe and as far afield as Borneo, to add to the original supplies from America. Although the name is a diminutive of the Spanish word for silver, platinum was not at first used for jewellery, but its exceptional resistance to corrosion made it valuable for some types of laboratory equipment, such as crucibles, and especially for sulphuric-acid rectifiers used in industry: with the making of large industrial vessels of malleable platinum the name of W. H. Wollaston is particularly associated.

Cobalt was obtained in 1733 by the Swedish chemist Georg Brandt—from the mineral cobalt (the oxide of the metal) which had long been employed to make blue glass—and was used mainly for reconversion to its oxide in purer form, which was likewise required chiefly for glass-making. Nickel was obtained by another Swedish chemist, Axel Cronstedt, from *Kupfernickel* or false copper, an ore found in Germany and Norway. It was roasted to remove arsenic, dissolved in acid, and further treated to remove impurities. Nickel itself was used mainly in alloys, especially German silver, the name given to a variety of alloys in which from 15 to 34 per cent. of nickel was combined with copper and a smaller proportion of zinc; the more nickel, the better the ware. From 1840 onwards German silver was regarded as a particularly suitable material for the new process of electroplating with silver and other metals (p. 499), the popularity of which helped to end the vogue of Sheffield plate.

In the second half of the nineteenth century the exploitation of metals was greatly accelerated in consequence of the huge industrial and commercial demand to be satisfied. Accordingly, there was a world-wide search for ores, intensified at intervals by the great profits that resulted from lucky discoveries. At the same time, the skills of the chemist and the engineer enormously improved the extraction and the working of metals—electrical methods, for example, became important by the end of the century.

The great new discoveries of mineral deposits, which affected the economic life of the whole world in this period, seem to have been due more to chance than to any new techniques suggested by geological theory. This is true not only of the great gold-mines in California and Australia, and the diamonds underlying Kimberley in South Africa, but even of such self-evident treasures as the lead-zinc deposits of Broken Hill in New South Wales, which form a conspicuous black ridge rising from a plain long frequented by sheep graziers.

Systematic prospecting received, however, a great impetus from the provision of new equipment. Soft rock was penetrated by rotating augers, harder rock by dropping chisels. The derrick was developed from its use as a ship's crane to facilitate the withdrawal of a complete line of boring tools without disjointing. Where samples were needed of strata passed through, a series of mechanically driven drill-tubes was employed, to which a more powerful and lasting 'bite' was given by the use of industrial diamonds; these, as they ground their way down, cut out a cylinder of rock which was held in the tube and could be brought up for examination. There were corresponding advances in methods of boring underground. Shot-holes in which to lay improved explosive charges began to be made by a rock-boring machine, which was brought into use when the Mont Cenis railway tunnel (p. 459) was being built in the 1860's. More effective pneumatic machines were devised later, which could be operated more than a mile away from the compressor. But while the best practice in the most advanced mining areas steadily improved, it would be unrealistic to suppose that the spread of mining into all parts of the world, so characteristic of this period, did not mean a continued dependence upon individual muscle and resource. The descent to an Australian mine, for instance, might still in the 1870's be achieved by the application of the counterbalance principle to the old-fashioned windlass, enabling one man to work alone.

One new problem created by the world's increasing demand for metals was how to concentrate primary ore deposits of low metal-content, which had increasingly to be used as rich secondary deposits near the surface became exhausted. There were several improvements made in the old process of washing—already highly developed in eighteenth-century Sweden (Fig. 251)—or panning the ore. One of these was a shaking-table, which made it easier to keep the 'dirt' suspended in the water while relatively heavy particles of ore sank to the bottom; by graduating the depth of a series of grooves, over which the water passed in succession, it was possible also to grade the residue according to fineness. An entirely new method, developed in the late nineteenth century, was the use of a powerful electromagnet, which easily separated ferrous from non-ferrous materials in the finely crushed ore; later it was adapted to separate minerals distinguished by only a slight difference of magnetic properties. Lastly, there was a process known as flotation, which was first applied to low-grade sulphide ores in 1860: the ore was mixed with water and a viscous oil, whereupon sulphide particles were absorbed by the oil and much of the impurity could be washed away with water. But this method used much oil, and it was not until 1901, at Broken Hill, that the modern method was developed, which uses less oil, agitates the mixture by air, and employs air-bubbles to carry up the ore particles.

FIG. 251. Concentration of copper ore by washing, from Swedenborg, *Regnum subterraneum*, 1734

Changes in the technology of extraction may be exemplified by copper, which was second only to iron in its importance, and was the first metal to be refined electrolytically on an industrial scale; moreover, copper smelting is an early example of an industry in which Britain came to lose a once well-established lead. At the beginning of the nineteenth century three-quarters of the world's copper was smelted in South Wales. At mid-century Swansea was still the effective centre of the world copper industry; and yet, of the 600 furnaces at work there in 1860, the last was extinguished by 1921. The basic cause of this great change was not the superiority of foreign technology, but the fact that, when new sources of supply were developed in Spain, Chile, and North America, there were unanswerable advantages in the ability to mine, smelt, and refine on a single site and on a scale commensurate with the vast new bodies of ore. In the last two decades of the century Arizona and Montana between them produced nearly half of the world's copper, and they provided the natural base for the main advances in technology. South Wales accordingly became more concerned with the manufacture of by-products. For generations the surroundings of Swansea had been polluted by the so-called 'copper smoke' containing sulphur dioxide, but in 1865 a new type of furnace began to be installed, so that sulphuric acid was obtained as a valuable by-product; from these beginnings an extensive industry was built up in heavy chemicals. Swansea also began to turn to the smelting of nickel and zinc ores, and to new methods for the extraction of precious metals.

One ingenious change in copper extraction was the introduction of the multi-hearth roasting furnace. The ore started at the top and was raked by rotating arms alternately to the centre and the circumference of successive hearths, so that it fell from one to the next; a single operation reduced the sulphur content as much as several days of slow roasting by the old method. Further elimination of sulphur and iron was required to convert this product, known as matte, into the blister copper, which was 98·5 per cent. pure. This was achieved from 1880 onwards with the side-blown converter, a direct imitation of the Bessemer converter. But although this product, when turned into 'tough pitch' metal (p. 488), was satisfactory for all older uses, up to and including fire-boxes of locomotives, it was not pure enough to act as a satisfactory electric conductor: the transatlantic cable of 1858, for instance, was made of copper that had only half the maximum possible conductivity.

In this case the new electrical industry itself produced the solution, for J. B. Elkington's patent of 1865 was for refining plates of blister copper by suspending them as electrodes in troughs containing saturated copper sulphate solution, which formed cells in an electrical circuit: pure copper was deposited on the other electrode. This electrolytic refining not only produced a copper which was a satisfactory electric conductor, but sludge from the cells yielded silver, gold, and other metals as valuable by-products. The first of the electrolytic refineries was built near Swansea, but the process spread to America in 1892; their location was in general determined by the availability of cheap electricity. At the end of the century Elkington's methods remained basically unchanged, except that it became the practice to use not blister copper, but 'tough pitch' metal for the electrodes.

The development of the world's supply of nickel went through two phases. In the first of these, nickel became readily available and cheap, as large deposits were discovered, first in New Caledonia in 1865, and then at Sudbury, Ontario, during the construction of the Canadian Pacific Railway in 1883. To separate it was difficult and the demand was small, until James Riley in 1889 showed the value of nickel in alloy steels (p. 486). Two new extraction processes were then developed. The 'tops and bottoms' process involved the addition of salt-cake (p. 533) and coke to a molten mixture of nickel and copper, which was poured into large pots, where the copper sulphide separated into a layer that floated on top of the relatively denser nickel sulphide; the melt was allowed to solidify and the two parts were then separated by breaking with a sledge-hammer. The treatment was repeated, and the so-called 'second bottom' contained 72 per cent. nickel. After further processing, the final purification was effected electrolytically. The other process, invented in the 1890's by the fertile brain of Ludwig Mond, was based on his chance discovery that carbon monoxide reacts with hot nickel to form a gaseous nickel carbonyl, which can be decomposed at a still higher temperature to form pure nickel. This method was used after removing the bulk of the copper by the 'tops and bottoms' process; it produced 99·95 per cent. pure nickel, and was established at the turn of the century.

In 1887 it was discovered that a very dilute solution of potassium or sodium cyanide could be used for gold extraction by the Forrest-MacArthur process, which could be economically applied to low-grade material such as quartzite rocks in which gold was very thinly dispersed. The process was economic when the quantity of gold was as small as a quarter of an ounce to a ton, and it was after this discovery that West Africa and the Rand became the main sources of supply; electrolytic methods were introduced for final purification. This was of great importance in a period when currency, credit, and the development of large markets for plate all depended upon the availability of gold.

Finally, one new metal was both recognized for the first time—although its existence had been suspected since shortly after 1700—and produced commercially within the space of half a century. This was aluminium, of which F. Wöhler obtained minute globules in 1845. It was more closely studied a little later by the French chemist, H. E. Sainte-Claire Deville, under the patronage of the emperor Napoleon III, who commissioned aluminium spoons for state ban-

quets and a rattle for the Prince Imperial. There were two stages in
Deville's process. In the first, bauxite, an ore containing 50–65 per
cent. alumina (aluminium oxide), was digested with caustic soda;
the alumina so purified was heated in a stream of chlorine to produce aluminium chloride. In the second stage hydrogen was passed
over the aluminium chloride and the vapour led over boats containing liquid sodium, which reduced the chloride to metallic
aluminium. The sodium, which was his most expensive raw material,
at this time cost at least 5s. an ounce, and during thirty-three years
of manufacture the price of Deville's aluminium never fell below
50s. a pound: its use was therefore restricted to luxury articles. This
remained the position, for although Deville later devised a potentially better process, based on making sodium cheaply by reducing
caustic soda at a high temperature with charcoal, he was defeated
by technical obstacles. The first to work this process satisfactorily
was an American chemist, H. Y. Castner. Failing to interest American
industrialists, he came to England, where he established the manufacture of sodium for aluminium extraction at Oldbury in 1888. He
planned to make 100,000 lb of aluminium a year, using sodium
produced at 9d. a lb, and had just overcome initial difficulties when
the way to success was unexpectedly barred by the development
of a much cheaper electrolytic process.

In 1886 C. M. Hall in America and P. L. T. Héroult in France
independently invented the modern method of aluminium manufacture by electrolysis of alumina dissolved in molten cryolite
(another aluminium-containing mineral, mined in Greenland but
later made synthetically). To make a ton of aluminium in this way
requires about 18,000–20,000 kW-hrs. of electricity: as with all other
large-scale electrolytic processes, the cost of electricity was an important factor. The first plant used electric power derived from the
Schaffhausen falls on the Rhine, and although France, America, and
Britain took the process up in succession, the Swiss were for many
years the main producers. Commercial production was much helped
by the fact that soon after the discovery of the electrolytic process
the preliminary process of purifying the bauxite ore with soda was
greatly improved by K. J. Bayer.

NEW METAL PRODUCTS

Although the late nineteenth century introduced the Age of
Steel—in 1900 the world output of mild steel was 28 million tons as

compared with 500,000 tons of copper—the working of other metals and of alloys remained so important as to justify a brief survey of the products of the metal-working industries as a whole; the history of armaments since 1750 will, however, be considered separately.

The greatly increased scale of working led to bigger ingots, which in the case of mild steel made by the open-hearth process might reach a weight of 5 tons; copper was normally cast in 2-ton ingots. Special steels, brasses, nickel silver, and other alloys, on the other hand, were still melted in crucibles containing not more than 200 lb of metal and were then hand-poured into moulds. Further treatment was by forging, rolling, pressing and drawing, welding, and plating.

The use of the forge hammer, which was made much easier by the introduction of Nasmyth's invention of the steam-hammer in 1842 (see Fig. 162), remained essential for shaping wrought iron before it was rolled, as long as that metal was in general use. But in the later nineteenth century forging, much of it by hand-hammering, was required chiefly in the copper industry in preparation for the final shaping of rolled plates, which by the 1870's might be of 2 tons weight. The rolling-mill, on the other hand, played the main part in the production of the bars, plates, and sections for structural engineering, the plates for the new iron and steel ships, plates for boilers, and the rails for the ever-extending railways. The three-high mill has already been described (p. 486). It began to be replaced in 1884 by the universal mill, which with its enormous power could take a cast-steel ingot unhammered and convert it into either a plate or a bar of any required width: this was the final answer to the problem of how to produce heavy naval armour plate. In 1861 a plate 12 in. thick and weighing 20 tons had been made by rolling together what had originally been sixteen separate $1\frac{1}{4}$-in. plates of wrought iron (Fig. 252). By the turn of the century, however, Krupps could roll a steel ingot weighing 130 tons and 3 ft thick into a 12-in. plate measuring 43 ft × 11 ft.

The production of thin sheet metal was important for the copper and brass industries, including, for example, the brass and Muntz's metal worked up in innumerable Indian bazaars. The rolling of thin sheets, first of iron and later of steel, for the making of tinplate, however, was particularly important: for many purposes the uncoated sheet metal could not be used because of rusting. There was an ever-growing demand for cheap containers, especially for preserving food, and until the Americans introduced the McKinley tariff in 1890 tinplate was virtually a British monopoly. The manufacture was located in South Wales and Monmouthshire, and the Americans built up their industry with the help of Welsh technologists. The method of forming the sheet metal by rolling, which continued unaltered from about 1825 onwards, was to work two bars at a time, heated to 790° C. They were rolled separately, then as a pair, and then twice doubled, so that the final rolling was completed in 'eights', the object being to secure a thickness which, when the tin had been added, would not greatly exceed one-hundredth of an

Fig. 252. Rolling 20-ton armour plate, Sheffield, 1861

inch. The hot rolled sheets were annealed, pickled, and immersed in oil before dipping in the tin-pot. They were dipped twice, greased, and then passed through rollers to regulate the thickness of the tin, which even in best-quality tinplate formed a coating less than one five-thousandth of an inch thick.

As tinplate rusted quickly out of doors, an important development—which began commercially at Wolverhampton in 1838—was the manufacture of corrugated 'galvanized' iron sheeting, which was in great demand in the gold-diggings at mid-century and since then has roofed the humbler buildings of half mankind. Corrugation, used in the ancient world to stiffen bronze, was first adopted for iron roofing, to increase the load carried by a given thickness, by R. Walter of Rotherhithe in 1828; eight years later the French chemist M. Sorel introduced the galvanization of sheet metal, a straightforward process of dipping in molten zinc, unconnected with the work of Galvani (p. 609).

Galvanized wire fences and barbed wire, the last-named an American invention, both played an important part from the 1880's onwards in the opening-up and parcelling-out of great tracts of land, particularly for cattle ranches. Wire had first been required in quantity a generation earlier with the advent of the stranded wire rope, which W. A. J. Albert introduced into the mines of Clausthal in 1834, and of the telegraph. Warrington became the centre of a new industry, using the 'Belgian train' of grooved rolls, which worked the metal as it was forced through holes of diminishing size and changing section—square, diamond, oval, and circular in succession. By 1862 this had been developed by G. Bedson into a continuous rolling-train of sixteen stands, alternating between the horizontal and vertical position so that the rod need not be turned, and working progressively faster so that the rod as it became thinner should not become slack. From 1882 onwards, further improvements were adopted in the type of mill erected in America to the designs of W. Garrett, enabling 50 tons of steel rod to be converted in nine hours into a single coil of $\frac{1}{4}$-in. diameter wire. Copper wire, introduced into telegraphy from the 1860's onwards, and used in rapidly increasing quantities for electrical conduction, was made according to steel-rolling practice. Ancillary wire-using trades, with increasingly complex machinery and growing output, were the long-established manufactures of nails, pins, and needles; umbrella-making; and the making of the wire netting which supplemented the use of the galvanized wire fence. An outstanding example of a new process was the 'patenting', introduced by J. Horsefall in 1854, which produced high-tensile steel wire by a continuous process, passing the single strand in succession through a heating furnace, a quenching bath, and a tempering bath of molten lead. The applications of its products ranged from steam-ploughing to piano-making, and were well advertised by its use in the Brooklyn suspension bridge, New York (p. 455), the cables of which were each composed of 6,400 separate wires of '100-ton' high-tensile steel.

Seamless tubes were a product of great importance to nineteenth-century engineering. In the case of lead the problem had been solved as early as 1790, when John Wilkinson took out a patent for casting a lead tube round a steel bar in a mould; in 1838 this was developed by C. Green for brass and copper tubes. He used a split cylindrical mould to form the original tube, which was then drawn through a succession of dies of decreasing diameter. This method became standard practice in Birmingham, and was used to make steam-engine condenser tubes for more than fifty years. The extrusion method also dates back to the late eighteenth century, having been suggested, but not practised, by Bramah in 1797. In 1820 a Shrewsbury plumber, T. Burr, devised a simple method by which a hydraulic ram forced lead to emerge in pipe form by pressing it between a circular centre-piece and a surrounding circular die. This was much used for the sheathing of electrical cables with lead, but it was not until near the end of the century that the means was found for applying this technique to copper and copper alloys, requiring to be worked at a high temperature. For the making of seamless steel tubes a satisfactory process was patented a quarter of a century after the German steel manufacturer R. Mannesmann first conceived the idea in 1860. A hot metal rod was drawn forward and outwards by rollers so that a cavity was formed, which was further shaped by a mandrel placed just beyond the rollers. Thomas Edison regarded this as the most impressive device on show at the World Exhibition held in Chicago in 1893.

A final example may be taken from British enterprise. In 1840 G. R. and H. Elkington introduced the use of electro-deposition to plate base metals such as copper, brass, or German silver with silver and gold, and found that there was enormous scope for the sale to the rising middle classes of a type of luxury goods which would seem more valuable than they were. Hostesses loaded with gold-plated jewellery presided over tea-tables and coffee-tables groaning with silver-plated pots, jugs, and spoons, and for a quarter of a century Britain enjoyed a virtual monopoly of this type of manufacture. By 1900, however, rising tariffs had closed many foreign markets, and the manufacture became centred in Germany.

ARMAMENTS

Although the growth of modern armament depended upon the explosives industry (p. 546) for more powerful projectiles, its basis was still the metal-working industries. Up to 1815, indeed, the main development in the art of war was the greatly increased use of cannon on the battlefield: under Frederick the Great and Napoleon they ceased to be dispersed among infantry regiments, and became twice as numerous in proportion to combatant troops as they had been in the smaller armies of the time of Marlborough. From Friedland (1807) onwards, great artillery concentrations played as large a part in Napoleon's victories as his ability to dispose of great numbers of conscripted troops.

As their number increased, the average length and weight of the field-pieces, cast in iron or bronze, was reduced, as was also the variety of calibre, while greater accuracy of aim was achieved by the use of the ballistic pendulum for measuring the velocity of the projectile: this had been described to the Royal Society by its inventor, Benjamin Robins, in 1742. The projectiles themselves were modernized to some extent. For the defence of Gibraltar in 1779–83 the British employed a shell which, unlike the older mortar-shells, was short-fused for firing from cannon, and soon afterwards Henry Shrapnel, an English artillery officer, began the development of his 'spherical case', successfully used in the reduction of Surinam in 1804; this became the most effective of anti-personnel missiles. The main factor, however, was the increased mobility of the guns. 'Horse artillery', designed to operate with cavalry—as other field artillery with infantry—was introduced by Frederick in 1759, and spread to the British and French armies in the 1790's, while the French in the last years of the old régime had started the use of pair-harnessing and standard six-wheeled limbers, together with interchangeability of wheels and other parts.

The flint-lock musket and bayonet were still the standard infantry weapons, the former commonly made by local gunsmiths with the help of water-mills for grinding and polishing. Pennsylvania alone manufactured 100,000 guns in the emergency of 1774. Eli Whitney's mass production of interchangeable parts two decades later has been referred to elsewhere (p. 356). The rifle, which had made a sporadic appearance in earlier times (p. 148), was used with effect by American 'minute-men' in the War of Independence, and as the Baker rifle, with seven grooves which made only a quarter-turn in a 30-in. barrel, was issued to the newly raised British Rifle Brigade in 1800. Its defects, however, were a strong tendency to foul the barrel and the difficulty of packing the bullet tightly enough because of the rifling. In America these were largely overcome by improvising a wad, which was packed round the bullet and fell out at its discharge: but the Baker rifle proved very inaccurate, and Napoleon withdrew from service such rifles as he found in use in France.

Basic changes in small arms followed only after the means of firing had been revolutionized. In 1809 Alexander Forsyth, a Scottish Presbyterian minister with sporting proclivities, patented a percussion powder, which led in turn to the invention of a percussion cap of steel, then of copper. Within ten years of Forsyth's invention, the flint-lock, which was very susceptible to damp, could be replaced by a weather-proof hammer action, the cap resting on the crown of a nipple which contained the flash-hole. The British War Office, however, was so slow in adopting the improvement that the first instalment of an award reached Forsyth on the day of his death in 1843. Meanwhile, the bullet itself had been redesigned by Captain J. Norton, as the result of his observation of the use made in South India of lotus-pith, with which the natives secured an airtight fit for arrows fired from blowpipes. He accordingly designed a tapered cylindrical bullet with a hollow base, which expanded on firing and effectively sealed the bore. In French hands the idea was finally developed into the Minié bullet (1849), and at about the same time a Paris gunsmith, Houiller, introduced the first expansive copper cartridge-case, which prevented the escape of gases at the breech. The way was at last clear for the adoption both of rifling and of breech loading.

A rifle of the Minié pattern was used by British troops in the Kaffir war in 1852, the year of its adoption by the French army, but was replaced by the Lee-Enfield, manufactured on American principles (p. 356); breech loading was not accepted in Britain until after the Austro-Prussian War of 1866, when it was embodied in the new Martini-Henry rifles. The Prussians had begun the use of a breech-loading rifle, the needle-gun, invented by J. N. Dreyse, in 1841, and were completely re-equipped by 1858. Its increased rapidity of fire and the advantage of loading in the prone position were important factors in their victory over the Austrians, who in 1866 were still using muzzle-loaders. But the firing-pin, which gave the weapon its name, was liable both to foul and to rust, while Chassepot's rifle, which replaced the Minié in France in 1866, outranged the needle-gun by several hundred yards. The Prussian victory over France in 1870–1 must therefore be attributed to other factors than the needle-gun, though the disciplined volley-firing of the Prussian infantry wrought great havoc, especially in stopping cavalry-charges.

With the Martini-Henry rifle the British army used the first metallic cartridge, which had an iron base and walls of thin coiled brass wire. When this was found to jam in action in the Sudan in 1882, it was replaced by a case, made by George Kynoch of Birmingham, which was already in wide use abroad. This was constructed of brass, solid drawn by a series of operations which included enough cold-working for it to withstand the explosive force of the propellent. Other improvements were made by a Swiss army officer, Eduard Rubin, especially the substitution of a copper envelope enclosing a lead core for the older soft lead bullet, which at high velocity failed to follow the twist of the rifling. After much rivalry among chemists a satisfactory smokeless powder, *Poudre B* (p. 548), was invented by P. M. E. Vieille in France; this changed the tactics, and even the appearance, of the battlefield, and made the French Lebel rifle of 1886 for a time the leading infantry weapon. The magazine rifle, like the Colt revolver (p. 356), was first seen in America, but the earliest general issue was of an eight-cartridge tubular type to the German army in 1884.

The machine-gun resembles the torpedo and the electrically fired mine in being an invention that was first developed during the American Civil War but of which the full implications did not become apparent before the wars of the twentieth century. It began with a ten-barrel revolving rifle, gravity-fed and rotated by a hand-crank, invented by R. J. Gatling, and still in use by Theodore Roosevelt's rough-riders in Cuba in 1898. The *mitrailleuse*, which had twenty-five barrels encased in a cylindrical metal tube and fired 125 rounds a minute, followed in time to figure as the French 'secret weapon' in the war of 1870. But it was Hiram S. Maxim's recoil-operated gun of 1884 which, though heavy and easily overheated, developed into the key weapon of trench-warfare.

When the nineteenth century closed, artillery developments were still the main field of the growing international rivalry in armaments. This was partly because the big gun was a factor common to land and sea warfare. From the improvement of the shell by H. J. Paixhans, adopted by the French in 1827, may be dated the necessity for warships to be built of iron and armour-plated, though the lesson was not learnt until a whole squadron of Turkish wooden frigates had been demolished by Russian shell-fire at Sinope in 1853. In 1861 the first all-iron warship, the *Warrior* (p. 374), had plates $4\frac{1}{2}$ in. thick; within twenty years the thickness demanded had grown to 24 in. On land there was a similar need of fortresses designed to withstand shell-fire—though two great defences, of Sebastopol by the Russians and of Plevna by the Turks, showed the high value of improvized earthworks planned by resolute commanders—and in particular, developments in the production of high explosives during the 1880's led to large-scale use of concrete roofs and armoured cupolas.

The detached forts and *enceinte* of Antwerp, designed in 1859 to hold a garrison of 100,000 men, are a reminder that small powers might invest heavily in static defences. But the possession of the most effective weapons of offence increasingly involved technical and financial resources which were only at the disposal of the great powers. Thus the German and Austro-Hungarian armies were distinguished by their possession of siege-trains of large howitzers,

FIG. 253. The American ironclad, *Monitor*

which fired with a steep trajectory. The British Navy, too, maintained its ascendancy at the cost of two expensive periods of experiment. The first was in the 1870's, when big guns began to be mounted in a turret, such as was originally designed by Ericsson to house the 11-in. guns of the *Monitor* (Fig. 253) and helped to maintain the Federal blockade of the South in 1862. The second was in the following decade, when watertight compartments, heavier armour plating (p. 496), torpedo nets, and a strong secondary armament were required for protection against the torpedo-boat.

In about 1850 wrought iron for a time returned to favour for gunmaking, as in the earliest days, and in 1855 W. G. Armstrong produced his first pieces at Elswick by a method of shrinking-on successive layers of metal, so that the outer layers shared in firing-stresses. Both rifling and breech loading of artillery had been used separately in the past; they were successfully combined in Sardinian and Prussian experiments of 1845 and 1846 respectively. At the siege of Sebastopol, however, the British artillery had to improvize a crude form of rifling; and although both improvements were then officially adopted, disappointment with the first breech loaders led to a reversion to muzzle-loading for all British guns during the period 1865–81. This is the more remarkable as the war of 1870 showed above all the superiority of Prussian breech-loading artillery, made in cast steel by Krupps (Fig. 254), to the bronze muzzle-loaders of the French. More than twenty French fortresses were captured in six months, while the encirclement and destruction of the main

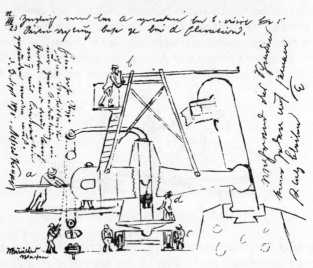

FIG. 254. Sketch by Alfred Krupp for mounting a heavy gun, 1875

French field army at Sedan was described by a contemporary as 'the ideal battle of cannon'.

Improved propellents called for constant improvements in the new alloy steels (p. 486) of which both guns and armour-plate were increasingly made. But at the end of the century the chief problem of the artillerist was to devise a true quick-firing gun, which could rival the rapid action of the new magazine rifle. The artillery that Whitworth supplied to the Federal government in the American Civil War was classified as quick-firing: but the main problem of how to absorb the recoil on firing, so that the gun need not be relaid, still awaited solution. The use of the resistance of water to flow through an orifice was suggested by (Sir) William Siemens in 1867. The first completely successful quick-firer, however, was the famous French '75', which also included elaborate devices to hold the carriage perfectly steady during firing. This was introduced in 1898, to fire both shrapnel and high explosive; in 1902 a shield was added.

Two novel uses of metal in warfare remain to be mentioned. The modern history of naval mining begins with the first metal containers filled with explosives, which were laid by the Russians off Kronstadt in the Crimean War. The self-propelled torpedo—as distinct from the boat-borne spar torpedoes of the American Civil War—was the invention of a Scotsman, Robert Whitehead, while working in Austria in 1864. By 1890 its steel body stored sufficient compressed air to propel a 200-lb. charge at 29 knots for nearly half a mile. But enough has perhaps been said to show what degree of truth lies behind Lewis Mumford's generalization, 'Bloodshed kept pace with iron production'.

NEW MATERIALS: COAL-GAS, PETROLEUM, AND RUBBER

THESE three diverse products, all of which first came into general use in the nineteenth century, although known much earlier, have at least one property in common: all have hydrocarbons as principal constituents. Coal-gas is rich in the hydrocarbon gas methane, petroleum is a complex mixture of liquid hydrocarbons, and rubber is a solid derived chiefly from the hydrocarbon isoprene. In 1900, when the automobile industry was still in its infancy, the part played by petroleum and rubber was still insignificant as compared with the part it plays today. Coal-gas, on the other hand, in the course of the century had reached its full technological development as a source of light and heat and as a source of power for a prime mover, the gas-engine (p. 601); by 1900, indeed, gas as an illuminant was fighting a losing battle against electricity. Its other uses remain, but in retrospect gas appears to us as something especially characteristic of nineteenth-century homes and workplaces and ever-spreading streets: we will therefore give it pride of place in this chapter.

ORIGINS OF GAS-LIGHTING

After the Flemish chemist J. B. van Helmont, at the end of the sixteenth century, had investigated the nature of, and had invented the name for, a gas (a Fleming's pronunciation of *chaos*), there was some desultory investigation of the inflammable air issuing from coal measures, which clearly bore some relation to the flame produced by the ignition of coal. It is significant that in England there were investigations in the neighbourhood of Wigan, of Whitehaven, and of Newcastle upon Tyne. From Wigan came the first communication to the Royal Society in 1667; from Whitehaven, two generations later, the piping of fire-damp, a scheme to light the town with it, and—it is said—the actual lighting of an office in this way by a colliery agent, Carlisle Spedding: but it was at Newcastle, about 1760, that the first fully authenticated attempt was made to light a room by coal-gas. A kettle was used as a retort, and the gas was passed along sections of clay tobacco-pipe to burners improvized by making holes in the clay. But no practical result followed from this or from the development of the tar-making oven which, unlike the early coking-oven, could have collected gas as well as tar. A Belgian professor, J. P. Minkelers, wrote in 1784 about the possibility of using coal-gas for ballooning, and was posthumously stated to have lighted his classroom with gas. But this, if it happened, was only one among half a dozen similar experiments, including the lighting of the Elector's castle at Dresden, which took place in various countries in the 1780's and 1790's but led to no commercial result. For that we must turn to the careers of Lebon and Murdock.

Philippe Lebon was an engineer of the Service des Ponts et Chaussées who from his childhood home was familiar with charcoal-burning. In 1791 he commenced the study of gas produced by heating wood, and concluded that it could be satisfactorily prepared in an iron retort, cooled, and then used for lighting, heating, or the inflation of balloons. He took out a patent in September 1799, only a couple of months before Napoleon seized power from the Directory; having failed to arouse the interest of the government, he began two years later a series of nightly exhibitions at a house in Paris, where gas distilled from wood was used both to warm and light the interior, to service a flame fountain, and to produce other lighting effects in the garden. Lebon not only demonstrated the practical usefulness of such a gas, but his eager imagination anticipated nearly all its later applications—the soft light burning in a glass globe, and the convenience of its distribution through the house by small pipes concealed in the plaster. But he got no farther: even before his untimely death in 1804, at the hands of robbers in the Champs Élysées, France was again at war, and the novel illuminant had somehow failed to kindle the imagination of the all-powerful First Consul. The French experiments had been important enough to bring one of James Watt's sons to Paris to investigate them even in time of war, and had inspired a German, F. A. Winzer, to tour a number of countries to stimulate interest in the principle of gas-lighting; but for the continuous history of the new illuminant we must turn to England, with its plentiful supply of coal for gas-making and wealthy mill-owners to back the new venture. As a class, they were accustomed to innovation; lamp-oil and candles were costing more because the war made it difficult to import whale-oil and Russian tallow; and they wanted a safer illuminant in order to cut down fire-insurance premiums.

William Murdock was a young Scots mechanic who rose to be Boulton & Watt's chief engine-erector in Cornwall. An interest in finding improved materials for preserving the bottoms of ships led him to work upon the making of tar by distillation of coal, and in 1792 he used gas generated from coal to light the rooms of a house in Redruth, Cornwall. Concerned with commercial possibilities, he experimented with coal of different qualities, various types of burners, and devices for storing enough gas to make a portable light. In 1798 he was called back to the Soho Foundry at Birmingham, where he used cast-iron retorts, brought to a red heat, to generate the gas, and illuminated the main building of the works 'during many successive nights'. Gregory Watt's report from France having made the firm aware of the risk that they might be forestalled by the French, Murdock resumed his experiments, with the result that in March 1802 gas flares were erected at each end of the main Soho building to celebrate the Peace of Amiens, and by 1804 he had brought his apparatus to a point at which Boulton & Watt were able to canvass for orders.

The first customers were the owners of a large Salford cotton-mill, who in 1806–7 installed over 900 gas-lights to illuminate the factory, a length of private road, and a private residence. Some of the burners were Argands, adapted from the Swiss oil-lamp of that name (p. 516), having an annular burner, with air introduced at the centre, and a surrounding glass cylinder, but the majority were of the type known as Cockspurs, consisting of three small holes in the end of a pipe. The six cast-iron pots used as retorts were 5 ft 6 in. deep; each was fed with about 15 cwt of coal from an openwork metal basket raised by a crane (Fig. 255). The hydraulic seal was hand-operated, and the gas was led via a dry main to an air-cooled condenser, from which the tar ran into a pit. The bell-shaped holders were of sheet iron 10 ft in diameter and 10 ft high; they were suspended in water to provide the necessary gastight seal and were supported at the centre by a rope pulley and counterweight, so that they could move up and down according to the amount of gas in them. As the gas was apparently neither washed nor purified, there must have been a very disagreeable smell when it was burnt, but as lighting costs were considerably reduced, even this first crude apparatus was deemed a success.

Murdock made various further improvements, including the indirect application of the furnace heat to the retort and the introduction of a jet of water at the bottom of the condenser, which eventually trickled away to the tar-pit with the tar, carrying other impurities with it. It is uncertain why Boulton & Watt, having made a flying start in the manufacture of gas apparatus, for which they were

Fig. 255. Murdock's gas-making plant for Phillips & Lee, 1806

doubly well equipped by the size and scope of their workshops and by the presence of Murdock on their staff, gave it up at the moment of expansion in 1814 (Fig. 256). At all events, though Murdock remained actively engaged in business for another sixteen years, the development of more efficient gas apparatus passed entirely into other hands.

Samuel Clegg was a generation younger than Murdock, and benefited from having had some scientific study under John Dalton at Manchester before he was apprenticed to Boulton & Watt, whom he joined in time to work on the gas illuminations for the Peace in 1802. By 1805, however, he had left the firm and had begun to install gas in factories at about the same period as Murdock. His first important improvement was the purification of the gas by liming the water through which it passed, and in 1810 (at Stonyhurst College, Lancashire) he brought in a separate liming machine. He also invented the hydraulic main for some of his clients' cotton-mills, and gave gas a great advertisement by installing it in the house and premises of Rudolph Ackermann, the famous London art-publisher, where two cast-iron retorts, holding about 1 cwt of coal apiece, serviced eighty burners, both for lighting and for heating. But Clegg's most important practical service was in connexion with the transition from local to general installation.

The idea of distributing gas throughout a district from a central generating station had first presented itself to the mind of the German immigrant, F. A. Winsor (formerly Winzer), who from 1806

FIG. 256. The 180-ft façade of the Soho works illuminated by gas for the Peace of Paris, June 1814

onwards was trying to secure a parliamentary charter and subscribers for a joint-stock company to illuminate London. In 1807 he was allowed to advertise his project by lighting part of Pall Mall, and, in spite of war-time conditions and the bitter opposition of Boulton & Watt and other interested parties, by 1812 he had secured a charter for The Gas Light & Coke Company. But neither Winsor nor the chemist F. C. Accum, who was brought in to help, had the necessary administrative or engineering experience, and the company was saved in its early months only by recruiting Samuel Clegg. As a result of his efforts, on 1 April 1814 the parish of St Margaret's, Westminster, was lit by gas; by December 1816 London had 26 miles of gas-mains. The growth of the practice of reducing fire-insurance premiums for public buildings and factories lit by gas made it certain that the system would spread.

As shown in Accum's *Practical Treatise on Gas-light* (1815), cast-iron retorts of circular section were used, but they carbonized the coal badly and were soon replaced by elliptical ones. The gas was cooled by passing it through a worm-tube immersed in the water in the holder, and was then purified with lime and washed. The wet-liming machine, however, was imperfect, the company being left with a noisome liquid, 'blue billy', which had to be concentrated and then carted away through the streets at night. Street distribution of the gas itself had not proved particularly difficult, as cast-iron mains had just been introduced for water. The service pipe to go into the houses was (and still is) known as 'barrel' because it was made like cheap gun-barrels from 4-ft lengths of strip iron, bent round a mandrel, and welded along the joint; to begin with, there was even some use of actual gun-barrels left over from the French wars.

THE GAS AGE

By 1817, when Clegg left The Gas Light & Coke Company owing to a financial disagreement, the use of gas was rapidly ceasing to be a mere experimental novelty. A dry-liming process was patented in the same year, and in 1819 Clegg's son-in-law, John Malam, perfected a meter for measuring output. In 1823 there were three rival gas companies at work in London north of the Thames, and the whale-oil interests were trying in vain to compete by 'cracking' animal fats in cast-iron retorts for the manufacture of oil-gas to light large buildings, such as churches, theatres, clubs, and shops. Gas-light was already seen to have many advantages to outweigh the expense of installation: besides its greater convenience, the supply cost only one-third or even one-quarter as much as the same amount of light derived from oil. As for technical advance, it may be noted that Clegg's immediate successor with The Gas Light & Coke Company, T. S. Peckston, who wrote the first modern text-book on gas, was in a position to lay down principles that prevailed until very nearly the end of the nineteenth century.

Retorts were mounted in benches of three, four, or five, and at a later stage in two banks set back to back. By 1850 they had come to be made of fire-clay with only the mouths of cast iron, and might be as much as 18 ft long and openable at either end; but charging and discharging was still arduous hand-work as late as the 1870's, even in a big London gas-works (Fig. 257). Lime was replaced by oxide of iron for purification only towards the end of the century. In the late 1830's extraction pumps were introduced, to remove gas from the retorts and make the washing and scrubbing more efficient:

this reduced the nuisance of ammonia corroding the fittings and poisoning the air. There were no meters for consumers until the second half of the century, so that gas was often charged for by the number of burners in use. The two standard types were the long narrow slit known as the batswing, and the fishtail burner, in which two jets of gas impinged; this was invented by J. B. Neilson, who

FIG. 257. Retort house of the Great Central gas-works

was foreman of the Glasgow gas-works, about ten years before he patented the hot blast (p. 478). The Argand burner, on the other hand, even in an improved form made standard by the British Government in 1869, was disliked by the public as being expensive, fragile, and smoky. But the opinion of the consumer is best indicated by the prevalence of special ventilating pipes called perdifumes, placed over the gas burners; the truth being that neither the quality of the gas itself, nor the precision with which the fittings were made, nor the technical skill with which they were installed, was adequate to protect the consumer against serious discomfort in small rooms. Thus in 1833 it was suggested in the *Mechanics' Magazine* that the best way to light a room by gas was to place the burner outside the window, and ten years later Michael Faraday was being consulted by the pundits of the Athenaeum as to how to mitigate what they called the stupefying effects of gas in the comparatively spacious rooms of their Pall Mall club-house. Great importance therefore attached to the introduction of the atmospheric burner, bringing air into the gas stream immediately below the burning-point, and giving much more complete combustion: this was first devised about 1840, but Bunsen's famous version of it—a source of heat rather than light—not until a new laboratory was being prepared for him at Heidelberg in 1855. Another thirty years were to pass before the yellow gas flare which heated the air, blackened the ceilings, and gave only a moderate degree of illumination for a great expenditure of gas at last gave place to the far more efficient incandescent gas-mantle, impregnated with oxide of thorium, together with a little oxide of cerium, invented by the Austrian, C. A. von Welsbach, for an industry to which electricity was by then providing a serious rival.

The gas-mantle staved off the doom of gas as an illuminant until beyond the end of the century of which it had helped to shape the social history. In its early years, Andrew Ure had claimed that gas-light adequately replaced sunlight, so that there was no moral obliquity in forcing children to work a twelve-hour day in the factories. A sounder humanitarian instinct was that which emphasized the civilizing influence of gas-lit streets, especially when they became usual in the poorer quarters of large towns. Gas-light improved the amenities of every place of public entertainment or instruction, just as it brightened the decorous domesticities of the Victorian home. Above all, it played an enormous though incalculable part in the development of the habit of reading among a population that became increasingly literate after the Elementary Education Act of 1870.

All this, of course, did not apply to Britain alone, but the combination of cheap coal and rapid urbanization caused gas-lighting to spread more readily in the island than elsewhere; as early as 1823, fifty-two English towns were lit by gas, and in 1859 there were nearly a thousand gas-works. There is something ironical in the fact that Boulton & Watt were caused to press on with their early experiments by Gregory Watt's report that the French were far ahead, for after Lebon's untimely death France lagged behind. Gas-lighting in Paris began with the Palais Royal in 1819, and a quarter of a century later the city had no more than 65,000 burners indoors and out. The successful illumination of a museum caused Baltimore to adopt gas-lighting for streets in 1816, followed by Boston and New York and—in 1837—by Philadelphia, but it did not figure commonly in American homes until after the Civil War. By that time gas as an illuminant had spread in some measure to all the principal towns of Europe—to Berlin, through an English company, in 1826, and in 1866 as far afield as Moscow. Gas-making appliances and pipes for Europe and America became an important British trade.

As for other uses of gas, Lebon's ideas inspired a Moravian, Z. A. Winzler, who in December 1802 gave at dinner parties food cooked on a gas-stove in a gas-heated dining room. But in the middle of the century gas-cooking (Fig. 258) was still something of a rarity, though practised, for instance, by the famous chef, Alexis Soyer, at the Reform Club in London. The gas-ring and the geyser, serving more modest needs, were both introduced in the 1860's, while in the 1870's gas-cooking came rapidly into popularity, the cooker assuming a design which hardly varied for the next fifty years. The gas-fire, however, which Winzler had also in a sense anticipated, was not developed with the use of radiants until 1880, and did not enjoy any great vogue until the end of the century. By that time the gas industry, seriously challenged (as we have seen) in the field of illumination, was bent on developing with increasing efficiency all those domestic and industrial heating functions which have been its mainstay since.

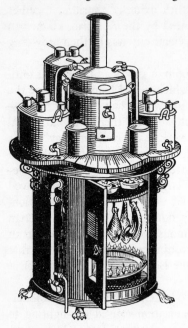

FIG. 258. Gas-cooker, designed to cook for a hundred people, c. 1850

EARLY EXPLOITATION OF BITUMINOUS DEPOSITS

The use of petroleum products long antedates the use of coal-gas. Between the Nile and the Indus there are at least thirty places where petroleum deposits appear on the surface, the concentrations being most numerous in the Mesopotamian region. For the Assyrians of the ninth century B.C. escaping gases marked 'the place where the voice of the gods issueth from the rocks'; the inflammable oil, mysterious and useless in the eyes of the ancients, was given the name of naphtha by the Babylonians as 'the thing that blazes'; and only the solid rock asphalt and the thicker seepages were deemed useful—for the preparation of bitumen. In the last three millennia B.C., mixtures containing bitumen were employed extensively for caulking ships, for waterproofing floors and even processional roadways, in a hard mortar for brickwork, and in medicaments. It was an important object of commerce in Mesopotamia, and known as such to both Strabo and Tacitus, but although the Mesopotamian production has a continuous history down to the present century, it was not of interest to the classical Roman world, which got what bitumen it needed in the form of wood tar or pitch, made cheaply available as a by-product of charcoal-burning. Naphtha had a limited, but militarily extremely important, use as an ingredient of 'Greek fire' (p. 268). Accordingly, the seepages in western Europe attracted little attention except for medicinal purposes, but in the fifteenth and sixteenth centuries at least there was a well-advertised trade in petroleum on that account (Fig. 259).

FIG. 259. Transport of oil in flasks, Modena, c. 1540

Although the burning gases and seepages of Baku had been described by Marco Polo, greater interest was aroused by sixteenth-century reports from the New World—of the seepages at Havana which could be used to caulk ships, of the bitumon with which the Aztecs made a chewing-gum, and of the asphalt lake in Trinidad, 3 miles in circumference, which Sir Walter Raleigh visited when he raided the island in 1595. Agricola's *De Re Metallica* described the skimming of oil from seepages, the use of heat to thicken it, and the separation of bitumen by the melting of rock asphalt; in 1625 the processing was more fully investigated in a small pamphlet published at Strasbourg. Careful distillation of the crude oil showed that, in addition to its medical uses, the various fractions were suitable for axle grease, paints and varnishes, for dressing leather, and as fuel for lamps.

Before the end of the century there was an English patent for treating sandstone shale at Pitchford-on-Severn in Shropshire, the name of which shows that the presence of bitumen there had long been recognized. The shale was ground in horse-driven mills and some oil was produced by distillation; the residue was boiled with water to extract pitch. The two principal products were a mineral 'turpentine' sold as medicine, and a pitch which, when thinned with some of the turpentine, provided a soft non-cracking material for caulking ships. Similar processes worked at Pontypool produced a black varnish for metalware, which was sold as 'Welsh' lacquer. The early eighteenth century, in which both these enterprises flourished, was also important for the invention of an asphalt mastic. This was the work of a Greek doctor, who in 1712 discovered the rock asphalt near Neuchâtel in Switzerland, mixed the powdered rock with hot pitch, and used the resulting mastic for floors and steps. The material was made tax-free in France in 1720, and further supplies of rock asphalt were found there and in several other European countries in the course of the century. But its use for pavements and then for roads (p. 435) did not begin until after 1800, and became important only when the French produced a better-quality mastic by the addition of mineral oil in 1832.

The modern petroleum industry, however, came from none of these sources but from the same demand as that which led to the creation of the gas industry. This was the demand for improved lighting, which grew up in the later eighteenth century as a concomitant of the industrial revolution. There was a steady improvement in the quality of lamps available; between 1783 and 1836 there were introduced in succession the flat-woven wick and the circular oil-burner with cylindrical wick and glass chimney known from its inventor's name as the Argand. But the better lamps only emphasized the poor illuminating quality of both the vegetable and the animal oils in use. Gas-lighting was unquestionably superior, but its virtual restriction to large rooms and to urban areas encouraged the attempt to find a satisfactory alternative.

A material known as 'coal oil' was pioneered by James Young, a former assistant of Faraday, who in 1848 began to develop for lubrication and other purposes the product of a spring of crude oil that welled up temporarily in a Derbyshire coal-mine. Young went on to manufacture a paraffin oil by dry distillation of torbanite, a brown shale, at Bathgate, Lothian, but the supply of this too gave out. In 1862, however, he turned to a more plentiful raw material and became the founder of the Scottish shale-oil industry. But before this he had learned, from the demonstrations of an American engaged in a rather similar manufacture, that refined naphtha from his works made an excellent illuminant. In the late 1850's, therefore, Young was selling a 'paraffin illuminating oil' in Europe and America, while his American competitors were making 'coal oil' from an asphalt-like mineral found in New Brunswick.

A more important American manufacture, however, was kerosene (from the Greek for wax), to employ the usual American name for what the United Kingdom knows as paraffin. This was developed by Abraham Gesner, a London doctor with geological interests, whose attention may have been directed to the oil industry through his friendship with the famous Admiral Cochrane, later tenth Earl of Dundonald, whose technological interests, which extended from naval improvements to the exploitation of Trinidad asphalt, have already been mentioned (p. 453). Gesner's patents provided for the dry distillation of asphalt rock to obtain a liquid, which was purified by treatment with sulphuric acid and lime and then redistilled. The new oil, kerosene, sold readily, together with a cheap lamp including a flat wick and glass chimney. By 1856 its inventor believed that it would completely supersede whale-oil, but three years later the situation was transformed by the drilling of the first American oil-well.

The drilling of deep holes in the earth's surface was no new phenomenon, though development was impeded by the lack of sufficiently hard drills, lack of mechanical power for drilling, and the uncertainty of success. But in 1830 the introduction of the derrick (p. 491) made it easier both to manipulate and to store the drilling apparatus, and by about 1850 the steam-engine had been brought in as a source of power. In the early nineteenth century exploratory drilling was usually undertaken in the search for either water or salt, and in America between 1840 and 1860 at least fifteen borings for salt struck petroleum; this led the American industrialist, G. H. Bissell, to consider the possibility of drilling in deliberate search for oil. But before doing so he sent, in 1854, a sample of oil from a Pennsylvanian seepage for examination by Benjamin Silliman, Jr., who had just succeeded his father, for half a century the immensely active professor of chemistry at Yale. Fractions were prepared by distillation, and Silliman's report pointed out that new products—quite apart from the illuminating gas, paraffin wax, lubricants, and excellent lamp-oil which were readily obtained—might be formed while the crude oil was being heated in the still. Bissell therefore went ahead, and his contractor, Edwin L. Drake, having drilled $69\frac{1}{2}$ ft through bedrock duly struck oil (27 August 1859), thus beginning the development of the Pennsylvanian oil-field (Fig. 260). Although the drilling of oil-wells had begun in Hanover in April 1857 and in the same year 300 tons were extracted from two hand-dug wells at Ploesti, Romania, it is the American event, occurring at the moment in that country's history when Americans were ready to give an industrial lead to the world, which has always

been regarded as the turning-point in the history of petroleum. Within fifteen years the annual output, still closely concentrated in Pennsylvania (Fig. 261), had reached 10 million 360-lb. barrels.

THE OIL-WELL INDUSTRY

America, with a rapidly expanding market for lamp-oil, now had a regular supply of crude oil from which to make the staple product, kerosene. At the same time, the Americans began to export their product, send-ing it in tins, packed in wooden cases, to world-wide markets, but chiefly to Europe, where in the very year of

FIG. 260. The Drake well, as it appeared in 1866

Drake's initial success they staged an important demonstration of paraffin lamps at the Ghent Flower Exhibition. Accordingly, we find that American drilling methods became increasingly important. The original 'Pennsylvanian system', which owed much to ancient Chinese practice reported by French missionaries, involved the use of hem-pen cables to raise and lower the drill. But flush drilling with hollow drill-pipes, through which water could be pumped down to the bit so as to clear the debris, had come into the petroleum industry from Europe, where it was first used to drill a 550-ft well near Perpignan in 1846. This method gave an average drilling speed of 3 ft an hour, which could be increased by the use of taller derricks—they reached 84 ft an hour before the end of the century—and of powerful steam-engines. In 1859 Drake still had to employ wrought-iron bits with steel cutting-edges, but the cheapening of cast steel gradually made a better material available. Diamond drilling, which could penetrate hard formations, was a French invention of the 1860's, taken up by the Americans and sold by them in England, where it was further improved upon by mining engineers. By 1886 a boring had reached a depth of 5,735 ft.

European and American drilling methods met especially in Galicia, where hand-dug shafts began to be superseded by percussion-drilling about 1862, but geological conditions caused serious hindrances until a Canadian firm introduced newer techniques first developed at Petrolia, Ontario. Galician experts spread to Germany, where a rapid-drilling machine was invented by A. Raky in 1895, and to the big Romanian oil-field, mechanical drilling having begun at Ploesti in 1880. The most important European event, however, was the growth of the industry in Russia. The first wells were sunk to the north of Baku in 1873; American drillers were brought in, who capped the spouting wells; and within the ten years the construction

FIG. 261. Oil-wells on Pioneer Run, Oil Creek, c. 1870

of the Baku–Batum railway opened up a wider market than via the Caspian Sea. When the smaller field at Grozny came into effective use, Russia's output reached its pre-revolutionary peak of $11\frac{3}{4}$ million tons (1901) and made her the largest oil-producer in the world.

One consequence of the use of a hollow drill, which by removing samples could reveal the structure of underground formations, was that the question of the origin of oil became of practical interest, with the result that prospecting ceased to be wholly dependent upon such vague surface indications as chance seepages. But the opening up of new oilfields in many parts of the world meant that the composition of the crude oil—which might differ at different levels as well as in different localities—was altogether too variable for direct use. Methods of refining, therefore, came to be of high importance, a fact of which John D. Rockefeller was keenly aware when he was organizing Standard Oil in the 1870's.

Distillation was already regular practice in the chemical and alcoholic fermentation industries. Horizontal cylindrical stills heated with steam (or later superheated steam) were used for petroleum; steam avoided the danger of a naked flame. Three fractions were separated according to their differences in boiling-point. The petrol or gasoline which distilled over first was for many years regarded as not merely useless but dangerous; the middle fraction gave the kerosene which was then wanted; and the residue with the highest boiling-point was sold as fuel without any attempt to extract fractions that would serve as lubricants. An additional wastefulness lay in the fact that the third fraction had to be drained off and the still itself allowed to cool between distillations. This batch process was used in America from the 1850's until the 1880's, but Europe, with more experience of distillation and more need to economize in fuel, soon introduced a continuous system.

As early as 1871 double stills were used in Galicia, the light fractions being obtained from the upper still, and the heavier fractions from the lower still, into which the residue from the upper one flowed, so that operation was continuous for three or four days at a time. At Baku continuous distillation was at first forbidden by the excise—a check to technological progress comparable to the hindrances that British industry had experienced earlier from the glass excise and the salt-duties (pp. 598, 531). By 1881 the Swedes, Ludwig and Robert Nobel, who were the great pioneers of the industry at Baku, had established and patented a bench of no fewer than seventeen stills; this method spread from eastern Europe to the Far East, though it was not favoured by Americans working there. Both the steam superheater and high-vacuum distillation (the latter allowing lower working temperatures and thus diminishing the risk of decomposing the less volatile fractions) were introduced first in Europe; up to the end of the century Russia in particular lay far ahead of America in the attention which the universities gave to refinery problems. This was largely due to the influence of the finance minister, Count Witte, who was a graduate of Odessa.

The French technologist G. A. Hirn, who had used superheated steam at Logenbach, then in French territory, adapted from the soap and fat industry the process of further refining the various fractions by chemical methods. About 1850 he introduced the use of sulphuric acid, washing the excess out of the oil with a solution of caustic soda. About 1870 air-stirring was introduced (in Budapest) to secure better mixing of the petroleum and the solutions with which it was treated. Other possibilities were to wash with caustic soda or to filter through beds of certain natural clays which have a strong decolorizing action but, except in Russia, the use of such clays hardly got beyond the experimental stage before the end of the century. At about the same time there was introduced the process of 'cracking', that is to say, heating under pressure to get a greater proportion of the lighter oils, the effect being to break the long chains of carbon atoms forming the molecules of the heavier and less volatile fractions; the first American use of this dates from 1862, when its purpose was to provide more lamp-oil, in contrast with modern use, which is to increase yield of petrol.

The main article of commerce continued to be paraffin or kerosene, which lit the lamps of half the world. The competition of gas in urban areas and—from the 1880's onwards—that of its more adaptable rival, electricity, made it increasingly desirable to find uses for the other fractions. Paraffin itself had shown the way by its extensive application in the kitchen. A modern type of paraffin stove was shown at the Paris Exhibition of 1878, and half a million were sold within ten years. But the first attempts to use for the same purpose the heavier products of distillation, later known as fuel-oil, were unsuccessful. In 1862 there was an American patent for a very primitive burner, merely a sheet along which the heavy oil flowed in parallel channels; this was followed almost immediately by the first proposal to ignite not liquid oil but a mist made by spraying hot oil by means of compressed air. This process, later called atomization, could also be carried out with superheated steam, and it soon served to heat both stills at Baku and the boilers of some Russian locomotives. Mechanical atomization of the fuel, the final stage in the evolution of this idea, though patented in America in 1868 did not become fully practicable until just after the end of the century. Meanwhile, in 1865 an article in *The Times* pointed out with considerable prescience the great potential value of fuel-oil for ships. Experiments were conducted but, in Europe at least, the relative costs of fuel-oil and coal provided no incentive to a change.

An alternative use for the heavy fractions was to produce lubricants, which had become an increasingly important article of commerce since the end of the eighteenth century because of the greater demands made by both vehicles and machinery. The shale-oil industry started by Young in Scotland (p. 516) had predecessors in

France and central Europe, which had begun to make lubricants from oil about a quarter of a century earlier. Oil-sands extracted with boiling water provided the basis for a lubricant made at Pechelbronn, and by 1853 mineral-oil lubricants were being made at Logenbach by distillation. Heavy machine-oils became a standard product of oil refineries, and by the 1880's were widely used on the railways. In France there was a special manufacture, from American crude-oil imports, of a very thin spindle oil, with which textile fibres were dressed before spinning.

Petrol, however, remained in general a worthless and dangerously inflammable by-product of the industry, whose most hopeful uses

FIG. 262. Transporting oil by water, Oil Creek, Pennsylvania, 1875

seemed to be for soldering-lamps and pressure-stoves, while the mixed paraffin hydrocarbons known as naphtha found a limited application in dry-cleaning and the extraction of oil-seeds. Old and new met, however, in a project to combine coal-gas with petrol, the method being to mix petrol vapour with the gas. But gas-oil (from the fraction intermediate between kerosene and lubricants), which was both cheaper and less dangerous than petrol, could be cracked at high temperatures to provide a more convenient means of enriching the coal-gas, and in the United States it was even possible to use natural gases for this purpose. As for the oil-engine, the Diesel engine, and the petrol-engine (Ch. 21), these feats of nineteenth-century inventive skill had little effect on the petroleum industry within this period. It took forty years (1860–1900) for the annual crude-oil production of the United States to reach 9¼ million tons, a figure that was quadrupled by 1914 and again by 1929.

The relatively small demand for petroleum products in the days before the Ford car is reflected in the primitive organization for transporting them. To begin with, Pennsylvania used wooden barrels (Fig. 262) in which cargoes even crossed the Atlantic; then came tin cans and sheet-iron drums, with tanks of iron or cement as their counterpart in the hold of a ship. Steam tankers developed slowly (p. 375), but the earliest came into service on the Caspian Sea in 1879 and its first ocean-going counterpart sailed from Batum for London in 1885; both were constructed for the Nobels in Sweden. Steel pipelines were built in the 1870's both in America and in Russia; by 1880 it was already a feature of the Standard Oil monopoly in America that it 'owns and controls the pipelines of the producing regions that connect with the railroads', as A. P. Hepburn reported.

EARLY RUBBER MANUFACTURE

The history of rubber resembles that of petroleum in that it was first employed outside the pale of European civilization; that its use developed rapidly during the nineteenth century; and that nevertheless it did not until the twentieth century take its place as a basic raw material, without which modern transport in particular could not continue. Of the differences, one of the most important lies in the fact that rubber is essentially a tropical crop, whereas petroleum is a natural deposit to be found in every clime. Another lies in the comparative simplicity both of the processing of rubber and of its adaptation to technological purposes.

The characteristic property of rubber is that of recovering its shape after deformation, qualities of which the Central and South American natives were well aware long before the era of Spanish conquest. They cut the bark and collected the liquid latex that slowly oozes out: this is a milky emulsion of rubber in an aqueous solution. The rubber can be made to coagulate, and separate from the water, by heating: the natives of Brazil achieved this by repeatedly dipping a wooden paddle into latex and holding it over a wood fire, so that it gradually became covered with a thick coating of rubber, which was then cut off. By the thirteenth century articles of rubber, including balls for games, were in common use among the Mayas and Aztecs; the desired shapes were obtained by carrying out the coagulation on moulds made of clay or other material.

Since the Spaniards from the days of Cortez and Pizarro were cognizant of both the industries and the amusements of the peoples they had conquered, and since by 1615 at latest they were themselves using rubber to weatherproof soldiers' cloaks, it seems to illustrate a remarkable national ineptitude that it was left for the French more than a century later to carry the study and the use of rubber to Europe. Charles de la Condamine, who had been sent by the French Academy of Sciences on an expedition to Peru, brought back caoutchouc, as the substance was then called, and in 1751, fifteen years after the expedition, he gave an account of it to the Academy, accompanied by a memoir by another Frenchman, Fresneau. One very early use gave caoutchouc its English name: Joseph Priestley in 1770 remarked on its usefulness for rubbing out pencil marks. Fresneau had made various elastic objects from freshly collected latex, but he pointed out the difficulty that the latex quickly coagulated, so that, for want of any means of reforming the rubber, articles could only be made on the spot. In consequence, the rubber which then began to be imported into Europe consisted only of bottles or large balls of native manufacture, and although French chemists quickly suggested the use of turpentine or ether as a solvent to bring the rubber back to a liquid state, the value of the new material was clearly limited by the difficulty of working it.

In France at the time of the Revolution a clumsy process of wrapping strips of oil-softened rubber round a bar, and applying a bandage until it was consolidated, produced tubes which were no doubt expensive but which found favour with surgeons, as did elastic bandages and other similar appliances. In England, at the same period, there was some experimental work in waterproofing fabrics and a patent for making air-beds. A rubberized fabric was used for a balloon in 1783, and by the beginning of the nineteenth century a combination of rubber and fabric served for garters and similar objects. No very striking results were achieved, however, until Thomas Hancock became interested; his patents were among the foremost factors in the development of the industry from 1820 to their expiry in 1858.

Dissatisfied with the existing practice of using turpentine as a solvent, which resulted in weak solutions that dried badly, Hancock's first idea was to use the rubber directly so as to make (to quote his own words) 'a better kind of spring than any then in use'. He cut strips or rings of rubber from the imported bottles, and made them up with leather or cotton to supply springy material for glove-wrists, braces, and slip-on boots and shoes, and to impart elasticity to shoe soles. But as business increased, Hancock found it difficult to import enough bottles of the right size to work from, and his cutting in any case left him with an uneconomic amount of waste rubber. He therefore experimented with a shredding machine, designed to tear the waste rubber to pieces inside a hollow cylinder fitted with revolving spikes. But the unexpected result of this treatment was to create not shreds but a homogeneous mass of solid rubber. In an enlarged form, and with the teeth restricted to a solid

FIG. 263. Large masticator for rubber

roller inside the hollow cylinder, this device became the masticator (Fig. 263), with which cylinders of rubber could be readily prepared. The cylinders could then be compressed in iron moulds to obtain blocks of any desired shape and size.

After this basic discovery of 1820, Hancock proceeded to make rubber sheets by shaving successive slices off a block. The ultimate size of the sheets made was unrestricted, as the pieces could be joined edge to edge when warm; they could also be cut down into thread, although this was not as strong as thread made direct from native rubber. Bottle rubber produced threads only about 5 in. long, limited by the size of the original bottle, but these short pieces could be warmed and then joined end to end. To make thread with fewer joints Hancock arranged for South American natives to send him cured rubber in the form of tubes, which he cut spirally on a lathe. This thread was used as warp for elastic fabrics and webbing.

Hitherto only pure rubber had been used: the next major development was to blend rubber with other substances. Hancock found that it was possible to mix pitch with rubber in the masticator, giving a cheaper product, but it soon became the practice to use a two-roller open type of mixing machine (Fig. 264), whose rollers, which could be heated if necessary, revolved in opposite directions and at different speeds. The action was a tearing one, which in the end concentrated all the rubber in a continuous sheet on the front roller. At this stage it was dough-like in consistency, and compounding ingredients could then be added. To make the quality as uniform as possible before further processing, the sheet would be cut and doubled over many times. This was the standard form of mixer until the close of the century.

FIG. 264. Rubber-mixing mills, with pipes for steam heating

Another important pioneer was Charles Macintosh, a Glasgow chemical manufacturer, who found that the coal-tar naphtha produced by the then rapidly developing gas industry was a satisfactory solvent for rubber. Strips of bottle rubber dissolved in naphtha made a varnish that could be brushed on to cloth, where the rubber remained as a viscous layer impermeable to air and water after the naphtha evaporated: if two pieces of such cloth were pressed together, with the rubber inside, a satisfactory compound fabric was obtained which had no tacky surface. The first factory for the production of 'mackintoshes' was opened at Manchester in 1824. Hancock made Macintosh's process more economical by the use of masticated rubber, and later, in partnership with Macintosh, he invented a spreading machine, of a type still in use, so that the cloth could be treated in long lengths at high speed. In 1836, one year before the introduction of the spreading machine for making rubberized fabric, an American inventor, E. M. Chaffee, performed a similar service in speeding up the preparation of rubber in sheet form. His calender pressed the rubber into sheets between internally heated heavy steel rollers, after which it was run between wrappers so that it should not stick together in its warm and softened condition. A calender erected from American drawings in 1849 is still in use at Bradford-on-Avon, Wiltshire.

At the beginning of the reign of Queen Victoria rubber manufacture was well established, at least in Britain: during 1830–40 imports of raw rubber rose from 23 to 332 tons. Apart from waterproof garments and rubber shoes, rubber was coming steadily into use for a large number of miscellaneous engineering appliances, and its use for a variety of surgical purposes still continued. Hancock's improved methods of manufacture had been introduced by him to France in 1828. In America, too, there was a rapid development of rubber manufacture after about 1830, chiefly for the production of rubber shoes. But there the British practice of enclosing the rubber in fabric, as in double proofing and elastic webbing, did not appeal; instead, much use was made of raw rubber or of rubber which was fabric-protected only on one side. In 1835 the extremes of the climate caused rubber goods to obtain a very bad name for losing their elasticity in the cold as well as going soft and tacky in the heat; although Americans, as we shall see, reacted strongly to the challenge of adverse conditions, the position of the industry was for many years more precarious among them than in Britain.

VULCANIZATION AND WIDER USES OF RUBBER

Charles Goodyear, a Philadelphia hardware merchant who had become interested in the problems of rubber manufacture, conducted a long series of experiments to try to improve the capacity of the material to withstand extremes of temperature. In one, he accidentally over-heated a mixture of rubber, sulphur, and white lead, and found that, although it was charred in the centre, the edges had a perfectly cured border; the resulting substance was relatively little affected by cold or heat, and could not be dissolved like the original rubber. In 1841 Goodyear was able to prepare the new material in continuous sheets of uniform quality by passing the mixture through a heated cast-iron trough, and in December a specification was lodged with the U.S. Patent Office. This was not in itself an application for a patent, and for financial reasons a British patent was not asked for until three years later. Since there was a strong prejudice against rubber in America, Goodyear tried to sell his secret to Macintosh, who was interested in finding a process for producing single-texture garments with a rubber surface that would become neither tacky nor brittle. The British firm refused to purchase a process that had not been patented, but Goodyear's samples were given to Hancock, who proceeded to work out independently the method employed in the manufacture; he obtained a British patent in November 1843, a couple of months before an application from Goodyear. Goodyear had at least shown him that the problem was soluble.

Vulcanization, as the name implies, is essentially a heating process. Sulphur was added to the rubber, together with other minor ingredients, and the temperature in the mixing machine raised until it was completely incorporated. The process was completed by heating the sulphur-treated rubber in the moulds in which the final product was to be made. Vulcanization removed most of the disadvantages associated with the use of rubber, the extent to which its properties were changed depending on the amount of sulphur added and the temperature and duration of the curing process. In 1846 an alternative form of vulcanization was invented by Alexander Parkes: in this method, suitable only for thin sheets or thin-walled articles, the rubber was dipped in a weak solution of sulphur chloride.

By the time Hancock's patent expired in 1858, the success of vulcanized rubber was assured. Heavy waterproof garments could now be replaced by something lighter; there was a growing demand for rubber shoes and other forms of footwear; and rubber was wanted in the engineering industries for valves, conveyor-belting, and various types of hose. As a consequence rubber imports into Britain had gone up by nearly 400 per cent. since 1840, and the day was rapidly approaching when only rubber for adhesives, erasers, or for such specialized uses as crêpe soles in footwear would be left unvulcanized.

The growth of the use of rubber in the nineteenth century— Brazil, which was the main supplier of the raw material, increased its output from 31 tons in 1827 to 27,650 in 1900—was closely related to the development of transportation. In the pre-railway age it was especially valuable for equipping the exposed traveller with waterproof outer-wear, including footwear, while in the railway age its use did much to increase the comfort of travel by reduction of jolting. As early as 1826 there was a patent for using cubic rubber blocks to replace steel springs in road carriages, and in 1845 rubber was being used to cushion the ends of railway carriages; rubber springs appeared in 1852. But even before the middle of the century Hancock had started the manufacture of rubber road tyres, which a hundred years later was to consume far more rubber than all other uses combined. The first road-vehicle tyres made by Hancock in 1846 were solid, about $1\frac{1}{2}$ in. wide and $1\frac{1}{4}$ in. thick, either attached to a metal hoop or sprung on to the wheel and held in position by flanges. But in the same decade of the 1840's a patent was taken out for pneumatic rubber tyres with an outer casing of leather: these 'aerial wheels', as they were called, were tested in Hyde Park and ran successfully for as much as 1,200 miles; they even spread to New York, yet the invention was soon completely forgotten. It reappeared in 1888 as an improvement upon solid rubber tyres, which had been widely used for bicycles since the 1870's, and the immediate success of Dunlop's pneumatic bicycle-tyre led to experiments with a larger number of canvas plies and thicker tread for use on the new motor vehicles. Michelin's first motor-tyre appeared in 1895, Dunlop's in 1900, and with the growing popularity of the motor-car there were fortunes to be made from the production of increasingly durable rubber compounds for this manufacture.

The other main application of rubber in the nineteenth century was to the electrical industry, especially in the insulation of cable (p. 620). For this reason increasing importance attached to the improvement of methods of extrusion, for which there had been patents as early as 1845. The method finally adopted was to drive the rubber to the front of a cylinder by means of a power-driven worm-shaft fitting closely to its walls. From the front of the cylinder the rubber would be forced round the wire through a heated die which gave it the required shape.

PLANTATION RUBBER

All this presupposed the existence of an almost indefinite supply of raw material—Britain, for example, by 1900 was importing 20,000 tons a year—such as existed in the case of petroleum and coal-gas. Rubber latex, however, was a liquid of rather variable properties derived hitherto from the bark of wild tropical plants, and the process of tapping the trees for rubber was in practice confined to South and Central America. Since the production of synthetic rubber lay far in the future, much importance attached to the two stages by which the twentieth-century supplies of plantation rubber came into existence.

The idea of deliberately cultivating rubber plants in the East and West Indies dates back to 1855, but it was not until 1873 that the India Office, having satisfied itself that the best of the rubber-bearing trees was the *Hevea* of South America, procured seeds from which six seedlings were raised and sent to Calcutta, where they failed. A second attempt was made with seedlings direct from Brazil, of which barely thirty survived: cuttings from them were distributed to Ceylon, Singapore, and Java. Finally, the services of an English planter resident on the Amazon were enlisted for the collecting of seeds from trees then actually being tapped. They were shipped promptly to Kew Gardens and were sown the day after arrival, with the result that nearly 2,000 plants were sent to Ceylon in August 1877 (Fig. 265) for distribution thence to Singapore and other destinations. At the end of the century seeds and plants by the million were being

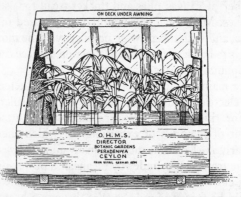

FIG. 265. Case in which plants were dispatched from Kew
to initiate the rubber plantation industry in the East

distributed from official sources over a wide area of the Far East and to British Guiana, Honduras, and the West Indies. The total cost of the initial venture, however, had been only £1,500.

Nevertheless, it was not until about 1895 that plantations came into effective production. Clearing and weeding, planting and cultivation all took time; there was also the training of the staff and the study of the best methods of tapping the latex. This led, about 1889, to the replacement of the native method of cutting the bark by a new one, in which a preliminary cut was made and then reopened at intervals, so as to produce the maximum flow of latex for the minimum damage to the tree. Considerable improvements were also made in the coagulation of the latex and in preparing the rubber for market.

THE RISE OF THE
MODERN CHEMICAL INDUSTRY

THE CHEMICAL INDUSTRY AND THE INDUSTRIAL REVOLUTION

As we have seen in Chapter 9, chemical products had, by the middle of the eighteenth century, become necessary for a very wide range of industries, and the demands of the textile industry were particularly heavy; there is, however, little truth in the often-made assertion that the textile industry was the parent of chemical science. The great expansion of the textile manufactures in Britain which began with the industrial revolution, together with the expansion of glass-making and soap manufacture, greatly increased the demand for alkali, and so great a strain was put on natural resources that before long the synthesis of alkali became essential. A satisfactory process for making soda from salt was devised by Nicolas Leblanc, physician to the Duke of Orleans, in 1787. This was of enormous technological significance as being the first industrial chemical process to be worked on a really large scale: for more than a century it was the very core of the heavy chemical industry.

Although Leblanc's process, which we shall describe later, was announced in 1787, it was not worked in Britain until nearly forty years later, an important factor in the delay being the excise duty on salt, introduced in 1702 and not finally abolished until 1823. Meanwhile, however, vegetable sources of alkali—in addition to the expensive natron that had been imported into Europe from Egypt since ancient times—were intensively exploited. An important new source of potash, made by leaching wood ashes, was Canada, where the sale of potash was virtually the only means by which the early settlers could earn ready money, if they lived in forest regions situated at a distance from the great waterways on which the lumber trade depended. By 1820 there were some 1,500 ships engaged in the business; by 1831 Canada was exporting 35,000 tons of potash and pearl-ash (the most refined grade) to Britain annually, this being approximately three-quarters of this country's total import. By the middle of the century, 4 million tons of hardwood were being burnt annually in Canadian asheries; Scandinavia, too, was a major source of wood ash. The ashes were extracted with water, the solution filtered through straw, and the extract evaporated to dryness; to make pearl-ash the crude product was roasted in a reverberatory furnace. Meanwhile, additional supplies of low-grade alkali—10,000 tons annually by the end of the eighteenth century—were being obtained from Scotland by the burning of seaweed, and from Mediterranean seashore plants under the name of barilla. Although synthetic soda quickly ousted the natural product as the Leblanc

FIG. 266. Extraction of soda from black ash, in the Leblanc process

process became widely established, the ashes of plants remained the main source of potash up to 1860, when the vast deposits of potassium salts at Stassfurt, south of Magdeburg, began to be worked.

In France the general shortage of alkali had been made acute by the difficulties arising from the wars, and in 1775 the Academy offered a prize of 2,400 livres for a satisfactory method of making soda from salt. In offering this award, they had reasonable grounds for hoping that it would soon be claimed, for the problem was already engaging the attention of a number of chemists. Although earlier attempts met with some success, the first to devise a process that could be satisfactorily worked on an industrial scale was Leblanc, who took out a patent in 1791. He opened factories at St Denis, Rouen, and Lille, but reaped no lasting benefit from what was to remain for a century one of the most fundamentally important of all industrial processes: he was swept away by the Revolution, and died in poverty, by his own hand, in 1806. His process was basically very simple: common salt was treated with sulphuric acid, and the resulting salt-cake (sodium sulphate) was mixed with coal and limestone and then

FIG. 267. Purification of soda by crystallization

roasted. Soda was extracted with water from the resulting 'black ash' (Fig. 266), and the solution was evaporated to dryness in open pans; if necessary, for example in glass-making, the product so obtained was further purified by crystallization (Fig. 267).

In Britain, somewhat similar processes, derived from France, began to be worked by, among others, William Losh and Thomas Double-day of Walker-on-Tyne. From 1802, after the Peace of Amiens, they worked the Leblanc process on a very small scale, but the first effectively to establish this in Britain was James Muspratt, an Irish chemical manufacturer who settled in Liverpool in 1822. In this neighbourhood he found the ideal conditions for working the process economically: salt, on which the duty of £30 per ton was repealed in 1823, lay in abundance beneath the ground, and coal and limestone were close at hand. A reason for the slow establishment of the Leblanc process is that the soap-boilers (Fig. 268), who were eventually among Muspratt's best customers, would

FIG. 268. Soap-boiling, mid-nineteenth century

not accept the synthetic soda and he had, at first, not only to give them his product but to supervise its use. This is all the more surprising in view of the fact that the synthetic product had a great advantage over the natural one in being of very consistent quality. In 1828 Muspratt entered into partnership with Josias Gamble and a new works was established at St Helens, which has since remained one of the great centres of the British chemical industry. Gamble was exceptional among chemical manufacturers of his day in that he had received some formal training in chemistry, under Professor Cleghorn at Glasgow; Muspratt, by contrast, had had an adven-

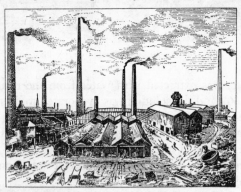

FIG. 269. St Rollox works, Glasgow, c. 1800

turous career in the Napoleonic wars, taking part in the British retreat from Madrid in 1812. No doubt the great difference of temperament between the two men was among the reasons for the termination of the partnership after only two years. In 1825 Charles Tennant began to make soda by the Leblanc process at Glasgow, where his St Rollox works (Fig. 269) soon became the largest chemical factory in Europe. In the 1830's it covered 100 acres and had over a thousand employees, and its immense chimney, 455 ft high, was a famous landmark. By 1840, at latest, synthetic soda had largely replaced barilla in Britain.

Sulphuric acid was, as we have seen, necessary for the first stage of the Leblanc process, and its manufacture on a large scale became essential. From the seventeenth century, Nordhausen in Saxony had been a centre for the manufacture of strong sulphuric acid by the distillation of green vitriol (ferrous sulphate), but production there was limited and very expensive. Joshua Ward—perhaps better known as the quack of Hogarth's *Harlot's Progress*—had begun to manufacture it at Richmond in 1737 by burning a mixture of sulphur and nitre (saltpetre) in the necks of large glass vessels containing a little water: after several combustions, the water became converted into dilute sulphuric acid, which was then concentrated by distillation. Ward was granted a patent in 1749, even though his process was basically the same as one used experimentally by the German chemist Johann Glauber in the seventeenth century and his

method was already being used in both France and Germany. By Ward's process the price of the acid was reduced from roughly £2 to 2s. a pound, but it was John Roebuck's 'lead-chamber' process that finally established this essential manufacture on a really firm basis and on a large scale. Roebuck replaced the fragile glass vessels (Fig. 270) by chambers consisting of sheets of lead, one of the few cheap metals resistant to the acid, mounted on wooden frames. Roebuck, who had studied chemistry at Edinburgh and Leyden, first worked his process at Birmingham, where he was a consulting chemist to

FIG. 270. Manufacture of sulphuric acid according to Ward, *c.* 1760

the local metal industry, but he shortly moved to Prestonpans; there, in greater isolation, he hoped to preserve the secret of his process, which he did not at first attempt to patent. But an employee left him and set up a rival works at Bridgnorth, and before long lead-chamber works were established elsewhere in Britain and in France. The first lead-chamber factory in France was built about 1766, at Rouen. The first in the United States was established at Philadelphia in 1793 by John Harrison, who had studied chemistry and industrial chemical methods in England: he soon had competitors at a number of centres, including New York. When Roebuck made a belated application for a patent, it failed on the grounds that the process was already widely used.

By the early nineteenth century various improvements had been made in the original process. In 1793 the French chemists Désormes and Clément showed that the quantity of nitre required could be much reduced by admitting air for the combustion of the sulphur, and in 1803 Tennant carried out the process of combustion in a separate furnace instead of within the lead chambers. In 1818 Hill of Deptford used pyrites as a source of sulphur—a change which became general for half a century after 1838, when Ferdinand II, king of the Two Sicilies, ill-advisedly gave a French firm the mono-

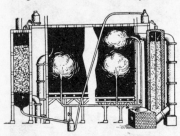

FIG. 271. Lead chamber in which sulphuric acid was made, c. 1813

poly of Italian sulphur, with the result that the price quickly doubled itself. About the same time steam jets began to be used in the chambers in place of the shallow layers of water at the bottom (Fig. 271). The size of the chambers was very greatly increased—by 1860 Muspratt had one of 56,000 cu. ft capacity, compared with the 200 cu. ft of Roebuck's original—and the process was made continuous. By 1830 the price of sulphuric acid had fallen to $2\frac{1}{2}d.$ a pound, and it fell still further when mineral saltpetre (sodium nitrate) began to be imported from Chile.

The action of sulphuric acid on salt in the first stage of the Leblanc process produced clouds of hydrochloric acid gas, a very noxious and destructive by-product which involved the early soda manufacturers in repeated litigation with their neighbours. Muspratt sought to abate the nuisance by expelling the gas through immensely tall chimneys—one almost 300 ft high—but in 1836 William Gossage, a Worcestershire chemical manufacturer, invented towers in which the gas was absorbed by a descending stream of water. This paved the way for the Alkali Act of 1863, which required manufacturers to absorb at least 95 per cent. of the hydrochloric acid.

Long before this, however, manufacturers had found in bleaching an important use for some of the hydrochloric acid. For centuries the traditional way of bleaching textiles had been by treating the fabric with buttermilk (or, after 1758, with dilute sulphuric acid) and exposing it to sunlight in bleach-fields (Fig. 272)—a very slow process, taking several months to complete, especially in northern latitudes, and requiring much space. Chemical bleaching was introduced in 1785 by the French chemist Berthollet, who showed that a solution (eau de Javel) made by passing chlorine through potash had a very strong bleaching action. Berthollet described this process to James Watt during a visit by the latter to Paris, and when he returned to Glasgow, Watt passed the information on to Tennant. Very soon Tennant introduced an improvement of his own: in 1799 he began the manufacture of bleaching powder by passing chlorine over lime. The introduction of bleaching powder, at first offered at £140 a ton

FIG. 272. Bleach-field, early nineteenth century

but by 1830 at £80 a ton, was an event of the first importance to the textile industry, for without it the cotton industry could not have achieved its enormous expansion; chemical bleaching was also a valuable innovation in the manufacture of paper. The British Government recognized its importance in 1815 by recommending that salt used for making bleaching powder should be exempt from duty. By 1830 annual production of bleaching powder in Britain was approximately 1,500 tons.

LATER DEVELOPMENTS IN THE MANUFACTURE OF SODA AND SULPHURIC ACID, 1830–1900

Although the nineteenth century saw an enormous expansion of the chemical industry in both its scale and the number of its products, three aspects are of particular importance. The first was the gradual obsolescence of the Leblanc process as it became replaced by the Solvay ammonia–soda process; the second was the development of the synthetic organic chemical industry, following W. H. Perkin's discovery of the first synthetic dyestuff in 1856; the third was the growth of the electrochemical industry concomitant with the development of large-scale methods for the production and distribution of electricity (Ch. 22).

The story of the development of the Solvay process is a logical sequel to that of the Leblanc process, which we have already considered. Although the technological importance of the Leblanc process is difficult to overestimate, it had certain inherent disadvantages, to one of which—the evolution of vast clouds of hydrochloric acid gas—we have already alluded. Gossage's absorption towers (p. 536) satisfactorily solved the problem of hydrochloric acid, but there remained the further serious problem of disposing of the noisome waste, known as 'galligu', which remained after the soda had been extracted from the black ash. The magnitude of the problem is apparent from the fact that for every ton of soda manufactured there remained no less than two tons of galligu. Apart from the inconvenience of disposing of it, the galligu was a serious source of financial loss, for within it was locked up most of the expensive sulphur used in making the sulphuric acid required for the first stage of the process.

In these circumstances, it is not surprising that even in the early days of the Leblanc process chemists turned their attention to the devising of an alternative. The essentials of what subsequently became the Solvay process were, apparently, worked out as early as 1811 by the French engineer and scientist A. J. Fresnel, but the practical difficulties of the process were such that half a century elapsed before it could be satisfactorily worked industrially. While Fresnel's contribution must not be overestimated, there is evidence that he knew that if carbon dioxide gas is passed into brine saturated with ammonia, sodium bicarbonate, a relatively insoluble salt, is precipitated. Sodium bicarbonate is easily converted into soda, merely by heating it; at the same time carbon dioxide gas is liberated and this can be re-used for the first stage of the process. The ammonia, too, can potentially be recovered for further use, since it is converted during the process into ammonium chloride; from this ammonia is easily liberated by treatment with lime. The lime itself is obtained as a by-product of roasting limestone to make carbon dioxide. Thus the process is to a high degree self-contained, the only waste product being calcium chloride which, although almost unmarketable, was at least not objectionable like galligu.

The story of the evolution of the ammonia–soda process is a long and involved one, of which we can consider here only the most important steps. As early as 1836 soda was being made in a Scottish works at Camlachie, at the rate of 2 cwt daily, by treating salt with ammonium bicarbonate, but this was a short-lived venture. Two years later two London chemists, H. G. Dyar and J. Hemming, patented a similar process which they worked for a time at their Whitechapel works. They soon ran into severe practical difficulties, however, arising mainly from the difficulty of preventing the escape of ammonia, a light and volatile gas. The Whitechapel works was visited by James Sheridan Muspratt—son of James Muspratt, pioneer of the Leblanc process in Britain—who was sufficiently impressed to persuade his father to invest some £8,000 in a plant to work the process at Merton. This venture met with no success. A number of other chemical manufacturers, in Britain, Germany, and France, attempted to work the Dyar and Hemming process but all were defeated by the practical difficulties, particularly that of conserving ammonia, which was relatively costly to manufacture. Of these ventures perhaps the most successful was that of Rolland and Schlösing, who about 1854 set up works near Paris to manufacture soda by what they claimed to be a continuous version of the Dyar–Hemming process; the factory was closed three years later, however, having made only 300 tons of soda.

The decisive step was made in Belgium by the Solvay brothers, Ernest and Alfred. Ernest Solvay's principal contribution was to introduce a carbonating tower, which made the process continuous; other, but somewhat less important, developments were in the kilns for liberating carbon dioxide from limestone and for calcining the sodium bicarbonate. Solvay filed his patent in Belgium in 1861: it is an interesting sidelight on the still relatively slow rate at which knowledge was disseminated that he was totally unaware of the considerable work done already in this field during the previous half century. The first works was built at Couillet in 1863, but there were still technical difficulties to be overcome and it was four years before the Solvay process was finally working satisfactorily. Once the teething troubles had been overcome, however, progress was very rapid and the big Dombasle works were built in France in 1876.

The ammonia–soda process was introduced into Britain by Ludwig Mond, who in 1872 acquired the British rights in a more extensive patent which Solvay had filed in Britain in that year. Mond entered into partnership with John Brunner and they established works at Winnington in Cheshire. Even then the ammonia–soda process proved obstinate, and before they finally mastered it the two partners were within sight of financial ruin. The process was being worked at Wyhlen, in Germany, by 1880, and at Syracuse, in the United States, four years later.

From that time onwards the ultimate triumph of the ammonia-soda process was no longer in doubt, but the operators of the Leblanc process, who had heavy capital investments in plant, put up a spirited resistance. The general course of the struggle is illustrated by the figures for world production of soda. In 1874 production was 525,000 tons, of which no less than 495,000 tons was made by the Leblanc process: by 1902, although the world total had risen to 1,800,000 tons, only 150,000 tons of this was made by the Leblanc process. During the same period the price of soda fell by more than half. That the two processes were for so long worked side by side, despite the undoubted superiority of the Solvay process, can be attributed to two principal factors. The first, and more important, was that during the middle decades of the nineteenth century numerous technical improvements were made in the original Leblanc process; the second was a series of amalgamations among the Leblanc operators, making it possible for them to produce more efficiently.

Of the technical improvements in the Leblanc process, some of the most important were concerned with the treatment of galligu to recover sulphur. Among the many able chemists who directed their attention to this problem were Gossage and Mond, but neither of them produced entirely satisfactory solutions. The first to do so was Alexander Chance, whose process was a development of Gossage's that was made possible, as he himself acknowledged, by the availability of improved machinery and appliances. Chance's process consisted essentially in blowing carbon dioxide gas through the galligu, when hydrogen sulphide is liberated from the calcium sulphide contained in it. By a process of double enrichment he obtained a gas sufficiently rich to be burnt in kilns devised by C. F. Claus: in these kilns the hydrogen sulphide was partially oxidized to water and sulphur, the latter collecting in a well at the bottom. In 1893 the Chance–Claus process was being worked in Britain on a scale sufficient to yield 35,000 tons of sulphur annually, which found a market for the manufacture of sulphuric acid.

Of others who made technical improvements in the Leblanc process, James Shanks must be mentioned: in 1861 he introduced much improved vats for the extraction of the black ash. About 1870 a notable improvement was made in the manufacture of the black ash itself. Originally it was prepared simply by stirring a mixture of salt-cake, limestone, and coke in a furnace, but this came to be replaced by a large revolving furnace, of which the first used in Britain were cast by Thomas Robinson of St Helens. These 'revolvers', generally about 10 ft in diameter and 20 ft long, could contain a relatively large charge.

Improvements were also made in the utilization of the hydrochloric acid gas produced in the first stage of the Leblanc process. Henry Deacon devised a method for the catalytic oxidation of the gas to chlorine, and in 1870 patented a process by which strong bleaching powder could be made from the resulting mixture of gases. More important, however, was a process devised by Walter Weldon, in which the hydrochloric acid was oxidized to chlorine by manganese dioxide: this was not a new process, but he was the first to solve the very important problem of recovering the expensive manganese for further use. Weldon's process quadrupled the output of bleaching powder and reduced its price in Britain to £6 a ton. In presenting him with the gold medal of the Société d'Encouragement, the great French chemist J. B. A. Dumas stressed the far-reaching consequences of the invention: 'By Mr. Weldon's invention, every sheet of paper and every yard of calico has been cheapened throughout the world.'

In the manufacture of sulphuric acid there had been, meanwhile, a revolution comparable with that in the manufacture of soda. As early as 1831 Peregrine Phillips, a Bristol vinegar manufacturer, patented a process for the manufacture of sulphuric acid different in principle from that of the lead-chamber process. Briefly, sulphur dioxide—made from sulphur or pyrites—was to be made to combine with oxygen in the presence of finely divided platinum, which served as a catalyst: that is, a substance which facilitates a chemical reaction without itself being consumed in it. The resulting sulphur trioxide was to be dissolved in water or dilute sulphuric acid, to form a strong acid. Like the ammonia–soda process, Phillips's was long defeated by its technical difficulties, the most serious of which was that the catalyst gradually became 'poisoned' and useless. This difficulty seemed less serious from 1852 onwards, when it was shown that materials much less expensive than platinum—notably iron oxide—

could serve as catalysts. Nevertheless, the so-called contact process made little headway until developments elsewhere in the chemical industry made it necessary to have sulphuric acid stronger than that obtainable by the lead-chamber process. This development was the growth of the organic chemical industry, which required increasingly large quantities not only of strong sulphuric acid but of the form known as oleum, which contains a considerable excess of sulphur trioxide. Until 1870 virtually the only source of oleum was the Nordhausen works (p. 534), whose product was, however, extremely expensive and limited in quantity. The contact process quite suddenly engaged serious attention, as it promised to supply large quantities of oleum at a reasonable price. There was, at first, no thought of competition with the lead-chamber process.

A decisive improvement in the contact process was made about 1870 by a German chemist, Rudolf Messel, who found that the poisoning of the catalyst could be avoided if the sulphur dioxide, originally derived from lead-chamber acid but later from pyrites, was first carefully purified. After the Franco-Prussian war Messel, with W. S. Squire, developed an industrially satisfactory form of the contact process which was worked from 1876 at Silvertown, where output eventually rose to 1,000 tons weekly. In Germany, which had become the main centre of the flourishing dyestuff industry, the contact process was quickly developed on a very large scale: by 1900 production was 116,000 metric tons and within three years it had almost doubled.

SYNTHETIC DYES

The manufacture of dyestuffs is only one example of a totally new branch of the chemical industry—the manufacture of organic chemicals—that developed in the last half of the nineteenth century. Originally, as its name implies, organic chemistry concerned itself with the study of substances found in living organisms, but as chemists identified the vast majority of these as compounds of carbon, organic chemistry became synonymous with the chemistry of all substances containing carbon, regardless of their origin. Carbon is unique in the facility with which its atoms will join together to form chains and rings: where the compounds of other elements are measured in hundreds or thousands, the compounds of carbon are numbered in millions.

Since the dyestuffs industry was the main customer for oleum, we may appropriately next consider the changes that had been taking place in it. In earlier discussion of dyeing, it has been pointed out that from very early times a considerable range of vegetable dyes has been used: in 1856, however, a discovery occurred which very quickly made an enormous number of new dyes available. This discovery was that of mauve, made by W. H. Perkin in 1856, but the story properly begins some ten years earlier. In 1845 the distinguished German chemist, August Wilhelm von Hofmann, had come to London at the invitation of Prince Albert to be the first superintendent of the Royal College of Chemistry. Hofmann was among the first to realize that coal-tar, cheaply available from the rapidly expanding gas industry (Ch. 17), could yield many different substances of great chemical interest. Among these substances was benzene. It was already well known that when this is treated with nitric acid it forms an oily yellow substance called nitrobenzene; if this is reduced, it yields aniline, so called because it was first prepared from indigo, for which the French and Portuguese name is *anil*. Hofmann found a very much better way of reducing nitrobenzene, and thus made aniline available cheaply and in large quantities if a use could be found for it. Among his students was Perkin, then a youth of only eighteen, who saw a resemblance between the formula of allyl-toluidine, a derivative of aniline, and the very important anti-malarial drug, quinine. Perkin conceived the idea, which we now know to be totally impracticable, of oxidizing allyl-toluidine to quinine. Disappointed in the result, he tried the same experiment with aniline: from the black sludge resulting from his experiment he obtained some purple crystals. Experimenting with the possibilities of this 'aniline purple' as a dye, he found that it would dye silk a brilliant mauve which was fast to light and not removed by washing.

Perkin sent a specimen of his dyed silk to Pullars of Perth, the dyers, who sent a most encouraging report upon it, saying: 'If your discovery does not make the goods too expensive, it is decidedly one of the most valuable that has come out for a very long time.' Perkin immediately patented his dye, and with the help of his father and elder brother built a works at Greenford Green, near Harrow, in 1857. While the new dye quickly achieved considerable success in Britain, it was its popularity among fashionable circles in France— where Perkin's patent unfortunately proved to be void—that finally established sales on a really large scale. Although the original mauve is now little used, it is still familiar to stamp-collectors as the dye of some early British penny stamps. Such was Perkin's success that by the age of thirty-five he was wealthy enough to retire from business and devote himself entirely to chemical research. In this he had a further conspicuous success in June 1869, when he perfected a method for the synthesis of alizarin, the red colouring matter of madder root (p. 267). In the event, the German chemist Heinrich Caro beat him by a single day in lodging his patent, but to this dramatic story we will return later.

The great success of Perkin's mauve led organic chemists to investigate energetically the possibility of making other synthetic dyes from aniline and its chemical derivatives. In 1859 Verguin discovered magenta, named after the town in northern Italy where Napoleon III that summer defeated the Austrians. Hofmann himself—who had at first been scornful of Perkin's forsaking of pure chemistry for industrial practice—showed that magenta (Fig. 273) could be the parent of a whole series of violet dyes. These were followed by a blue dye, rosaniline blue, discovered independently in France and in England: this suffered from the disadvantage of low solubility in water, but the defect was removed when Edward Nicholson discovered that sulphonating the dye with oleum converted it into a soluble form. It was soon found that this process of sulphonation was widely useful: apart from rendering many dyes more soluble it also made them strongly acid, which had certain technical advantages from the dyer's point of view. Aniline black was discovered—or rather rediscovered, for it had been observed in 1834—by John Lightfoot in 1863. In its original form it had the defect of gradually acquiring a dingy green tinge, but this was overcome by chemical modification. Meanwhile, a young German chemist, Peter Griess, had discovered the so-called diazo compounds, which subsequently proved of very great importance in the manufacture of dyestuffs: although there were earlier examples, the first really successful dye of this kind was Bismarck brown, prepared in 1863. Such was the avidity of manufacturers for new dyes, that this was being manufactured in Manchester by Ivan Levinstein in the following year.

While chemists had been inventing synthetic dyes of totally new kinds, another profitable line of research was being followed. This concerned the synthesis of some of the traditional natural dyes: that this was possible was the result of rapid strides concurrently being made in theoretical organic chemistry. In 1869 two German chemists, K. Graebe and K. Liebermann, achieved a conspicuous success by synthesizing alizarin; their first process was not, however, industrially practicable, as it was too expensive to compete with the natural product. The solution of the problem came as the result of a laboratory accident which showed that the essential process of sulphonation could be carried out only with very strong sulphuric acid and at a high temperature. This key discovery was made by Caro, working for the Badische Anilin-und-Soda Fabrik; he (as previously

FIG. 273. Cauldron fitted with mechanical stirrer for manufacture of magenta dye, c. 1860

mentioned) lodged his patent in Britain the day before Perkin lodged one for the same process. In the end a satisfactory solution was arranged, for the Badische Fabrik gave Perkin licence to manufacture alizarin in England. The European madder growers, whose crop in 1868 was some 70,000 tons, were ruined by the discovery, but the long-term result was not without advantage, for considerable areas of land were liberated for food production.

In 1897 synthetic indigo came on the market, and the story of this development is in many ways curiously similar to that of alizarin. The first process—invented in 1880 by Adolf von Baeyer—proved, like the first synthesis of alizarin, to be too complicated and expensive for industrial development. Again, it was a laboratory accident, acutely interpreted, that finally pointed the way to success. One of the raw materials required for the making of synthetic indigo was phthalic anhydride, which can be obtained by the oxidation of naphthalene: the breaking of a thermometer during an experiment showed that mercury sulphate would catalyse the reaction and enormously increase its speed. The perfecting of the process took seventeen years and is said to have cost the Badische Fabrik £1 million. Within a few years there had been far-reaching effects on the Indian indigo growers: the export of Indian indigo fell from about 19,000 tons in 1895 to little more than 1,000 tons in 1913, and a million acres of land could then be used for other purposes.

It is impossible to list here all the new synthetic dyestuffs that became available before the end of the nineteenth century. It must suffice to mention, in addition to those named, methylene blue, discovered by Caro in 1876, and its derivative methylene green, discovered by Fischer in 1878. The first synthetic dye that would dye cotton directly was Congo red, discovered by Böttiger in 1884. Primuline yellow was first prepared by Green in 1887.

Before leaving the dyestuffs industry we must mention a very important change in its structure that took place in the last decades of the nineteenth century. Although the first synthetic dye was made in Britain and the early industrial development of the new industry took place largely there, by 1900 the centre of activity had been decisively transferred to Germany. The number of patents relating to dyes filed in Britain each five-year period was 20 in 1860 and 52 in 1900: the figures for Germany, for the same years, were 8 and 427 respectively. For this, various reasons have been advanced: important factors were certainly the greater availability of raw materials in Germany; a better system of technical education, with strong financial support from the state; and a readiness to use technically qualified men in all branches of the business. A measure of the grip that Germany had established is given by the fact that, when war broke out in 1914, only 20 per cent. of the dyes used in Britain were of domestic manufacture, a grave strategic disadvantage; even the dyeing of military uniforms presented a serious problem.

EXPLOSIVES

While the dyestuffs industry was developing, an equally important development was taking place in the manufacture of explosives. Until the middle of the nineteenth century virtually the only important explosive, whether for military or civil purposes, was gunpowder

(p. 268). This was probably first used for blasting in England about 1670, following earlier use for the same purpose on the Continent; it was regularly used in Cornish mines by 1689. Some of the hazards of its use were removed when William Bickford, in 1831, invented the miner's safety fuse.

Shortly before the middle of the century it was discovered by C. F. Schönbein that if cellulose is treated with nitric acid, a highly inflammable and explosive product results. In 1846 he came to Britain and, in association with John Hall & Sons at Faversham, began the manufacture of gun-cotton, so called because cotton was the cellulosic material normally used. A disastrous explosion in the following year put a stop to this enterprise, and similar unhappy experiences on the Continent led to a general lack of confidence in nitro-cellulose. Similar doubts attached to nitroglycerine, which A. Sobrero, an Italian chemist, had discovered, also in 1846. It was Alfred Nobel who first showed that nitroglycerine could be made safe by absorbing it on a kind of clay known as kieselguhr: this product was known as dynamite. Although it could be safely handled if reasonable care was used, dynamite exploded violently if touched off with a detonator such as mercury fulminate (p. 549). This discovery resulted in a considerable expansion of the high-explosives industry. In 1875 Nobel invented blasting gelatine, which consisted largely of nitroglycerine with a small addition of collodion cotton; technical difficulties, however, prevented the manufacture being established until some ten years later.

The nitroglycerine for these purposes was made by treating glycerine—a by-product of soap manufacture—with a mixture of strong sulphuric and nitric acids. This was a hazardous operation, as the reaction itself could generate sufficient heat to explode the mixture; an essential precaution for success was therefore to keep the mixture cool. Originally the manufacture was carried out by hand in small batches, but from about 1880 larger-scale manufacture began. Hand-stirring was replaced by mechanical stirring or—in order still further to reduce the risk of dangerous local heating—by stirring with compressed air. After completion of the nitration, the mixture was normally drowned in a large volume of cold water from which, being immiscible with water, the nitroglycerine separates and can be isolated. As this method wasted acid not used up in the process, a later practice was to allow the original mixture to settle in tanks until the nitroglycerine separated and could be run off and washed, the final washing being done with an alkaline solution to remove excess acid. Nitroglycerine works were normally built on the sides of hills so that all movements of liquid could be effected by gravity, thus obviating the risk of explosive material being left behind in pumps. Although all these precautions could not make the manufacture of nitroglycerine entirely safe, the hazards were very greatly reduced. In Britain the most satisfactory conditions for explosive manufacture were codified in the Explosives Act of 1875, and similar legislation was introduced in other countries to safeguard the workers in the industry.

Meanwhile the manufacture of gun-cotton was being developed. This was not put on a satisfactory basis until 1866, when Frederick Abel showed that its stability depended upon complete removal of all traces of the mixture of sulphuric and nitric acids used in its preparation: the only satisfactory means of doing this proved to be maceration of the product so that the washing water penetrated it thoroughly. As practised at Waltham Abbey, Abel's method consisted of first degreasing the cotton with alkali, and then washing and drying it. It was then treated with a mixture of roughly three parts of concentrated sulphuric acid and one part of concentrated nitric acid. After several hours excess acid was removed centrifugally and the nitrated cotton was washed with a large volume of water. It was then subjected to prolonged boiling with soda solution, which removed almost all the remaining traces of acid. Finally, to ensure that no acid remained, the nitro-cotton was reduced to a pulp and subjected to further thorough washing.

As has been indicated, the first uses of the new high explosives were for blasting in mines and quarries, but attention was early directed to their use as propellents. As early as 1846, Schönbein demonstrated the possibilities of gun-cotton as a smokeless propellent for artillery shells. In 1864 a smokeless powder for shot-guns began to be made by nitrating wood, but it was not until some twenty years later, when *Poudre B* was developed in France and ballistite by Nobel, that nitroglycerine and nitro-cellulose became important in the munitions industry. *Poudre B* consisted of approximately 70 per cent. of gun-cotton made in the ordinary way, and 30 per cent. of so-called soluble gun-cotton made by carrying out the nitration process with a higher proportion of nitric acid. Ballistite consisted of a mixture of nitroglycerine and soluble gun-cotton, together with a little camphor. It was later found that ballistite was liable to deteriorate during storage owing to evaporation of the camphor, and this led to the introduction of cordite, in which a little petroleum jelly was added as a stabilizer. Cordite owes its name to the fact that in the final stages of its preparation it was converted into a paste which was forced through dies, emerging in the form of cord, which was either wound on a drum or chopped into short lengths; *Poudre B* and ballistite were marketed in the form of flakes. The only other important high explosive introduced before the end of the nineteenth century was picric acid. Although this was known as early as 1788, almost a century elapsed before it began to be used as a high explosive for shells, known in Britain as lyddite—from Lydd in Kent, where it was tested on the ranges—and first used in action at Omdurman (p. 305): it was made by the nitration of carbolic acid (phenol).

FIG. 274. Manufacture of mercury fulminate

All these high explosives differ materially from gunpowder in the method by which they are detonated. Whereas gunpowder will explode merely by application of a naked flame, the detonation of nitro-cellulose and nitroglycerine must be effected by percussion. The standard means is to use a percussion cap containing a very small amount of a more sensitive explosive: mercury fulminate—made by treating a solution of mercury in strong nitric acid with alcohol—is normally used (Fig. 274). This is readily detonated by the firing pin of a rifle or gun and its explosion will, in turn, initiate the explosion of the contents of the cartridge.

SOME ELECTROCHEMICAL PROCESSES

Having considered two major lines of development of the organic chemical industry—the manufacture of dyes and high explosives—we may now return to the manufacture of inorganic substances and consider some completely new processes made possible by the development of the electrical industry (Ch. 22). Here the work of an American chemist, Hamilton Young Castner, demands special consideration. Castner began his career, as we have noted (p. 495), by devising a new method for the manufacture of sodium, which he intended as an intermediary for making aluminium. Unfortunately for Castner, his aluminium process was rendered obsolete, just when commercial success seemed secure, by the development, in 1886, of an electrolytic process with which his own could not compete. Castner's only remaining asset was his process for manufacturing sodium cheaply, but as the demand for sodium was then extremely small, the value of this asset was doubtful. It was not long, however, before Castner himself had found new uses for sodium. First, he established a process for manufacturing sodium peroxide—a valuable bleaching agent, especially for the straw hats then very fashionable for both sexes—by burning sodium in a current of air. He next began to manufacture sodium cyanide by passing ammonia over molten sodium: the first product of this reaction was sodamide, which could be converted into sodium cyanide by pouring it over red-hot charcoal. In 1894 he improved on this process by one in which sodium cyanide was made in a single stage by reaction between ammonia, charcoal, and sodium. After some initial difficulties—arising from the fact that the gold-mining industry was accustomed to the use of potassium cyanide—Castner was able to establish a large market for sodium cyanide in Australia, America, South Africa, and in other countries where the Forrest-MacArthur cyanide process (p. 494) was being applied for the extraction of gold.

These developments had quite unexpected consequences: instead of having surplus sodium, Castner now had difficulty in making sufficient to meet the demand. He therefore turned his versatile mind to the problem of an improved method of manufacture and eventually concentrated his attention upon making it by the electrolysis of fused caustic soda. At first, however, he met with only limited success, because of the impure state of even the best caustic soda then available commercially. He therefore decided to seek an industrial method for making pure caustic soda, and again he turned his attention to electrochemical processes. It was well known that electrolysis of brine resulted in the formation of chlorine at the anode, and of caustic soda and hydrogen at the cathode, but there was no satisfactory method of separating the resulting caustic soda from unchanged salt. Castner solved this difficulty by using an electrolytic cell in which the cathode consisted of a layer of mercury: sodium released from the brine formed an amalgam with the mercury, and this in turn reacted with water in a separate compartment of the cell to form caustic soda. The mercury was made to circulate by means of a rocking device, and the process was made continuous by periodically replenishing the brine and removing the caustic soda. This process enabled Castner to make almost pure caustic soda, a product previously unknown to the alkali trade. The chlorine evolved during the reaction was a valuable by-product, for it could be converted into bleaching powder.

In 1894 Castner sought international patents for his process, but in Germany he found he had been anticipated by an Austrian chemist, Carl Kellner, who had formed a company to work his process near Salzburg and had sold the other European rights to Solvay & Company in Brussels. Although it is questionable whether Kellner's process would have been satisfactory in practice, Castner preferred to reach agreement with him rather than face prolonged and costly litigation. In consequence the two men exchanged their patents and processes, and for this reason what Castner invented is now always known as the Castner-Kellner process.

Two factors were essential for its successful working: cheap and abundant electricity and a good local supply of salt. Neither of these was available at Oldbury, where Castner had first set up his works, and the new company, the Castner-Kellner Alkali Company, was established at Runcorn, in the Cheshire salt area. It began operation in 1897, initially producing some 20 tons of caustic soda and 40 tons of bleaching powder daily. In the United States a pilot plant was established at Saltville, Virginia, and the success of this led, in 1896, to the building of a much bigger works at Niagara Falls, where cheap electricity was obtainable (p. 618).

Another important application of electricity was in the manufacture of phosphorus, this being in great demand by the middle of the nineteenth century for the manufacture of matches. This element had been discovered in 1669 by Brand; until about 1890 the general method of preparing it was to treat either bones, or some mineral form of phosphate, with hot sulphuric acid. This treatment yielded a syrupy solution of phosphoric acid, which was then mixed to a paste with some form of carbon, usually powdered coal or charcoal. The paste was dried, powdered, and then charged into large fireclay retorts, the necks of which dipped under water contained in long troughs. When the retorts were strongly heated, phosphorus distilled over and condensed under the water. From this stage onwards, great care had to be exercised in the manufacture, as phosphorus is spontaneously inflammable if exposed to air. The crude material was purified by treatment with sodium dichromate and sulphuric acid, and was then soldered into tins for dispatch.

Its property of spontaneous ignition in air early directed attention to the possibilities of using phosphorus for making fire. As early as 1680 Robert Boyle was using sulphur-tipped splints drawn through paper impregnated with phosphorus, but a further century elapsed before any sort of match became at all generally used. In 1780 the 'phosphoric candle' appeared in France. This consisted simply of a strip of paper, with its tip impregnated with phosphorus, sealed in an easily broken glass tube: on breaking the glass, the paper quickly burst into flames. For the first half of the nineteenth century the 'instantaneous light box' was popular in Europe and the United States. The equipment consisted of a bottle of strong sulphuric acid and a packet of wooden matches tipped with a mixture of potassium chlorate, gum, and sugar. When the splint was dipped into the acid and quickly withdrawn, it burst into flame.

The first match of modern type, however, was sold by John Walker of Stockton-on-Tees in 1827. The wooden match was tipped with a mixture of potassium chlorate, antimony sulphide, gum, and starch. These 'Lucifers' were made to ignite by striking them against sandpaper or some other rough surface. In 1831 Charles Sauria, in France, re-established phosphorus in matches by using it to replace the antimony sulphide in Walker's composition.

Apart from the hazard of fire, phosphorus was gravely dangerous to those who handled it because of the highly poisonous nature of its vapour: the resulting necrosis of the jaw ('Phossy jaw') was first characterized in 1839. Great interest was therefore aroused by the discovery in 1845, by Anton Schroetter of Vienna, that if ordinary phosphorus is heated in a closed vessel it is converted into an amorphous form which is neither spontaneously inflammable nor poisonous. Schroetter's patent was acquired by Arthur Albright of Birmingham, and amorphous phosphorus was displayed at the Great Exhibition in 1851. At first, however, the new form of phosphorus proved unsuitable for what it had been hoped would be its main use, namely the manufacture of matches. Eventually, however, J. E. Lundström of Jönköping, Sweden, solved the problem of making 'safety' matches with Albright's product, of which they subsequently bought very large quantities. The safety match incorporated amorphous phosphorus in the striker on the box, but there was no phosphorus in the head of the match. This development led to a greatly increased demand for phosphorus, and consequently to improvements in its manufacture. Gas-fired furnaces were introduced in France, but a much more important development was the patenting of an electro-thermal process in 1888. In this, an electric furnace is charged with a mixture of mineral phosphate, coal, and sand: phosphorus vola-tilizes and is condensed. The process is a continuous one, a fresh charge being added to the furnace as slag is removed.

ARTIFICIAL FERTILIZERS

In the last half of the nineteenth century an important new use developed for sulphuric acid, compensating for the diminishing demands of the Leblanc industry as it met competition from the Solvay process. Superphosphate, made by treating bones or mineral phosphate with sulphuric acid, is one of the most important of all agricultural fertilizers. Although manufactured by James Murray in Dublin as early as 1817, the first to establish a large-scale industry was John Bennet Lawes who, from 1834 onwards, carried out exten-sive agricultural experiments on his estate at Rothamsted, where he was joined by J. H. Gilbert in 1843. In that year he established a superphosphate factory at Deptford Creek, near London, and in the 1870's was manufacturing some 40,000 tons annually. His raw material was at first bones, but as these became increasingly scarce and expensive, mineral phosphate was used.

Superphosphate is a convenient means of supplying plants with phosphorus, one of the elements essential for their growth. No less important, however, are nitrogen and potassium. Today, most nitro-genous fertilizers are derived from fixation of the nitrogen of the air, but until the end of the nineteenth century the principal source was mineral sodium nitrate; this occurs in many places, but in indus-trially important quantities only on the west coast of Chile, where it is known as caliche. When first discovered, these deposits were in Bolivian territory, and they were the cause of the war that Chile fought with Peru and Bolivia, ending in 1881; at one time the tax on nitrate exports was 80 per cent. of Chile's total revenue. The caliche is crushed, and extracted with hot water until a saturated solution is obtained; when this is allowed to cool, almost pure sodium nitrate crystallizes out. In 1900 production of sodium nitrate was approximately 1,350,000 tons, of which the bulk went to Europe as an agricultural fertilizer, although by that time the United States was already using 170,000 tons annually for the same purpose. Until

1870 the main source of potassium was the ash of plants, a reminder of the necessity of potassium for plant growth. From the 1860's onwards, however, increasing quantities of mineral potassium salts became available from the vast deposits at Stassfurt.

OTHER DEVELOPMENTS, 1830–1900

Some other developments of the chemical industry can be considered only briefly here. By the middle of the century alcohol was being required in increasingly large quantities for industrial processes, and the high rate of duty to which it was subject was a serious hindrance. In 1855, however, the Board of Inland Revenue in Britain agreed to the sale of industrial alcohol free of duty, provided that it had first been made unfit to drink by the addition of methyl alcohol; similar concessions for 'methylated spirits' were granted in other countries. Industrial alcohol was made by fermentation processes similar in principle to those used for the manufacture of alcoholic drinks. For industrial purposes, however, the process of distillation had to be modified in order to obtain a nearly pure alcohol: this was made possible by the invention of the Coffey still—which remained in use for the rest of the century—by Aeneas Coffey about 1830. For technical reasons, it is not possible by distillation alone to obtain alcohol of more than approximately 96 per cent. purity: if necessary, the final traces of water must be removed by means of quicklime or some similar dehydrating agent.

Methyl alcohol, required for various industrial chemical processes as well as for denaturing ethyl alcohol, was normally obtained by destructive distillation of wood; acetic acid, familiar as the active principle of vinegar, was obtained at the same time. A residue of charcoal was left in the stills, and this found a use in the manufacture of gunpowder. Wood was also a source of oxalic acid, required for bleaching, for calico-printing, for metal polish, and a number of other purposes: it was made by mixing sawdust with caustic potash and heating the mixture in iron vessels. The oxalic acid was extracted with hot water from the resulting charred mass.

The development of the photographic industry (Ch. 23) called for increased quantities of both bromine and iodine, which were also required for medical purposes and for the manufacture of certain synthetic dyestuffs. Bromine, first isolated in 1826, occurs in the form of bromides in sea-water and in the Stassfurt deposits: it can be liberated by treating bromides with chlorine. Iodine occurs in seaweed and was formerly a by-product of the kelp industry. The potassium iodide present in kelp was concentrated by crystallization and then treated with sulphuric acid: manganese dioxide was added to liberate the iodine, the mixture was distilled, and the iodine condensed in earthenware vessels. Towards the end of the century, however, the chief source of iodine was Chilean caliche, which contains recoverable quantities of sodium iodide.

The growth of the textile industry during this time stimulated the demand for alum and caused attention to be directed to fresh sources of supply. In Britain the existence of alum-containing shales near Guisborough and Whitby had been known since the fifteenth century; the shale was burned in heaps and the alum was extracted from the ash. At the end of the eighteenth century it was discovered that some of the waste from Scottish coal-mines consisted of an alum-containing shale and a large works was built in Renfrewshire to exploit the discovery, the output of which, together with that of another works opened in Stirlingshire in 1812, had risen by 1835 to 2,000 tons a year. In 1845 Peter Spence, a British chemical manufacturer, obtained a patent—resulting from an accidental discovery —for manufacturing alum by treating burnt shale and iron pyrites with sulphuric acid; iron sulphate was obtained at the same time. Spence established an alum works in Manchester and eventually became the world's largest manufacturer of this important chemical.

SOME CHEMICAL CONTRIBUTIONS TO MEDICINE

Iodine, like bromine, was required for the photographic industry and for making dyes, but an important further use was as an antiseptic, following the pioneer work in this field by Joseph Lister, who was the first to see the practical significance of Pasteur's discoveries in relation to human infections. Lister himself usually employed carbolic acid, obtained by distillation of coal tar, as an antiseptic. Iodoform, first made in 1822, was introduced as an antiseptic in 1878.

Lister's elucidation of the principle of antisepsis enabled much greater advantage to be taken of the earlier discovery of anaesthetics. Anaesthetics enabled surgeons to perform operations that would otherwise have been quite impossible, but death still often followed surgical operations not from lack of skill on the part of the surgeon but through infection of the wound. The history of anaesthetics may be said to date from the discovery by (Sir) Humphry Davy, in

1799, that inhalation of nitrous oxide alleviates physical pain: he suggested that it might be used in surgical operations, but this suggestion was not followed up at the time, although 'laughing gas' parties became fashionable. The use of nitrous oxide in dentistry dates from 1844, when Horace Wells, a Connecticut dentist, carried out a number of extractions with its aid. A little earlier an American surgeon, C. W. Long, successfully used ether for a minor operation, and in 1846 the success of a surgical operation at the Massachusetts General Hospital, in which ether was used, led to its more general use, particularly as an anaesthetic in obstetrics. For this last purpose, however, it was not altogether satisfactory, and Long's search for an alternative led to the discovery of the value of chloroform. Opposition to the use of anaesthetics during childbirth rapidly disappeared when John Snow administered it to Queen Victoria at the birth of Prince Leopold in 1853. From that time onwards nitrous oxide, ether, and chloroform became firmly established in medical practice, and corresponding demands were made upon the chemical industry for their manufacture.

The manufacture of ether presented no particular difficulties except those resulting from the exceptionally inflammable nature of the product. Nitrous oxide was made by the cautious heating of ammonium nitrate. The normal method, due to Eugène Soubeiran, consisted of treating alcohol with sulphuric acid: on heating, a mixture of steam, alcohol, and ether distills off. The less volatile steam and alcohol are condensed first, and the more volatile ether passes on to a purifier in which it is condensed. Chloroform was usually prepared by distilling a mixture of bleaching powder with water and alcohol, but the medical need for exceedingly pure chloroform led to the introduction of a better process in the 1870's.

Ether, chloroform, and nitrous oxide are all examples of anaesthetics administered by inhalation. The first local anaesthetic was cocaine, introduced by Carl Koller in 1884. It is a natural alkaloid extracted from the leaves of the coca plant, and initially proved particularly valuable in the surgery of the eye. At the very end of the century a whole series of synthetic substitutes for cocaine was prepared.

TEXTILES

THE textile manufactures have always been given pride of place in the history of the industrial revolution, as the classic example of an industry which within the space of about two generations was transformed and expanded out of all recognition by the impact of technological development. The cotton manufacture, indeed, was doubly fortunate, for the mainly English inventions which first cheapened the final product were followed immediately by the American invention of the saw-gin, which provided an enormous increase in the supply of cheap raw material. Until the last decade of the eighteenth century raw cotton was brought to Europe either from its ancient home in the Levant or from the British and French West Indian islands; the American mainland did not grow enough for its own needs. The teeth, brushes, and fan of Whitney's gin (1793)—operated manually at first—removed the seeds from the cotton-boll so easily that even short-staple cotton, which alone could be grown far inland in America, repaid cultivation. Between 1790 and 1810 the output of raw cotton in the United States rose from $1\frac{1}{2}$ million to 85 million lb; for good and ill, the reign of King Cotton in the South had begun. When the Civil War came in 1861, American slave plantations were satisfying five-sixths of an ever-increasing world demand for cotton: Britain took fully 1,000 million lb a year, the rest of Europe about two-thirds of this quantity, and America rather more than one-third.

What did this enormous increase in cotton textiles mean for humanity? To some extent one form of cloth ousted another: the uniformity, strength, and elasticity which characterize cotton fibre enabled it to compete successfully against linen and to some extent silk, while the expansion of the woollen industry in the nineteenth century, though great, would have been much greater but for the world-wide vogue of cheap cotton materials. Much more important was the general availability of the new material. Apart from the few rich, mankind had never before had access to so plentiful, varied, and healthy a supply of clothing: for cotton was cheaply manufactured, easily printed and dyed, and readily washed.

It has been said, however, that Whitney's cotton-gin prolonged slavery in the United States for several generations: as the number of slaves grew from 700,000 in 1790 to 3,200,000 in 1850, the cost of cheap plantation-cotton in terms of human degradation was certainly great. Long after emancipation had been completed in 1865, many of the share-croppers of the southern states cultivated the cotton by the same manual methods as their enslaved fathers for a minimum cash reward. The British cotton-spinning factories, too, were long notorious for their employment of child labour. In the early days, small bodies were found aptest for cleaning clumsy machinery, often built of wood; at all times, the need for a large number of 'piecers' to watch for and tie together broken ends of thread made the use of children economically attractive. In Britain the employment of children under nine in textile factories was stopped in 1833, but that of 'half-timers', older children spending one-half of their schooldays in the mill, remained legal until 1918: as Britain was the pioneer in factory legislation, conditions in other countries can be inferred. On the other hand, by providing outside the home large-scale employment suitable for women of any age, cotton gave them a new chance of economic independence, and of a substantial addition to family earnings. By 1850 the wages, hours, and standard of life of adult factory operatives in the industry, which then employed one-fortieth of the population of Britain, were almost certainly better than had been enjoyed by any major group of industrial workers in any previous age.

Finally, the position of cotton textiles as Britain's premier export trade influenced both international and imperial relations, as in the attitude taken to the American Civil War and in the denial of a protective tariff to Indian cottons in the 1890's.

SPINNING-MACHINERY, 1760–1850

The first successful spinning-machines belong to that same great decade of the 1760's, the first of the reign of George III, in which the annexation of Canada marked Britain's triumph over France, and Watt's first experiments with the steam-engine prepared the way for the use of the new prime-mover, which was for a time to make the whole civilized world the economic fief of the British. Although in the earlier part of the eighteenth century improved processes had been developed, as we have seen, in the traditional woollen industry and in the luxury manufacture of silk, it is now appropriate to concentrate our attention upon cotton. The elasticity of cotton fibre makes it easier than other fibres to spin by mechanical means; the fact that it was a comparatively new industry encouraged experimentation unhampered by tradition; and the supply of the raw material responded readily to the stimulus of a growing trade.

Richard Arkwright's spinning-machine may not have been his own original invention, for it is impossible to say how much he owed to the use of rollers by Bourn and Paul (p. 105) and to the work of other pioneers less ruthless than himself. If James Hargraves invented his jenny in 1764, six years before he patented it, then Arkwright's water-frame is almost certainly later, although his patent is dated the year preceding that of Hargraves, which was in any case invalidated by some previous sales of his machine. Even the name water-frame, which came rapidly into use, is misleading, since Arkwright's original specification was in fact for a machine to be driven by a horse. Nevertheless, Carlyle was justified when, looking back from seventy years later, he called him 'this man that had to give England the power of cotton'. The spinning-frame required the use of much stronger forces than those of the human hand or foot, and so it began the factory system. By producing the first satisfactory cotton warp it made possible the manufacture of all-cotton goods, and led on to Arkwright's other improvements and contested patents, from which Carlyle's 'much inventing barber' emerged as the prototype of the cotton-spinning capitalists that dominated Lancashire and much else for a century and a half. It was at Arkwright's request that Parliament in 1774 abolished the ban on painted and printed calico and halved the excise duty on them, which had been 6d. a yard.

In Arkwright's machine (Fig. 275) four horizontal wooden bobbins held the rovings of raw cotton, which had been cleaned, carded, and made ready in a slightly twisted roll for spinning. The roving was then drawn down through two pairs of rollers, the second of which moved faster than the first so as to elongate it, and continued down to the bottom of the machine through the arm of a flyer attached to a spindle. The spindle also carried a bobbin—the speed of which was reduced in comparison with that of the spindle by the primitive device of a piece of worsted twisted round its base—on to which the spun yarn was finally wound, uniform winding being secured, as in some earlier wheels, by pins placed on the flyer. In contrast to this, Hargraves's spinning-jenny, as improved by Haley of Houghton Tower soon after its first invention, was a light machine more suitable for weft than for warp or the strong hosiery yarn for which Arkwright's invention was first employed. In the case of the jenny (Fig. 276) the rovings were drawn out, from bobbins placed at the bottom of the frame, by pulling back a bar which slid to and fro on the upper part of the frame. Two rails were pressed together to hold

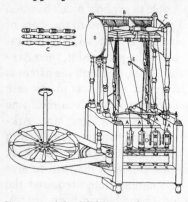

FIG. 275. Arkwright's water-frame spinning machine

the roving fast while the bar was moved farther back and the roving was twisted by spindles placed at the opposite end of the frame; the bar was then moved forward again, while a wire pushed the thread down so that it could be wound on to the spindles.

Hargraves was a carpenter as well as a weaver, which makes it easier to understand how—according to tradition—the idea of his invention came to him from watching the continued action of a spinning-wheel that had been knocked over by accident. Samuel Crompton, however, the inventor of the mule, was a substantial yeoman, though he devoted himself to textiles instead of the farming of the family lands. His home at Bolton was within 20 miles both of Preston, the scene of Arkwright's invention, and of Blackburn, where was first produced the jenny that was the basis of his experiments. The work was done between 1774 and 1779, a period which he refers to as '4½ years at least wherein every moment of time and power of mind as well as expense which my other employment would permit were devoted to this one end'. The result was a machine, never patented, of which the earliest surviving model is in France. One reason why it was not patented is implicit in the name of 'mule', which was given to Crompton's machine before the end of the century because it was regarded as a hybrid of the two earlier inventions, one of which was strongly defended by existing patents. The thread was drawn between rollers, as in Arkwright's water-frame, but the rollers were placed at the far end of the frame, and there was a carriage, as in Hargraves's invention, which was drawn back at the same rate as the rollers gave out the roving. But before the carriage had been drawn back to its full extent, the rollers were stopped; they then gripped the material while the carriage went back more slowly and the spindles, which were mounted on it, continued to twist. Next the spindles were turned back a little to free the yarn, after which the carriage was pushed back and a wire 'faller'

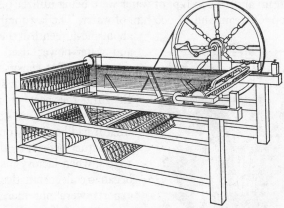

FIG. 276. Hargraves's spinning-jenny as improved by Haley

guided the yarn on to the spindles. The result was that for the first time a yarn could be spun which was both fine and strong. Moreover, the fact that the speeds of the rollers, the spindles, and the carriage could be varied independently of each other made it possible to vary the type of yarn at will.

While the mule was still a hand-driven machine, its convenience of operation called attention to the problem of improving the preparatory process. Carding-machines were already in existence, but Arkwright and others worked hard at their improvement. By 1785 he could card continuously by the use of a cylinder covered with card-teeth, from which the cotton was removed by a comb. It was then passed under rollers and through a funnel, so that a narrow coiled carding fell into a can. To secure uniformity, several cardings were drawn from their cans and passed under rollers which united them, the resulting sliver being dropped finally into a roving-can, which was rotating slowly so as to give the roving the necessary twist. The net result was that Arkwright had an almost continuous power-driven process to prepare the rovings for spinning.

In 1785, the year in which the cancellation of Arkwright's spinning patent as unoriginal made the water-frame available to all, the balance was finally tipped in favour of large-scale enterprise by the erection of a Boulton & Watt steam-engine to drive the machinery of a spinning factory at Papplewick in Nottinghamshire. From 1790 the use of steam-power spread simultaneously with, though not at the same pace as, the expansion of the cotton industry: in 1835 about 35,000 h.p. of steam and 10,000 h.p. of water were being utilized; in 1850, 71,000 h.p. of steam and 11,000 h.p. of water. The last total is only about one-fifteenth of the steam- and water-power used at the time of the first census of production in 1907, but it sufficed. In 1812 the cost of making cotton yarn was one-tenth of what it had been only one-third of a century before; by the early 1830's, when factory inspectors began to collect statistics, cotton exports were not merely four times those of woollen goods, but they constituted one-half of all British exports. It followed that inventions were for the most part made for cotton and later applied, where possible, to other fibres. It will therefore be convenient to continue the story of the cotton inventions down to the middle of the nineteenth century before returning to consider briefly the fortunes of the other textile manufactures.

FIG. 277. Batting cotton by hand

As might be expected, power was applied at an early date—from 1800 onwards—to the processes known as willowing and batting (Fig. 277), which opened up and cleaned the tangled fibres of raw cotton before it was rolled into fleecy masses or 'laps' to be fed into the carding-engine (Fig. 278). These machines in turn became larger and more elaborate, though it was not until after 1850 that the problem was solved of how to clean the outer half-cylinders (which had the teeth on the inside) without stopping the machinery twice a day for it to be done by hand. An earlier device to safeguard the winding of the rovings on bobbins—at which stage the tenuous thread breaks very easily—solved the problem of keeping the winding speed exactly

the same as the speed at which the rovings emerged from the rollers:
speed was adjusted by having the bobbins driven separately from the
spindles through a strap which slid along a conical drum, so providing continuously variable gearing. There was a rack mechanism
to stop the machine when the bobbin was full, and a differential
motion to keep the speed of the bobbins constant in relation to the
spindles. The differential motion, patented by a Mansfield tinsmith
in 1823 and used by Henry Houldsworth of Glasgow to perfect his
machine in 1825, had also been patented by an American, Asa
Arnold, in 1822. This early ex-
ample of American technological
achievement, like many later
ones, illustrates the fact that the
solution to any urgent problem
might present itself independently at the same time to
workers in different countries,
though it is also possible in this
instance that Houldsworth saw
a model of Arnold's invention,
which was brought to England
in the year of his own patent.
The increasingly cosmopolitan
character of the industry is
further exemplified in the in-

FIG. 278. Carding-engine at work, c. 1850

vention of a device to make spinning continuous with carding, instead
of the can of roving having to be carried from machine to machine.
This was the work of a Swiss, J. G. Bodmer, who had lived for many
years in Lancashire; but Lancashire ignored what America and the
Continent found convenient.

A fundamental problem, involving many years of work, was that
of rendering the mule fully self-acting. By 1800 John Kennedy, a
Manchester spinner and machine-maker, had solved the problem to
the extent that the outward journey of the carriage, including the
change of speed, was controlled automatically and only the winding-
on was done by hand. But the operation still required a skilled craftsman, with the result that the important spinners' strike in 1824,
just after the repeal of the Combination Laws, caused the problem
to be put to Richard Roberts, a machine-maker in Manchester who
had worked with Maudslay. He and his partners spent £12,000 on

his second patent (1830), and the profits for the first nine years amounted to no more than £7,000, with the result that in 1839 the patent was extended for seven years; there were also rival inventions. But Roberts's machine was fully self-acting and might well be acclaimed as almost perfect. In spite of its success, however, at mid-century the finer counts were still being spun on the older type of hand-mule, which had been improved by a coupling system, so that one spinner could control up to 1,200 spindles. Secondly, a new form of water-frame, called the throstle (Fig. 279), came into existence after 1815 to meet the need for a strong yarn for use in power-looms; an improved American version of this, known as Danforth's frame, with a revolving conical cap over the spindle to conduct the thread to the bobbin, produced a softer cotton yarn, but it was more wasteful. Finally, in 1828, John Thorp of Providence, Rhode Island, invented ring-spinning, but this did not make its decisive impact upon the industry until after 1850.

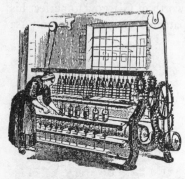

FIG. 279. The throstle in use, c. 1850

IMPROVEMENTS IN WEAVING

Meanwhile, the great growth of the cotton industry had likewise involved great developments in weaving; as compared with spinning, however, the improvements were less overwhelmingly associated with cotton. Thus the main further development in the hand-loom was the introduction of the Jacquard loom in silk-weaving, the only other significant improvement being the addition of a device to take up the cloth on the beam automatically; this was patented in 1805 and came into widespread use for all hand-woven textiles as the 'dandy loom'. But the fact that the invention of the power-loom sprang from the needs of the cotton industry is made clear by the pioneer inventor himself. Straying from his Leicestershire rectory to the cotton-spinning valley of the Derbyshire Derwent, Edmund Cartwright 'fell in company with some gentlemen of Manchester, one of whom observed that as soon as Arkwright's patent expired so many mills would be erected and so much cotton spun that hands could never be found to weave it'. This chance encounter in the summer of 1784 engaged the attention of an active mind—Cartwright was accustomed to doctor his parishioners as well as preach to them—and the result was a series of patents progressing towards the solution of the problem.

Cartwright himself considered that he completed his invention in 1787, in which year he set up a factory of his own at Doncaster, but it was in 1791 that a Manchester firm introduced it experimentally into the cotton industry, only to have their factory burned down for their pains. The Doncaster venture was also closed a couple of years later, when the inventor himself went bankrupt, but Cartwright had shown the way, though with a very imperfect machine. The action of the shuttle, which was driven by a spring, was too sudden; the single-shaft drive was found to be too harsh; and the mechanical provision for sizing the warp—which the hand-loom weaver could do as

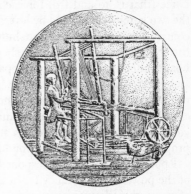

FIG. 280. Loom as shown on penny token issued in Barnsley, Yorkshire, 1811

necessary—was not very satisfactory. Consequently there was a period lasting to the end of the Napoleonic wars in which the power-loom continued to be experimental and hand-looms were still very widely used (Fig. 280): a quarter of a century after Cartwright set up his factory at Doncaster there were only 2,400 power-looms in the whole of Britain. But in the 1820's the number multiplied tenfold, while in 1850 the cotton industry employed almost a quarter of a million power-looms and probably no more than one-fifth that number of hand-looms. By then the power-loom was also predominant in the worsted branch of the woollen industry, which makes unfulled cloth from long, combed wool (p. 96); this, though taking its name from Worstead, in Norfolk, had been largely developed in the West Riding of Yorkshire by big capitalists who favoured specialization and had ready access to both swift streams and coal.

The first major improvement was a machine, invented in 1803, which laid the size on to the warp by rollers, brushed it in, and dried it with a current of hot air. This remained in use for half a century, but in 1839 an alternative method was devised, by which tapes made up of warp threads were passed through a trough of size and then dried by passing them round heated cylinders. Meanwhile, in 1813 William Horrocks of Stockport devised a power-loom in which the speed of the batten was varied to suit the period that it was desired to allow for the passage of the shuttle through the shed. About ten years later it provided the basis for a standard type of loom constructed by Richard Roberts. In this machine the batten moved twice (that is, to and fro) for each movement of shed and shuttle; the two latter were worked by levers; and there was a special device to control the instant at which the shuttle began to move. In the event of the shuttle being caught in the shed, its failure to enter the shuttle-box resulted in an automatic stoppage, but there was no provision to stop the machine if a weft thread happened to break. In the following twenty years a series of improvements gave the drive of the shuttle exact force, added a stop-mechanism for weft breakage, and provided for rough-surfaced rollers at the sides, which kept the cloth properly stretched as it was wound on to the cloth-beam.

Roberts was also partly responsible for perfecting the application of the power-loom to fancy fabrics. The raising of the different sets of warp threads was contrived by using wheels with projections which caused the appropriate healds to be lifted by levers. By 1838 eight changes of pattern could be worked in this way, and eight years later Squire Diggle of Bury mechanized even the drop-box—the device which the hand-loom weaver operated in order to get weft of different colours: plates of different thicknesses were carried on an endless chain, and the thickness of the plate determined which shuttle was brought out of the drop-box. However, in the 1830's power-driven Jacquard looms (p. 570) had begun to be introduced from the silk industry into the making of worsted. The superior quality of the Jacquard system made it certain to triumph in the end, though up to 1850 even its cheaper form, the 'dobby', was not found cheap enough for the cotton industry.

SPREAD OF TEXTILE MACHINERY, TO 1850

Although there is hardly an example of a textile invention which has not been applied to more than one of the main textile industries, a review of the position which they had severally reached as regards power-weaving by the middle of the nineteenth century illustrates how various were their needs. The cotton and worsted manufactures had in the main adopted it, as we have seen. In the making of woollen cloth other than worsted, however, the thread was too fragile to allow the shuttle to move faster than it already did in the hand-loom, so it was not until the power-loom reached an advanced state of development in the 1840's that its use began to spread. By way of contrast, we find that in silk-weaving power had been brought even into the cottage industry, and that Coventry in 1832 presented the striking spectacle of rows of cottages backed by steam-engines.

In the case of linen, the yarn was inelastic and the warp could not be subjected to the strain which was normal to power-loom operation; consequently, it was not until after 1850 that the problem of adaptation was seriously attacked.

The successful power-spinning of linen thread from flax depended primarily upon the earlier processes of heckling and drawing. The heckling of the bundles or stricks of flax so as to separate the long fibres of 'line' from the shorter ones of

FIG. 281. Heckling-machine in use in England, c. 1850

'tow' was extremely difficult to mechanize, for each strick required to be combed on both sides in turn and then in the reverse direction. A successful machine was produced by a Frenchman, Philippe de Girard, in 1832, and improved subsequently in England, perhaps by the mechanic who brought it over; but there were similar machines of English origin (Fig. 281). The strick was placed between two vertical sheets of combs which moved in opposite directions, depositing the tow upon brush cylinders at the bottom of the machine, while the holder from which the strick was suspended moved up and down so as to help the teeth to penetrate deeper into the flax. But in 1850 all flax for fine yarn was still heckled by hand. The fine dust which the preparation of flax released into the air caused so much pulmonary disease that British recruiting officers were at one time forbidden to enlist recruits who had worked in flax mills.

Once separated, the short tow could be spun like cotton, but the line required very careful preparation if the yarn was to be uniform.

The earliest patent for using Arkwright's machinery to spin line dates from 1787: the rollers were placed farther apart than for cotton, the flax was pressed with heavy weights, and the natural gum was softened by passing the thread over wet cloth during spinning. Only three years later Matthew Murray, working for John Marshall of Leeds, patented the use of tight leather straps, between which the flax was drawn out to pass under a loaded roller. This method avoided wetting the thread, and the product proved to be more elastic, though not so strong and silky in appearance. In 1810, however, a prize of a million francs, offered as part of Napoleon's policy of stimulating the French textile industries, led de Girard to suggest three improvements in the preparation. He was too late to win the prize, but his processes were in part adopted and developed in Britain. De Girard proposed that the fibres should be soaked in a hot alkaline solution both before drawing and immediately before they went to the spindles; the actual drawing was to be done by passing the material, when dry, through combs or gills. Gill-drawing was taken up in England in 1816, the combs being fixed to revolving cylinders which were placed between the drawing-rollers in such a way that the fibres were drawn faster than the movement of the combs. A steeping process, not unlike de Girard's, also came into use by the 1840's, though hot water was used and not alkali.

The worsted branch of the woollen industry has a history parallel with that of linen thread, since it was the preliminary process, the combing, which proved most difficult to mechanize. The first attempt to solve the problem was made by Cartwright in 1792, using a circular revolving comb from which the long fibres or 'top' were carried off into a can, and a smaller cylinder-comb for teazing out short fibres or 'noils', which were taken off by hand. The first successful machine was, however, one patented in Britain in 1827, but mainly of French origin. This used two circles of combs working into each other, with drawing-rollers to carry off the top, while the noils were cleaned from the teeth by hand. This machine was still in use in England in the middle of the century, though by that time a third system had been developed more or less independently by Josué Heilmann of Mulhouse, France, and by G. E. Donisthorpe and S. C. Lister in Bradford. Heilmann, it may be noticed in passing, made his invention originally for the combing of fine cotton: this method used a nip to hold one end of the sliver that was being combed, two or more combs to carry out the process thoroughly, and a brush cylinder and knife to clear the noils. In contrast, the machine-spinning of worsted presented few difficulties. To begin with, Arkwright's machinery was used, with the rollers at a greater distance from each other to suit the greater length of wool fibres. At a later period, however, the throstle was used for spinning in England, and the mule in France, a divergence which enabled the French to produce the finest worsted.

The carding-engine to prepare the short wool for cloth began to be power-driven in the early 1770's in Yorkshire, where water-power was generally available. This was done according to the method patented by Daniel Bourn, with cylinders working against each other. Later there was a double process: the first carding-machine 'scribbled' the wool, which came off as a fleece, and the second, using parallel strips of card, made it into flat pieces a yard long, which were then rolled by means of a corrugated roller. About 1822 John Goulding of Massachusetts succeeded in making carding and the preparation of the roving into a continuous process, but although his machine appeared in France and Germany in the 1830's and had been patented in Britain, virtually no use was made of it on this side of the Channel: instead, the rovings continued to be prepared on the hand-machine known as the billy. The spinning of wool, too, continued to be often performed on the jenny, long after the mule had been adapted for the purpose by removing one pair of rollers, at Leeds in 1816. Indeed, the self-acting mule was not used at all until well after 1850.

As regards cloth-finishing, the gig-mill—nominally illegal under a statute of Edward VI—continued to arouse bitter opposition, especially in Yorkshire, where its destruction was one of the main objects of the Luddites in 1812, and hand-raising of the nap, perhaps in consequence, still survived in 1850. Some of the newer patents provided for raising the nap by means of wire cards, which might prove cheaper and more durable than the teazle (p. 96), but the natural material continued in use and, indeed, is still grown in Somerset. In 1802 the gig-mill was exported from England to France. Machinery for nap-shearing, on the other hand, begins with Delaroche of Amiens, who used power to operate several pairs of shears simultaneously. The first English patent was granted only three years later, in 1787, his, but until the great post-war depression the Luddites and similar demonstrators caused it to be less widely used in England than in France. The first rotary-shearer was invented by an American, Samuel

Dorr, and was introduced into France in 1812, but did not flourish in England until rather later, although patented in 1794: the machine was drawn over the cloth, and operated rather after the fashion of the modern lawn-mower. By 1850 hand-shearing was almost extinct.

In spite of the fact that Lombe's silk-throwing mill at Derby (p. 100) preceded the first cotton-mill by over fifty years, the silk industry was not immediately caught up in the wave of industrial progress. Few improved machines were introduced in Britain until the relaxation of duties in 1826, and even after that the Piedmontese were still using the same type of machine as Lombe had copied more than a hundred years before. In 1825 John Heathcoat patented a cocoon-reeling machine, but the main development was in the use of unreelable silk from damaged cocoons and similar sources. Such material could not be thrown, but it could be de-gummed by a steeping process and then spun; by the middle of the eighteenth century its hand-combing and hand-spinning was an established cottage industry in England. In 1792 the spinning of waste silk was begun on the model of the cotton-spinning factory, the silk fibres being first chopped up into shorter lengths corresponding to those of cotton. In the 1830's, however, the machinery of the flax-spinner was adapted for spinning the longer fibres of silk, and the cutting of the fibres was then discontinued in favour of carding or combing them into separate groups according to length.

The silk industry, however, was associated with a most important step in the mechanization of the loom, namely the advance which eliminated the use of the draw-boy in operating the apparatus of the draw-loom. It was natural that the weaving of patterns should be a special feature of the luxurious fabrics of silk. It was, and still is, a characteristic French luxury trade, while Napoleon I's personal interest in textile developments helps to explain the fact that what J. M. Jacquard invented in 1801 was applied within eleven years to 11,000 draw-looms.

In relation to earlier inventions, what Jacquard did was to combine needles with hooks, change the perforated cylinder into a perforated prism, and—most important—provide a lifting-mechanism (known as the 'griffe'), which the weaver himself operated with a treadle. This apparatus, which was fixed above the loom, had a number of wire hooks suspended from it, to which the neck-cords holding the warp threads were attached. Each hook passed perpendicularly through the eye of a horizontal needle, one end of which protruded through a frame and was kept in its normal position by a spring. Any perpendicular hook thrust aside by the needle missed the bars in a frame, which would otherwise lift the hook and attached warp threads. The face of the prism pressed against the ends of the needles, but was perforated in such a way that the pressure was effective only where the perforations placed on the card over the face of the prism were incomplete. Each time the treadle moved, the pattern of perforations on the card changed and the weft passed through a correspondingly changed series of warp threads.

The Jacquard machine did not appear in England—at any rate in any quantity—until the 1820's, when an English improvement made the harness more compact, so that it could be used in the cottage industry as well as in factories. By 1832 there were some 600 Jacquards in Coventry; by 1850, power-looms in the British silk industry, which numbered

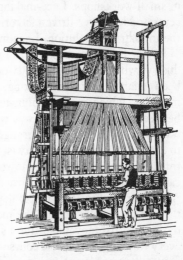

FIG. 282. Jacquard loom for weaving ribbons, scarves, etc., c. 1840

only 309 in 1835, had grown to 1,141, and it may be supposed that these were nearly all of the Jacquard type (Fig. 282).

HOSIERY AND LACE-MAKING

Before tracing the further history of the main textile industries in the second half of the nineteenth century, it will be convenient briefly to consider developments as a whole in the ancillary industries of hosiery and lace-making, both of which were by 1900 machine industries of considerable importance, while hosiery was rapidly rising into its twentieth-century position as the third among the British textile trades. The two industries are closely connected; indeed, machine-made lace grew out of the older frame-knitting industry in Nottingham at a time of depression in its staple trade of cotton and silk hosiery. They are parallel also inasmuch as each of them is a way of making up thread into fabric otherwise than by interweaving —the looping process of the knitter and the thread-twisting of the lace-maker. Their history after 1750, however, presents a remarkable contrast. Knitting, which ever since Elizabethan times had been conducted by means of an intricate machine, the stocking-frame (p. 106), was only slowly adapted to the use of power, and as late as 1870 the majority of hosiery workers were engaged in hand-work at home or in small workshops. Lace-making, on the other hand, became concentrated in power-driven factories at a comparatively early stage in the industrial revolution. Lace may therefore be considered first.

It was John Heathcoat, a framesmith attached to the hosiery industry, who, in 1809, about twenty years after hosiery frames had been adapted for lace-making, introduced the first satisfactory machine, which made bobbin-net by the use of thin brass disks, between which the thread was wound. As they passed through the warp threads, which were arranged vertically, the latter were moved to each side in turn, so as to twist the bobbin threads round the warp threads. The bobbins were in two rows, to save space, and jogged on carriages in grooves along a bar running the length of the machine. As the strength of this fabric depended upon bringing the bobbin threads diagonally across, the machine had to provide, in addition to the forward movement, for a sideways movement of each bobbin every time the lengthwise course was completed. A high standard of accuracy in construction was essential for success, which helped to preserve for Nottingham its long-continued supremacy in the building of lace-making machinery. Of more immediate interest is the fact that such a machine, even though it at first wove only narrow lace, required considerable strength as well as great skill in the operator, who had to work eight handles and two treadles. Thus there was every incentive to use power, and the mechanical problem was solved in the main within ten years: Heathcoat, for example, used the waters of the Exe to run the disused woollen factory at Tiverton, his intended removal to which provided a motive for the destruction of his premises at Loughborough by the Luddites in 1816.

Not content with the rapid change-over from pure handicraft to the use of a power-driven machine within a single generation, lace-makers proceeded to elaborate their machinery so as to imitate the more complicated forms of hand-work. Another framesmith, John Leavers, brought out a variant of Heathcoat's machine in 1813, which was better adapted for making patterned lace because it used only a single row of bobbins. Heathcoat, as we have noted, had used two sets of bobbins to save space, but Leavers obtained the help of a watch-maker to manufacture bobbins and carriages that were half the thickness of Heathcoat's. In 1821, however, Leavers emigrated to the north of France, where the industry had already been established for some years through an illegal cross-Channel traffic in artisans and machinery. But it was in Nottingham twenty years later that Hooton Deverill made the first fully successful application of the French Jacquard to lace-making. It then became possible to reproduce most of the traditional patterns of hand-made lace in both narrow and wide pieces; vibrations caused by steam engines used for power ceased to be a cause of damage, as in the case of the original Leavers machine; and with the adaptation of the original bobbin-net machine to the making of curtains, the industry was fully equipped for rapid expansion, until neither window nor petti-coat was complete without its adornment of machine-made lace.

FIG. 283. Hand-operated stocking-frame, *c.* 1876

The stocking industry, meanwhile, had made what might seem a promising advance when Jedediah Strutt, later the partner of Arkwright, solved the problem of producing ribbed hosiery by placing a row of vertical needles between the horizontal needles of the standard Lee machine. This was in 1758, but it did not lead to any solution of the more delicate problem of adapting the needle, sinker, and presser-mechanism to the use of power. Moreover, the prejudice which the Nottinghamshire Luddites of 1811 showed against a type of framework knitting—for making garments cut from straight pieces of fabric with no selvedge—which savoured of mass production, must have lent force to the argument that the introduction of power was unnecessary in a handicraft industry (Fig. 283) which was both overcrowded and extremely localized: the villagers of the east Midlands took very low wages and had no prospect of alternative employment. Thus little came of a machine invented by the elder Brunel in 1816, which had the needles arranged in a circle, so that the turning of a handle produced a straight tube of fabric—a product obviously inferior to the fully fashioned stocking.

In the 1840's, however, the possibilities of the power-driven circular frame began to be appreciated in both Germany and England, and at this time two important inventions were made by Matthew Townsend of Leicester. One was for a circular rib-frame, enabling a non-fashioned seamless hose of reasonable elasticity to be put on the market. The other was the device of the latch needle, the hinge of which was opened and closed by the threads, so that no presser was required for knitting the coarse fabrics for which this type of latch was suitable. Then came a series of attempts to apply power to the flat frame, which produced the fully fashioned work. This culminated in the work of William Cotton, who in 1864 invented a machine that proved to be adaptable to the making of a dozen or more hose simultaneously and to the knitting of fashioned garments of all kinds. Cotton, who was originally employed by a Loughborough firm, was one of the first specialized hosiery-machine builders. In 1890 America followed this up by developing a type of seamless hose that required only a small seam across the toe to finish it, and that compensated to some extent for the fact that it was unfashioned by having loops of varying size so as to make the lower part of the leg tighter than the upper.

But the main line of development lay in mechanizing the process of seaming the garment after it left the knitting-machine. The power-driven sewing-machine provided the solution, and in 1887 American inventors developed a two-thread machine, working at the rate of 3,000 stitches a minute, which provided the secure and well-trimmed seam needed to prevent knitted garments unravelling.

THE SEWING-MACHINE

The sewing-machine stands by itself as an invention which, though not directly concerned with any of the traditional textile processes, in the second half of the nineteenth century did more than any speeding-up of those processes to extend the usefulness of, and enhance the demand for, textile products. It also stands apart because it was the first major consumer appliance. While some of its special applications brought into the factory new industries remote from the textile trades—shoe-making and bookbinding are examples—its proper place, like Victorian woman's, was in the home, and it was the housewife whose yearly stint of work was revolutionized. It is significant that all the main inventions were made in the United States of America in the pioneering days, when women had much work to do outside the home as well as many tasks within it.

The sewing-machine does not imitate the process of hand-sewing but makes a special kind of stitch, the lock-stitch, by the use of a double continuous thread and a special type of needle, in which the eye is near the point. A Massachusetts mechanic, Elias Howe, invented the lock-stitch, but his machine could sew only straight seams of limited length. The toothed plate that moved the material forward after each stitch and made it possible to turn the cloth (so as to form a curved seam) was the idea of a Michigan cabinet-maker, but it was Isaac M. Singer, with a small shop in Boston, Massachusetts, who in 1851 produced the first practical domestic sewing-machine (Fig. 284). This was the first machine to have a straight needle; it also had an adjustable presser-foot to hold the material in place when the needle moved upwards, and was worked by a foot-treadle. The alternative chain-stitch was invented in the same year.

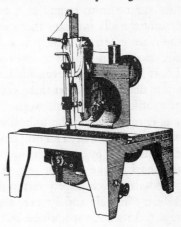

FIG. 284. Isaac Singer's sewing-machine, 1851

In the same decade a big sewing-machine industry sprang up in the United States, and Germany followed suit in the 1870's. The fact that the systems of instalment purchase and of 'sale and service' began in this connexion shows how heavy the demand was for home use, while the invention of a shoe-sewing machine in 1861 and of a welt-machine ten years later shows how readily its use spread beyond the field of textiles. In the textile trades themselves it came into use wherever fabrics were stitched or seamed, and by 1859 the band-knife had been adapted from the band-saw of the furniture industry to cut through the many thicknesses of cloth required for the repetitive work of the ready-made clothing industry, which rapidly expanded. By 1880 there were special sewing-machines that could move along the surface of a carpet, and by the end of the century America had a blind-stitching machine designed to stitch half-way through the thickness of the material.

THE TEXTILE INDUSTRIES, 1850–1900

In the history of the textile industries proper, the period 1850–1900 produced no technical changes comparable in importance to those of the earlier industrial revolution, or even to the sewing-machine. Indeed, some of the most important developments in textiles sprang from events of a non-technological character. In the case of the silk industry there was the serious outbreak in 1853 of the disease *pébrine*, which in a dozen years reduced the output of silk cocoons in France to less than one-sixth of its former weight. Louis Pasteur then began his investigation into the causes of silk-worm disease, and after three years isolated the bacilli of *pébrine* and of another disease of silkworms, and pointed out that their spread was encouraged by the unhealthy conditions in which the worms were reared. The need for proper ventilation and cleanliness had been demonstrated by an Italian investigator half a century earlier, but the shock of the disaster caused the general adoption of Pasteur's proposals, which largely restored the prosperity of the natural silk industry in Italy and France, though the Far East had meanwhile regained its ancient position as the main producer. Even more remote from technology was another major event of the 1860's, namely the cotton-famine resulting from the Federal blockade of the South during the American Civil War. It was then that the cotton industry finally discarded the hand-loom weaver, while every one of cotton's rivals, excepting silk, received a natural impetus towards increased mechanization. The silk industry in Britain was at that time languishing under the effects of the Cobden-Chevalier treaty of 1860, which enabled French silks to come in duty-free. But the long-term result was the adoption of improved—or at least more profitable—silk-making techniques from abroad.

The spinning of long-fibred silk waste, though envisaged in the early part of the century, depended for its success upon the invention of satisfactorily economical methods for dressing or combing the silk waste so as to separate the long fibres. A steam-driven silk-dressing machine, of circular design, had been patented by Bauwens and Didelot in France in 1821, and continued in use throughout the century. A combing-machine for silk was invented in 1859 by the

British wool-comber S. C. Lister, but this rejected too much of the expensive fibre, and it was not until 1877 that he invented a satisfactory self-acting silk-dressing machine. This carried combs and cards on an endless belt, caused the teeth to penetrate more deeply into the tufts of silk as the action proceeded, and collected the shorter fibres on the cards so that separate drafts of different qualities could gradually be accumulated. A similar machine had been invented in Alsace twenty years earlier by de Jongh, from whom Lister may have derived his ideas. In any case, by 1890 Lister's machine had been abandoned in Britain in favour of a flat dressing machine, while the Continent was still using chiefly the circular form.

The other main change was quite clearly of continental origin. In 1857 it was discovered by accident at Krefeld, on the Rhine, that preliminary treatment of silk with certain metallic salts before dyeing made the product both more lustrous and much heavier. In the case of some spun silks, it proved possible to increase the weight as much as ninefold, and when applied in moderation the practice could be defended as improving both the feel and the appearance of the product. British dyers imitated the practice from their French and German rivals; a report on the industry in Britain published at Manchester in 1885 says: 'The dyer's chemistry is almost wholly needed nowadays for the weighting of silk, and not for the dyeing of it.'

In the other textile industries, the only parallel to this weighting of silk is the introduction of the 'mercerizing' of cotton. John Mercer was an English calico-printer and dyer, who in the middle of the century patented the treatment of cotton with caustic soda, the effect being to render the fibre more elastic and more readily dyed. The fact that caustic soda (p. 550) was still expensive, and that a 20–25 per cent. shrinkage of cloth occurred in the process, prevented Mercer from having any commercial success, but in 1895 the process was taken up again by the Krefeld dyers, R. Thomas and E. Prévost, first for yarn and then for piece goods; they found that when the mercerizing was done under tension the result was a permanent gloss not far inferior to that of spun silk.

If cotton could be made competitive with silk by improving the finish, wool could likewise be made competitive with cotton by altering the basis of the raw material. This was done by the use of ragwool made from old woollens, a substance which was first woven into 'shoddy' to meet the demand for uniforms for the Peninsular

War. By the 1830's the rag-tearer or 'devil' had been equipped with teeth instead of the original blades, so that it was capable of tearing up the better qualities of cloth, which could be manufactured into a superior product called 'mungo', a name whose origin is obscure. But it was not until the 1850's that the use of stronger teeth in the devil, as well as the development of an acid process for removing the cotton fibre from mixed fabrics and the increasing popularity of

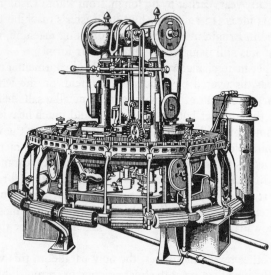

FIG. 285. Noble's combing machine, 1887

the dust and refuse from the shoddy industry as an agricultural fertilizer, made shoddy a big factor throughout the woollen (but not the worsted) industry. It was then that part of the West Riding of Yorkshire 'rose on rags to riches'. By 1880 something like 40 per cent. of the British woollen industry's raw material came from this source, and the fact that new wool was less in demand as a raw material meant that goods made from it also became rather cheaper.

In the preliminary textile processes, the key event was the long-delayed triumph of machine-combing, which took place in the 1850's. The Heilmann comb, it is true, dates from 1845, but its use did not spread into the English worsted industry to any great extent. It served best for the combing of very short wools and of cotton; it was therefore used on the Continent for fine wools, in

Lancashire as well as Alsace for fine cotton, and also in the Belfast linen industry. But the machine that gave new life to the Yorkshire worsted industry was the Lister–Donisthorpe nip machine of 1851, which was elaborated later and safeguarded by Lister's determination in buying up rival patents. Its final triumph came with the expiration of Lister's monopoly in the 1860's, and by the 1880's it was even being used for short-fibre wools. In its fully developed form (Fig. 285) the circular horizontal comb enclosed two smaller comb-

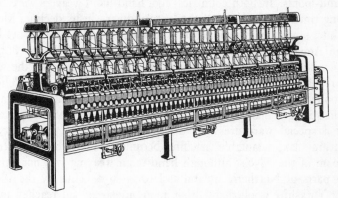

FIG. 286. Ring spinning-frame, 1888

rings, the fibres were drawn through pins in each of the smaller circles, and the protruding 'tops' were taken off by vertical drawing-off rollers, while the inner pins held the 'noils' for removal at a later stage.

In the case of spinning, the principal development of the period was the increasing use of the American ring spinning-frame (p. 564), even in Lancashire, while it completely dominated the American spinning mills, which by 1900 had 42 per cent. of the capacity of the British. It worked faster than the throstle, and in the 1880's began to compete with the mule. Its advantages were that it wound and spun continuously and needed only unskilled labour, its disadvantage that it produced yarn with too much twist for fine wefts. In its developed form the ring spinning-frame (Fig. 286) consisted of spindles revolving in the centre of stationary rings, with a light C-shaped traveller in place of the flyer. By drawing the traveller round the ring as it passed through, the yarn was twisted, while the vertical movement of the ring built up the 'cop' or conical head on the bobbin.

Weaving, which was far less mechanized than spinning in 1850, underwent correspondingly greater development in the next half-century, though hand-loom weaving survived on the Continent on a considerable scale for at least a generation after its virtual demise in Britain. The power-loom did not predominate in either the cotton or the woollen industry of France or Germany before the 1880's, and at the close of the decade Krefeld resembled the French silk-weaving district round Lyons in its four-fifths dependence upon hand-looms. In both countries, too, hand-loom weavers were for a long time characteristic of the linen industry in its decline. Meanwhile, power-loom weaving of fancy fabrics had been improved by the Americans William and George Crompton, and in 1863 an open-shed loom was invented in England which relieved the warp threads of strain; this became the general loom for the more delicate woollen fabrics. Linen, on the other hand, required something heavier and stronger than the cotton power-loom, and with the assistance of a special warp-dressing to compensate for the inelasticity of natural flax, a suitable machine became established in the trade boom of the 1850's, although hand-loom weaving was not extinct in parts of Northern Ireland as late as 1932. Thus by the 1890's the Yorkshire woollen and Irish linen industries had reached much the same position as the English worsted and cotton industries, where power had finally ousted the hand-loom in the 1850's and 1870's respectively. A lighter version of the loom used for linen was also applied to jute, of which the manufacture at Dundee from Indian raw material received an important stimulus when supplies of Russian hemp were cut off during the Crimean War.

The power-loom was likewise applied increasingly to the various and complicated weaves of the carpet (Fig. 287). The draw-loom had been applied to the ingrain carpet at Kidderminster in 1735, and ninety years later the Jacquard was used in the same town to help the manufacture of the Brussels carpet. But the key event was the invention, by E. B. Bigelow of Massachusetts, of the Brussels power-loom, which was improved in England and came into regular use for both Brussels and Wilton carpets in the 1850's and 1860's. The automatic insertion and withdrawal of strong wires with looped ends was the means employed to raise the looped pile of the Brussels type, while thinner wires with a knife blade at the end raised and then severed the loops to create the rich Wilton pile. The power-loom at the same time became applicable to the cheaper 'tapestry' carpets, which replaced the expensive use of differently coloured warp threads by having the design printed on the drum round which the warp threads were passed. By the 1870's these were ousting the original Brussels carpets. Power-weaving was then being applied even to the luxurious chenille carpet, which had chenille cloth woven into it; finally, in 1876, H. Skinner of New York developed a machine for making the Royal Axminster pile.

The third great change in weaving was the introduction of the automatic loom, invented by J. H. Northrop of Massachusetts in

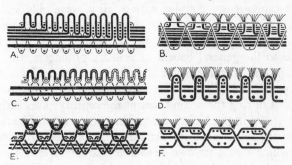

FIG. 287. Carpet weaves: (A) Brussels; (B) Wilton; (C) Tapestry-Brussels; (D) Tapestry-Velvet; (E) Chenille-Axminster; (F) Imperial-Axminster

1895, which has been described as 'the loom of the twentieth century'. It spread first in the United States rather than in Lancashire, where strong trade unions existed to protect the interests of an abundant labour force; the capital cost, which was three times that of an ordinary loom, was also a serious deterrent. The vital improvement which it embodied was a method of changing the cop without stopping the loom. This was done by means of a kind of hopper containing cops, but its use involved the development of several other inventions, including a self-threading shuttle and a warp-stop motion. In its completed form, it left the weaver with nothing to do but repair breakages of warp or weft and refill the hoppers as required.

Looking back at the changes in the textile industry in 1750–1900, it becomes possible to make some further generalizations. From the point of view of the worker, although there was temporary unemployment among certain groups, the only large class that suffered severely were the hand-loom weavers, who, as we have seen, fought a long and losing battle against the machine. In Britain at the time of the Chartist movement (1838–48), which vainly sought to help them, they had numbered at least a quarter of a million souls, subsisting in some cases, as attested by a Government inquiry, on total family earnings of 5s. weekly. The replacement of hand-work by machine-work in general reduced physical effort, though the work load and its mental strain increased, and the machine-worker normally earned more than the corresponding hand-worker. From the point of view of the entrepreneur, the improved techniques meant a steady increase in capital costs, coupled with a fall in wage bills, so that, as compared with the past, capital charges loomed larger than labour charges. As regards the product, the demand for the raw materials increased to the general benefit of primary producers, the manufactured product became better and often cheaper, and world trade expanded correspondingly. The consumption of raw cotton was quadrupled during the second half of the century; five-sixths of it was still grown in the United States. Increasing mechanization also enhanced the importance for Britain of the textile engineering industry, which found its own profitable markets overseas in competition with the product itself; this had been a considerable trade long before it was legalized by Peel in 1843.

Lastly, we may summarize the international aspect. To begin with, the progress of textile techniques strengthened the role of Britain, and to a less extent America, as inventive pioneers. Germany, France, and Belgium also played a vigorous and enterprising part, too often ignored in Britain, thereby reinforcing the industrial supremacy of Europe. But by 1900 it would be clear to a reflective and dispassionate mind that the leadership in output and invention was passing to the United States of America, and might in due course pass again to the teeming millions of Asia, whom Lancashire in 1900 still envisaged chiefly in the passive role of textile consumers.

POTTERY AND GLASS

NEITHER pottery nor glass-making rivalled the position of the textile manufactures, as transformed by the industrial revolution. The growth of the pottery industry in scale and technique was far less spectacular, and depended less upon machinery. It was only in the second half of the nineteenth century, when the main textile changes were already completed, that the manufacture was put upon a truly scientific basis. Yet pottery, unlike cloth, gave a direct stimulus to the whole course of technical change because of the part it played in electrical equipment and in the more modern forms of building structure. In the case of glass-making, the character of the material made its transformation into a machine industry a still slower process. It was, indeed, far from complete even in 1900, but the important part that improved optical glass played in the growth of science makes this, too, an instance of a manufacture whose development had repercussions in various industrial fields.

THE POTTERY INDUSTRY IN THE EIGHTEENTH CENTURY

In the history of pottery-making, the central event of the industrial revolution is undoubtedly the mass production of cheap but effective earthenware in the once obscure Staffordshire district known ever since as The Potteries. But the developments in this case begin with continental instead of British discoveries, discoveries which—instead of producing something new like Arkwright's machine-spun yarn— were to put Europe at last on a level with the ancient skills of the Chinese potter. The period from 1680 to 1749 has been described as 'the most fertile in the annals of Chinese ceramics'. Its blue and white porcelain, transparent enamels, and monochrome glazes were brought to Europe, especially by the Dutch; they were admired in every capital—Queen Mary II, for instance, brought the vogue to England from The Hague—and, as in earlier centuries, zealously imitated.

It was in 1710 that success came in the long struggle to reproduce the quality of Chinese hard-paste porcelain, the struggle which had given Europe various soft-paste imitations as well as the beautiful delft ware (p. 94), which often used Chinese designs for decoration. The first maker was J. F. Böttger, chemist to Augustus the Strong of Saxony, who used alabaster or marble as a fluxing agent, a particularly white china clay from the Erzgebirge as his main material, and an improved type of kiln which permitted firing at a temperature of 1,300–1,400° C. Thus the manufacture of Dresden china in conditions of strictest secrecy at Meissen antedates by a full generation the popular ware which we are now to consider. Indeed, it took thirty years of experiment to produce a second hard porcelain to rival it. That was achieved in 1768 at the French state manufactory at Sèvres under its chief chemist, P.-J. Macquer, and in the same year the discovery was made independently by a Plymouth chemist, William Cookworthy, who two years later moved the manufacture to Bristol for the sake of the local coal-supply, whence it spread to a site at Hanley in The Potteries.

A parallel development, in which England played a rather larger part, was the making of soft porcelain, which had, for instance, been produced at Sèvres before they were able to make the more prized hard porcelain. The soft paste was produced in the eighteenth century at half a dozen different centres in England, only one of which, Longton Hall, was in The Potteries. This is important for its introduction of new materials, including soapstone (a hydrated magnesium silicate), which was brought into regular use at Worcester in 1752. Two or three years before this the first London porcelain factory at Bow, followed shortly after by a more important works at Chelsea, began the use of bone-ash as an ingredient. Although the idea had been conceived in Germany earlier, and was adopted at Sèvres later, this manufacture of bone-china, which spread to the other English soft-paste potteries, was the first wholly distinctive English contribution to European ceramics. Nevertheless, we must look elsewhere for the series of industrial changes that gave Staffordshire its world market.

The Staffordshire industry of the Tudor and Stuart era had been based upon the red-burning clays of the neighbourhood, the availability of galena (lead sulphide) for glazing, and the coal that was increasingly important as the timber supply began to dwindle: Tunstall and Hanley were early coal-mining centres, but the first potters dug coal for themselves. A dairy industry clustering round Uttoxeter, Staffordshire, provided a local market for butter pots, and there was a wider distribution by pack-horse, donkey, and river transport. Two Saxon potters from Delft, David and John Elers, who are believed to have arrived in England with William of Orange in 1688, introduced salt-glazing from the Continent and a higher standard of refinement and accuracy, doubtless related to the fact that they had once been silversmiths. Pipe clay from Devon came into use to coat the inside and decorate the outside of vessels, so that the red or brown product of Staffordshire might have some of the aesthetic appeal of porcelain or delft. This in turn led to the development, probably made by John Astbury about 1720, of Staffordshire's first truly competitive product—a salt-glazed ware that was white throughout. The making of this involved two changes, the use of white-burning clay fetched from a distance and the addition to it of calcined flint: both materials could be conveyed by water up the Weaver or the Trent. The resulting stoneware provided the much-prized

Fig. 288. Mill for grinding flint or clay, 1844

qualities of translucency and hardness, and brought some of the refinement of imported porcelain within the reach of a less wealthy class; it was this expanding market which first made the fortunes of The Potteries.

Technologically an important development was the introduction of the flint-mill, as the flints after calcination in a kiln had to be ground to an extremely fine powder before mixing into the clay. On account of the havoc wrought by silica dust in the lungs, grinding under water was patented as early as 1726. The grinding machine itself was preferably of stone, in order to avoid the discoloration imparted by iron; the machine was a heavy one (Fig. 288), and this encouraged the use of water-power and the steam-engine at an early date. James Brindley, for example, was a builder of flint-mills before he turned to canals. The purpose of the flint was not only to lighten the colour of the ware, but, by firing it at a high temperature, to impart increased hardness: much greater attention was therefore given to the working of the kiln. About 1750 the practice began of double-firing, first to produce the biscuit stage (Fig. 289), and again after the application of the glaze, while a special shallow kiln was also brought into use to accelerate the drying of the clay. At the same time banks of kilns began to replace the original single structures, often measuring only 8×6 ft; new devices were found for controlling their temperatures; and salt-glazing was gradually abandoned.

Enoch Booth of Tunstall, who introduced double firing into Staffordshire, was also a pioneer in the replacement of the practice

FIG. 289. Biscuit oven, nineteenth century

of dusting the ware with powdered galena before it was fired: instead it was dipped, after the first firing, in a slip of liquid glaze containing a lead oxide (Fig. 290). This brought the cream-coloured Staffordshire earthenware nearer to the degree of perfection which eventually gave it a world market. Production increased rapidly in the 1750's, and about 1768 Booth made a further improvement by adding china stone to the china clay already present in the body: this body was the original basis of the industrial achievement of Wedgwood.

Josiah Wedgwood was a potter's son who was throwing pottery on the wheel by the age of nine. In 1759, aged twenty-nine, he set up his own business at Burslem within 3 miles of the site of the pottery works and village of Etruria which he established ten years later, and of the mansion where he mixed experimental clays in secrecy and resided until his death in 1795. One of his first successes was a green-glazed ware, but the most important product was an improvement upon the cream-coloured ware manufactured by Booth. For this he used a mixture of 4 parts flint to 20–24 parts of the whitest clay obtainable, which he fired twice and glazed with what was essentially flint glass; the product had no decoration, but it appealed by its attractive shape and was comparatively cheap. It secured an enormous advertisement when, Queen Charlotte having accepted a set in 1762, it became known as 'Queen's ware' and its

FIG. 290. Dipping biscuit-ware in glaze, c. 1840

fortunate manufacturer was appointed royal potter. But Wedgwood, whose use of the name Etruria attests his classical enthusiasms, was much concerned with the more purely artistic side of ceramics: his employment of John Flaxman to design white ornamentation as effective relief on a coloured ground, his output of portrait medallions, and the classic shapes given to his fine jasper ware, may be quoted as examples. His taste for the classical or sentimental motif, in place of the exotic Chinese or the French rococo, suited the expanding bourgeois society that he served. Since Wedgwood's multifarious interests also ranged from the scientific examination of pottery materials and methods to such purely commercial developments as the promotion of the Grand Trunk Canal, which passed alongside his kilns at Etruria, it is clear that he was ideally qualified to raise the status of the industry as a whole. In 1777 the value of the annual output of The Potteries was only £75,000, though this was five times what it had been half a century before, but ten years later there were two hundred master-potters there, with an average of a hundred employees each.

It remains to enumerate some of the technical improvements which ministered to this growth: pride of place may be given to the introduction of the steam-engine. A Newcomen engine was the first steam-engine to be installed in The Potteries: this pumped water back

for re-use by an existing water-wheel, and belonged to a pottery which later passed to the growing firm of Spode. Wedgwood ordered one of Watt's engines in 1782, proposing to use it both for grinding flint and pigments and for the mixing of clay, a decision that proved important not only in the history of the pottery industry, of which it eventually changed the whole tempo, but because of its effect on the fortunes of Boulton & Watt by providing a much-needed new market for their engines before the textile industry was ripe for them.

But there were also numerous improvements which speeded up, or added to the value of, a handicraft process. Thus throw-

FIG. 291. Pressing flat hollow-ware, *c.* 1814

ing on the wheel had been supplemented by 1750 by reviving the ancient use of moulds—of cast metal, plaster of Paris, or lightly baked clay—for stamping out small vessels, a method which was employed even for Wedgwood's portrait medallions. In the end the mould-cutter prepared the first design in alabaster and then transferred it to a stoneware duplicate, thus providing a means of making any number of plaster moulds for the object; he became in consequence one of the most important workers in the industry. Pressers, who made the cheap, flat hollow-ware by this means (Fig. 291), likewise became more numerous than throwers. Another move towards mass production was the invention of transfer-printing: the required pattern was engraved on a metal plate, which was then inked, so that the design could be taken up on paper and transferred to any number of articles. Later refinements ranged from the provision of a semi-hand-made article, which had the transfer imposed merely as an outline to guide the decorator, to full-scale picture printing, such as ornamented the lids of pomade-pots for Victorian dressing-tables.

Although it would be wrong to think of mass production as the only aim of the industry, there was a natural tendency to concentrate on what could be worked most easily and effectively. In the case of porcelain, for example, England did not attempt to vie with the Continent in the making of the hard paste, but continued with its soft paste bone-china. In 1797 the second generation of the great dynasty of Spode added felspar to the bone-ash, producing the easily worked English porcelain material of the present day. So also in the sphere of decoration with metal, the difficulty that gilding was easily rubbed off was met by the introduction of 'fired gold'—gold-leaf mixed with honey, which could be applied before firing—providing a rare example of a pottery process in which Europe was not anticipated by the East. The production of lustre ware, intended to look like metal, was achieved by application of a metallic compound over the glaze, to be fired in a reducing atmosphere so that the metal itself would be liberated; it shows the eighteenth century engaged in the kind of facile imitative manufacture which we think of as an unsatisfactory characteristic of our own age. Wedgwood's only patent, as it happens, was one taken out in 1769 for making an encaustic gold bronze.

NINETEENTH-CENTURY DEVELOPMENTS

At the close of the eighteenth century, thanks largely to the genius of Wedgwood, the size and scope of the English pottery industry had been transformed, and machinery and labour-saving devices had been introduced to a degree which enabled it for a long time to function satisfactorily as a large-scale handicraft. It depended to a great extent on the availability of an ample supply of cheap labour. There is a close parallel with the coal industry in this respect, as also in the tendency for pot-making to be a hereditary trade; in the exploitation of child-labour, which went on much longer at the kilns than in the mines; and in the considerable physical risk to the worker. But what chiefly enabled the pottery industry to function efficiently in the first half of the nineteenth century without any important further change was a division of labour to which there was no parallel in the coal-mines. As early as 1790, some 160 employees engaged in the cheaper kinds of work at Etruria were distributed among at least twenty distinct occupations.

By 1850 the most artistic forms of pottery fully satisfied the requirements of the leisured classes, and the substitution of cheap earthenware for wood and pewter as the tableware of the masses in all civilized countries was virtually completed. The Great Exhibition included such curiosities of ceramics as the largest porcelain dish in existence, a Hungarian product that attracted the eye of Queen Victoria and secured a most profitable royal order. By 1860 there was a porcelain flute, in 1885 a Dresden china fireplace, and at the Paris Exhibition of 1900 a 'Ceramic Palace', of which the interior was constructed exclusively of Sèvres porcelain. It was perhaps fortunate that further development came to the industry largely through the demand for new end-products. These included great numbers of porcelain and steatite insulators for telegraphic and other electrical uses; containers for acids and other chemicals, required by the rapidly expanding chemical industry; and fire-bricks for steel-smelting, such as were made of calcined dolomite or Austrian magnesite for the Gilchrist–Thomas process. By the last decade of the century porcelain for sanitary fittings had also become a large-scale manufacture, at least in America. Besides these new uses of pottery there was a great expansion in the use of clay products in the building industry. Brick-making machines, which cut ten bricks at a time from a length of clay, on the model of a sausage-machine, were introduced in Britain by mid-century, yet the demand for bricks was such that in 1871 brickyards still employed half as many workers as all the potteries. Besides the ubiquitous brick walls, in many places interlocking tiles were used for roof construction; there was also a steady demand for hollow bricks for light-weight partitions and non-inflammable floors and ceilings for tall buildings.

The Potteries owed their location partly to the presence of a plentiful supply of cheap coal. The characteristic bottle kiln (Fig. 292) was developed there without much regard for fuel-efficiency, not to speak of the pollution of the atmosphere: about 1800 it was reckoned that $2\frac{1}{2}$ lb of coal were used to fire 1 lb of clay. One line of advance was to change the fuel, with which object experiments began about 1855 in various countries with coal- or producer-gas or, a good deal later, electricity. Another was to redesign the kiln: F. Hoffman, for instance, in 1858 patented the first continuous circular kiln, which had a series of openings to enable the fire to be moved from one to another. Even more important was the tunnel kiln, developed in Denmark—where the need to economize in fuel was very great. The first was built in 1839, but it became more effective after 1877, when a type was patented which burned producer-gas or coal. This in turn was followed in the next year by the more economic annular tunnel kiln, set up almost simultaneously in London and in Hungary. The improvement of the kiln was accompanied by the development of ancillary machinery—grinders, crushers, and mixers for the raw

FIG. 292. Bottle kilns in The Potteries

materials, and mechanical presses to form the simpler of the finished products, including tiles as well as bricks, porcelain insulators, and household crockery.

In the long run, however, the most significant change was the gradual substitution of scientific methods for the empirical approach of countless past generations. There was for the first time a rational analysis of the raw materials, exact measurement of kiln temperatures, and the formulation of rules of procedure to prevent minute cracks (crazing) forming on the surface of the pot.

Among the practical results of the new approach, we may notice the long battle which resulted in the prohibition of the use of soluble lead in glazes, a protection against lead-poisoning important to the consumer but more particularly to the workers in the industry. There was also more variety in the colouring of glazes; uranium, for instance, was first used for this purpose in 1853. Finally, it became easier to imitate not merely the china of the Far East but rival Western products. Thus British bone-china was manufactured in Sweden with a body so greatly improved that as many as ten plates could be placed one above the other in saggars; even the famous *pâte-sur-pâte* technique of Sèvres was successfully copied by the Dresden china-works at Meissen in 1878. By 1900 what had once been the most individual of industries had become largely standardized and mechanized and even—in Ohio at least—elevated to the rank of a university faculty.

PROGRESS OF GLASS-MAKING

The history of glass-making bears a broad resemblance to that of pottery, inasmuch as the craftsman and the ancient, and often secret, traditional process were not quickly swept aside by industrial change. Indeed, development was even slower, because there was not such a great mass-market in the earlier period—we use more cups and plates than glasses—nor at a later stage were the uses of glass in industrial equipment so numerous. In building development, however, glass was as important as bricks and tiles, and the maker of glass sheets, unlike the potter, had the special problem of increasing the dimensions of his product to suit new window requirements.

The closest link with the scientific advances of the period of the industrial revolution is in the steady progress of optical glass. It was in 1758 that John Dollond, a practical optician, was awarded a patent for the achromatic lenses that he had been constructing, con-temporaneously with Moor Hall, for about a quarter of a century; they were made by cementing a convex lens of crown glass to a con-cave lens of flint glass. With the conquest of chromatic aberration, the mathematical theory of which was worked out in 1760 by Samuel Klingenstierna of Uppsala, the early drawing-room pieces were suc-ceeded by large observatory telescopes. Large reflecting telescopes, such as the 40-ft instrument which Herschel completed in 1789, also came into use. Improved methods of making optical glass became the object of research not only among manufacturers but among interested scientists such as Herschel and Faraday, who took charge of the Royal Society investigations of the matter in 1824. A significant discovery had been made in 1798 by P. L. Guinand, a Swiss clock-bell founder, whose bell-founding experience suggested to him the idea of stirring the molten flint glass in the crucible with a fire-clay stirrer, in order to distribute the heavy lead oxide more evenly and so to form a homogeneous mixture, an absolute essential for good optical results. With denser glasses the range of refractivity could be extended. The quality of light transmission was also improved because air bubbles in the mixture were more completely dispersed. Guinand's secret process was developed chiefly at a Bavarian works in collaboration with the spectroscopist, Joseph von Fraunhofer, and enabled the Munich optical institute to produce large lenses of fine quality.

Fraunhofer's work was complemented in Britain by that of Vernon Harcourt, the son of an archbishop and father of a Chancellor of the Exchequer, whose experiments were nevertheless hampered by lack of resources. Moreover, until 1845 British excise rules (p. 598) severely obstructed manufacture, so that even the glass for lighthouse lenses and prisms was usually imported. After the deaths of

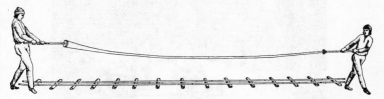

FIG. 293. Drawing glass tubing, preparatory to laying it on the 'ladder'

Guinand and Fraunhofer, the secret of the stirrer was purchased by a French glass-maker, Georges Bontemps, who in 1837 made an agreement to share it with the English firm of Chance Brothers at Birmingham. Finally, when the revolution of 1848 drove Bontemps to England, a new plant was set up under his supervision, and Chance Brothers became established in the manufacture of both crown and flint glass for telescopes, and of a lighter quality for the new requirements of camera lenses.

In general, however, the great difficulty of handling molten glass was an effective barrier to progress. No attempt was made to produce tubing and rod mechanically, to say nothing of bottles. Tubing was produced by gradually blowing a gob of glass into cylindrical form, which was then drawn out between two workers (Fig. 293) while a third measured the diameter with calipers; when the size was right he cooled the glass, to make it set, by flapping the air with a sheet of leather to create a draught, and it was cut into lengths on a horizontal 'ladder'.

Crown window-glass was still in common use in England in 1800. The distinctive small round sheet of glass, with the bull's eye or 'crown' in the centre, was made from a globe of glass which was attached by a lump of molten metal to an iron rod (or pontil) at a point diametrically opposite to that at which it was held on the blow-iron. The removal of the blow-iron then left a small opening in the globe, which was reheated and spun until centrifugal force caused the flat glass suddenly to flare out into the shape of a disk. It was then whirled about on the pontil until it became cool enough to be cut away (Fig. 294).

A better system of making sheet glass, from blown cylinders, was introduced into England in 1832 by Chance Brothers and Bontemps.

FIG. 294. Glasshouse for making crown glass, c. 1800

Although the new method, already established in Germany and France, required five types of skilled workers, it was cheaper, produced bigger sheets, and was free from blemish in the centre. The method was as follows. A ball of glass weighing anything up to 40 lb was blown into a globe, and this was swung in a deep trench so as to give it the shape of a cylinder. The two ends were then cut off preparatory to slitting the cylinder lengthwise with a diamond tool: when softened by reheating, it would unroll into a flat sheet. For better-quality sheet the cylinder was opened out on a glass-covered stone, smoothed by rubbing with a block of wood, and finally passed through an annealing kiln. But after only seven years Chance Brothers devised a process by which the sheets could be ground and polished like plate glass: this involved the grinding away of irregularities from the surface while the sheet was relieved from strain by being laid upon a bed of moistened leather, resting upon slate, to which it was made to adhere by suction.

The manufacture of plate glass was introduced into England from northern France in 1773, and a company established at Ravenhead near St Helens in Lancashire three years later was famous for its casting-hall, 130 yds long by 50 yds wide, which was one of the largest industrial buildings of the age. Although some experienced French workmen were available and the first managers were French, the business was at best a struggling one, hampered by expensive breakages, until the outbreak of the long French wars saved it from the competition of the manufacture in France, which had a full century's experience behind it (p. 110). Yet the process had the enormous advantage that cast plates could now measure 160×80 in., as compared with the maximum of 50×30 in. for plate glass made by the old blowing process. The batch mixture included 25 per cent. of broken plate glass (cullet); it was prepared for use by fritting, a process which gave a uniform paste-like mix-

FIG. 295. Casting plate glass, c. 1780

ture, and was fused in crucibles placed in a high-temperature furnace. Stourbridge clay with an admixture of burnt clay provided the material for these crucibles, which had to withstand both intense heat and the action of the molten glass, and they were covered—an English innovation for use with smutty coal-fuel. The casting (Fig. 295) was done originally on a copper table, but in the 1840's cast iron was substituted. As early as 1789 a Boulton & Watt steam-engine was introduced for the grinding and polishing processes. The grinding implement was a sheet of glass, fastened to a plank and a horizontal wheel, which was moved freely about on the surface of the plate, after the latter had been plastered down with lime or stucco on to a stone table fitted with a rim to retain the water and sand which formed the grinding material. The polishing was done with a felt roller mounted on a wooden bow, using finely powdered Tripoli stone or emery (Fig. 296).

As the annual amount of building in Britain approximately doubled during the period 1821–5, the demand for window-glass

rose proportionately. Some of this was met by the blowing of more
cylinder glass, and a new crown-glass company was formed at

FIG. 296. Buffing or polishing plate glass for mirrors

FIG. 297. Casting-hall at Union Plate Glass Works, Lancashire, c. 1843

St Helens in 1826. But the most important development was the
Union Plate Glass Works at Pocket Nook (Fig. 297), with four
furnaces and twenty annealing kilns, which clearly foreshadowed the

extension of the industrial revolution to the glass industry. Yet it was not until 1845 that a change in the British fiscal policy made expansion fully practicable.

Before then, both glass-cutting and glass-engraving had passed through their greatest period, when their products compared with porcelain in their appeal to a limited class for whom expense was no object. Glass-cutting by hand was a highly skilled operation, for which Britain had a high reputation because of the excellent quality of the early crystal glass upon which it was practised. Designs, which were mainly geometrical, were ground in with an iron wheel fed with sand (Fig. 298). The glass was then smoothed on a wheel of fine sandstone fed with water, and repolished on a wooden wheel fed with water and putty-powder. Engraving was used for thinner ware, with freer designs put in by small rotating copper wheels. These wheels were

FIG. 298. Grinding a cut-glass vessel, *c.* 1840

smaller than those used for cutting, and a single delicate design might require the use of fifty such, the diameters ranging between 1/8th and 4 in.

Lastly, we may notice that in 1750–1850 there were important advances in glass coloration. Bottles were still mainly black or very dark green because of the iron and other impurities in the raw materials. Glass for plain tableware, on the other hand, was made with purer materials in order to ensure that it was virtually colourless. But artificial colours were required increasingly for many purposes, ranging from stained-glass windows downwards: cobalt compounds had long been used for blue, and the metal itself was first identified in 1742; nickel, uranium, and chromium compounds were used for producing other colours; and in 1826 the way of making true copper red glass (p. 95) was rediscovered by the versatile Bontemps. It was not until the 1830's, however, that it was discovered that the yellow colour imparted to glass by such materials as powdered coke or anthracite was due to the presence of sulphuric impurities in these materials. In general, the substances used to colour glass were still the traditional ones: progress came chiefly through the use of more highly purified compounds and through more careful control of the atmosphere and temperature of the furnaces.

GLASS-MAKING, 1845–1900

The repeal of the century-old British excise duties on glass in 1845, followed by the final extinction of the window tax in 1851, may be taken as a convenient starting-point in considering the newer developments in the second half of the nineteenth century. The constant supervision practised by the excise officers rankled with the manufacturers, and the effect of the duties themselves was tersely summed up by the economist, J. R. McCulloch, in 1833: 'A man with 125 per cent. duty over his head is not very likely to make experiments.' When the goods became cheaper, demand increased, and the consequent pressure of the workers for higher wages provided an additional incentive for experiments in mechanization. From 1859 onwards there was a series of patents in various countries for bottle-making machines, and in 1887 the semi-automatic Ashley machine, used at Castleford in Yorkshire, provided the first commercial success. Molten glass was collected manually on an iron and dropped into a mould; a plunger was pressed into the glass to form the neck, and compressed air then expanded the glass to fill the mould. Next, the neck was held by hand and inverted; a second mould, the blow-mould, then closed round the glass, which was blown up to form the completed bottle. In 1898 M. J. Owens in America built the first experimental hand-gun, which mechanized the first process in the manufacture. As regards the economy of labour, five handworkers produced about 150 bottles an hour, whereas two men working two improved Ashley machines could make 200; by the end of the century an Owens machine could make 2,500 bottles an hour. Plunger and mould also came into use for the simpler process of pressing out glass articles such as pie-dishes and bowls.

A more immediate sequel to the removal of the excise duties in Britain was the increased trade enjoyed by Chance Brothers who, on taking over the sheet glass process in 1832, had improved upon it by blowing a cylinder as much as 6 ft long by 16 inches in diameter: the firm supplied the glass for the Crystal Palace in 1851. In 1884-7, as a sequel to much unsuccessful experimentation (which began with Bessemer in 1846), Chance Brothers developed a rolled-plate process, in which molten glass was poured on to an inclined plate, passed between a pair of rollers, and then ground and polished.

Mechanization in this case, as in that of glass containers, depended to a considerable extent upon improved furnaces. Those in use up to 1850 were directly fired and extravagant in fuel, but in the 1860's the Siemens regenerative furnace, as was previously related (p. 484), was applied to glass-making. Gas-fired furnaces of the new type produced a much higher temperature, which among other advantages facilitated the dispersal of air bubbles, but in consequence reduced the life of the traditional fireclay pots. The result was their replacement by tank furnaces, used at first to hold only the quantity of melted glass required for a single day's work, but later to provide a continuous flow of glass, with the batch melting at one end and emerging at the other refined and ready for working. This system was introduced in Britain by 1872, but not until 1888 in America, where fuel was generally cheaper and glassworks were smaller.

As regards the chemical composition of the glass, the higher temperature of the new Siemens furnace made it possible for expensive soda to be replaced by salt-cake (sodium sulphate, p. 533), but in 1863 the development of the Solvay process for making soda reversed the trend. More generally, a feature of the time was the careful scientific study of the materials used: in 1875, for instance, the chemical composition of what was then regarded as the most durable glass was defined, and proved to be near to that still used for windows. More important, for science at least, was the continuance of the study of optical glass, particularly by Ernst Abbé and Otto Schott, who in 1886 joined Karl Zeiss in beginning manufacture at the famous Jena glassworks. Just after the end of the century they were able to list about eighty different optical glasses, and in a very few years they had introduced, to an extent of at least 10 per cent. of the mixture, no fewer than twenty-eight elements not previously used in glass-making.

THE INTERNAL COMBUSTION ENGINE

INTRODUCTION

ALTHOUGH the complexity of the internal combustion engine and the course of its evolution from a primitive to a practical form make it very comparable with the steam-engine, its story can be relatively briefly told in the present context. Although, as we have seen, the steam-engine neither started the industrial revolution nor even played the decisive part in its early phases, it subsequently had a decisive effect on many technological developments in the nineteenth century. By contrast, although the main features of the modern internal combustion engine had appeared by 1900, its enormous influence on world civilization was not felt until well into the twentieth century. Moreover, as the steam and the internal combustion engines have a good deal in common—the heart of both being a piston in a cylinder—some of the general principles of operation have already been discussed. In passing, it may be remarked that this similarity to the steam-engine was to a certain extent a hindrance to the development of the new engine: early inventors tended to adopt features of steam practice that were not suitable for internal combustion engines. An interesting, if extreme, example of the lingering influence of old on new is provided by a French patent for a petrol horse (Fig. 299) taken out as late as 1897.

Although the internal combustion engine effectively came into the field a century later than the steam-engine, its history is just as long, for both can be considered to have derived from the experiments of Huygens and Papin with a gunpowder engine (p. 314). As will be recalled, the hazards and difficulties of recharging such an engine, and of sweeping out the products of combustion, caused Papin to turn his attention to steam, and so to set in train experiments that resulted in the first Newcomen engine of 1712. With the internal combustion engine, as with so many inventions, the fundamental idea was conceived long before there existed either the means of putting it satisfactorily into practice or a strong incentive to develop them. In the nineteenth century the ready availability of coal-gas, and later of very volatile petroleum fractions for which there was no existing demand, caused thoughts to turn again to internal combustion engines; at the same time, the growing understanding and mastery of electricity provided an extremely convenient system of ignition, although not the only one used in early engines.

But the incentive was still not very great. Although by far the most important modern application of the internal combustion engine is in transport by land, water, and air, this application can scarcely have entered the thoughts of early inventors. Apart from the fact that the steam-train and the steamship must have seemed to many to represent near-perfection in transport by land and sea, the fuel of the earliest internal combustion engines was coal-gas which, depending on connexion with, or frequent recharging from, a mains supply, offered no obvious possibilities for locomotion. Moreover, the weight-to-power ratio of early engines was very high and their running speeds were low: not until the very end of the century did light, high-speed petrol-engines make their appearance. In consequence, all the early engines were stationary ones, designed for industrial use.

FIG. 299. The petrol horse: a novel form of tractor patented in France in 1897

GAS-ENGINES

Although the seventeenth-century gunpowder engine can fairly be regarded as the ultimate ancestor of the internal combustion engine, nearly two centuries elapsed before such an engine was successfully developed. A gas-engine patent was lodged in Britain in 1794, and thirty years later gas-engines were used for pumping, but even the Great Exhibition included only a single example, one introduced by Drake in 1843 in the United States. Not until 1859, when a French Engineer, Etienne Lenoir, built a gas-engine that in most respects was designed according to current steam-engine practice, was any real success achieved. Up to date in so far as ignition of the explosive mixture of gas and air in the cylinder was effected by an electric spark generated by an induction coil, it lacked, among other essential features, any provision for compressing the mixture before it was fired. Its performance did not stand comparison with contemporary steam-engines of the same power, but it was nevertheless a landmark as the first non-steam-engine able to work continuously under industrial conditions. Not for nearly twenty years was a fully successful gas-engine built: this was N. A. Otto's horizontal engine of 1876 (Fig. 300), of which 50,000, of about 200,000 h.p. in all, were sold in the first seventeen years after its introduction by the German firm of Otto & Langen. This engine worked upon the so-

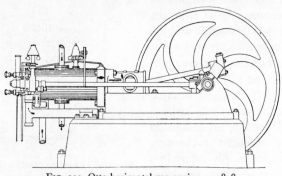

FIG. 300. Otto horizontal gas-engine, *c.* 1878

called Otto cycle, after 1890 almost universally used for all internal combustion engines. The principal exceptions are cheap lower-power engines—designed for motor-mowers, light-weight motor-bicycles, and similar purposes—which often work on the simpler two-stroke principle: compression was applied to this type of engine by Sir Dugald Clerk in Scotland in 1878. The Otto cycle, controlled by valves which regulate the intake of fuel and expulsion of the products of combustion, consists of four strokes. In the first stroke the explosive mixture is drawn into the cylinder; in the second, the mixture is compressed by the piston and then ignited; in the third, the force of the explosion drives the piston back again; and in the fourth, the returning piston drives out the gaseous products of combustion, ready for the cycle to be repeated. Although probably an independent invention, the Otto cycle was clearly anticipated in an unexploited French invention of 1862.

Otto's success effectively demonstrated the possible uses of gas-engines and by the end of the century their improved size, efficiency, and reliability, and the development of special gaseous fuels, made them fully competitive with steam-engines. In 1881 the largest gas-engine was of 20 h.p.: by 1917, at which time it reached the peak of its popularity, 5,000 h.p. engines were in use.

OIL-ENGINES

Meanwhile, important developments in fuel utilization had taken place that were to determine the main line of evolution of the internal combustion engine: liquid fuels derived from petroleum began to supersede gas derived from coal. For this, two principal reasons are apparent. While the long-distance piping of gas is now commonplace, this was not so in the nineteenth century. Gas was then available only relatively close to the works at which it was manufactured: this generally served domestic and industrial consumers in a single town area. Although the power requirements of non-urban areas throughout the world were growing, only the biggest installations would justify the establishment of gas-manufacturing plant for power alone. To use a liquid fuel, easily transported and stored, capable of being fed to engines by gravity, and yielding more heat per unit of weight than coal, was therefore very attractive. Moreover, at just this time the petroleum industry—originally developed, as we have seen, to meet the demand for illuminants and, after 1878, for heating—could offer just such a fuel at a competitive price. Although the dangerously volatile lighter fractions, which at the outset presented a serious disposal problem to the petroleum industry (p. 520), were destined to be the most important fuels for internal combustion engines, higher kerosene fractions were used first.

The use of fuels of relatively low volatility presents technical problems different from those involved in the use of petrol, which vaporizes freely at normal temperatures. To prepare a suitable explosive mixture with air in the cylinder, fuel oils must either be vaporized by heating or converted into an exceedingly fine spray. Once an engine is running, the vaporization of the oil and the explosion of a properly balanced mixture in the cylinder of an oil-engine can be effected spontaneously by the great heat generated in the compression stroke. While this has the very great advantage of making it possible to dispense with an external ignition system—which even today is the most important single cause of failure of petrol-engines—it has attendant disadvantages. The very high degree of compression necessary for spontaneous ignition demands stronger, and therefore heavier, construction, so that oil-engines do not lend themselves to light-weight, low-power design; moreover, they tend to run roughly at low speeds. In consequence, oil-engines have found little favour for motor-cars, but they are very extensively used for the heavier forms of road-transport, and as large stationary and marine engines they have been enormously successful.

Although the ignition of the mixture in the cylinder of an oil-engine will eventually take place spontaneously as a result of the heat of compression, some means of starting from cold must normally be provided: only exceptionally high compression-ratios will bring about ignition of oil-air mixtures merely by turning the engine over a few times. In an engine built by Brayton, an American engineer, in 1873, initial firing was facilitated by turning the engine over with the aid of a cylinder of compressed air, recharged by the engine itself once spontaneous ignition had been established. A more successful oil-engine, built in sizes up to 100 h.p., was that patented by Dent & Priestman of Hull in 1886. Operating on the four-stroke Otto cycle, it was started by pre-heating the cylinder; the success of a mobile unit introduced in 1889 for agricultural use is a reminder of the growing power demand of rural areas. In these engines the heavy-oil fuel passed before combustion through a pre-heater heated by the exhaust gases. A notably successful engine was the Ackroyd-Stuart, first produced in England in 1890 and manufactured in large numbers by Ruston & Hornsby of Lincoln.

The Diesel engine, first patented by Rudolf Diesel in Britain in 1892, and first successfully manufactured in 1897, is notable for the very careful attention given to thermodynamic principles (p. 341) in its design: these principles Diesel set forth in detail in 1893 in his *Theorie und Konstruktion eines Rationellen Wärme-motors*. His object, eventually shown to be not wholly practicable, was to prevent the engine temperature rising above that of the compressed gas in the cylinders, so making cooling unnecessary; he sought also to increase efficiency by lowering the temperature of the exhaust gases. Diesel's thermodynamic ideals were never fully achieved in practice, and after a few years the main, but exceedingly important, distinction of the Diesel engine from other oil-engines was its exceptionally high compression ratio, which favours high thermal efficiency.

PETROL-ENGINES

The essential principles of the petrol-engine are the same as those of the gas- and oil-engines already described: the main differences are in the systems of fuel injection and ignition and in the fact that it is essentially a high-speed engine. Although an Austrian engineer, Siegfried Markus, is reputed to have built in the period 1864–74 several vehicles propelled by petrol-engines (p. 393), the acknowledged pioneer was the German engineer, Gottlieb Daimler, who had for some years been interested in the design and construction of gas-engines. His first petrol-engine, patented in 1885, was a single-cylinder vertical machine, air-cooled, working on the Otto cycle. The explosive mixture was prepared by sucking air through petrol in a float-chamber, and it was ignited by an externally heated tube inserted into the cylinder head. In the following year this engine was successfully applied to a bicycle, then to a carriage. Within three years Daimler had constructed a two-cylinder engine, in which the two pistons drove one crank: originally it was proposed to fit valves in both pistons, but this intention was never realized in practice. This engine was built in considerable numbers, not only for the motor-car industry but also for small boats and as a stationary engine.

Simultaneously with Daimler, another German engineer, Karl Benz, was building engines that were specifically for motor-cars. His single-cylinder engine of 1885 differed from Daimler's in being horizontal, in having electrical ignition, and in being relatively slow-running. Applied first to a three-wheeled car (p. 393), the engine proved conspicuously successful when it was used, as a $3\frac{1}{2}$ h.p. unit, in a four-wheeled vehicle in 1893; production of this continued up to 1901. Its system of ignition by an electrical induction coil—powered by an accumulator and fitted with a rotary contact-breaker, driven from the engine, to ensure that sparking occurred at the right point in the four-stroke cycle—was soon widely adopted by other manufacturers. The spark itself was produced in a removable plug, of essentially modern design, fitted into the cylinder-head. The carburettor was of the surface type, similar in principle to that of Daimler's engine, except that volatilization was assisted by the heat of the exhaust and there was a shutter that served as a choke to control the admixture of air.

After 1893 Daimler, and subsequently other manufacturers, used the modern float-feed carburettor (Fig. 301) invented by Wilhelm Maybach. The petrol level in the chamber of this carburettor is kept constant by a float working a needle valve. The float-chamber communicates, through a very fine jet, with the inlet of the cylinder: the suction from the cylinder causes an exceedingly fine spray of petrol to be injected into the air-intake. Up to the First World War the only other alternative to the original surface-type and the float-feed carburettor was the Lanchester wick-carburettor fitted to Lanchester engines, which we shall consider later, from 1897. In this, air was drawn over a series of wicks dipping into a small chamber constantly replenished from the main fuel tank.

Within the period now under consideration, only single- or twin-cylindered petrol-engines were in use; multiple-cylindered engines

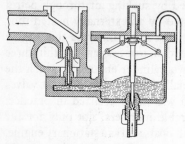

came into general use much later. Although, as we have seen, Daimler introduced a twin-cylindered engine in 1889, the design of such engines presents considerable engineering problems. The fundamental difficulty is that with a four-stroke engine there is only one power stroke for every two revolutions of the crankshaft. From the

FIG. 301. Early float-feed carburettor

point of view of engine balance it is desirable, supposing that the cylinders are arranged alongside each other, that one piston should be rising as the other falls. The effect of this, however, is that the crankshaft receives power impulses in two successive half turns, but receives no power impulses at all during the next full turn. This can be overcome if the pistons rise and fall together—one making the first stroke of the cycle while the other makes the third—but this throws the engine out of balance and imposes excessive strain. A solution, but one not widely adopted because it has attendant difficulties, is to use horizontally opposed cylinders. Within the period in question, other ingenious devices were used by a number of manufacturers, of whom perhaps the most successful was F. W. Lanchester. His engine applied the principle of horizontally opposed cylinders, but instead of one crankshaft there were two, one above the other (Fig. 302). Each piston was connected to both crankshafts, which carried separate flywheels, but which were geared together so that they turned in opposite directions; the chain-drive to the rear axle was, of course, taken from only one crankshaft.

Most early engines were air-cooled: Diesel, as we have seen, paid particular attention to keeping the engine temperature low in order, among other things, to obviate the need for a cooling system. The cooling effect of the air can be increased by increasing the external surface area of the cylinder by means of fins, and the draught resulting from the vehicle's own motion also assists, and can if necessary be increased by a fan, as in the Lanchester engine. The circulation of the lubricating oil—effected by hand-pumping on many early cars but already mechanized in the first Lanchester —also promotes cooling. Additional cooling by means of a water-circulating system had, however, also appeared before 1900: it was

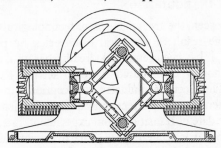

FIG. 302. Twin-cylinder Lanchester engine, 1897–1904

a feature of Henry Ford's first motor-car of 1896 and also of early Lanchesters, though not of the original model.

CONCLUSION

Such, in brief, was the main line of evolution of the internal combustion engine up to 1900, by which time many tens of thousands had been constructed. Although its full social impact was not felt until the twentieth century, it is to be noted that all the fundamental problems had been solved: it is fair to say that a modern motor-car engine contains no feature that would surprise a nineteenth-century engineer. The greatest change has been from custom building to mass production, and even the latter lies only just beyond our period, for the Ford Motor Company was founded in 1903 (p. 395).

A very significant feature of the evolution of the internal combustion engine in general, and of the petrol-engine in particular, is the relatively small contribution made by British engineers; Lanchester is a conspicuous exception. This becomes all the more striking if comparison is made with the history of the steam-engine. The way in which Continental and American inventors outnumbered British supports the general thesis that the Great Exhibition of 1851 marked the climax of Britain's inventive supremacy.

THE ELECTRICAL INDUSTRY

HISTORICAL INTRODUCTION

As we have seen, the great majority of technological developments were the result of empirical discoveries by practical men: indeed, it has been remarked already that until comparatively recently technology contributed more to science than science to technology. The electrical industry is exceptional in that its birth and development were the direct consequence of scientific research; moreover, the date of transition from experimental science to useful industry can be fairly accurately set. The key event was the practical demonstration of electromagnetic induction by Michael Faraday, announced to the Royal Society on 24 November 1831: within a very short time electromagnetic generators were being manufactured commercially. While our main concern here must be with practical applications, it is necessary first to put the subject in perspective by a brief consideration of the events that led up to this historic discovery.

It was known at a very early date that if amber (*elektron* in Greek) is rubbed, it acquires the power of attracting certain very light bodies, such as feathers or scraps of paper. William Gilbert, physician to Queen Elizabeth I, and famous for his *De Magnete*, a comprehensive treatise on magnetism to which little could be added for two centuries, knew of some twenty substances which exhibited the same curious property as amber. He concluded that the 'effluvium' responsible for the phenomenon was widely distributed.

Philosophers of the seventeenth and eighteenth centuries found the phenomenon interesting and established some of the properties of static electricity, that is, an electric charge as distinct from an electric current. In 1660 von Guericke invented a frictional machine to generate a continuous supply of electricity. Shortly afterwards Francis Hauksbee demonstrated that charged bodies may repel as well as attract each other, and in 1729 Stephen Gray made the very important contribution of distinguishing between conductors (mainly metals) and non-conductors. In the 1730's the French physicist Charles Du Fay discovered that electricity induced by rubbing could be of two kinds, now called positive and negative respectively, while in 1754 John Canton, a weaver's apprentice who became a Fellow of the Royal Society, put the science of electricity on a quantitative basis by devising an instrument to measure electricity, based upon the repulsion of like-charged balls of pith suspended by threads. This important instrument was standardized by the Italian, Alessandro Volta, so that investigators in different laboratories could compare results, and was redesigned, as the gold-leaf electroscope, by Bennet in 1787; the electroscope enabled Canton to show that a charged body induces a charge on any other that it approaches.

Meanwhile, Musschenbroek had invented the 'Leyden jar', by means of which substantial quantities of electricity could be accumulated from an electrical machine and then rapidly discharged: such a jar is, in effect, a large condenser. In Philadelphia, Benjamin Franklin, by flying kites during thunderstorms and obtaining sparks from the end of the cord to which they were attached, identified lightning as an electrical discharge. These experiments led to the invention of the lightning conductor, soon widely used to safeguard buildings, especially munitions stores and others of a particularly vulnerable nature. The discovery resulted in a curious interplay between science and politics. There arose a controversy, which ought to have been settled by experiment and observation, as to whether the tips of lightning conductors should consist of points or knobs. Franklin rightly advocated points, but when the American colonies revolted, with Franklin prominent among the rebels, George III allowed himself to be drawn into the quarrel and supported the use of blunt-ended conductors. He went so far as to try to induce the Royal Society to support his view, but the President, Sir John Pringle, despite the dangers of offending the Society's royal patron, stood firmly by scientific principle and made a classic reply: 'Sire, I cannot reverse the laws and operations of nature.' Franklin, who was then in France negotiating the famous alliance that ensured the success of the rebellion, expressed the hope that George III would bring the thunder of heaven upon himself by dispensing with lightning conductors altogether.

At this time other important research was being carried out in Italy. Luigi Galvani's experiments on the twitching of frogs' legs, which he wrongly attributed to a special form of animal electricity, attracted the attention of Volta, who showed that the source of the electricity in the experiment was, in fact, the contact between two different metals in a solution. From this developed the voltaic pile, consisting of alternate plates of silver or copper and zinc—a choice made as a result of systematic experiment—separated by flannel or paper soaked in brine. This discovery was communicated to the Royal Society in 1800: its enormous importance lay in the fact that it provided a simple and convenient source of a continuous electric current and thus greatly facilitated experiment. An electric battery of this kind is essentially a machine for converting the energy released in chemical reaction, which would normally appear largely as heat, into electrical energy. Within a matter of months, large electric batteries were being built in many laboratories on Volta's principle, and with its help a series of important discoveries was made. Water was easily decomposed by the electric current into hydrogen and oxygen, providing analytical proof of its composition to support the conclusions of Lavoisier, reached by methods of synthesis. Using the great pile built for the Royal Institution in London, Humphry Davy isolated by electrolysis a whole series of new metals—first potassium from potash, and then sodium, barium, strontium, and magnesium. In 1802 Davy noted that when a spark is continuously struck between two pieces of carbon a brilliant light is emitted: this is the principle of the arc-lamp (p. 630), although its practical development had to await a cheaper source of electricity. It was also observed that an electric current heats the conductor through which it passes, a discovery put to practical use later in the incandescent filament lamp.

Of more immediate importance to the development of the electrical industry, the Danish physicist, H. C. Oersted, described in 1820 the magnetic field that surrounds a conductor carrying an electric current. In Paris A. M. Ampère almost at once put this observation on a quantitative basis, establishing the relationship between the strength of the magnetic field and that of the electric current that produces it. It was also established that movement of a continuous conductor in a magnetic field causes an electric current to flow in it. In such ways the fundamental relationship between electricity and magnetism was established, but there remained the vital step of turning the relationship to practical use: this step was taken by Faraday. In September 1831 he used the interaction of electric and magnetic fields to produce mechanical motion. First, on 3 September, he made a wire carrying an electric current circle round a fixed magnet; on the following day he made a magnet circle round a wire carrying a current. Although Faraday's device was purely experimental, and was not intended for practical use, it represented a very big step forward. Not only had he devised the first electric-motor but—because a dynamo is essentially an electric-motor working in reverse—he had pointed the way towards the conversion of mechanical into electrical power. Although many practical difficulties had still to be solved, the development of the modern electrical industry became possible.

From this point, the story of the rise of the electrical industry in the nineteenth century may conveniently be told under three main headings: generation, distribution, and utilization.

THE GENERATION OF ELECTRICITY

Before considering the magneto-electric generators that resulted from Faraday's discoveries, the story of the electric battery may be concluded. As we have seen, the original voltaic cell gave a great stimulus to the experimental study of electricity. Nevertheless, it had serious imperfections, among which were the strong tendency of the voltage to fall, due to accumulation of the products of chemical reaction, and the steady dissolution of the expensive copper plates. Of various improvements, the first major one was the Leclanché cell of 1866. In this, the two electrodes consist of rods of carbon and zinc respectively, immersed in a solution of ammonium chloride: the familiar 'dry' battery, introduced towards the end of the century, is based on the same principle. The Leclanché cell was excellent for supplying intermittent current as it would remain active for long periods without attention, but still possessed the defect that the voltage fell on continuous use. The growing needs of the electric telegraph (p. 624) for a reliable cell, giving constant voltage and capable of prolonged output, led to the development of a cell that had been invented by J. F. Daniell in 1836. In this, the electrodes are of copper and zinc, each dipping into a different electrolyte—solutions of copper sulphate and sulphuric acid respectively—separated from each other by a porous pot. The Daniell cell was improved in 1853 by J. C. Fuller, who prolonged its life by using zinc sulphate in place of sulphuric acid; in this form it was much used for telegraphic purposes until replaced by a chromic-acid cell in the 1870's. For tropical use, the Daniell cell was developed in 1862 as the Minotto cell.

The cells we have hitherto considered are what are called primary cells. Storage cells or accumulators, which can be charged from some other electrical source and discharged as required, derived largely from the work done in the 1860's by a Frenchman, R. L. G. Planté: his batteries were demonstrated in 1878 and came into use about two years later. The Planté cell consisted essentially of lead electrodes in the shape of large plates immersed in sulphuric acid. On charging, the positive plate became coated with lead peroxide; on discharging, the chemical reaction was reversed. By a complicated system of charge and discharge the electrodes were made 'spongy', so increasing their effective surface area and consequently the electrical capacity of the cell. This electrical 'forming' of the plates was obviated by another French inventor, Faure, who applied a paste of sulphuric acid and red lead to them; later inventors devised improved methods of causing the paste to adhere. By the 1880's storage batteries were being used for such purposes as lighting railway carriages and propelling road vehicles (p. 390). A serious limitation, however, was their weight: in 1888, for example, a 660 ampere-hour accumulator, designed for general lighting purposes, might weigh as much as $2\frac{1}{2}$ cwt.

Although batteries were, and indeed remain, an extremely convenient source of electricity for a great many purposes, the widespread use of electricity for heat, light, and power depended upon the development of mechanical methods of generation. The first mechanical generator was shown in Paris within a year of Faraday reading his classic paper to the Royal Society in 1831 by an instrument-maker, Hippolyte Pixii, in whose hand-turned generator the coils were fixed and the horseshoe magnet rotated. But before another year had passed, a machine was demonstrated at a Cambridge meeting of the British Association for the Advancement of Science in which the opposite principle, namely rotation of the coils relative to a fixed magnet, was utilized; this is now general practice. From 1834, at latest, rotating-coil generators were being made commercially in London.

The earliest generators produced alternating current: that is, the direction of flow constantly reversed, with a frequency depending upon the speed at which the machine was turned. This was looked upon as a most serious disadvantage—partly, at least, because all workers were accustomed to working with the direct current provided by batteries—but towards the end of the century it was realized that for large-scale use alternating current had decisive advantages over direct (pp. 615–16). For the time being, however, the problem of the conversion of alternating into direct current was solved by the invention of the mechanical commutator: a commutator designed by Ampère was fitted to an early generator made by Pixii (Fig. 303).

Other developments quickly followed. A simple rectangular coil rotating in a magnetic field produces current whose voltage fluctuates considerably, in accordance with the speed of rotation. To obviate this, a combination of coils, the armature, was devised: as the maximum voltage was generated in each coil in succession, the irregularities were largely evened out, and at a given speed of rotation a fairly constant voltage could be generated. By 1825, electromagnets, excited by batteries, were being used by William Sturgeon, founder of the first English electrical journal, *Annals of Electricity*, as alternatives to permanent magnets. From this there sprang a further development of the utmost importance, namely the principle of self-excitation. In 1855 the Danish engineer, Søren Hjorth, obtained, but never exploited, a British patent showing a

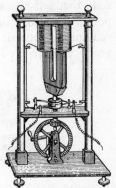

Fig. 303. Early generator by Pixii, fitted with commutator to provide direct current

clear realization that, once the machine had been started, the electromagnets could be activated not by external batteries but by diversion of part of the electricity generated; the initial excitation was, however, to be provided by permanent magnets. Ten years were to elapse before it was realized that electromagnets possessed enough residual magnetism in their soft-iron cores to provide the magnetic field necessary to start output from an electric generator. The discovery of the principle of self-excitation is attributed to C. F. Varley (Fig. 304), who disclosed it in a patent that was filed at the end of 1866 but not published until the summer of the following year. In the meantime, Werner von Siemens—reputedly the originator of the word 'dynamo' —had demonstrated the principle to the Berlin Academy of Sciences, and his brother William had shown it to the Royal Society in London; at this last meeting Charles Wheatstone also demonstrated a generator working on the same principle. Other inventors were working on the same idea at the same time. Henry Wilde, an electrical manufacturer whose ideas stimulated Siemens, almost completely enunciated the self-excitation principle in a paper read to the Royal Society in April 1866, and later in the same year an American inventor, Moses Farmer, wrote to Wilde in terms which indicated that he too had independently discovered the principle. Claims have also been made that as early as 1861 the Hungarian physicist Anyos Jedlik had employed the principle at Budapest in an experimental machine. The details of these claims need not concern us here, where it suffices to state that self-excitation was firmly established by 1866. The importance of this discovery was that it made the electric generator self-contained: that is, a machine that had only to be rotated to produce electricity for as long as desired. With the application of a

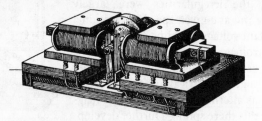

FIG. 304. Self-excited generator of C. F. Varley, 1866

steam-engine to rotate the armature, convincingly demonstrated in England in 1857 in connexion with the generation of electricity to supply arc-lamps for lighthouses (p. 630), the large-scale use of electricity was brought a step nearer.

There were, nevertheless, important technological improvements still to be made: in particular, generators capable of giving satisfactory service over long periods had still to be designed. An improved armature was provisionally patented by Werner von Siemens in 1856, and was extensively used although it had inherent defects: it generated so much heat—representing waste of power—that on large machines water-cooling was necessary. A better, ring-shaped armature was devised in 1860 by an Italian physicist Antonio Pacinotti, but the description he published four years later attracted surprisingly little attention. Much more decisively important in its practical consequences was the similar ring-armature of Z. T. Gramme, introduced in 1870: Gramme dynamos, mainly designed to .be driven by steam-engines, could supply current continuously without overheating and within a few years were in wide use.

Gramme's ring-armature (Fig. 305) was improved by Emil Bürgin of Basle, by R. E. B. Crompton in Britain, and by the Swedish engineer Jonas Wenström. In Germany, the Siemens & Halske Company replied to the challenge of Gramme's design by introducing the drum-armature (Fig. 306), which eventually replaced the ring-armature. In the 1880's the young Ferranti, following an earlier suggestion by William Thomson (later Lord Kelvin), designed an armature with a continuous winding of copper wire.

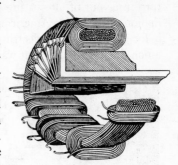

FIG. 305. Gramme's ring-armature, 1870

Meanwhile, the possibilities of the arc-lamp for lighting streets and large buildings, and more particularly of Edison's and Swan's filament lamps (p. 634) for domestic use, had—together with the growing needs of industry—made necessary the design and construction of electric power generators of substantial size. Before describing these, however, it is convenient to consider a remaining difficulty which excited much controversy. The earliest generators, it will be recalled, were regarded as unsatisfactory because they provided alternating current, and commutators, not infrequently a source of trouble, had to be employed if direct current was required—as, for example, for electrochemical purposes. By the 1880's, however, it was being increasingly realized that alternating current had definite practical advantages. A major factor was that for long-distance transmission, power losses

FIG. 306. Dynamo with drum-armature, 1876

were much less for high voltages than low, and for technical reasons high-voltage direct-current generators presented great difficulties in construction. Conversion of alternating current from high voltage to low for ordinary use was easily effected by a transformer, the principle of which had been elucidated by Faraday in 1831, although some fifty years elapsed before it came into general use. On the other hand, the coupling of alternators in power-stations presented great practical difficulties. The argument took a decisive turn in favour of alternating current when, in 1893, George Westinghouse—a strong American protagonist of the system—adopted it for the first hydro-electric generators at Niagara Falls. Even so, much direct-current plant was installed and even today, when alter-

FIG. 307. Deptford power-station, 1889

nating current is almost universal for general use, isolated pockets of direct-current mains supply still exist.

We have already seen (p. 510) that the development of the gas industry was much influenced by Winsor's realization that the future lay not with local generation but with distributing gas from large central works. In the electrical industry Ferranti occupies a position analogous to that of Winsor in the gas industry eighty years earlier: his advocacy of wide distribution at high voltage found practical expression in 1889, when the power-station he had designed and built at Deptford for the London Electricity Supply Corporation came into operation (Fig. 307); the plant included four 10,000-h.p. steam-engines, driving 10,000-volt alternators, and two 1,250-h.p. engines, driving 5,000-volt alternators. Ferranti also fathered 176 inventions, including an alternator, cables, and an electricity meter to measure consumption by his company's customers.

The Deptford power-station was the prototype of modern installations, but it was not the first substantial one. As early as 1875 a Gramme generator was installed at the Gare du Nord in Paris to supply power for arc-lamps, and in the same year a mill at Mülhausen and the Menier chocolate factory (p. 414) at Noisiel-sur-Marne were among other concerns that adopted the system. Wanamaker's store in Philadelphia installed a generating plant in 1878 so that it could be illuminated with arc-lamps; in New York, Edison's Pearl Street generating station (Fig. 308) was in operation in 1882. In London, the Holborn Viaduct plant was opened a few

FIG. 308. Pearl Street generating station, New York, 1882

weeks before the Pearl Street station, and the installation of arc-lamps at the Gaiety Theatre in the same year widely advertised the capabilities of contemporary generators. In 1883 a small power-station—taken over by the London Electricity Supply Corporation —was built to light the Grosvenor Gallery, and surplus electricity was sold to local consumers; a power-station to meet local needs in Brighton was built in 1887.

In the account of the steam-engine (Ch. 11) it was pointed out that Parsons began to experiment with turbines primarily because the electrical industry required for its dynamos engines capable of a higher speed of rotation than seemed possible with the reciprocating steam-engine; in 1888 his first turbo-alternator—working at 4,800 revolutions a minute—was installed in the Forth Banks power-station. This had an initial capacity of 75 kW; by 1900, however, he had built two 1,000-kW turbo-alternators for Elberfeld, Germany.

Meanwhile, the growing demand for electricity caused attention to be turned to the possibility of utilizing one of the oldest sources of mechanical power, the water-wheel, whose early development has been described elsewhere (p. 311). This had been dramatically improved by Benoit Fourneyron in 1827 with his outward-flow water-turbine, which gained him a prize from the French Société d'Encouragement. One of his earliest machines operated at 2,300 r.p.m. under a water head of about 350 ft. Such heads of water were not common in Europe, however, and there Fourneyron's machines were displaced by Jonval's more suitable axial-flow turbine, introduced in 1843. This was followed by the inward-flow turbine, which was conceived by Poncelet in 1826 and built in crude form by Howd in New York a dozen years later; it was much improved by James Francis and by James Thomson, who developed the vortex wheel in 1852. About 1870 a British mining engineer, Lester Pelton, working in the Californian gold-field, discovered—following an accident to a simple water-wheel—that fast and powerful wheels could be worked by directing high-pressure water jets at hemispherical cups placed round the circumference. Within twenty years a 500-h.p. Pelton wheel, worked by a jet fed by a 400-ft head of water, was in use in Alaska.

The first great hydro-electric installation—designed to have an ultimate capacity of 200,000 h.p.—was commenced at Niagara in 1886, after some sixteen years of planning. It was originally intended to equip it with Jonval turbines, but in the event two Fourneyron outward-flow wheels, each generating 5,500 h.p., were originally used by the Niagara Falls Power Company in 1895. Very soon, however, turbines of the Francis type were adopted. Jonval axial-flow turbines were also in use there at an early date.

While hydro-electric schemes became increasingly important, their successful operation demanded both an exceptional combination of local circumstances and, as a general rule, very considerable capital outlay. At the end of the nineteenth century, coal-fired steam-engines were still the main, and not very economical, prime movers in electrical power-stations: in the following three decades output per worker in American power-stations was trebled, and in the third of those decades alone coal consumption per unit of electricity generated in America and Britain fell by almost 44 per cent.

DISTRIBUTION

As we have seen, the 1880's saw the beginning of general recognition of the economic advantages of central power-stations generating electricity at high voltages and serving large areas: acceptance of this principle brought with it new problems of distribution, both practical and economic. The distinction between conductors and insulators had been made in the eighteenth century, and the insulation of wires for electrical work became an important part of the task of the early investigators. The high conductivities of metals, especially copper and silver, were recognized at an early date and wires of these metals—and of the cheaper, but more easily corroded and less highly conducting, iron—were widely used. For some purposes the insulating properties of air were sufficient, so that it was necessary to provide insulation—for example, glass, ceramic, or sulphur—only at the points of support. Continuously insulated wires were, however, increasingly demanded, and at first these were made by laboriously winding them by hand with silk or cotton and then coating them with protective varnish. By the 1840's, however, other insulators and methods of mass-producing insulated wires were being used, the development of the electric telegraph (p. 626) providing a powerful stimulus. From the 1850's the expansion of the electrical industry in general, and of the electric telegraph in particular, called for enormous numbers of porcelain insulators for telegraph-poles, and from 1888 ceramics based on steatite began to be used for the same purpose. Towards the end of the century oil-sealed insulators began to be used to prevent leakage at high voltages through surface films of moisture.

For underground cables, necessary in most urban areas because the authorities would not allow overhead wires, Hancock in 1848 invented a machine that continuously coated wire with gutta-percha (obtained from the percha tree in Malaya); within a short time means had been found for enclosing several wires, each insulated from the others, within a single gutta-percha sheath. But gutta-percha was not very satisfactory as it was liable to perish. Vulcanized gutta-percha was introduced in 1850, but difficulties arose from corrosion of the copper by the sulphur used in vulcanization (p. 527), and in the following year attempts were made to insulate telegraph wires with bitumen. Although this first attempt was not a success, bituminous substances were later widely used for power cables. As mechanical strength and resistance to abrasion and severe working conditions became increasingly important, armoured cable began to be used. Lead-covered cable was introduced in 1850; for less exacting conditions fabric coating was used. The modern practice of identifying the elements of a multi-strand cable by giving each strand a different colour was begun in 1852.

By the end of the century, india-rubber had become accepted as the best, although relatively expensive, insulating material for general-purpose cables. As with vulcanized gutta-percha, difficulties arose through chemical combination between the copper wires and the sulphur in the vulcanized rubber, but this was overcome by tinning the wire before sheathing it. The particular problems of the Deptford power-station led Ferranti to explore the possibility of paper as an insulator for high-voltage work: this very ambitious venture was embarked upon when there were not only no existing generators or transformers capable of operating at more than 2,500 volts, but no cables suitable for distribution of the supply. Ferranti's experiments with conductors consisting of concentric copper tubes, separated by spirally-wound waxed paper, proved so successful that this design became standard practice for many years. This type of cable had certain intrinsic advantages apart from that of fulfilling the heavy duty required of it. It was particularly suitable for use with alternating current because it had a much lower electrostatic capacity than was easily obtainable with any other insulating material. Moreover, the concentric design had the advantage that the cable had no inductive effect on neighbouring telegraph, telephone, or other electrical installations—a major consideration as the electrical network beneath city streets increased in complexity.

By the end of the century, three main systems of underground distribution of electricity were in use. In one, the cables, separated by wooden bridges, were completely embedded in bitumen in cast-iron troughs: a disadvantage of this system was that it was not possible to withdraw a cable in the event of a fault developing. If provision for withdrawal was considered necessary, the cables were laid separately through channels in 6-foot lengths of bituminous concrete, itself an insulator: draw-boxes were provided at intervals so that in the event of a failure the short length of cable affected could be removed without disturbing the whole system. In the third system, the cable was heavily protected so that it could be laid direct in the ground: the conductor was surrounded successively with paper, bituminized cotton, and lead, and then further armoured, generally with more bitumen, steel wire, and an outer coat of bituminized fabric.

By the middle of the nineteenth century the demand of the electrical industry for copper, a relatively expensive metal, had become so considerable that serious attention had to be given to economizing in its use: the first Atlantic telegraph cable of 1858, for example, incorporated no less than 17,000 miles of stranded copper wire. In 1881 Lord Kelvin, addressing the British Association for the Advancement of Science, enunciated a scientific principle that could be used as a guide for the most economical construction of a conductor. The following year John Hopkinson, professor of electrical engineering at King's College, London, patented the three-wire system of distributing direct current, which provided a means of supplying two two-wire circuits from a single generator operating at double the voltage required for either circuit, thus permitting a saving of copper of up to 50 per cent. Later attempts in the nineteenth century to economize still further by using five-wire systems proved unsatisfactory for technical reasons.

TELEGRAPHY AND TELEPHONY

The relaying of visual signals from one station to another was carried out in ancient times; the smoke-signals of the Red Indian are reminders that very primitive means suffice for simple messages. Aeschylus, in the *Agamemnon*, described the sending of signals by means of torches: his account is doubtless based on his experiences with the Athenian army in the Persian wars. The Greek historian Polybius also describes communication by means of fire-signals, and seventeen centuries after his death the beacons that gave England warning of the Spanish Armada in 1588 exemplify a method used in many countries to give early warning of danger. The special problems of communication between ships, or between ships and shore stations, led the future James II, while Lord High Admiral, to design a set of naval flag-signals, which were systematized by Kempenfeldt and Earl Howe at the time of the great maritime wars against France in the last decades of the eighteenth century.

The possibilities of such visual systems were much improved with the invention of the telescope, but telegraphy, in the modern sense of the term, is largely a product of the French Revolution, when French forces were fighting on many fronts and speedy communication between the armies was a matter of the first importance. Among the ardent supporters of the Revolution was Claude Chappe who, in 1790, applied his mind to the problem of long-distance telegraphy. Although he investigated the possibilities of the electric telegraph, his final recommendation was for a series of stations, equipped with semaphore arms and telescopes and usually not distant more than 10 miles from each other, by which messages could be relayed according to a predetermined code (Fig. 309). In 1793 Chappe became Ingénieur-Télégraphe, with instructions to set up a line of stations between Paris and Lille: the first message—announcing the recapture of Le Quesnoy —was passed in August 1794. Before the end of the century Paris had been similarly linked with Brest and Strasbourg, and by the time the Chappe system was finally abandoned in the middle of the nineteenth century the network comprised some 3,000 miles. Reports from France led the British Admiralty to establish a similar system of stations—the main difference being that movable shutters were used in place of semaphore arms—between London and Deal, and later between London and Portsmouth: hence the Telegraph Hills of the Ordnance Survey maps, then just beginning. A temporary break in the fighting in 1802 led to loss of interest in these schemes, but a line of stations between London and Plymouth was completed in 1806. At about the same time, a semaphore system was installed in the United

FIG. 309. Model of a Chappe telegraph station

States to connect an island off the coast of Massachusetts with Boston, to convey information about shipping. As the primary demand for the telegraph was, however, for urgent military intelligence, it is not surprising that the conclusion of hostilities with France led to the Admiralty system falling into disuse, although the line from London to Portsmouth was not finally closed until the middle of the century. Ship-to-ship communication was, however, not neglected by the Admiralty: for example, by varying the combinations of two revolving crosses, 400 standardized messages could quickly be passed.

Working under ideal conditions, such visual systems could transmit messages surprisingly quickly: it is said that a short message could be sent from London to Deal within a minute. There were, however, obvious inherent disadvantages. The system was extremely extravagant in manpower: at its maximum, the French system included over 500 separate stations. It was, moreover, extremely vulnerable to climatic conditions, as poor visibility over any one section of the route could seriously, if not completely, disrupt the exchange of signals. The semaphore system justified itself when swift communication was vital and expense was unimportant, but it was clearly of limited value for ordinary civil purposes.

The future lay with the electric telegraph, but the necessary stimulus for its development was not provided until the 1830's, with the expansion of the railway network in Britain. The development of the telegraph is particularly associated with the names of William Cooke and Charles Wheatstone, but long before their time a variety of ingenious forms of electric telegraphic apparatus had been designed and demonstrated. Although most of these are out of the main line of evolution they may be briefly mentioned.

The first, and surprisingly detailed, reference to an electric telegraph was a proposal from an anonymous correspondent published as early as 1753 in the *Scots Magazine*. This provided for twenty-six separate wires, corresponding to the individual letters of the alphabet, to be suspended between the transmitting and receiving station, the words of the message being spelt out in full letter by letter: as each wire was connected with a machine generating static electricity, a corresponding pith ball could be moved at the receiving station. Le Sage put forward a similar scheme in the 1770's (Fig. 310). A few years later, in Paris, M. Lomond demonstrated a telegraph similar to Le Sage's but having the notable improvement of a single conductor instead of twenty-six separate ones: the letters of the message were distinguished by a code. In 1795, in Spain, Francisco Salvá employed a multiple-wire scheme and his proposals attracted royal patronage. In further experiments he reverted to single-wire working and it is alleged, although the evidence is inconclusive, that an experimental line was established between Madrid and Aranjuez, the spring residence of the royal family. Yet another electrostatic telegraph was devised by Francis Ronalds in London, and its working over 8 miles of wire was demonstrated in 1816: the Admiralty, however, informed him that they then had no interest in telegraphs of any kind.

The advent of the voltaic battery, which provided a far more convenient source of electricity, brought electrical telegraphy substantially nearer practical realization. Among the pioneers of its use was a German inventor, S. T. von Soemmering, whose equipment was based on that of Salvá. In 1810 he demonstrated his telegraph to Baron Schilling, one of the attachés at the Russian Legation in Munich, who was greatly impressed with its possibilities: so much so, indeed, that for many years he devoted a great deal of his time to its further development. The electric battery provided a convenient means of transmitting a strong signal at will, but means of

FIG. 310. Le Sage's electrostatic telegraph, c. 1774

receiving it were still so primitive—Salvá had even suggested utilizing a shock experienced by the operator—that messages could be transmitted only very slowly. This obstacle was overcome when the relationship between magnetism and electricity was established. The discovery that an electric current flowing through a coil could cause a movement in a magnet suspended near by (p. 610) was an event of great importance to telegraphy, and quickly attracted the attention of both von Soemmering and Schilling. From 1822 Schilling experimented with a number of electromagnetic detectors (Fig. 311) and devised a code for single-needle working, resembling that later put forward by Samuel Morse. In 1836 one of his instruments was seen by Cooke in Heidelberg, and from this stemmed the first successful large-scale system of electric telegraphy.

On his return to England Cooke carried out various experiments with an electromagnetic telegraph, and was commissioned to install one on the Liverpool–Manchester railway. Encountering technical difficulties, he consulted Wheatstone, then professor of natural philosophy at King's College, London, who had himself been experimenting with a similar form of electric telegraph. Recognizing the similarity of their interests, the two men entered into a partnership which was unfortunately marred by constant quarrels concerning their relative contributions to the development of the invention.

The partners obtained their first patent in June 1837, and later in the same year they demonstrated a five-needle telegraph to the directors of the London and Birmingham railway. This demonstra-

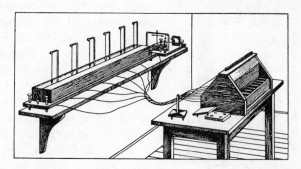

FIG. 311. Schilling's electric telegraph, *c.* 1825

tion produced no immediate results, as the directors were not fully convinced of the value of the invention to them. The directors of the Great Western Railway were more discerning, and in 1838 Paddington and West Drayton were connected: four years later the telegraph was extended to Slough. This telegraph line, and its possibilities, attracted enormous publicity in 1845 when a suspected murderer was seen to board a London-bound train at Slough: the news was telegraphed to Paddington, and he was arrested on arrival and subsequently hanged. The receivers on this installation were of a two-needle kind (Fig. 312) requiring the message to be coded. Although Wheatstone always favoured receivers which directly recorded the letter being transmitted, it gradually became clear that codification was by far the most satisfactory system, and this gradually came into general use. For the code now universally used we are indebted to the American inventor Morse, who had experimented independently since 1832. His earliest instruments were relatively crude, but after a first public demonstration in September 1837 they were redesigned with the help of the ironmaster Alfred Vail.

The later 1840's were a period of expansion of the telegraph service, resulting in Britain from the success of the Paddington to Slough installation, and in the United States from Morse's good fortune in completing the first line, linking Washington with Baltimore, one day before the Democratic Convention met in the latter city to choose its Presidential candidate. On the Continent, too, the importance and convenience of the electric telegraph were widely recognized. So great were the demands on Cooke and Wheatstone that in 1846 they formed the Electric Telegraph Company, which within six years had installed some 4,000 miles of telegraph in Britain. In the United States, four years after Morse's initial success in 1844, Florida was the only state east of the Mississippi which the telegraph had not reached. Intensive competition between rival American companies ended with the formation of the Western Union Company in 1856; in Britain, an Act of 1868 allowed the Postmaster-General to acquire, work, and maintain electric telegraphs.

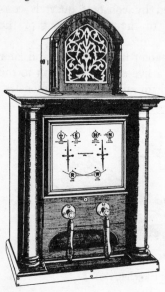

FIG. 312. Two-needle telegraph by Cooke and Wheatstone, 1842

Telegraphic systems had also been developing on the Continent, and it is not surprising that when London was linked with Dover in 1846 Wheatstone suggested a submarine cable to France that would link London with the European network: after one unsuccessful attempt in 1847 and another in 1850 (Fig. 313), this project was finally realized in 1851. Among the results of this were that the opening and closing prices of the funds in Paris were known before the close of business on the London Stock Exchange. Within six years a far more ambitious programme, the linking of Britain with the United States, was attempted. The story of the transatlantic cable cannot be told in detail here, but it is a remarkable record of triumph over practical and technical difficulties. In the first venture, in the summer of 1857, the cable broke and was lost after 300 miles of it had been laid. After a second failure, the two continents were successfully joined in August 1858: but the cable broke down and after a few weeks became quite unserviceable. A redesigned cable, the first to be laid by the *Great Eastern* (p. 373), was lost in mid-Atlantic in a depth of 12,000 ft, though subsequently recovered. Not until 1866 was final success achieved and a permanent and satisfactory telegraphic link established between the Old and the New Worlds.

FIG. 313. Cross-channel cable-laying, August 1850

By 1862 the world's telegraph system covered approximately 150,000 miles, including 15,000 miles in Britain, 80,000 on the Continent, and 48,000 in America. Telegraph offices (Fig. 314) made possible the very speedy transmission of messages throughout the system. By 1872, when the Mayor of Adelaide exchanged messages with the Lord Mayor of London, almost all the principal cities of the world were linked together.

The telegraph was devised to transmit messages, generally coded, which had to be written by hand at the receiving end. A method of printing the message was invented by 1845, and was developed in the United States as 'House's printing telegraph'. Wheatstone patented a printing telegraph in 1860. The transmission of speech, however, presented quite different problems. Although an electric telephone was demonstrated in Germany as early as 1861, the first practical instrument permitting commercial exploitation was that of

Alexander Graham Bell, whose invention was to some extent inspired by the researches into the reproduction of sound made by the German physicist Hermann Helmholtz. In 1876 Bell patented his invention, incorporating an electromagnetic microphone, and it was demonstrated to the British Association in the following year. The first telephone company in Britain was formed in 1878. Originally visualized as a means of oral communication between two points, the telephone exchange—which in Britain first appeared in 1879—made conversation possible between any pair of a large number of local subscribers. Inter-urban lines soon followed.

FIG. 314. Telegraph office, London, 1850

Meanwhile, a third and even more revolutionary method of communication by electrical means was being developed. In the latter half of the nineteenth century Faraday's experimental discoveries in electromagnetism were being translated into mathematical terms by Clerk Maxwell, whose theory, in its fully developed form, was published in 1873 in his classic *Treatise on Electricity and Magnetism*. Maxwell demonstrated that the propagation of electrical disturbances resembles that of light, and he asserted the identity of the two phenomena, concluding that 'We can scarcely avoid the inference that light consists in the transverse undulations of the same medium which is the cause of electric and magnetic phenomena'. Maxwell's views were so unorthodox that many of his contemporaries had difficulty in accepting them. Recognition of their validity owed much to the work of a German physicist, Heinrich Hertz, who discovered the electric waves whose existence had been deduced by Maxwell as an inevitable consequence of his theory. On his appointment as professor of physics at Karlsruhe in 1885, Hertz turned his attention to verifying Maxwell's theory by experiment. He quickly showed that a flow of current in one electrical circuit could result in a corresponding flow in a similarly 'tuned' circuit not directly connected with the first. Waves radiated by the transmitter could be detected by the appearance of a spark at a small gap in the receiving circuit.

Hertz proved the general similarity of electric and light waves, the essential difference being in the wavelength; waves of approximately 24 cm wavelength were employed in his own experiments. Hertz did not concern himself with the practical possibilities of his invention: not until 1895 did Ernest (later Lord) Rutherford transmit messages over a distance of three-quarters of a mile at Cambridge, and it was not until the very end of the century that the experiments of Guglielmo Marconi put wireless telegraphy on a practical basis. Marconi used waves of approximately 300–3,000 metres wavelength; not until very much later were relatively short waves, such as

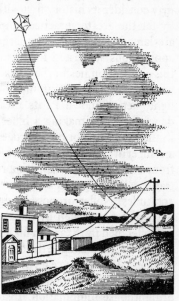

Fig. 315. Receiving station at Signal Hill, Newfoundland, for Marconi's first transatlantic wireless signal, 1901

Hertz had used in his laboratory experiments, used for long-distance communication. Marconi's most spectacular achievement, the sending of a wireless signal across the Atlantic, falls just after the end of the period with which we are here concerned, taking place on 12 December 1901 (Fig. 315).

ELECTRIC LIGHTING

The basic principles on which electric lighting is based had been established at the very beginning of the nineteenth century. As we have noted (p. 610), (Sir) Humphry Davy, as early as 1802, had remarked the brilliant light that was emitted when an electric spark was struck between two carbon electrodes. It was also known that the passage of electricity through a conductor caused the latter to become heated: this is the principle of the incandescent filament lamp, in which a conductor is heated to so high a temperature that it glows and emits light. Not until the latter half of the century, however, were these two discoveries turned to practical account.

As the arc-lamp is the earliest form of electrical illumination we may consider its history first, although the electric filament lamp had by far the greater practical importance. For technical reasons, the arc-lamp is suitable only for large installations, and one of the earliest applications suggested for it was in lighthouses. The beginning of this application lies in the work of a French pioneer, F. Nollet, who proposed using the Drummond light in lighthouses. The Drummond light, better known in its theatrical application as the limelight, depended upon making a block of lime incandescent by heating it in the intensely hot oxyhydrogen flame. It was invented in 1826 by an officer of the Royal Engineers, Thomas Drummond, who graduated from survey work to an important position in the Irish administration: light signals were observed over a distance of more than 100 miles. Nollet proposed to generate the appropriate mixture of oxygen and hydrogen by the electrolytic decomposition of water.

Nollet died in 1853 with his ambitions unfulfilled, and his financial supporters then sought the advice of an English engineer, Frederick Holmes. After some years of experiment the project was abandoned, but his interest in it led Holmes to a more practical and direct form of lighthouse illumination. Instead of using the electric current to decompose water, he suggested that it should be used for an arc, and in 1857 he staged a demonstration for the Brethren of Trinity House, London. His generator, of an expensive but very efficient design pioneered by the French engineer Baron A. de Meritens, was steam-driven and had an output of about 1½ kW. The demonstration was so successful that full-scale trials were requested at once, to take place at the South Foreland lighthouse. The equipment was put into operation there with conspicuous success in December 1858, and four years later Dungeness lighthouse, too, was equipped with arc-lamps. The arc-lamps used at the South Foreland were Duboscq's improvement of a type originated by W. E. Staite in 1846.

Among the technical problems Staite had to overcome was that of preparing carbon of sufficient purity and hardness for the electrode. A further problem with all carbon arc-lamps is that the electrodes burn away, so that the gap between them is variable and thus the intensity of the light changes. At first Staite tried to overcome this with a clockwork mechanism, but he soon changed this in favour of one driven by a falling weight and regulated—through the thermal expansion of a copper rod—by the heat of the arc, which increases as the length of the spark increases. Later, in collaboration with W. Petrie, Staite made further improvements, but there was only slight interest because batteries were still the only practicable source of electricity for the purpose then generally available in Britain. Not until the dynamo had been further developed was a satisfactory source of power available for arc-lamps: a number of large installations were completed both in Britain and on the Continent within a few years of the advent of Gramme's ring-dynamo in 1871.

FIG. 316. Jablochkoff's arc-lamp, 1876

In 1876 an arc-lamp of new and improved design was introduced by Paul Jablochkoff, a Russian army telegraph engineer who had settled in Paris. In this, the carbon electrodes were vertical and parallel—instead of opposed end-to-end as in other types—and the arc was struck between the tips of the rods. No mechanical regulation was provided, the use of alternating current ensuring that the electrodes burned away at the same rate. In 1877 eighty Jablochkoff 'candles' (Fig. 316) were introduced in a department store in Paris; in the same year the West India Dock in London was similarly lighted, followed by Billingsgate market, Holborn Viaduct, and part of the Thames Embankment. The performance of the lamps was further improved by using copper-plated carbon electrodes. Meanwhile, however, the incandescent-filament lamp, which we will next consider, had been developed to such an extent that by the 1880's it was being sold in hundreds of thousands, with the result that,. except for special purposes, the arc-lamp was superseded.

The possibilities of incandescent-filament lamps attracted the attention of inventors from the 1840's: that some thirty years elapsed before such lamps came into use was due to the technical difficulties of their construction. Two major obstacles had to be overcome. Firstly, the filament had to be constructed of an electrical conductor that could be heated to incandescence without melting, and this severely limited the choice. Secondly, as almost all substances combine with oxygen when so heated, the filament had to be enclosed in a high vacuum, and satisfactory means of achieving this were not available to the early inventors.

Staite demonstrated an incandescent-filament lamp in Britain as early as 1847, but the filament, although it consisted of a high-melting alloy of platinum and iridium, had a very short life because of

FIG. 317. Evacuation of electric lamp bulbs with a mercury air-pump, *c.* 1883

residual air left in the container; other contemporary inventors, using platinum filaments, encountered the same problem and failed to solve it. Not until 1865, when the mercury pump (Fig. 317) was invented, was it possible to obtain a satisfactory vacuum. This development encouraged Joseph Swan to resume experiments with carbon filaments that he had begun about 1847, when he had witnessed Staite's demonstration and had become aware of an American patent, lodged by J. W. Starr in 1845, which included the use of carbon filaments. Swan's first carbon-filament lamp was made in 1848, but its life was too brief to be useful; his first satisfactory model was not made until 1878 (Fig. 318), the filament being made by carbonizing a thread of mercerized cotton (p. 577). Meanwhile, after early experiments with platinum, Edison in America had developed lamps incorporating filaments made by carbonizing slivers of bamboo, this material being chosen because Edison believed that it gave a particularly strong filament (Fig. 319). Whichever type of filament was used—Edison's, in which the original structure of the carbonaceous material was deliberately retained, or Swan's, in which a dense homogeneous structure was sought—contact had to be made with the external electric supply through the evacuated glass container. For this purpose, platinum wires had to be fixed into the glass, the choice of this expensive material being dictated by the fact that it was the only metal then available whose expansion on heating is the same as that of glass: if the thermal expansion were different, some cracking of the glass, with fatal impairment of the vacuum, would be inevitable.

Initially, Swan took no steps to patent his inventions; by contrast Edison, as with all his inventions, took the fullest possible advantage of the patent laws. The result was that Swan, despite his originality, found his way blocked by Edison. However, the balance was redressed when, made wiser by events, Swan patented in 1880 a process for removing the last traces of air from the filaments by 'flashing' them before the bulb was finally sealed: this gave longer life and diminished the internal blackening of the bulb, due to deposited carbon, that had quickly reduced the efficiency of early carbon-filament lamps. In 1883 Swan likewise patented an improved method for the preparation of fila-

FIG. 318. Swan's experimental carbon-filament lamp, 1878

ments. In this, cellulose was dissolved to form a syrupy liquid, which was then extruded through a fine nozzle into a coagulating bath. The resulting thread was then wound on formers, shaping it as a characteristically looped curve, and carbonized by baking.

After some legal skirmishes, Edison and Swan recognized that their interests were better served by co-operation than by competition; accordingly, the Edison & Swan United Electric Light Company Limited was founded in 1883. Until the original carbon-lamp patents expired in 1893 this company had a monopoly of manufacture in Britain, and potential competitors were driven to the Continent. Among those who took this course was C. J. Robertson, who had been associated with another inventor, St George Lane-Fox,

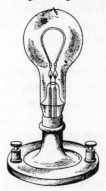

FIG. 319. Edison's carbon-filament lamp, 1881

a past experimenter with both carbon and metallic filaments. Robertson equipped and managed a number of electric-lamp factories on the Continent.

Surprisingly, in view of its later immense success, the possibilities of the incandescent-filament lamp were not at first generally recognized: in Germany, for example, Werner von Siemens—keenly on the alert though he must have been for new uses for his electric generators—declined, even as late as 1881, an invitation to take up a European licence for Edison's patents. The new type of electric light at first spread slowly, but then more quickly as its use in a number of well-known buildings demonstrated its value. From 1881 the debates of the House of Commons were illuminated by incandescent lamps, and in the same year an elaborate installation of over a thousand lamps was made at the Savoy Theatre, London. The new fashion was followed next year by the British Museum and the Royal Academy. Its convenience for transport was soon recognized, both an ocean-going ship and a train being fitted with the new lamps in 1881; but another five years passed before the first house-to-house installation in the United Kingdom was made in Kensington, London.

The success of the carbon-filament lamp did not deter inventors from seeking to make a satisfactory metallic filament, and by the end of the nineteenth century they had achieved a measure of success that brought the end of the carbon lamp in sight. One of its last strongholds was on board warships, where its resistance to the shock of gunfire prolonged the demand for it. For the reasons previously stated, the choice of metals was extremely limited, and even when its physical properties were known to be satisfactory, the conversion of the metal into a sufficiently fine and uniform wire might entail formidable difficulties. In 1898 von Welsbach, pioneer of the incandescent gas-mantle (p. 513), introduced filaments of osmium (melting point 2,700° C.) and just after the turn of the century tantalum (melting point 2,996° C.) was used. The future, however, lay with tungsten, with its much higher melting point (3,410° C.): although very intractable, this came into general use for lamp filaments about 1911.

By 1900 the supremacy of incandescent lamps over all others for domestic use was fully recognized: they were convenient, clean, safe, and reliable. Their adoption was, however, controlled by the rate of the development of public electric-supply services. Electric lighting was an accepted feature of urban life by 1900—though gas-lighting was still a competitor not to be ignored—but its penetration into the countryside was necessarily slow.

With growing use of electric lamps, produced in millions by the end of the century, attention had to be paid to the standardization of fittings. At first, connexion of the mains supply was made directly to the protruding ends of the platinum wires that supported the carbon filament. From the 1880's, however, a clear distinction began to be made in British practice, on the one hand, and American and Continental practice on the other. Britain adopted the bayonet holder now familiar there, while Edison from the beginning used the screw-type holder. By 1900 the fuse—made of low-melting tin wire which would liquefy and break the circuit if the current exceeded a predetermined maximum—was in general use.

THE ELECTRIC-MOTOR

As we have seen, the principles of the dynamo and the electric-motor are the same: if an electric potential is supplied to direct-current dynamos of the types we have considered, the armature will revolve. Indeed, in 1873 Gramme staged in Vienna a demonstration of two of his generators (p. 614) so arranged that either one would serve as a dynamo to provide electricity to drive the other as a motor. For reasons of efficiency, however, the design of dynamos and motors must differ. Gramme's machines were, in any event, suitable as motors only with direct current, whereas, as we have seen, alternating current gradually gained the ascendancy for large-scale generation towards the end of the century. The first alternating-current motor was invented in 1888 by Nikola Tesla, and was manufactured in America by Westinghouse.

For tramway and railway traction work, however, within the period with which we are concerned, the direct-current motor predominated: even when the source of supply was alternating current, preliminary conversion to direct current was common practice. Thus on the Central London Railway each locomotive was fitted with four 120-h.p. direct-current motors. The initial source of supply was 5,000-volt alternating current, which was transformed down to 305 volts at three sub-stations; this in turn was converted to 500-volt direct current, supplied to the locomotives through a third rail, of special high-conducting steel, supported on porcelain insulators. At the end of the century, this was looked upon as one of the most successful examples of the application of electricity to traction achieved up to that time.

A very important feature of the electric-motor is its convenience: it can be operated wherever a cable from an electric supply can be brought. By the end of the nineteenth century the usefulness of this was beginning to be recognized in industry generally. The noisy and cumbersome system of overhead shafts, with pulleys and belts for every machine to be driven, began to give way to individual electric-motors for each machine, which might be of less than 1 h.p. apiece. At first, the tendency was to mount the electric-motor a short distance away from the machine it was to drive, the power being transmitted by a belt, but by 1900 some designers, especially of machine tools, had begun to incorporate electric-motors as an integral part of the machine. Some machines even incorporated several electric-motors, each driving a separate part of the mechanism.

In retrospect it seems surprising that the use of electric-power, which held such great possibilities for electrochemistry as well as for factory purposes and traction, should have developed so slowly up to 1900 in all spheres except that of illumination. The electrical industry was important nowhere except in Germany—where Siemens & Halske had given it a flying start—Britain, and the United States; in the last-named country it employed in 1899 only 42,000 wage-earners, a number that was to rise by 1929 to nearly 330,000. The reason appears to lie largely in a double difficulty. On the one hand, electricity did not easily come into use industrially except in new branches of technology, because in its early stages of development it could not compete on a cost basis with established steam-power as a prime mover. On the other hand, the use of electricity for lighting was characterized by a short peak-period both in the day and in the year: average demand was often no more than 10 per cent. of capacity, which meant that large-scale production was too costly in overhead expenses to be readily undertaken. After 1900 the growth of electric traction—where the far-sighted Werner von Siemens twenty-one years before had pointed the way (p. 383), and where the new-style electric locomotive was the equal of the locomotive steam-engine in efficiency and in some respects its superior—was an important factor in spreading the load throughout the twenty-four hours.

PRINTING, PHOTOGRAPHY,
AND THE CINEMA

Iᴎ the present chapter we are to consider three forms of technology which are clearly distinguishable from most of the subjects discussed in this book by the fact that their impact is not direct but indirect, their indirect effect being, indeed, enormous. At the present day the availability of cheap mechanically printed books and papers is a big, often the biggest, factor in the spread of any new technology. By 1900 photography, at first designated merely as 'the new art', was already playing an indispensable part not only in science and medicine, but in the whole field of industry and commerce. As for cinematography, although its special interest lies in the fact that it is one of the few art forms created by the machine age, and its growth has been stimulated mainly by the needs of entertainment, this too has made a considerable contribution in recent years to the researches upon which technological development increasingly depends.

But in treating these three together it is important to bear in mind the broad historical distinction. In the age of Dr Johnson, printing was already 300 years old, and from the point of view of the user, as distinct from the maker, the printed book was a physical product not essentially different from the books we read today. Photography, on the other hand, was a creation of the nineteenth century: indeed, a period of only fifty years spans the gulf between the first daguerreotype and the Kodak snapshot. As regards the cinema, it is an instance, like that of the motor-car, in which the essential technological inventions belong to the late nineteenth century but the main social impact to the twentieth century: the first public screening of a film as we know it today was in 1895.

THE CASTING AND SETTING OF TYPE

There had been no basic changes in the working of a printing-press between its first inception and the early nineteenth century. Printing was an industry where, in Britain at least, the seven-year apprentice-ship was strictly enforced, but the proportion of apprentices to journeymen was so high that there was plenty of unemployment among the latter, while the former—some of whom began work at the age of nine—often served as labourers rather than trainees. In the first three centuries of its existence the rate of output of the press is estimated as having increased threefold, or perhaps as much as five-fold, but the average quality of the printing deteriorated. Each letter was still both cast and set by hand, and the maximum speed of an expert founder was about six letters a minute, which is very roughly equivalent to ten minutes for a line, or more than half a day's work for a page. Nevertheless, neither type-casting nor type-setting machines made rapid progress because of the opposition of a relatively well-organized body of workers.

The first effective type-casting machine was an American inven-tion of 1838, operated either by hand or by steam-power. The machine brought the mould up to the nozzle of a pot containing molten type-metal, opened the mould for the metal to flow in, closed it so as to give it its shape, and then tilted the reopened mould for the type to fall out. From America, where the opposition of workers was smallest, the machine spread to the book printers of Leipzig, to Edinburgh, and by 1851 to England: the catalogues for the Great Exhibition of that year were printed with its help, and the machine itself won a medal for the Leipzig firm of Brockhaus. The machine then became generally accepted; within a generation *The Times* was using a rotary caster with a hundred moulds and an output of 60,000 letters an hour. This meant that a newspaper could dispense altogether with the laborious process of redistributing the type after use; instead, it was thrown straight into the melting-pot to reappear as new type for the next day's issue.

In the case of composing machines the part played by the news-paper and periodical publisher was even greater, since he had the maximum incentive to override all opposing considerations, in-cluding the cheapness of labour as well as its hostility to the machine, in order to set up his material more quickly. The first and most ob-viously attractive proposal was for a machine which would bring down from a separate magazine each required character (a term which includes figures and punctuation marks besides small and capital letters), selecting them if necessary from more than one fount. A technical difficulty was that the characters were very small and would easily stick. However, by 1842 Henry Bessemer, later the inventor of the converter, in association with a firm at Lille, had produced a machine commonly known as the Pianotype (Fig. 320), which was employed to set up the first number of the *Family Herald*. One operator worked a keyboard, which was rather like that of a piano, and a second 'justified'—that is, spread out the material evenly into lines; they achieved a speed of 6,000 letters and spaces an hour, but the fact that the machine could be operated by women created

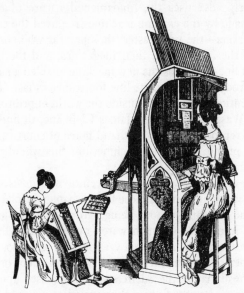

FIG. 320. An early type-composing machine

prejudice. In 1856 there appeared the Alden machine, containing no less than 14,626 parts, which came into use in book publishing. About ten years later a Lancashire newspaper proprietor applied a principle which we have already seen at work in connexion with loom harness (p. 106). A perforating machine made on a roll of paper a pattern of holes corresponding to the sequence of letters required; the roll was then passed through the character-holding machine, in which little levers, actuated by the pattern of holes on the roll, caused the different characters to fall in succession on to a travelling belt; the lines were then 'justified' as before. By the time of the Caxton quatercentenary celebrations in 1877 there was already an electrically driven type-setter, and the variety of inventions was becoming so great that *The Times* was alleged to have cellars full of discarded machines; yet, when allowance was made for the frequency with which they went out of order, these machines were not fast enough to secure general adoption anywhere, though newspapers were always eager to try them.

By 1886 newspapers were able to use a more successful machine based on a completely different principle. The etymology of the name 'linotype' (from 'line o' type'), however distasteful to the purist, clearly advertises the fundamental nature of the change. Each line made by the existing machines required the co-operation of three workers—the type-caster, the operator who controlled the selection of the letters from their magazines, and the person who justified the line—whereas the new machine enabled a single skilled worker to produce the complete line four times as fast. This epoch-making invention began quite outside the world of printing, with the desire of a Washington lawyer, James Clephane, to find a satisfactory way of reproducing his shorthand notes of court cases; he had first tried a primitive writing-machine, but this would not provide copies in quantity.

Clephane came in touch with an inventor who devised a method of casting a whole line in one piece from a papier-mâché mould, the first machine for this purpose being a rotary-impression machine built by an immigrant German watch-maker, Otto Mergenthaler. He later constructed an improved version with a keyboard controlling a number of vertical bars, each of which had cut on it in relief a letter of the alphabet: these letters were impressed upon a strip of papier mâché the length of a line, thus providing a mould from which a line of type could then be cast. Mergenthaler next saw that the first cumbrous stage could be omitted by assembling a magazine of matrices, that is to say, moulds from which the individual characters were made by the founder, so that a line could be set at a time. When the single-letter matrices were moved pneumatically to an assembly point, there still remained the problem of adjusting the spaces between the words so as to 'justify' the line, for which purpose he adopted an existing patent for wedge-shaped spacers to press downwards until the line was full. After the matrices forming the particular line had done their work, a distribution bar carried them back to the magazine. But since every machine required to be equipped with some hundreds of matrices, there was also the difficulty of the economic provision of enough punches from which to manufacture them: most opportunely, a mechanical punch-cutting machine was perfected, also by an American inventor, J. G. Benton. The Linotype (Fig. 321) as used universally at the present day was virtually completed by 1890, and quickly spread from America to Great Britain and later to the Continent. By 1900 it was already in use for a score of London daily newspapers and for some 250 other British metropolitan and provincial newspapers and periodicals.

In the 1890's America led the way again in the introduction of the Monotype machine for the setting of books. This machine also used the principle of a perforated roll of paper on which the keyboard operator recorded what was to be printed, very much as though he were typewriting; both the keyboard and the caster, which could be entirely separate, were worked pneumatically. The caster had a square matrix-holder of steel, which commonly contained 225 matrices in an area not exceeding 16 sq. in., and the required matrix was brought into position over the mould by the perforated pattern on the paper.

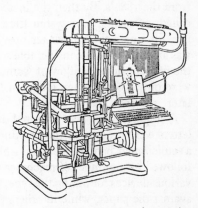

FIG. 321. The Linotype 'blower' composing machine, 1886

At the moment when the particular matrix was clamped into position a jet of molten type-metal was forced into the mould and the type was cast. The Monotype machine, producing a long strip of type matter on what is known as a galley, possessed the advantage over the Linotype that if necessary a single letter could be corrected at a time; given a satisfactory press, this would enable the book-printer to turn out by machine work as satisfactory as that produced by the older traditional methods. But before we examine the development of the press it will be convenient briefly to consider the typewriter.

THE TYPEWRITER

The typewriter is in effect a printing-machine which uses a keyboard to set and print a single letter at a time. Unlike the printing-press proper, it is compact and portable; but its usefulness is, of course, strictly limited by the small number of serviceable copies that it can produce. Even so, it represents an important advance in the use of machinery to replace the laborious copying of hand-written documents and cumbrous methods of duplication, such as the use of glutinous ink for enabling the writing to be transferred to moistened sheets of thin paper, a method patented by James Watt in 1780. Although various types of writing-machine, including some that embossed paper for the blind, were invented in the eighteenth and early nineteenth centuries, the extensive use of the typewriter dates only from the 1880's. By then the increasing size of business enterprises called increasingly for systematic correspondence and record-keeping, for which the typewriter provided the means. Its introduction was also an event of considerable social significance, since it brought the first considerable flow of women into office work: in 1881 there were only 7,000 women clerks in England and Wales; thirty years later, 146,000.

A 'typographer' was invented at Detroit in 1829, in which the letters were brought to the printing position as required by moving a semicircular band of metal on which they were mounted. This was followed by a number of machines of rather similar design and with various devices for inking the type, which in some models was struck against the paper, while in others there was a small hammer which struck the paper against the type. The arrangement of type characters on a curved band survives in a machine called the 'Varityper', which is still used to make type-plates for offset printing because it is easy to change the band for different alphabets. The prototype of the modern typewriter, however, was the *machine kryptographique*, invented by a Marseilles printer in 1833, with the modest claim that it would write 'almost as fast as a pen': this was the first machine to have each character mounted on a separate bar. The same principle was followed by the American printer, C. S. Sholes, who used a horizontal platen and inked ribbon and, after making some thirty models, solved the problem of rapid fingering. The main difficulty in this was the tendency for the type-bars to clash whenever two keys were touched in very quick succession; he solved this problem by arranging the keyboard substantially as it is arranged nowadays, so that letters which occur frequently in juxtaposition are placed widely apart.

Sholes's machine was manufactured from 1873 onwards by the Remington Company, who had begun as firearms manufacturers and had already branched out into the manufacture of agricultural implements and sewing-machines. Although the shift-key system was introduced in 1878, typewriters with a double keyboard, for small and capital letters respectively, continued in use until the 1890's, when the increasing practice of touch-typing made the use of the larger keyboard undesirable. Other improvements made before the end of the century, which both enhanced and attested the growing popularity of the machine, were the arrangements for making the text fully visible during typing, the introduction of a tabulator, and the reduction of size and weight so as to provide a truly portable model.

THE MODERN PRINTING-PRESS

Since the application of (electric) power to the typewriter lay far in the future, the history of the typewriter bears no resemblance to that of the printing-press proper, which was becoming heavier, larger, swifter, and more powerful as the nineteenth century advanced. It was not until 1800 that the third Earl Stanhope employed iron instead of wood in the first successful attempt to produce a press that could handle both heavy formes of type matter and delicate wood-engravings, such as those of the school of Thomas Bewick. At a price of 90 guineas—double the cost at that time of a wooden press—he provided a machine of iron which rested upon a wooden tee. After the bed had been run under the platen in the usual way, the latter was applied to the type by a combination of lever- and screw-motion which exerted a sufficient uniform pressure for the entire type-surface to be impressed at one pull. This was followed about 1813 by the independent American invention of the Columbian press, the first to eliminate the screw: the platen was driven down by means of a system of levers and counterweights, the topmost lever being surmounted by a heavy metal eagle, the position of which could be adjusted to vary the pressure. The inventor, a Philadelphia cabinet-maker named George Clymer, introduced his press successfully to the English market, where it was improved into a machine called the Albion. This applied the pressure by means of an elliptical steel bar which rotated above the platen-head, applying the maximum pressure as it reached the perpendicular. As great strength of impression was combined with light weight and simplicity of operation, the Albion (Fig. 322), surmounted by a Royal Coat of Arms on the counterweight in place of the American eagle, enjoyed great popularity in England and to some extent elsewhere. First built in the

1820's, in the 1860's it was being sold in thirteen sizes costing from £12 to £75, and at the end of the century was chosen by William Morris for the Kelmscott Press.

Printing is commonly thought of in terms of the newspaper and periodical and of the book, but there was a third class of work whose needs technology had to satisfy. It is estimated that late-Victorian Britain had about 2,000 newspaper establishments, while its book-printing firms were confined to two dozen towns, but the jobbing printers numbered at least 8,000. Their average business was certainly small, but taken as a whole they represented a prodigious demand for all kinds of individual and local needs, ranging from visiting cards to catalogues, pamphlets, and, above all, handbills. These remained a staple form of advertising as long as the daily newspaper was something of a luxury in the homes of the masses—it is recorded that in 1861 it was possible to collect 250 such items during a walk round the City and West End of London—and even after the popular newspaper came in with the *Daily Mail* in 1896, they still had their uses in commerce if produced cheaply enough.

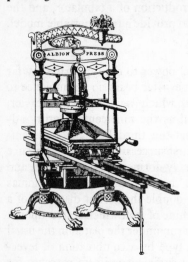

FIG. 322. Early form of Albion press invented by R. W. Cope

It was for such purposes that Steven Ruggles of Boston, Massachusetts, invented in 1851 a press with a vertical bed, enabling both the type and paper to be always in view except at the actual moment of impression, and a small chase, measuring $4\frac{1}{2} \times 7\frac{1}{2}$ in., which was well suited to the jobbing-trade. The method of operation was that the platen, hinged at the base of the press, rocked to and fro as it made the successive impressions; the chase was held on a flattened section of a cylinder, round which the ink was conveyed on the rollers. The foot-treadle, which Ruggles had employed even earlier, provided a satisfactory mode of operation, and when introduced to Europe in a slightly modified form at the International Exhibition of 1862, the machine became immediately popular. The name Cropper, taken from its first English manufacturers, became attached to all treadle-platens (Fig. 323), which even in the twentieth century are often worked without power, either by foot or by hand.

A system of mass production was, however, essential to the development of the modern newspaper: this required not only the application of power but an alternative to the cumbrous traditional method which produced every sheet of printed matter by the bringing together of two flat surfaces, supporting respectively the inked

Fig. 323. H. S. Cropper & Company's 'Minerva' press, 1860

type and the paper. As early as 1810 a London book-printer, Thomas Bensley, using the ideas of a Saxon immigrant, Friedrich Koenig, was printing the *Annual Register* by steam in an adapted hand-press provided with automatic inking-cylinders. The printing was done at the rate of 800 sheets an hour, but there was no important future for the device until Koenig in the following year—perhaps as the result of an indirect contact with an earlier patentee, the scientist William Nicholson—for the first time brought into use the cylinder, from which the mass-produced printed matter of the present day has resulted. Koenig put the paper on to a large horizontal cylinder, the circumference of which was divided into thirds and which could be held stationary in three corresponding positions. Each time the cylinder made one-third of a revolution it carried forward a new sheet of paper, fed in at the top, and at the bottom printed a sheet which could then be removed. At each movement the type-bed was propelled backwards and forwards, so Koenig almost immediately decided to use two cylinders, in order to utilize the movement of the type-bed in each direction.

Only *The Times* proved enterprising enough to buy the machine, which on 29 November 1814 produced the first steam-printed newspaper at the rate of 1,100 impressions an hour—about four times the output of a hand press. Before returning to Germany in 1817, Koenig had made the first 'perfecting' machine, that is to say, a machine with two single cylinders, the second of which printed the reverse side of the sheets, which were fed through both cylinders in a single operation. *The Times* adopted this, too, and with modifications made by their engineers ran it until 1828, when they introduced a machine of their own design. This had four cylinders and gave 4,000 impressions an hour from a single bed of type, the reverse side of the sheet being left blank for later news. Meanwhile, the perfecter had been improved by an English press manufacturer, David Napier, who invented grippers which held the paper while the impression was made and took it over for the perfecting cylinder to operate. The perfecting cylinder revolved twice for each sheet printed, being raised at the second revolution so that the type-bed could run back without touching it (Fig. 324).

A further increase of speed was possible only if the type-bed also could be made to rotate—an idea that had occurred to William Nicholson and which was put into practice as early as 1813 by Bryan Donkin, inventor and engineer. Four trays of type were secured to a revolving spindle, which had on one side of it an inking-cylinder fed by inking-rollers made from a composition of glue and treacle: at the other side, it came into contact with a four-leaved device on which the paper was mounted to take the impression. The Cambridge University Press tried to use this machine for Bible printing, but though ingenious it proved a failure, which contributed only the new composition-rollers to the development of the industry.

Success came instead from an American invention, which was first installed by the *Philadelphia Public Ledger* in 1846, spread to Paris in time for the Revolution of 1848, and in 1857 reached England, where the abolition of the stamp duty on newspapers (though not the duty on paper) two years earlier had opened a wide field for newspaper development. The inventor, Richard March Hoe, was the son of an immigrant from Leicestershire who had been making printing presses since about 1805. The machine had five horizontal cylinders, one large type-cylinder in the middle and four smaller cylinders surrounding it; the type was held in cast-iron beds, and was fastened down with wedge-shaped rules between the columns to prevent centrifugal force causing it to fly out as the cylinder rotated; automatic grippers inserted the sheets between the smaller cylinders and the large ones as they turned. Although something

FIG. 324. Flat-bed cylinder-press made by Napier, *c.* 1819

similar, but with vertical cylinders, had been devised by the engineers of *The Times* and was to be seen in a smaller version printing the *Illustrated London News* at the 1851 Exhibition, *The Times*, followed by many other newspapers, changed over to a ten-feeder Hoe (Fig. 325). This could provide 20,000 impressions an hour, but as the paper had to be fed in from five different levels, twenty-five men and boys were required to tend it.

Cast-iron beds full of movable type were a clumsy and even dangerous fixture when attached to a rapidly revolving cylinder. Newspapers, therefore, took over the practice of stereotyping—an invention of the previous century that had come into common use soon after 1800 for books, such as Bibles and school books, which were frequently reprinted: it enabled a new impression to be made at any time from a solid plate, which was cast in a mould of papier mâché or some similar substance prepared from the original type. Applying this method to the newspaper, the *New York Herald* had the first plates made to fit the curve of the cylinder. The method spread rapidly, since it possessed the additional advantage that duplicate plates could be made as required without any setting-up of type beyond that needed to make the original mould. Another device, which first came into use in Philadelphia in 1865 and was patented independently next year by *The Times*, was to print from a continuous roll of paper. This had been proposed by Rowland Hill, the

FIG. 325. Hoe ten-feeder printing press, *c.* 1860

inventor of the postage stamp, in 1835, but the tax on newspapers at that time required a stamp on each sheet and the taxing authorities were inexorable. It is perhaps significant that by 1870, only fifteen years after the removal of this incubus, a rotary press was available which after cutting the printed roll folded the sheets ready for the news-vendor.

PAPER-MAKING, BINDING, AND ILLUSTRATING

It remains to consider the three auxiliary crafts, as they may be called: those of the paper-maker, the book-binder, and the illustrator. The great growth of the reading public after the middle of the nineteenth century caused a great increase in the demand for paper, even before the excise duty was abolished in 1861. In Britain, for example, the provision of the first municipal libraries in 1850 stimulated interest in books; after the newspaper tax was repealed (1855), the number of newspapers trebled in forty years; and in only thirty years the introduction of the penny post caused the number of letters delivered to rise to 917 million a year, more than ten times the number in 1839. This demand for paper could not be met from the linen and cotton rags and straw which were the chief raw materials then in use. Esparto grass from Spain and North Africa began to be imported about 1855, but the real solution was the use of wood-pulp, which had been experimented with for about two centuries. The pulp was first prepared commercially by the use of grindstones immersed in water containing ready-cut logs, but this did not remove resin and other deleterious impurities; from 1873 onwards chemical wood-pulp was developed, made by boiling wood chips with soda or sulphite solutions. This provided most of the material for the great rolls of the newspaper industry; the manufacture of paper in continuous lengths by machinery had been patented by N.-L. Robert in France in 1798, and was developed in Britain from 1803 onwards by the stationers H. and S. Fourdrinier with the help of the previously mentioned Bryan Donkin. Art paper, increasingly in demand for illustrations, was made by loading the paper with china clay or gypsum.

The mechanization of bookbinding began rather earlier, for boards backed with paper were an economy introduced during the Napoleonic wars. Before this the usual binding material was leather, whether used by the publisher for the whole edition or, as often, by the binder for the customer who had bought the book in sheet form. About 1825 the cheaper cloth case came into use, and since this was made separately, for attachment by glue and tapes to the sewn sheets, it became possible to produce it by machinery. A rolling-press to consolidate the sheets before binding—an operation previously performed by hand with a 14-lb hammer—and a blocking-press to replace the hand-tooling of the cover had made their appearance by the end of the same decade. Various unsatisfactory devices were tried for sewing and casing, such as stitching with iron wire—its employment was one of the younger Baedeker's few mistakes—or coating with a flexible rubber solution, both of which resulted in the speedy disintegration of the volume. About 1878, however, sewing-machines became generally available (p. 575), and in the 1890's Europe adopted from America methods of mass-binding with automatic folding and feeding-in of the sheets.

In the field of book illustration some of the outstanding achievements date from the early days of printing. Before the end of the eighteenth century not only were the techniques of the engraving, the etching, and the mezzotint (p. 241) at their height in Britain, but the use of the stippling process and, a little later, the substitution of steel plates for copper were giving new facilities for the art of book illustration. The high prices now paid for such marvels of the wood-engraver's art as Bewick's *History of British Birds* (1797 and 1804) remind us that there is a more serious loss involved in modern mass-methods of illustration than in the desuetude of hand-made papers and hand-tooled bindings. On the other hand, the development of the newspaper illustration, leading to its nineteenth-century culmination in the first use of photographic processes for this purpose (p. 659), was one that for better or worse enabled the events of the day to impinge upon the public mind in a wholly new way.

A woodcut is to be found in a pioneer English news-pamphlet of 1513 celebrating the victory at Flodden Field; but on the Continent they had been used even earlier for such news-sheets as the Nuremberg Chronicle (1493), and in the succeeding two and a half centuries such publication was more regular, and therefore more important, there than in England. At the close of the eighteenth century two major English newspapers habitually illustrated important events, but a much more frequent practice in the early newspapers was the insertion of very small woodcuts to drive home the message of a medical or other advertisement. More elaborate engravings appeared in the broadsheets which sold both news and views regarding such major events as the Peterloo riot or the Cato Street conspiracy; crudely daubed to enhance the horror, they gave rise to the expression 'penny plain, twopence coloured'.

In the course of the 1820's the use of more powerful presses made it easier to secure a satisfactory impression from a hand-engraved wood-block surrounded by type. This coincided with a big development of new newspapers and periodicals, including periodicals which made illustration the medium of instruction as well as of entertainment. Charles Knight's *Penny Magazine* in 1832–45, which at one time sold 180,000 copies a week, and his *Penny Cyclopaedia* (1833–44), may be compared with *Punch* and the *Illustrated London News*, which date from 1840 and 1842 respectively, as showing the appeal made by lavish illustration to widely differing classes.

Coloured illustrations were in the main too expensive for widespread use in periodicals, but nevertheless their production also underwent considerable development at this time. There was, for instance, a process called chromo-xylography, employing a separate hand-cut wood-block for each colour; this was in effective use by William Savage about 1820, was further developed by G. Baxter, enjoyed a great vogue after mid-century for religious subjects with the Viennese firm 'of Knöfler, and later still adorned the children's books of Kate Greenaway, which were said to have 'dressed the children of two continents'. At the other extreme, there was a stencilling system, each stencil enabling a different colour to be applied to a black outline carried on a travelling band; this was used for French fashion-papers early in the century and for cheap picture-postcards at the end of it. The most important process, however, was chromolithography.

The lithographic process itself had been invented by Alois Senefelder of Prague just before the century opened. The drawing was made with a special greasy pigment, either on the stone itself, in which case it had to be drawn in reverse, or upon a specially prepared paper for transfer to the stone. In order to print, the stone was first wetted and then inked, with the result that the ink adhered only to the prepared surface, from which it could be transferred to the paper with great accuracy. This process was excellent for such purposes as cartography; for book illustration it was a drawback that each picture had to be pasted in by hand. The colour-process required the use of a separate stone for each colour, and the best products were as beautiful as they were expensive. Lithographers fought hard to avoid the mechanization of their art, but in 1852 the power-press was introduced for it and in the 1870's grained zinc plates replaced the stones and greatly speeded up the process.

But in the last quarter of the nineteenth century the most revolutionary changes affecting all types of illustration were those which resulted from the introduction of photographic processes into printing. The earlier history of photography must therefore be considered next.

EARLY HISTORY OF PHOTOGRAPHY

The late conception of the idea of the photograph is perhaps the most remarkable aspect of its history. The camera obscura was available for photography by 1685 and the chemical effect of sunlight on silver salts known in 1727. The first impermanent experiments in making 'the light write' are reported in a communication to the Royal Institution, London, by Thomas Wedgwood and (Sir)

Humphry Davy, in 1802. Yet photography in its early form, the daguerreotype, was not generally available until 1839.

The fact that a pin-hole admitting light to a dark room—which is the literal meaning of camera obscura—projects an inverted image of external objects on to the opposite wall was recognized at the end of the first millennium A.D. by Alhazen, an Arab writer on optics, who proposed its use for the observation of solar eclipses. Advantage was taken of it for this purpose in the sixteenth century, when the Louvain astronomer, Gemma Frisius, published an illustration of the means by which he had observed the eclipse of January 1544

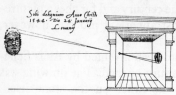

(Fig. 326). In the course of that century it was improved by the introduction of a lens in place of the pin-hole, a diaphragm, and a concave mirror to rectify the image. Such devices were used by

FIG. 326. The first illustration of a camera obscura. Gemma Frisius, 1545

artists in tracing the outline of views and for topographical surveys; in the seventeenth century the camera became portable, and the distance between lens and screen was made variable so that the image could be focused (Fig. 327). It remained only for the achromatic lens (p. 592) to be introduced, together with some form of shutter, to render the camera obscura fully suitable for photography.

In 1727 J. H. Schulze of Nuremberg demonstrated that it was the sun's light, and not its heat or the air, that darkened silver salts. Thomas Wedgwood, a younger son of the great potter, tried to employ silver nitrate to record the image of the camera obscura, but all that Davy and he, using silver chloride, were able to report in 1802 was that the image of a leaf or of a painting on glass could be reproduced upon paper or white leather, chemically coated, after two or three minutes' exposure to sunlight. Since further exposure darkened and ultimately destroyed the image, the practical value of the experiment was very small: the fixing of the image is an essential part of the photographic process.

Photography really begins with the work of the French physicist, Joseph Nicéphore Niepce, from which his partner, L. J. M. Daguerre, evolved the daguerreotype process in 1839. By the same date an Englishman, W. H. Fox Talbot, had developed an independent photographic process which was the first to possess what is nowadays regarded as an essential feature of photography, namely the ability to print many positives from the single negative. However, it was neither the metal plate on which Niepce took his photographs nor the paper sheets on which Fox Talbot took his, but the collodion glass plate, introduced in the 1850's, which proved to be the first fully practical medium for photography.

Niepce began his experiments in 1816, using silver chloride as the light-sensitive substance, and after ten years took the world's first

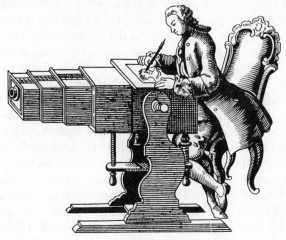

FIG. 327. Artist's camera obscura, 1769

photograph from his window at Chalon-sur-Sâone, with an exposure of eight hours. It was taken on a pewter plate covered with a thin layer of bitumen of Judea (a kind of asphalt) which had been applied in solution. A solution of oil of lavender 'developed' the plate by dissolving the bitumen wherever it had not been hardened by the light during exposure; the undissolved bitumen then gave the highlights of the picture and the underlying pewter the shadows, the result when dried being permanent. Niepce also used his bitumenized plate for a process of photo-etching. His process, however, had three major disadvantages: it was slow, the image was not sharp, and it produced only a single copy. It was his partner Daguerre, a scene-painter for the Paris Opera, who substantially eliminated the first two disadvantages: his photographs were shown at an historic joint meeting of the French Academy of Sciences and Academy of Fine Arts on 19 August 1839, and caused the artist Paul Delaroche to exclaim with dramatic exaggeration, 'From today painting is dead!' The portrait-painter at least could hardly regard himself as seriously threatened by an alternative which at that time would have required a sitter capable of remaining motionless in full sunshine for at least a quarter of an hour.

The daguerreotype was taken on a silvered copper plate bearing a thin layer of silver iodide, formed by exposing the plate to iodine vapour, and required for most outdoor subjects not more than half an hour's exposure. It could be developed in twenty minutes in a box containing vaporized mercury, tiny globules of which settled on the silver iodide in proportion to the degree to which it had been affected by the light. Excess silver iodide was washed away with sodium 'hyposulphite' (still the most common fixative and still known as 'hypo', although it is actually sodium thiosulphate), leaving the polished silver to form the shades. Unfortunately, the mercury forming the highlights easily came off the plate, which had there-fore to be covered by glass. Although no copies could be made, inanimate objects, including views, could be satisfactorily recorded, and an elaborate equipment, of which the 'official' version was made by a relative of Daguerre, found a wide sale for about twenty years in both Europe and America; the standard outfit, including a camera with an f/14 lens, weighed about 110 lb (Fig. 328). Its spread was helped by the fact that the French Government in effect bought the rights from the inventors, so that use was restricted by patent only in Britain, where Daguerre had put in an early application. One or two improvements were introduced almost immediately. Petzval's short-focus lens had a working aperture of f/3·6 and was thirty times as fast as Daguerre's original. At the same time the sensitivity of the plate was much improved by treating it with bromine vapour or chlorine as well as iodine vapour; in this way exposures were reduced to 10–90 seconds. A further ingenious reduction in the time of ex-posure was devised by Wolcott in New York, who introduced a camera—analogous to the reflecting telescope (p. 592)—in which the lens was replaced by a concave mirror. This made a large working-aperture possible, though definition was poor, and enabled its in-ventor in March 1840 to open the world's first photographic portrait studio; London had one a year later.

Meanwhile, Fox Talbot had been experimenting since 1835, employing paper coated with silver chloride both for the reproduc-tion of such things as botanical specimens by a technique not very different from that of Wedgwood a generation before, and—more important—for making rather indistinct pictures of views of his home at Lacock Abbey. These last were taken with cameras only 2½ in. square, fitted with microscope lenses; the exposure was thirty minutes. He made his process known in 1839, after the first announcement of the daguerreotype but before the official description of it to the two Academies. Two years later he patented the calotype process, in which the exposure was reduced to a period of from one

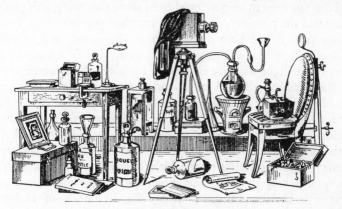

FIG. 328. Daguerreotype outfit, 1847

to five minutes for outdoor subjects. Fox Talbot's sensitive material, like Daguerre's, was silver iodide, formed not more than a day before use as a thin film on paper which was brushed successively with solutions of silver nitrate and potassium iodide; the sensitivity to light was increased by further treatment with gallic acid, the sensitizing properties of this having been discovered in 1837 by J. B. Reade, another British pioneer. The image formed was a latent one, which became visible only when the exposed material was warmed and which was then fixed with 'hypo'; it was also a 'negative' one, the highlights of the subject appearing as dark deposits of silver and the shadows as white paper. Although positives could be printed in quantity from these paper negatives—an extremely important difference from Daguerre's process—and although Fox Talbot set up his own printing-works establishment at Reading, the calotype, protected by patent, never became very popular in England.

In France, however, Blanquart-Evrard in 1851 replaced Fox Talbot's slow printing-out method by one in which the positive prints were developed like negatives, which meant that some hundreds of copies could be made in a day instead of half a dozen; careful processing and the use of a chloride of gold toning-bath overcame the tendency of Fox Talbot's prints to fade and gave permanent results. Another Frenchman, Gustave Le Gray, in the same year made a further improvement to Fox Talbot's process by using a waxed paper, which was not only more transparent but had the great advantage that it could be prepared as much as a fortnight before use and did not need to be developed until some time after; this greatly simplified the problems of the itinerant photographer.

However, it had been apparent from the outset that, in every respect except weight and perhaps fragility, the best material for carrying the light-sensitive silver salts was glass plates, which would be cheaper than silvered metal and more transparent than even waxed paper. The difficulty was to find a substance that could be used as a base for the silver salts, to hold them firmly in position during the development processes. Niepce de Saint-Victor, a relative of the earlier inventor, successfully introduced egg-white (albumen) in 1847, but the resulting material was relatively insensitive and did not remain long in use except for purposes requiring fine detail, such as the making of magic-lantern slides. In the year of the Great Exhibition its place was taken by the wet collodion process of the London sculptor F. S. Archer, a process which because of its speed and fineness—and independence of Fox Talbot's patent—was almost universally employed for nearly thirty years. The material was prepared by coating glass plates with a mixture of potassium iodide and collodion (nitrocellulose dissolved in ether); it was sensitized immediately before use by dipping in a solution of silver nitrate and had to be used wet—hence the name of the process. For portrait purposes the collodion negative, slightly under-exposed or underdeveloped, was turned into a kind of positive by bleaching it with nitric acid or mercuric chloride, and was then mounted over a black background. Its quickness and simplicity made the ambrotype—so called perhaps from its amber colouring—a popular form for cheap portraiture. As for landscape photography, though the wet plate was the fastest photographic process yet devised, its advantages were counterbalanced by the need to convey something like a hundredweight of equipment—much the same as the weight of Daguerre's outfit—on a day's outing. Since it was unusual to enlarge, the plates might be as much as 12 × 16 in., requiring a correspondingly large and heavy camera, to say nothing of the dark-tent and its chemical equipment (Fig. 329), without which the material could not be prepared or developed.

FIG. 329. Travelling photographer's dark-tent, *c.* 1865

PHOTOGRAPHY FOR THE AMATEUR AND THE ILLUSTRATOR

The important change, however, which according to the advertisements made photography a subject that 'a person of average intelligence could master in three lessons', was the production of a satisfactory dry plate—satisfactory in the sense of being fast, keeping well, and permitting development at leisure. Gelatine and collodion emulsions were both applied for this purpose, but the first fully successful invention was that of a gelatine emulsion containing nitric acid, cadmium bromide, and silver nitrate; when the emulsion had been 'ripened' by heat, the resulting film was twenty times faster than a wet collodion one. In 1878 large-scale production was begun by the pioneer Liverpool Dry Plate Company and other British firms; an automatic machine soon made it possible to coat glass plates with the emulsion at the rate of 1,200 an hour, and the plates were exported all over the world. By 1900 the sensitivity of the plate had been further increased so as to permit a minimum exposure of one-thousandth of a second, which meant that photography could be virtually instantaneous. Effective use of such high sensitivity demanded corresponding changes in the camera: the focal-plane shutter for high-speed cameras was invented by William England in 1861. At the same time much attention was given to the design of lenses, particularly to the elimination of chromatic and spherical aberration in fast lenses working with large apertures.

With the use of the ready-made dry plate, photography as a hobby came for the first time within the reach of the ordinary amateur. It was also at this time that its usefulness in the sphere of printed illustration was developed beyond the pasting of photographs into the pages of books, a process which began with Fox Talbot's work, *The Pencil of Nature*, in 1844. Since the same decade of the 1880's witnessed the birth of cinematography, it may be fairly claimed that the photographic art was at this time developing its modern scope and place in society. Use was accompanied by misuse, as when the searching vulgarity of the modern television camera was anticipated

FIG. 330. 'Detective' camera concealed in the crown of a hat, 1891

by the concealed 'detective' camera, a toy of the 1890's (Fig. 330), although in point of fact the miniature camera was still very much lacking in precision at the end of the century.

The main line of development, however, in the 1880's and 1890's was the lightening of the photographer's equipment and the simplification of its working. Thus the introduction of the gelatine dry plate brought with it gelatine printing-papers, including bromide paper so sensitive that for the first time small negatives could be enlarged by artificial light; the quarter-plate ($4\frac{1}{4} \times 3\frac{1}{4}$ in.) thereupon became the normal size for the amateur. The camera itself could then be reduced in size proportionately, but it still required a magazine inside the camera or a changing-bag if the plates were to be changed in daylight. The replacement of glass plates by roll film was therefore a most important advance. Celluloid, a plastic material which consists of nitrocellulose mixed with camphor, though first invented for solid mouldings by the versatile English chemist Alexander Parkes in 1855, was named and developed by J. W. Hyatt of Newark, New Jersey, who in 1888 produced clear sheets 0·01 in. thick, potentially suitable for use in photography. The first attempt to coat them with photographic emulsion produced a material that was still too thick and insufficiently flexible for the roll of film of which inventors were in search; but in December 1889 the American firm of Eastman succeeded in produc-ing and patenting a celluloid roll-film which gave it virtually a world monopoly for the rest of the century.

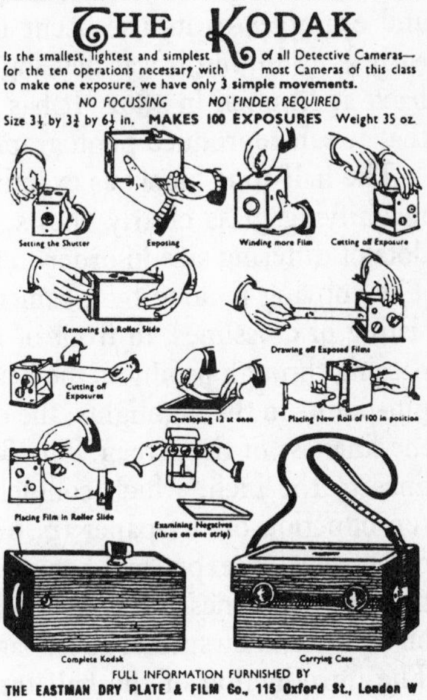

In the previous year George Eastman had introduced his Kodak camera, which broke quite new ground, as the advertise-ment clearly showed (Fig. 331). The small size and modest weight, the reduction from ten to three in the number of opera-tions needed to make an ex-posure, the long roll of film enabling a hundred pictures to be taken before reloading, and the fixed-focus lens—these fea-tures enabled the camera, like the bicycle, to enrich the leisure hours of the many. Eastman, moreover, astutely provided a

FIG. 331. Advertisement for Kodak box camera, 1888

full service of development, undertaking to return the camera with mounted prints and a new film loaded ready for use.

It was through photography that another landmark in the history of leisure was reached with the publication of the first fully illus-trated paper in England, the *Daily Graphic* of 4 January 1890. The photographic line-block or 'zinco' had been employed to some extent by the *Daily Telegraph* and other newspapers in the preceding decade, but it now became the means of enabling illustration, if desired, to predominate over letterpress. A negative made from an artist's line-drawing was placed in contact with a sensitized zinc plate under powerful lamps, and then rolled with printers' ink in a dark room. All the sensitive material except that corresponding to the lines of the drawing could be rubbed off with water; the zinc plate was then etched so that these lines stood out in relief, and was finally mounted to type-height on a block of wood ready for use. Only four years later the *Daily Graphic* had advanced to the employment of half-tones, though they did not become a regular feature of newspapers, as distinct from weeklies, until well into the following century. The half-tone process was achieved by a series of inventors and examples of its use occur in the *New York Daily Graphic* as early as 1880; but it was developed commercially by Georg Meisenbach at Munich in 1882. It has the great advantage over the zinco that it can reproduce photographs and wash-drawings.

The half-tone block, as examination of any of its products with a magnifying glass clearly shows, uses a system of regularly spaced dots of differing size in order to reproduce the tones of the original. The copying is done by a camera which has a special screen, consisting of crosslines, in front of the negative plate, so that the light passing through produces the heaviest dots in the shadows and mere pin-points in the highlights, the quality of the effect depending upon the fineness of the screen. The finest screens were at first about 135 lines to the inch, which could be used to full advantage only for reproduction on art paper (p. 649) for binding up with the letter-press pages in expensive books, while at the other end of the scale there were 80 lines to the inch in half-tones suitable for reproduction on ordinary newsprint; these last were often touched up by hand. The introduction of the half-tone block also made possible a new method of printing in colour. The 'three-colour' process involves the taking of three photographs through filters, each of which reproduces from the original only one of three primary colours (yellow, red, blue); the blocks are then successively printed—one on top of the other in exact registration—each with the appropriate coloured ink. But many technical difficulties had to be overcome before such letterpress colour-printing became fully established.

For fine work in small quantities there was already available a purely photographic process, requiring no screen and also suitable for the making of colour plates, best known as the collotype. Since its effectiveness depended upon stable climatic conditions, it became established first in France and Germany, and the machinery for it was not made in Britain until 1893. A reversed negative was imprinted by light upon a glass sheet which had been coated with a gelatine emulsion containing potassium dichromate. The lightest parts of the negative, corresponding to the shadows of the original, let through the most light to the gelatine, making it hard; conversely, the darkest parts of the negative kept the light away from the gelatine, leaving it soft. A mixture of glycerine and water was then applied, which the gelatine absorbed in proportion to its softness; when ink in turn was applied, it was repelled in exact proportion to the damp- ness of the gelatine, which was determined by its glycerine content. Although superb colour effects could be obtained by the collotype process, it did not lend itself to three-colour work as the half-tone process did: more plates were needed, with the result that the cost was prohibitive for most purposes, including book illustration.

Another photographic process adopted for illustrations before the end of the century was photogravure, originally invented by Fox Talbot in 1852. A positive photograph was printed on a polished copper plate, a screen of crossed lines was printed on top, and the plate was then etched in such a way that the acid ate deepest into the parts corresponding with the heaviest shadows; when the plate was inked and wiped, ink remained in the pits on the plate. Other changes included the application of the half-tone process to lithography and the use of aluminium printing plates.

DEVELOPMENT OF CINEMATOGRAPHY

The cinema as a major social force belonged to a later period than 1900. The first public film-show in the modern sense was held in Paris in 1895; the word 'cinematograph' came into English the follow- ing year, from the French. Its root in the Greek word for 'move- ment' draws attention to the central problem with which inventors in the later nineteenth century were wrestling, namely how to give the illusion of movement by taking and projecting a series of photo- graphs with regular but very short intervals between them. The in- vention was built upon the photographic processes we have just been considering, but the possibility of creating a spectacular illusion depended upon the physiological phenomenon known as persistence of vision, which causes the retina of the eye to record an impression for a brief period after the image itself has disappeared.

Persistence of vision, which we may therefore make our starting- point, was familiar to Ptolemy, who in his second book on optics (about A.D. 130) observed that a coloured sector of a disk, on being rapidly rotated, would impart its colour to the whole disk. But what was a commonplace of observation was given its first and possibly decisive twist towards practical use by J. A. Paris, an English physician, with his invention of the 'thaumatrope' in 1826. In this, a cardboard disk had drawn on its two surfaces two quite distinct objects, such as a tree and its foliage (Fig. 332): when the disk was spun by hand the two images were combined, showing the tree in

FIG. 332. The 'thaumatrope', 1826

full leaf. From this it was but a short step, taken in half a dozen years, to the idea of a disk spun in front of a mirror, so that a progressive series of drawings could be viewed in swift sequence through a slot, thus giving the illusion of movement which is the essence of cinematography. An improved form, known as the 'wheel-of-life', had a ribbon of drawings placed inside a slotted horizontal wheel, so that several people could see the illusion simultaneously (Fig. 333).

Under various names the wheel-of-life enjoyed many years of popularity, and as late as 1869 so eminent a scientist as Clerk Maxwell proposed one of the many improvements, namely substitution

FIG. 333. The wheel-of-life

of concave lenses for simple slots. But the most important development of the idea in the middle of the century was the linking of it with the magic lantern. The use of a powerful light with a reflector and a lens to project a picture from a painted glass slide on to a screen was first devised in 1645 by A. Kircher, a German Jesuit teaching at Rome, and in 1736 the Dutch physicist, Pieter van Musschenbroek, had brought motion into the lantern show by passing a second slide across one providing a stationary background. This kind of device provided a popular nineteenth-century entertainment, but it was the needs of military instruction which prompted an Austrian artillery officer, Baron Franz von Uchatius, to adapt the ribbon-drawings from the wheel-of-life. His first attempt, in which a series of drawings was projected through a rotating slide, was in 1853; the second and more successful method proposed by him was to rotate the light source and not the slide, but even then the number of drawings that could be got on to a single slide restricted the period of projection to 30 seconds.

Uchatius's work in adapting the magic lantern for showing consecutive drawings had been preceded three years earlier by the invention of a process that would make photographic positives available for it on glass slides. It was not, however, until 1874 that photography—a whole generation after its first invention—was used to record a continuous movement by stages with a view to its reproduction. This was achieved by the French astronomer, P. J. C. Janssen, who wished to record the transit of Venus across the Sun on 8 December 1874. He fitted the eyepiece of his telescope with a clockwork mechanism, so that at regular intervals the turning of a disk brought a slit into line with the eyepiece and caused a photograph to be taken on a revolving photographic plate; in this way the slow movement of the planet across the Sun was recorded in a series of forty-eight pictures.

The technique was transferred in the course of a very few years from astronomy to natural history, where there were innumerable problems of motion—such as the action of the horse's legs in the gallop and the nature of the flight of birds—which could never be settled by the unaided human eye. Thus in 1878 an expert photographer, E. Muybridge, was employed by a wealthy Californian sportsman finally to settle the ancient question whether all four legs of a galloping horse ever leave the ground simultaneously. He developed the use of a battery of numerous cameras placed a foot apart and triggered off by strings stretched above the ground, so as to provide an equidistant series of photographs of a horse passing along a track in front of the cameras: the pictures showed that there were brief periods when all four legs were raised (Fig. 334). The system was later improved by causing the shutters of the cameras to open at equal intervals of time instead of at equal distances travelled by the moving object. Exposures as short as 1/2000 sec were achieved, and the final result was an imposing analysis of animal and human locomotion, some 20,000 photographs being published before Muybridge's death in 1904. Meanwhile, the French physiologist, Étienne Jules Marey, who was in communication with Muybridge and Janssen, began in 1882 to use what he called the *fusil photographique*, in which twelve exposures a second were made on a rotating glass plate, each exposure being 1/720 sec. This introduction of the principle of intermittent motion was of the first importance, although it was not very satisfactorily achieved with this particular apparatus and the pictures were small. The new invention of photographic paper enabled Marey in October 1888 to demonstrate to the French Academy of Sciences his *chambre chronophotographique*, embodying the essential principles of the modern cine-camera. Though his cameras were primitive and none of Marey's films was projected until ten years later, this was the true beginning of the cinema industry.

In Marey's camera (Fig. 335), the ribbon of photographic paper was moved by a hand-crank from a supply spool to a take-up spool, recording images formed by the lens at the rate of ten to twelve a

FIG. 334. Muybridge's apparatus to analyse the movements (*below*) of a galloping horse

second; a shutter with a small square window rotated between the lens and the photographic paper and cut off the light each time the paper was moved. A brake worked by a cam behind the lens stopped the film each time the shutter was opened, and there was a simple device to prevent the film tearing when it was drawn forward for the next exposure.

The cosmopolitan character of the invention is shown by the work done in several countries in the period between the introduction of Marey's camera and the first public film show in December 1895. Improved methods for securing the intermittent movement of the film were devised by an assistant of Marey's in France; by an English group, who gave a demonstration of their cine-camera to the Bath Photographic Society in 1890; and most conspicuously by the great American inventor, Thomas Edison, who in 1887 thought of using moving-pictures in conjunction with his phonograph. In 1889 he saw Marey's work in Paris, and in 1891 patented a camera in which toothed wheels interlocked to secure the intermittent movement of the film, though this did not become public knowledge until the patent was issued six years later. Far more important, however, was Edison's introduction of a 35-mm celluloid film having four perforations on each side of the image, which allowed the film to be passed through either camera or projector by sprocket wheels and simplified its exact alignment.

In April 1894 Edison opened the Kinetoscope Parlor on Broadway, New York, where a single viewer sat at a peep-hole in a wooden cabinet to see the film, which was lit from behind by an electric lamp and was moved by a small electric-motor; the one-slot rotating shutter showed forty-six pictures a second. Although the Kinetoscope Parlor attracted immediate attention as a fairground peep-show and some machines were exported the same year, it is remarkable that Edison did not think it important to find a means for projecting to larger audiences. He was also satisfied to make his films with a camera weighing almost a ton, so that the subject-matter to be recorded had to be brought to the camera and not the camera to the subject.

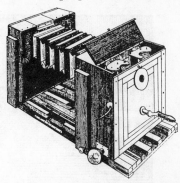

FIG. 335. Marey's cine-camera

The final step was taken in France by two brothers, Louis and Auguste Lumière, who were photographic manufacturers in Lyons. They were influenced by Edison's kinetoscope, and especially by his use of perforations at the edge of the film, which they reduced to one for each picture; also by the success in Paris of the *théâtre optique*, in which pictures hand-painted on gelatine had been projected life-size in succession on to a screen. They solved the problem of intermittency by a claw-movement employing two pins to engage with the perforations; these pulled down the film while the light was cut off by a semicircular shutter, and returned to their original position each time the picture was exposed. This became a standard arrangement in most cine-cameras and some projectors. At the same time, what is still the standard frequency for silent films was introduced, namely sixteen pictures a second. The Lumières filed their first patent on 13 February 1895: in June, with a fine sense of occasion, they filmed the arrival of delegates at a congress of French photographic societies, projecting it only forty-eight hours later; and three days before the end of the year they opened a public cinema in the basement of a café on a Paris boulevard, which quickly attracted an attendance of 2,000 a night. The strength of the international competition may be illustrated once more by the fact that within two months R. W. Paul and B. Acres exhibited moving pictures independently at the Finsbury Technical College in London, with an

FIG. 336. Typical film laboratory, late nineteenth century

expertise that enabled them to show the Derby of 1896 on the night of the event; they also devised the Maltese-cross mechanism which soon became the standard means of producing the necessary intermittent motion.

Soon after the end of the century what might almost be described as a second battle of the gauges—since both developing and printing apparatus and projector must correspond exactly with the width and perforations of the film used in the camera—ended in the general acceptance of 35 mm. The batches of film employed at that time were not more than about 30 yds long and the practice was to wind them for development and fixing on to long lattice-work drums (Fig. 336).

The taking of the early films was as primitive as their processing— a hand-cranked camera steadied on a wooden tripod, with sunlight as the only illumination whether indoors or out. Public and sporting events were the chief subjects. By the middle of 1896 there was an enterprising camera-man at work in Australia, and within another two years the film camera accompanied the advance of Kitchener's

FIG. 337. Scene from Méliès's *L'homme à la tête de caoutchouc*

army against the Khalifa in the Sudan. Meanwhile, the imaginative film grew from small beginnings: items shown to the boulevardiers of Paris in December 1895 had such titles as 'The Baby's Meal' and 'The Arrival of a Train'. The elaborately produced modern film waited until more capital had been attracted to the industry, but Georges Méliès, the expert conjuror who founded Star Films, was busily at work from 1896 onwards showing the combination of imagination and ingenuity which turns entertainment into art (Figs. 337, 338).

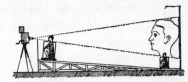

FIG. 338. Device by which Méliès's film (Fig. 337) was contrived

Although sound films were not introduced until the 1920's, with the development of the thermionic valve, the idea was conceived as early as 1887 (p. 664). Edison's phonograph, patented in January 1877, successfully recorded and reproduced sound by means of sound-tracks cut on cylinders coated with tinfoil. The quality of the reproduction had been improved by Emile Berliner, inventor of the gramophone, for which disk-records were effectively introduced in 1897. In the following year a young Danish engineer, Valdemar Poulsen, invented the magnetic recording of sound.

AGRICULTURE AND FOOD

ALTHOUGH agriculture and food has last place in Part II of this book, whereas in Part I it was almost first, the reason is not that its importance had become less fundamental. On the contrary, the period of industrial revolution in Britain, in Europe, and wherever else machine industry spread, posed problems of food-supply more difficult than any that had faced mankind since the earliest days of technological progress. Not only did the population of Europe increase in the course of the nineteenth century by 200 millions, but of that great increase a much larger proportion than at any earlier time in European history was engaged in manufacturing, commercial, and various other activities that did not directly contribute to the food-supply. Much of this huge industrial output was, of course, being exchanged on very advantageous terms for foodstuffs (and raw materials) of both European and extra-European origin, but technological progress of many kinds was needed to make such exchanges possible.

Thus justification for leaving this topic until last lies in the fact that so many other technologies played a prominent role in the advance of food production. Cheap transport, for example, enabled each industrialized country to make much more profitable use of its agricultural areas, almost irrespective of their distance from the urban markets. Even more important, cheap transport was the predominant factor in the opening-up of vast regions of the United States, Canada, Australasia, and the Argentine, from which—as also from tropical areas—an enormous quantity of foodstuffs was brought to Europe in the railway and steamship era. Moreover, progress in the actual technology of food production depended very much upon basic changes which occurred first in other contexts. It was, for instance, when cheap cast iron became generally available that agricultural implement-making ceased to be the virtual monopoly of local carpenters and blacksmiths, and efficient standardized equipment began to be purchased on a large scale from manufacturers of agricultural machinery. The steam-engine, again, was adapted from the factory and the railway line to the stackyard and the field and, through the employment of the steamer for trawling, to the harvest of the sea. Pipe drainage of agricultural land and improvement by the use of superphosphate, basic slag, and other artificial fertilizers are further examples of the contribution of industry to agriculture.

Agriculture, like manufacturing industry, profited both directly and indirectly from the growth of science. Lavoisier, for example, in 1778 started a model farm at Fréchines, where he doubled the yield of wheat within ten years. Sir Humphry Davy's lectures on agricultural chemistry were introduced at the Royal Institution in 1803 at the direct request of the Board of Agriculture. In 1835 J. B. Lawes and J. H. Gilbert began their famous collaboration at Rothamsted, where their experimental station contributed to the prestige of English high farming in its golden age. But it was not until after mid-century that the work of Justus von Liebig culminated in the foundation of modern agricultural chemistry, and the impact of Pasteur on stock-keeping is even later. It is broadly true to say, therefore, that until very near the end of the nineteenth century agricultural techniques, even more than those employed in industry, were still improved empirically, as a result of experimentation by practising agriculturists and manufacturers, rather than as the result of scientific investigation.

Great importance, therefore, attaches to the social milieu. In agriculture, to a larger extent than in most industries, social pressures tended to preserve obsolete methods. Subsistence agriculture was a self-contained way of life, the overthrow of which was often harder than the replacement of hand labour by machinery in an established manufacture. The big open fields, divided into small strips and cultivated in accordance with an agreed three-yearly (or two-yearly) rotation, were a feature of medieval village life that had deep social roots and could not anywhere be abolished without great upheaval. Moreover, there was no part of the Continent—except possibly the Netherlands and some regions of Scandinavia—where in 1750 agriculture was not, to a much greater extent than any other industry, under the direct control of a class of big landowners whose relationship with lesser tillers of the soil was still more or less feudal in character. On the continent of Europe there were indeed some rulers, such as Frederick the Great of Prussia, whose personal intervention gave a direct impetus to agricultural advance, but nowhere did circumstances produce a combination to rival the aristocratic agriculturists who gave the lead in Britain and the class of substantial farmers who were able to follow that lead: numerous agricultural associations, of which the Bath and West of England Society, the Highland and Agricultural Society, and the Smithfield Club are perhaps the most famous, were founded in the last quarter of the eighteenth century to foster this common purpose. Thus for about a hundred years Britain replaced the Netherlands in setting the standard in efficiency and modernization. Then, in the later nineteenth century, as we shall see, there came a twofold change. Cheap farming products from overseas were allowed to swamp the British market to the detriment of farming standards, whereas on the Continent agriculture was sheltered behind a tariff wall and technical assistance was provided by the state. At the same time, the huge success which resulted from the opening up of the American Middle West and other areas of virgin soil, combined with a shortage of labour, meant that America became the natural centre of technological advance.

From the light soil of the Netherlands there had come into the northern and eastern counties of England—and by about 1767 into Scotland as well—a small type of plough, requiring fewer draught animals, whose distinctive characteristic was a triangular frame; it is also significant that the curved mould-board was partly covered with an iron plate. The development of an all-iron plough was then completed by Robert Ransome, founder of the Ipswich firm of that name. In 1789 he introduced the chilled cast-iron share, of which the under surface had been cooled more quickly than the upper surface, so that the blade was self-sharpening through wear; a few years later he also devised an iron plough-frame with easily replaceable standard parts. The extension of the tilled area during the Napoleonic wars also led to the introduction of iron frames for harrows as well, and to the use of a heavier implement, called the cultivator, which could be mounted on wheels and had strong curved prongs penetrating deeply into the soil. The cast-iron roller, made in two or more sections for easier turning, likewise came into use in this period, though it was not until 1841 that the superiority of cast iron to wood or stone for this purpose was most strikingly demonstrated in Crosskill's clod-crusher with its serrated disks (Fig. 339). We may perhaps mention here the first appearance of the lawn-mower, which

Ransome began to manufacture in 1832: its inventor, Edwin Budding of Stroud, took the idea from the shearing of cloth.

Progress was not, of course, uniform. There were plenty of wooden ploughs still in use in England in 1850, when steel mould-boards, to which sticky soil will not cling, were being introduced by John Deere on the American prairies; and the small farmer everywhere was in the nature of things seldom able to do more than stare at, and perhaps secretly envy, the equipment of his more well-to-do neighbour. In 1782 Jethro Tull's seed-drill (*see* Fig. 22), made public by

FIG. 339. Crosskill's clod-crusher

his book in 1731, had been improved by introducing gears for the distributing machinery; and the drill was successfully adapted from the distribution of small seeds, such as those of sainfoin, to that of large seeds, and from large seeds to the distribution of manure and fertilizer. His horse-hoe was similarly elaborated into a machine that would hoe between several rows of crops at once. Yet the seed-drill, with which the rationalizing and mechanizing of farming processes virtually begin, was still described in Morton's *Cyclopedia of Agriculture* in 1851 as 'steadily progressing'. In the last quarter of the eighteenth century Thomas Coke, who showed that on cornland at Holkham it saved $1\frac{1}{2}$ bushels of seed and gave an additional yield of 12 bushels an acre, had found that its use spread at the rate of only a mile a year.

Since harvesting was the most labour-consuming operation in agriculture, it is rather surprising that the reaping-machines invented in Britain and America from 1780 onwards were left ineffective for half a century. Patrick Bell, a Scottish Presbyterian counterpart to Edmund Cartwright, won a prize from the Highland and Agricultural Society for a cumbrous-looking machine, which at first used scissors, rather than the modern knife and cutter-bar principle, and which the horses were required to push (Fig. 340). This first attained some popularity in the 1850's, when it was manufactured by Crosskill as the Beverley reaper. Meanwhile, in 1833, the American Obed Hussey had invented a more practical machine designed to be

FIG. 340. Bell's reaping-machine

pulled, but this in turn was gradually replaced by the better-known machine of Cyrus McCormick (Fig. 341), who made a series of improvements upon his original patent of 1834 and finally set up manufacture in Chicago in 1848; by 1860 Hussey had gone out of business, and McCormick was producing 4,000 machines a year. In England McCormick's invention was given much advertisement by the Great Exhibition in 1851, *The Times* remarking that it was 'the most valuable contribution from abroad . . . worth the whole cost of the Exposition'. At that date the parallel process of haymaking was still entirely unmechanized, apart from the use of an iron horse-rake to gather up the loose hay. But in 1856 American hayfields began to be mown by a machine equipped with a flexible cutter-bar so as to follow the unevennesses of the ground; as the price of labour there was such that the mower paid for itself in forty days' operation, it quickly became established.

In the further processing of grain crops the most primitive hand instrument was the flail, which had been used from time immemorial to separate the grain from the straw and the husks; under the open-field régime this had provided the only regular, albeit very unhealthy, employment when winter weather made outdoor work impracticable. The first successful machine for the purpose was that invented by a Scottish millwright, Andrew Meikle, in 1784, in which a drum was rotated inside a curved shield, arranged like a mudguard on a wheel but with only a very small clearance: grain was fed in between drum and shield so that the husks were rubbed off. This type of machine came quickly into use, especially in Scotland and the north of England, the power being often obtained from horses, though in 1842

FIG. 341. McCormick's reaping-machine

Ransomes won a prize from the Royal Agricultural Society for the application of locomotive steam-engines to threshing (Fig. 342). Meanwhile, a winnowing machine had been developed for the further separation of the corn from the chaff by the use of a fan and sieves, which were respectively turned and shaken by rotating a handle outside the box through which the grain was passed. The way was thus prepared for a more complicated type of machine, which combined threshing with cleaning apparatus and screens for grading the corn; in the later nineteenth century these were usually engine-driven and were moved from farm to farm under their own steam according to the contractor's engagements.

As winter feed for cattle became an increasingly important part of the farm economy, machines with chopping knives and crushing rollers were developed for the treatment of chaff, root crops, and cattle cake, the last a product of the residue left after expressing the oil from various oil seeds. On the model farms that were the glory of the great estates in the 1850's (Fig. 343), large barns would house a variety of such machines and probably a privately owned threshing 'drum', all of which would be driven by shafting from a stationary steam-engine.

AGRICULTURE: THE PRODUCTS

The new equipment, as we have indicated, served new purposes. After 1750 farm practice increasingly broke away from the medieval system, which at best ran at two-thirds pressure, for the land lay

FIG. 342. Steam-driven threshing-machine, c. 1840

fallow one year in three. Since the enrichment of the soil by animal droppings had long been a familiar aspect of animal husbandry, particularly as regards sheep, and since the value of fodder crops, enabling a larger head of stock to be carried through the winter, was emphasized in the earliest printed books on farming, it is difficult to see why the movement spread no quicker than it did. Clover and turnips were both well established in the Low Countries by 1650; clover was also being grown by then in north Italy, sainfoin in France, and lucerne perhaps in southern Spain. The year 1650 is in fact the date of the first printing of Sir Richard Weston's book, *A Discourse of Husbandry used in Brabant and Flanders, showing the wonderful improvement of land there, and serving as a pattern for our practice in this Commonwealth*. Yet another full century passed before England set to work seriously upon the enclosure movement, without which she could not have taken the lead in European agriculture. The Low Countries, on the other hand, already had such modern features as the laying down of arable periodically for leys; a specialized dairy industry exporting both butter and cheese; potatoes grown as a field crop; the systematic accumulation of organic manure both from farm animals and from towns and industry; and a general abolition of the fallow year.

Thus the Low Countries, where almost every conceivable type

FIG. 343. Model farm, England, 1859

of agriculture down to market gardening and bulb growing was practised in a compact area, were the original pioneers. For example, when Frederick the Great of Prussia set to work to transform the sandy wilderness of his possessions, the dairy husbandry which he established, the drainage programme over which he quarrelled with Hanover, the enthusiasm for potatoes which his subjects resisted as far as they dared, and much else came to his country primarily from Holland.

The system of alternate husbandry commonly known as the Norfolk four-course rotation was an adaptation to English soil of a seven-course rotation practised in Flanders. The industrial crops of the Flemings, including hemp and flax, oil and dye plants (p. 70), were omitted on this side of the Channel, as was the provision for a long ley period in which the arable was sown with grass seed. From the light lands of East Anglia the four-course rotation spread to the lowlands of Scotland and to districts in Northumberland and the Yorkshire and Lincolnshire wolds which had not known the plough before. By 1850 it had become the standard English practice and had spread widely from there to the Continent, though it seems to have originated independently in parts of Italy and was also in use at an early date in the Moselle valley.

The alternation of cereals with roots and green crops (most commonly in the order wheat, turnips, barley, clover) had truly spectacular advantages. It was not only that the total of land under cultivation in any given year was increased by one-third, but the soil conditions in the years allotted to cereals were improved, so that wheat became established in many areas where from time immemorial only rye had been grown. Weeds always flourish among grain: for that reason the heaviest soils continued to require an occasional interruption of the four-course system as long as the ground could be worked only imperfectly with animal-drawn implements. In general, however, the hoeing of the root crop and the smothering of the weeds by its foliage in the later stages of growth kept that particular enemy within reasonable bounds, while results showed that the clover crop actually fed the soil—though many generations were to pass before scientists were able to attribute this correctly to the fixation of atmospheric nitrogen by bacteria-carrying nodules on the roots. At the same time, both turnips and clover provided winter forage for large additions to flocks and herds: these crops could be fed to them in field, fold, or yard, with a consequent provision of manure to enrich the soil.

The most important end-product was grain, of which an increased supply was badly needed by an increasing population both for food and, in the case of barley, for drink. But stock-keeping also underwent a transformation, not only because the additional supply of fodder increased the number of beasts, but because quality came under control when enclosed fields took the place as grazing ground of the unenclosed stubble and waste, where selective breeding had been impossible. Among the stockbreeders who were quick to seize their chance the best-known name is that of Robert Bakewell of Dishley, the creator of the new Leicester sheep, small in size and great in value. His object in this case was to produce the maximum weight quickly in the joints of most value: he once let his famous ram, Two-pounder, at 800 guineas for the season, and altogether his rams might let for as much as 3,000 guineas. He was secretive by disposition, but his method clearly was one of in-breeding with carefully selected stock to develop the points of most value: his Midland black horse, which farmers sold profitably in London for coach and dray work, was so powerful in relation to its size that the agricultural expert, William Marshall, described one of the Dishley stallions as 'being in *reality* the *fancied* war horse of the German painters'. With cattle, however, Bakewell was less successful than Charles Colling of Ketton, near Darlington, who with his elder brother Robert developed the Durham shorthorn. Among many other breeds, Ayrshire cattle deserve mention because they are said to have been improved by importations from Holland, and among many other breeders, Coke of Holkham may be singled out because his interest in Devon cattle and shorthorn sheep had a widespread influence through his public position—he was Member of Parliament for Norfolk for fifty-five years—and open-handed hospitality. Finally, the publication in 1791 of the *Introduction to a General Studbook* led the way to the recording of pedigree herds and flocks as well as of thoroughbred horses.

The Continent, as well as Great Britain, learned about the improved methods of cropping and breeding, not only from seeing what was done at Holkham by Coke or at Woburn by the Duke of Bedford, but from the propaganda writings of men like Arthur Young and William Marshall, which culminated in the establishment in 1793 of a deliberately propagandist Board of Agriculture, proposed by Marshall but with Young as its first Secretary. Although the French wars interrupted the free exchange of ideas, improved farms consciously based on the English model were to be found as far away as Oslo, Norway. Nevertheless, it would be wrong to suppose that agricultural progress at this time was a British monopoly. The regional agricultural societies of England and Scotland had their counterpart elsewhere: the Royal Agricultural Society of Denmark, for example, dating from 1769, was older than any comparable British institution, and the Philadelphia Society for Promoting Agriculture (1785) numbered both Washington and Franklin among its members. A presumed debt of Scotland to Dutch cattle has already been mentioned. Again, while the spread of the potato as a field crop in Ireland, where 1½ million acres were given to its cultivation before the famine in 1846, may safely be attributed to English ventures dating from the seventeenth century, it is questionable how much its spread in Prussia from 1730 onwards owed to English example, and its establishment in Bavaria in the 1780's was certainly due largely to the American-born Benjamin Thompson, Count Rumford, who had spent only half a dozen years in England. Again, tobacco and maize are examples of crops that came into greater prominence on the Continent than in Britain. It is also easy to understand that military powers with highly centralized governments, such as France and Prussia, required no English example in the development of stud farms and stallions to serve peasants' mares in order to improve the quality of both cavalry and army baggage-trains.

The two best examples of Continental enterprise, however, are the sugar-beet and the merino sheep. The first is a new development which in the long run has partly replaced a transoceanic source of supply; the other a development which has met with an opposite fate since the Australian wool-supply became predominant in about 1850. The discovery of a beet rich in sugar was made by the German chemist A. S. Marggraf in 1747; to develop a source of supply alternative to the sugar-cane became important during the British blockade of the Continent in the French wars at the end of the century. The first sugar-beet factory in the world was built by F. Achard in Silesia in 1801–2, while Napoleon demanded the establishment of the crop in France, Germany, and the Low Countries. The result was that by 1840 France had fifty-eight sugar-beet factories, while the industry was also carried on in Germany. Sir Humphry Davy, however, advised against the development of a beet-sugar industry by Britain, for whom her control of the seas in any case made the matter less urgent.

As for the merino sheep, this was a jealously guarded Spanish monopoly which other powers broke into by various means. Napoleon, for instance, included merino sheep among his demands at the secret treaty of San Ildefonso in 1800. There had been other earlier importations into France, as also into Sweden, Prussia, Austria, and Saxony. In Britain merino breeding was one of the many farming activities in which George III took a personal interest, and the first importation was arranged for him by Sir Joseph Banks, President of the Royal Society. But the British market was for mutton as well as wool; by 1840 Britain had few pure merino flocks, but flocks of merino type were prominent in France and especially in north Germany.

Although the conservation of animal manure to enrich the field crops—rather than an increased supply of meat, dairy products, or even wool—was central to good husbandry in this age, other methods of enriching the soil were coming increasingly into vogue.

The ancient practice of marling—that is, spreading a light soil with an excavated clay containing limestone—which in Britain had become confined to Cheshire and Kent, was revived in Norfolk and elsewhere. The clay under the peat of the Fens was laboriously dug up and old turf and clayey soil used after burning. British improvers also imitated the practice of the Low Countries in using organic industrial waste from soap-boiling, from tailoring, and even the scraps of horn left over from the handle-making of Sheffield cutlers. From this there developed a large demand for bones, which were spread on the land after crushing or, later, solution in sulphuric acid; in the 1880's human bones that had whitened on the Balkan battlefield of Plevna were being purchased for this purpose. Meanwhile, Peruvian guano (sea-bird droppings), whose merits for this purpose had been described in Portugal as early as 1602, became an important import to Britain in the 1840's, while in 1842 J. B. Lawes of Rothamsted established the artificial-fertilizer industry in England with his manufacture of superphosphate (p. 553). A generation later, the Chileans began to exploit the vast sodium nitrate beds which, until the advent of methods of fixing atmospheric nitrogen just after 1900, supplied at least two-thirds of the nitrate requirements of the whole world.

Broadly speaking, half-way through the nineteenth century British farming practice still held the lead, though something like the same level was achieved in the Low Countries, parts of northern France, western Germany, Prussia, and the plains of north Italy. British agriculture had, indeed, suffered a severe setback when the termination of the Napoleonic wars deprived farmers of their monopoly. The Board of Agriculture came to an end in 1821; nearly two decades elapsed before the foundation of the Royal Agricultural Society 'proclaimed the alliance between practical farmers and men both of capital and of science'. The advantages which then for a time confirmed British agriculture in its European pre-eminence were the rapid growth of population and the comparatively high purchasing power of the industrial towns; the availability of agricultural machinery, when required, in the 'workshop of the world'; the existence of a powerful upper class with a traditional interest in agriculture and a readiness to invest capital in it for social as well as economic reasons; and lastly, the fact that in the 1850's and 1860's the British, unlike the French, the Germans, the Italians, the Austrians, the Americans, and even the Danes, were at no time seriously constrained to beat their ploughshares into swords.

AGRICULTURE: WORLD CHANGES, 1850–1900

In the third quarter of the nineteenth century, however, a change of balance began to be noticeable, which in the fourth quarter shifted so decisively that Britain and Europe had clearly ceased to be the main centre of agricultural advance. For the transoceanic world, from being a producer of raw materials and of foodstuffs which, with the exception of sugar, were of a non-essential character, became suddenly transformed into a bountiful supplier of necessities. It was the wheat, meat, dairy produce, and tropical products from overseas which enabled Europe, and especially Britain as its most industrialized country, to feed a population that was still rapidly increasing almost everywhere (except in France), and what was more, to give it on the whole a more nourishing and more varied diet. Economically this was not achieved without strain and distress, especially for corn-growing farmers in Britain who were not sheltered by any tariff, but also for very many of the pioneer agriculturists in the prairies of the New World itself, struggling as best they could against a steady decline in the price of the wheat that was their sole cash crop. They were all too often at the mercy of railway monopolists and the banks, or as one of their newspapers succinctly expressed it in 1890: 'There are three great crops raised in Nebraska: one is a crop of corn, one a crop of freight rates, and one a crop of interest.' Nevertheless, what was being accomplished cannot be viewed otherwise than as one of the outstanding triumphs in man's exploitation of his physical environment.

The area brought under cultivation in the United States between 1860 and 1900 is estimated at over 400 million acres, that is, more than ten times the area, cultivated and uncultivated, of England and Wales. Coming events cast their shadow as early as the period of the American Civil War (1861–5), when three successive bad harvests in Britain occasioned a temporary dependence upon imported American wheat sufficient to damp down British protests at their being deprived of southern cotton: in 1901 United States wheat exports reached an all-time maximum at 239 million bushels. By that time the United States was becoming industrialized, and Canada (with Australia and the Ukraine) was taking her place as a wheat producer, but the effect on Europe had already been comparable to that of the influx of precious metals three centuries before. The methods used in this tremendous feat of exploitation were primitive as regards tillage but very advanced in their economy of manpower (Fig. 344). The seed was drilled into a shallow furrow; instead of manuring there was a reversion to frequent fallow years; and the hope of a plentiful return from virgin soil was balanced against the risk of drought, hail, or a plague of grasshoppers. On the other hand, the four years of civil war gave a tremendous impetus to the use of the labour-saving McCormick reaper, which after 1858 had a highly

FIG. 344. Large-scale ploughing, Dakota, *c.* 1880

successful rival in the Marsh harvester, with a kind of chute which delivered the crop on to a table ready for binding. Just twenty years later J. F. Appleby made a supplementary invention of crucial importance—a binder-and-knotter, using balls of manila hemp and sisal twine, which worked eight times as fast as existing wire-binders and did not leave fragments to stick in machinery and the throats of cattle. Cultivating machines of various kinds were also developed, such as the Lister for maize, which ploughed, sowed, and covered simultaneously; steam-driven tractors began to be used as well as big threshers (Fig. 345) and finally the combine, which processed 30 acres of standing corn into wheat sacks in one day. By 1899 the annual output of agricultural implements in America, including export sales, was worth 101 million dollars, as compared with 7 million dollars fifty years before.

Meanwhile, the opening up of new territory by the transcontinental railway, which brought the farmer to the land and carried his wheat crop from it, was also a decisive factor in the growth of a meat-packing industry. Where in pre-railway days the Indian and the bison alone had flourished, the cowboy and his cattle ranged freely for about two decades. The quality of the stock which had been first imported by the Spaniards was improved from British strains, and a technique was developed of fattening for slaughter, sometimes with 'blue grass', but chiefly with maize, of which 75 bushels were needed for each animal over a five months period. By 1886 there were about 45 million cattle on the ranges, but the range system then rapidly declined as the farm frontier advanced and asserted its lawful rights with the new barbed wire. In the end, too, the cattlemen found it to

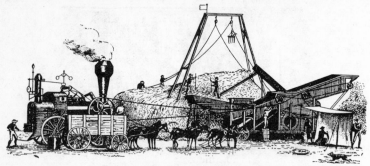

FIG. 345. Threshing in California, 1883

their own interest to replace the hardy longhorn (still familiar in films) by better breeds for which the open range would in any case have been unsuitable.

For Australia and New Zealand, flocks and herds were a source of wealth preceding any important export of meat. Merino sheep, imported both from South Africa and from George III's model farm at Kew, flourished in Australia on open ranges; by 1820 Captain Macarthur's first venture of 1797 had grown to an average of nearly four sheep per head of population. For a long time to come the wool only, and not the mutton, constituted the principal export of Australia: hence a great struggle to grow wheat in a land where low rainfall, lack of phosphates, and a stubborn soil—the stump-jump plough speaks for itself—delayed success until the 1880's. Meanwhile, cattle grazed on open ranges, as in America, and although this did not lead, as there, to an important industry in canned meat, it led to dairying, so that when refrigeration began in the 1880's butter and cheese could be sent across the world together with beef, mutton, and lamb. New Zealand, beginning a little later with easier conditions of work, followed the same general trend of development so far as agriculture is concerned, though its exports never included any substantial quantity of beef. But the Australian beef was driven out of the export market soon after 1900 by the new and more popular chilled beef of the Argentine.

Tropical agriculture likewise benefited from the new opportunities which modern transport provided and which the white man—in this case the entrepreneur and capitalist rather than the settler—was quick to seize. Old trades were energetically, if not always successfully, transplanted: India and Ceylon, for example, became great producers of tea, though an ambitious attempt to transfer coffee-planting from the British West Indies to Ceylon proved an almost complete failure. Sugar plantations, which in the British West Indies suffered from the same handicap as coffee, namely a chronic labour shortage after the emancipation of the slaves in 1833, were successfully introduced as far afield as Queensland; at the end of the nineteenth century, out of a world sugar supply of 12·4 million metric tons, 6·4 million still came from canes. Together with tea and coffee, which thanks to an increasing supply of sugar played an ever larger part in European life in the nineteenth century, must be mentioned cocoa—the cheaper and more popular variety of drinking-chocolate. The word itself dates from the end of the eighteenth century, but it was in the second half of the nineteenth century that the cocoa-bean became an important export from the West Indies, the Gold Coast, and finally Nigeria.

Products of tropical agriculture that were wholly new, so far as the European trade was concerned, include West African palm-oil, made from the fruit of the tree, which began to reach Britain in 1772 and was used largely in candle and soap manufacture but to some extent also in foodstuffs. For the latter purpose, however, the fat derived from oil seeds, particularly groundnuts, was more important: the first groundnuts were brought from Gambia in 1830 and half a century later they were used in the new manufacture of margarine. The popularity of the West Indian banana, which began to reach Europe only in the 1870's—though Americans were eating it extensively a generation or so earlier—illustrates the importance of the European market for transoceanic fruits of all kinds, which developed as rapidly as the means of conveyance, whether in the refrigerated hold or the sealed can, could be contrived. To this subject of food management and preservation, which was becoming increasingly important with the increasing remoteness of consumer from producer, we must shortly turn.

Brief reference must, however, be made to the technical progress of British and European agriculture during this period, when for the first time in Europe's history her own food producers were ceasing to be her main source of supply. Until the catastrophe of the 1870's, the tilled area in Britain was still being improved both in extent and quality. It was in this era that the cylindrical clay-pipe, the pipe-making machine, and the provision of government drainage loans—all three innovations of the mid-forties—at last made possible the

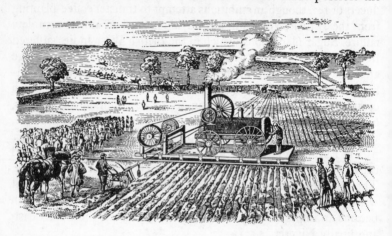

FIG. 346. Steam-ploughing demonstration, England, *c.* 1851

general drainage of heavy land. There was an increasing use of fertilizers; machinery for cultivating, reaping, and processing crops was more widely adopted, and much of it was now harnessed to steam. Steam-ploughing (Fig. 346) came to be something more than a curiosity, though the many farmers who could not afford both horse and engine kept to the more familiar and more adaptable power of the horse. Productivity was also increased by the development of improved types of seed, such as Squarehead Master wheat and Chevalier barley. Moreover, in the breeding of livestock British farmers maintained their lead—which they have never wholly lost—as it was comparatively easy for them to keep large pedigree herds, thanks to new feedingstuffs, including the maize and compound cake (made partly from palm-nuts) which the free-trade system made readily available to them from overseas. British husbandry was even able to surmount a big epidemic of cattle plague, which necessitated the slaughter of as many as 10,000 cattle in a single week just after the belated passage of the Cattle Diseases Prevention Act of 1866.

No such measures, however, could save the situation in the 1870's, when a series of bad seasons culminated in the almost continuous rain of the summer of 1879, which spoilt the hay as well as the corn harvest and was accompanied by serious outbreaks of disease, both of foot-and-mouth disease among the cattle and of liver-rot in sheep. The treachery of the English climate was, of course, no new phenomenon, but from 1879 onwards English farming lost its old resilience, because the flow of cheap corn imports from outside Europe, which the bad seasons helped to establish, acquired an ever-increasing momentum, due to favourable conditions of production and transportation against which the English farmer could not compete. In the last thirty years of the century the corn-growing area in England and Wales shrank from 8,244,392 acres to 5,886,052 acres. Broadly speaking, the farmers who still made a good living were no longer to be found among those who could put most capital into increasing the wheat crop, as in the days of high farming, but among dairy farmers, fruit and vegetable growers, and among specialists in home-grown beef and mutton. Their wares continued to be preferred at home to the imported article, and a good many prize animals were still sent abroad. In other respects the landed interest, as a whole, was forced to economize at the expense of technological progress.

Broadly speaking, the situation on the Continent was less depressing than in the United Kingdom, because almost every government erected a tariff-barrier and in other ways showed solicitude for the well-being of its rural population, which in most cases was a larger proportion of the whole than in Britain. Bismarck, for example, when imports of rye, oats, and barley from Russia doubled in two years—the spread of the European railway network made this a more immediate danger to the German farmer than the American wheat— three times increased the tariff. But even in Germany, where the work of Liebig had given a great impetus to scientific agriculture, not only as regards the chemistry of the soil but through the study of animal feedingstuffs, the last two decades of the century, though they saw $2\frac{1}{2}$ million acres added to the area under crops, were a period of much slower advance than their three predecessors. In

France, where large, highly capitalized estates were far fewer than in Germany, the slowness of technical advance may be measured by figures for the use of machinery, collected in 1892. At that date there were 3½ million holdings of all sizes, of which 1 in 14 possessed a horse-hoe, 1 in 15 a threshing-machine, only 1 in 140 a drilling-machine, and 1 in 150 a reaper. France was, however, using increased quantities of artificial manure, especially after the discovery of the North African phosphates at the time of the French occupation of Tunisia in 1881.

Italy, like most European countries apart from France, bore silent witness to the relative decline of her agriculture in the great efflux of her population to the American continent. One outstanding feature, no doubt related to the continued predominance of large landowners, was the fact that, in contrast to the rest of Europe, Italy had a larger quantity of sheep in 1900 than in 1850. Holland suffered less than many other countries because she had long been a dairy and cattle-keeping country; the Dutch still found it profitable to reclaim land by extracting the peat for fuel and laboriously mixing sand and farm-yard manure with the clay subsoil to make it manageable and fertile. Denmark, more than any of her neighbours, found salvation, when corn-growing ceased to be profitable, in a technical efficiency which was made possible by a high level of rural education and the inspiration of the folk high schools, and in a determination to seize every advantage from a system of agricultural co-operation. Thus the invention of the mechanical cream-separator (p. 693) led to the establishment of co-operative dairies, while the smooth working of the co-operative bacon factories resulted from the production of a standard pig, so nicely adapted to suit the English palate that the product of British sties was almost everywhere regarded as inferior. In Norway, on the other hand, the impact of American wheat was even more catastrophic than in England: in the 1880's many of the poorer farmsteads were left entirely untenanted, and for four years the movement to the American Middle West, particularly the Dakotas, was on such a scale that the total population left in the homeland actually shrank.

FOOD MANAGEMENT: FISH SUPPLIES AND WHALING

The action of the reindeer hunter, who in the loneliest regions of northern Europe still buries his kill under a loose heap of stones on the windswept hillside, knowing that the cold air will preserve the meat until it suits him to return, is a reminder that the art of storing and preserving food is older than agriculture itself. It became vastly more important, of course, in the second half of the nineteenth century when, as we have just seen, huge new supplies of food, including meat and dairy produce, became available for transoceanic markets. It will be convenient, however, to consider first another foodstuff which had long been in plentiful supply but whose use was

FIG. 347. Landing and curing cod, Newfoundland, 1715

limited by the problem of how to preserve it—a problem which had only very partially been solved.

The harvest of the sea, including the flesh and oil of the largest of mammals—'that great Leviathan whom Thou has made to take his pastime therein'—had attracted the daring and enterprise of mankind for long ages before the Psalmist wrote, but the usefulness of a cast-up whale-carcass, to say nothing of fish caught at an uncertain number of days' sail from the shore, was severely limited by its rapid deterioration. From the Middle Ages European man had, as we have already noted (p. 63), dried, salted, and smoked fish on a considerable scale (Fig. 347). In the seventeenth and eighteenth centuries the whale was hunted increasingly for its oil and the whalebone—

horny plates in the mouths of toothless whales, through which they filter their diet of plankton from the sea—highly valued as material for corsets, umbrellas, and even springs. The quarry, however, had been virtually exterminated in temperate European waters; whaling became concentrated in the Arctic, where Dutch and English ships worked along the edge of the ice from Spitzbergen to the Davis Strait. In the same period, Dutch, British, and French herring-

FIG. 348. Preparation and smoking of herring, France, c. 1770

busses drove their traditional trade (p. 64) in fishing-grounds ranging from the Shetland Islands to the Thames estuary, according to season, and the curing of the fish was an important activity in the coastal towns of all three countries (Fig. 348). Within living memory, the poorer students at Scottish universities stocked up for the winter with a barrel of herrings and a sack of oatmeal.

It was an achievement of the nineteenth century that, when the growth of towns and industry was making freshwater fish a rarer delicacy than ever, sea fish in prime condition became more widely available. Three interrelated factors may be distinguished. One was the increased efficiency of the fishing boats. As they became larger it became more practicable to carry a big sea-water tank, in which line-caught fish could be kept alive at sea, in many cases for at least a week. In shallow coastal waters, trawling, in which the net gathers the fish up from the sea bottom, was an alternative method that had been practised to some extent since the fourteenth century; it caught many fish, but they were mostly dead when hauled on deck. But this method could be developed to full advantage when the Dogger Bank area began to be exploited, about 1850, and steam was used, first for carrier-vessels to link the fishing-fleet with the market and, from about 1883, for the actual trawlers and for herring-drifters. The second factor was the railway, which connected the fishing ports expeditiously with inland industrial markets. The use of ice in the transportation of fish, which is the third factor, had begun before 1800 for such luxury trades as the dispatch of Scotch salmon to London, and was an essential feature of the growing railway traffic; it also made possible the longer preservation of the catch at sea. A Yarmouth trawler-owner, Samuel Hewett, began to employ it in his boats about 1855, and Norwegian ice was soon imported on a large scale, enabling Britain's east coast fishing-fleet to range as far afield as Iceland. By 1900 the ice was factory-made and in plentiful supply; but as its preservative qualities are strictly limited, whether for sea or land transport, cold storage was preferred as an alternative for large-scale operations. Experiments in the freezing of fish were, however, unsatisfactory, for it was not until much later that the secret of avoiding deterioration in the thaw was found to lie in a very rapid freezing.

Whale-hunting, meanwhile, had undergone a much more dramatic transformation. By 1850 the Arctic right whale was becoming very scarce, and it needed only the disappearance of the crinoline and the substitution of steel busks for whalebone in corsets to make the chase hopelessly unremunerative. The 1860's likewise saw the decline of the American industry, based on searching in warmer waters for the sperm whale, which has teeth instead of whalebone but is rich in oil and spermaceti, an excellent material for wax candles. The Civil War dispersed the whaling-fleet, which found a use as block-ships, and thereafter the American whaler fought a losing battle against cheap paraffin (p. 517). The period of adversity resulted in longer voyages and the development of new techniques.

In the course of a five-year voyage a ship would visit both the Arctic and Antarctic and in between would cruise in search of sperm whales in the tropics. This was made more profitable by the practice, first adopted by the Americans, of stripping the blubber from the dead whale while it floated alongside the ship. The blubber was minced, and was boiled in cauldrons which were set up on brickwork on the deck and fuelled with the oil-soaked scrap; the oil was then barrelled and sent home by freighter from the nearest convenient port. The type of ship used was a wooden sailing-ship, from which the attackers approached the whale in a small rowing-boat (Fig. 349)

FIG. 349. Hand-harpooning, nineteenth century

—though an adult sperm or right whale is likely to be 60 ft in length—hurled a harpoon at it with rope attached, and when the speared beast was sufficiently exhausted by its wound and the towing, hauled in the line and dispatched it with long lances. Thus whaling was inexpensive of everything but manpower, and even this cost is said to have been much reduced by desertions, since the crew did not receive their pay from the profits until the end of the long voyage.

The largest whalebone whales, such as the 90-ft blue whale, had always been virtually immune from human attack: they were too large and active to approach, and—unlike the sperm and the right whale—if killed, sank to the bottom. It was a Norwegian, Svend

FIG. 350. Harpoon cannon, 1870

Foyn, who about 1860, while hunting the smaller whales off the Norwegian coast, developed the modern whaler and harpoon-cannon (Fig. 350). The whaler is a small steam-boat fast enough to approach any whale. The cannon fires a very heavy barbed harpoon on a 400-fathom rope, the head of which contains a charge designed to explode after entering the whale's body: this may kill outright, but its primary object is to cause the barbs to spread out in the flesh, so that the rope cannot be shaken off. In the first ventures in north Norway the dead whale was towed as it was to harbour; but when Foyn applied his invention to the great whales of the Antarctic, there was an arrangement of pulleys and springs on board the whaler, to take the strain if the wounded beast pulled the line suddenly taut, and a steam-winch to haul up the carcass from the depths, so that it could be inflated with air from a hose-pipe before towing to the nearest convenient shore-station to extract the oil. Such shore-stations were set up, mainly with Norwegian labour, in various parts of the world where whales were to be found.

By the end of the century whales, especially the largest species, were becoming scarce and attention began to be concentrated upon the Antarctic, the first shore-station being established in South Georgia in 1904. The floating factory, which could haul the largest carcasses on board ship for treatment, did not come until a generation later, but already the hydrogenation process for converting the oil into hard fat had made the whale an important source of raw materials for both soaps and margarine.

PROCESSING AND PRESERVATION OF FOOD

The widespread use of margarine, which was first invented in the 1860's by the French chemist, H. Mège-Mouries, and the bitter struggle about its name—the term 'margarine' is a misnomer, which has been enforced by law in Britain since 1887 in place of the more alluring 'butterine' then preferred by its manufacturers—provide an interesting illustration of the commercial importance of the application of science to the processing of foodstuffs. Neither hardened whale-oil nor many others of the fats used in the production of margarine could have been employed as food in an earlier generation. Moreover, much of the food that mankind had used from time immemorial could be used only at or near the place of production until food technology, roughly about the time of the Great Exhibition of 1851, began to develop the numerous modern processes of preservation. At that date the population of England and Wales, the most urbanized major area in Europe, was still almost exactly one-half rural: as the urban areas grew, the problem of maintaining, let alone raising, the standard of diet would have been quite insoluble by the old methods. The three staple products—bread, meat, and milk—illustrate this. Corn was still ground mainly in small water- or wind-driven mills scattered all over the country, and bread was still commonly baked at home in the south as well as the north: only incompetent housewives bought ready-prepared food, except in emergency. London's meat-supply still entered the capital mainly on foot. The best milk in the large towns was still that produced by suburban cow-keepers up to the time of the great outbreak of cattle plague in 1865, when necessity compelled dairymen to organize the train-borne supply more carefully. As for canning, its use was still largely confined to naval expeditions, particularly those of polar explorers; even so, a high proportion of the large consignment supplied to Sir John Franklin for the ill-fated *Erebus* and *Terror* in 1845 proved to have gone bad.

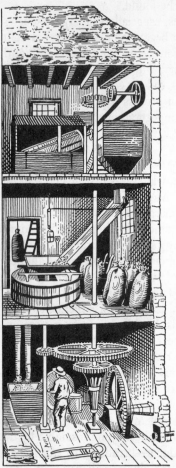

FIG. 351. Water-powered English flour-mill, *c.* 1850

But before we consider the new large-scale methods of food preservation, of which canning was the first, brief reference must be made to the later history of older methods of treating food for preservation, convenience of use, or increased palatableness. Popular taste was one factor in the supersession of the old stone-milled flour, though there was also the fact that it kept less well, because its relatively high content of oil tended to go rancid. Both the 'low milling' of England (Fig. 351), in which the millstones were all the time kept close together, and the 'high milling' of Hungary and the Continent in general, which dealt with a more brittle grain by bringing the grindstones closer together in stages, gave place by degrees to roller-milling. This process, first introduced in Hungary about 1840, passed the grain through a series of pairs of spirally fluted rollers, followed by pairs of plain rollers, so as to produce some five or six different qualities of flour from the same wheat. The product was very white; economical in use (because it absorbed more water); made tall, well 'piled' loaves; and had superior keeping qualities. In the late 1870's this type of milling, which became very popular in America for the hard red spring and winter wheat of the Middle West, accompanied the American grain to

Britain. Marketed in standardized blends from large mills situated mainly at the ports, this new flour suited the needs of large bakehouses, which employed kneading and other processing machines and the steam-heated ovens that began to appear after 1850. The use of machinery to produce reliable standard quantities and qualities of flour and other ingredients was even more important to the biscuitmaker—of whose service to the housewife even Mrs. Beeton expressed approval—for his reputation depended upon maintaining an absolutely uniform product.

As regards milk, the development of the milk-train was helped by the use of a water-cooler at or near the place of origin, and large churns of tinned steel plate were introduced for its conveyance between the farm and the roundsman's cart. Milk bottles were beginning to appear by 1900, but only for milk that had been 'pasteurized' against tuberculosis by Pasteur's method of heat-sterilization. In the history of butter-making the principal event was the invention of the centrifugal cream-separator by Gustav de Laval in 1877, which enabled the larger dairies to economize both in the labour of skimming and in the space that had previously been occupied by the large shallow pans where the milk was set for the cream to rise. Cheeses—which, in western Europe at least, are of all foodstuffs the one characterized by the largest element of traditional local idiosyncrasy—began to engage the attention of bacteriologists. In the United States, Canada, and Australia, though not in its original home in the West of England, a factory-made 'cheddar' cheese was produced, and the discovery that the ripening-agent in cheese is an enzyme that produces the best results when working at rather low temperatures incidentally vindicated an ancient practice among Somerset farmers, who ripened their cheeses in the cool caves around Cheddar Gorge. About the same time as butter and cheese came to be made by large-scale processes, experiments were also directed towards preserving milk. There was a British patent for 'condensation' as early as 1835, but the American, Gail Borden, who concentrated milk by evaporation in a vacuum and then sold the product from open vessels like ordinary milk, was the true pioneer; he also produced a canned condensed milk which was preserved by the inclusion of sugar. Borden's first factory, for unsweetened evaporated milk, was opened in 1860: the manufacture was greatly stimulated by the American Civil War of 1861–5. Unsweetened condensed milk was not canned until twenty years later, when a Swiss immigrant,

J. B. Meyenberg, established in America a process with which he had long been experimenting in his native country for sterilization in a pressure-cooker. Dried-milk powder was made in England as early as 1855, sodium carbonate being added to the milk before evaporation and cane-sugar afterwards, so as to produce a dough that could be satisfactorily ground to powder after drying; pure dried milk first appeared on the American market just before the end of the century.

Sugar as a preservative had, however, a much longer history than that of its use in sweetened condensed milk. A domestic conserve of fruit prepared with sugar was known as a preserve by 1600 and as jam by 1730; but it was the agricultural depression of the 1870's which caused English farmers to search for a new market for their fruit and so led to the growth of jam factories. Then, before the discovery of means of storing fruit pulp to make an inferior jam out of season, jam-makers added orange marmalade and other confections to their wares in order to maintain a continuous output. The methods employed were purely empirical, for the makers knew nothing about pectin and until about 1900 did not even use a jam-boiling thermometer. But the sales were enormous, especially in industrial areas, where a highly flavoured spread for bread that was cheaper than butter and economical in use was widely needed; jam also served to make margarine more palatable.

Breweries resembled jam factories in that they replaced what had once been a common domestic activity, but home brewing had been on the decline since the later Middle Ages: changes in modern times took place within a well established local industry.

The rise of porter brewing after 1722 was particularly important, for it provided for the first time a product with good keeping properties that could be widely distributed. British brewers not only built up a nation-wide market, helped by the establishment of the canal network, but a large export business, especially with the Baltic and, later, with the East: India pale ale enabled the Briton abroad to enjoy his national drink in perfect condition despite its long and slow journey.

London was already famous for its large breweries, such as Samuel Whitbread's, which employed a capital of £271,240 in 1790: by the early nineteenth century, eleven big concerns satisfied most of the thirst of the metropolis. But small-scale brewing by one licensee in three was the practice in the English provinces, and conditions in other beer-drinking countries, such as Germany and the U.S.A., were roughly similar. In 1873 there were still some 4,000 American breweries, with an output of 10 million barrels: seventy years later the breweries were one-ninth as numerous, the output eight times as great. An important factor in the change was the growing substitution of scientifically based techniques for the purely empirical methods on which small firms had always relied; this began with the publication in the 1860's of Pasteur's studies of yeast fermentation.

CANNING AND REFRIGERATION

Canning differs from preservation with sugar, not only in its far wider applicability, but in the circumstance that failure could be extremely dangerous, even fatal, so that the canner was far more anxious than the jam-maker to put his trade upon a scientific basis. Pasteur's studies of bacteria in the 1860's made a scientific approach possible, but it was not until the late 1890's that the fundamental principles of preserving food in cans were firmly established. Briefly, two essential conditions must be fulfilled. First, the food to be preserved must be sufficiently heated throughout its bulk to destroy harmful enzymes and bacteria: in many early instances lack of success was due to failure to sterilize material at the centre of large containers. Second, the containers in which the sterilized material is kept must be hermetically sealed, to prevent its reinfection by airborne bacteria and moulds. The process had been originated by a Paris confectioner, François Appert, to whom Napoleon awarded a prize first offered in 1795 to improve the condition of provisions for the Revolutionary armies. His method at the outset was to place the food in glass bottles or jars, which were then loosely corked, immersed in boiling water, and finally sealed down as tightly as possible. The use of tinplate (p. 496) canisters or cans was an English improvement, patented by Peter Durand in 1810 and taken up by Bryan Donkin (p. 646), who combined with others to set up in Bermondsey the earliest English cannery; they supplied their soups and preserved meats to the British Navy during the American War of 1812. The final sealing of the cans was done by soldering.

It was soon recognized that better results could be achieved if the process of heat sterilization was carried out at temperatures a little higher than that of boiling water: excessive heating, however, was to be avoided because of its effects on the taste and quality of the food. To achieve the necessary increase in temperature, Appert had used autoclaves resembling pressure-cookers (p. 317), and it was a member of his family who about fifty years later first provided them with pressure-gauges giving more precise control. An alternative was to use a bath of boiling calcium chloride solution, patented in Britain in 1841, as the boiling-point of such a solution is substantially higher than that of water. The latter method was practised in Britain about the middle of the century, the food being partly cooked and the cover of the can almost completely soldered on before placing it in the bath; the steam-hole was then soldered and the heating of the hermetically sealed can continued a little longer. Stephen Goldner employed this process for canning the soups of the Franklin expedition in 1845: he used large cans, and much of the soup went bad. Worse was to follow, for in 1850 the same supplier had a total of 111,108 lb of tinned meat condemned, belonging to the same Admiralty contract. The probable cause was his use of tins greatly in excess of the earlier maximum of 6 lb: the heat did not penetrate the contents, with the result that sterilization was incomplete. Although canned meat had begun to be imported from Australia in 1847 and the first salmon cannery had just been established at Cork in 1849, the industry as a whole suffered a temporary set-back, although canning still proceeded on a considerable scale (Fig. 352).

Though canning was made progressively safer, it was not until the end of the century that studies at the Massachusetts Institute of Technology finally established the fact that cooking at a temperature of 240–250° F. for periods varying with the commodity and the size of the container was necessary for all products of low acidity, such as meats, fish, and vegetables. Where the acidity is high, however, as in the case of fruits, the boiling-water bath gives adequate protection against damage by bacteria. Meanwhile, a new stimulus had been given to the industry in America—where it had been introduced from Britain as early as 1817—by the needs of the armies in the Civil War, and in Britain by the scarcity of fresh meat resulting from the cattle plague (p. 685). From 1868 onwards P. D. Armour and others began to develop the gigantic meat-packing concerns, with carcasses processed on an assembly-line, for which Chicago became famous. Fruit and vegetables, on the other hand, could be canned more economically in the localities where they grew: in the period 1870–1900 the number of such canneries in the United States rose from 97 to 1,813. The elimination of gluts and scarcities, the provision of a varied standard diet, and the release of the housewife from tedious duties in the kitchen, all made a strong and popular appeal.

There were numerous ancillary inventions, ranging in the decade 1893–1903 from a picking-and-shelling machine for peas to the 'iron Chink', a device for mechanizing the various preliminary processes in the salmon canneries when Chinese labour was excluded from California. But the making by hand of the tinplate canister,

FIG. 352. A Houndsditch cannery, 1852

which was still the usual practice even in the 1860's, would have set serious limits to the growth of the industry. As early as 1847 a drop press to make the flanges of the disks forming the two ends was invented in America; twenty years later there was a machine to solder the side-seams; and by the end of the century the manufacture of the lapped-seam can was entirely automatic (Fig. 353). The type of can prevailing in the twentieth century has locked side-seams and double seams at the ends. A machine for making such seams was available at Wakefield as early as 1824, and by 1870 the firm that made it was recommending the use of a rubber composition for perfecting the seal. But the modern open-topped type of can did not come into common use until a rubber composition for perfect joint-ing of can-ends was patented in America in 1896–7.

The advantages of refrigeration for preserving food were well known through the increasing use of ice, not only in the fish trade but (from about 1850) in the all-year-round curing of bacon in ice-cooled cellars, to say nothing of the familiar luxury uses of ice in the serving of wine and other drinks and sweets: as early as 1805 it was exported from New England to the West Indies. Since demand clearly exceeded natural supply—Trevithick was told in 1828 that

FIG. 353. Automatic machinery for making tin cans, late nineteenth century

'as much as £100,000 a year was paid in this place [London] for the use of ice'—ice-making machines began to be patented in the 1830's and became numerous in the 1850's, the cooling effect depending either upon the expansion of compressed air or upon the evaporation of very volatile liquids such as liquefied ammonia. James Harrison, who had emigrated from Glasgow to Australia and became editor of the *Melbourne Age*, made an improved ether-compression machine—which enabled him not only to work an ice-factory, but to provide an Australian brewery in 1851 with a refrigerating machine that made it possible to brew satisfactorily even in hot weather—and in 1873 to furnish a public banquet with meat, poultry, and fish which had been frozen for six months. Both Harrison and T. S. Mort, a fellow-Aus-tralian who had established the first meat-freezing works at Sydney in 1861, had a clear idea of the enormous commercial possibilities of the frozen-meat trade; they tried to adapt their plant for shipping frozen meat to England, but it broke down at sea. However, in 1877 frozen mutton was successfully shipped from the Argentine to Le

Havre in a ship equipped with ammonia-compression machinery; owing to a collision, the voyage took six months, but the hard-frozen meat remained in excellent condition. A compressed-air refrigerator was thereupon fitted to a British ship, which in February 1880 returned to London from Australia with 40 tons of frozen beef and mutton; in the same year a sailing-ship with the same type of plant carried the first mutton and lamb from New Zealand. By 1900 a special type of ship was conveying carcasses by the million from Australia, New Zealand, and the Argentine; dairy produce, fruit, and vegetables soon followed where meat had led the way.

Frozen storage at approximately 14° F. was found to be less satisfactory for many products, such as eggs and apples, than chilling or cool storage at about 30° F. This had been tried about 1870 for conveying beef from the United States to England in a ship's hold cooled by a mixture of ice and salt. In 1879 the same trade was attempted with the use of a compressed-air refrigerating machine: helped by the shortness of the voyage, American chilled beef came to dominate the British market for beef imports until well after the turn of the century. Not until much later, however, were the technical problems of freezing and thawing without serious effect on quality satisfactorily solved, especially in the case of meat.

Two other methods of preserving food must be mentioned for the sake of completeness. One is dehydration, which towards the end of the century was commonly applied to eggs as well as to milk. In general, however, public taste was not disposed to appreciate such products except under the necessities of war, or, in the case of vegetables, as a preventive of scurvy on board ship; they were employed, however, in the food industries. The second is the employment of chemical preservatives and so-called 'improvers', which was likewise of importance in the food industries rather than in the home. This was to an increasing extent controlled by law to prevent use of harmful substances: in Britain the first Food and Drugs Act was passed in 1875. Similar legislation in the United States followed an outcry against the issue of military meat rations 'embalmed' with formalin during the Spanish War of 1898.

EPILOGUE: TECHNOLOGICAL AND GENERAL HISTORY

A SHORT HISTORY can achieve clarity only at the risk of dogmatism. The present work, in seeking to lay before the reader the salient features in the development of many widely differing technologies over a vast period of time and without restriction to a single country or people, has had no space in which to express doubts or reservations, much less to attempt any systematic justification of the choice made of themes and examples. Yet the danger of dogmatizing and stating conclusions is greatest in a branch of history which, except as a subject of discrete and episodic studies, is almost wholly new. In his treatment of politics, constitutions, economic factors, and even social and cultural changes the historian nowadays either follows a beaten path or deviates knowingly, and shapes his argument to fit. The historian of technology, on the other hand, while his work impinges upon all these older types of history—and, as he hopes, contributes something to each of them—is himself still at the pioneering stage, when the most important thing is to open up the subject.

It is, indeed, part of the fascination of this study that, in its earlier and later phases alike, it contains so many puzzles. Technology is rooted, as we have seen, in the Palaeolithic stage, the hundreds of unrecorded millennia during which occurred man's evolution of his first tools, the key-event of all and one about which much would be written—if we could tell how the process of finding out began. After something like half a million years there came the dimly seen phenomenon that we identify as the Neolithic revolution and the beginnings of the loom, the sail, the wheel, the kiln, and other fundamental inventions, which in turn converted Neolithic barbarism into the earliest civilization. The where, the when, and the how of all this is still largely matter for conjecture. Lest it might be supposed that such uncertainties belong only to the period before written records began, we may instance the first two artificial prime-movers, namely the water-mill and the windmill, the art of glass-blowing, and the introduction of the three-field system, which transformed the productivity of medieval agriculture in the north, as examples of technological innovations which first affected Europe in historic times, but whose origins nevertheless are not satisfactorily accounted for by the evidence available. The same is true of the great majority of the inventions and discoveries, often of exceptional importance, with which China enriched the world during the first millenium and a half of the Christian era.

Not only the events themselves but the pattern of causation is often hidden from view. Thus we cannot at present determine whether the great discoveries and inventions of the early world were each made once and then slowly and intermittently diffused through migration and trade, or were made independently in different cultural regions when circumstances were equally favourable. Even in modern times the speed with which an invention is accepted for general use is subject to many not easily calculable hindrances. Such are the pull of conservatism and convention, especially where consumer interests are directly involved, and the handicap imposed on any society where capital is not available for innovation—an important reason why the Russian inventors of the later nineteenth century played little part in general technological progress. A second fruitful cause of obstruction is the misleading precedent, such as caused the first iron ships to be built in accordance with restrictions imposed by the use of timber and some early aeroplanes to be designed as orni-thopters. The frustration of many excellent inventions is also seen to occur through lack of constructional material or of interest in the product—or of both, as in the case of Thomson's pneumatic rubber tyre, patented more than forty years before Dunlop's. Similar fac-tors, which have left no trace, must often have affected the fortunes of inventions made in early times.

Apart from the history of particular inventions, there is still much uncertainty as to the influence which different forms of society have exerted both upon the transmission of established technologies and upon the creation of new ones. As regards the ancient world, there is virtually no information extant to show, for instance, how super-visors or foremen obtained the technical knowledge for organizing the large-scale enterprises that were commonly manned by slaves; the fact that classical literature expresses little but contempt for the study of industrial processes heightens the mystery. Apprenticeship, as an organized extension of the natural practice by which the father taught the son his trade, may be traced back as far as the Code of Hammurabi, but in Europe at least its fullest development dates from the establishment of the medieval craft guilds. When combined with the right of search, by which guild officials were entitled to ensure that all goods were made 'according to the laws, orders and ordinances of the trade'—a power still being granted by the English Parliament in 1650, and later—the fact that every skilled craftsman had normally served his time explains how skills and processes were successfully transmitted from generation to generation. The system did little or nothing, however, to help inventiveness: the guilds, being founded on the social solidarity of all master craftsmen, were quick to denounce the over-ingenious for 'unfair' competition; and, if ingenuity could not be entirely suppressed, they sought to restrict the use of any new process within narrow limits of place and occupation. In the Middle Ages the inventor often worked furtively, like the alchemist; many trade secrets were handed down inside the family; and those inventions which by their nature must be practised openly, such as the use of the fulling-mill, flourished first at a safe distance from the guildhall.

In the modern world both the making of inventions and their diffusion have been stimulated by the growth of patent law, which secures a temporary profit to the inventor and the ultimate availability of his invention to the public. But the system became fully effective only towards the end of the nineteenth century. Moreover, the stimulus given to invention cannot be judged merely by the date of effective patent legislation in the different countries: there are also differences of principle. French law favoured the inventor by not requiring him to define the limits of his claims; American required him to define them very broadly; British with more precision; and German law so precisely as to subordinate the inventor's interest to those of industry. Modern patents are usually taken out in several countries and their validity is not infrequently tested in the courts: the influence of patents upon the progress of invention, though obviously important, could therefore only be properly assessed in the light of a sufficient number and variety of international-business histories, and these are still largely unwritten.

The examination of applications for patents was among the first duties entrusted to the Royal Society in 1662, a clear example of the growing relationship between scientists and technologists that is characteristic of modern society. The growth, however, is by no means easy to trace. To begin with, the scientist sought the aid of the skilled crafts to provide the equipment with which to pursue the study of natural phenomena. The learned societies, which were an early product of the scientific movement, also exercised some direct influence upon technology by organizing the systematic collection and publication of data to illustrate existing conditions in its various branches as well as 'exact histories'—to quote a Royal Society statement of its intentions in 1718—'of all sorts of curious and beneficial trades in any country'. In this field, however, the early work of the Royal Society in England was outshone by the programme that the French Academy of Sciences entrusted in 1711 to Réaumur, and still more by the unofficial labours of Diderot, who provided a rival to their *Descriptions of the Arts and Crafts* in his more liberally conceived *Encyclopaedia*. The period of the eighteenth century in which the processes of industry were being made known in this way to the educated classes is that in which they were also becoming increasingly complex, so that the uneducated more and more rarely had the comprehensive grasp of their craft essential to progress. Black and Lavoisier are early examples of scientists who showed the basis in theory of industrial inventions that had been arrived at empirically; with Davy and Faraday the balance begins very gradually to tip the other way, towards the scientific advance which precedes and conditions the advances of technology.

But if we try to ascertain the stage in its history when technology became in general the dependant of applied science, the answer is still obscure, even with the nineteenth century's comparative plenitude of records, and varies widely from industry to industry and country to country. In Britain, for example, where the first industrial research laboratory was established about 1873, science did not triumph until the greatest age of industrial advance was past. In Germany, on the other hand, the most spectacular achievements of her chemical and electrical manufactures were squarely based on the research departments of the universities and the training of scientifically minded technicians in a carefully planned network of technical institutes and trade schools. As for America, her rise as an industrial power belongs to both the old and the new. The Massachusetts Institute of Technology opened its doors in the year that the Civil War ended; the funds for the land-grant colleges, pledged to promote 'agriculture and the mechanic arts', were authorized in 1862. But ten years later, when Andrew Carnegie admitted the first professional chemist—'a learned German'—to his Pittsburgh steel-works, the action, as he tells us with relish in his autobiography, was 'something our competitors pronounced extravagant'.

On the morrow of the Great Exhibition of 1851, Lyon Playfair had declared that 'Industry must in future be supported not by a competition of local advantages, but by a competition of intellects'. It is a commonplace of technological history to suggest that Britain in the following half-century fell behind in the newer competition because her men of intellect were not suitably trained. That too little attention was paid to science at Oxford and even at Cambridge, that Britain possessed nothing comparable to the technical colleges of Germany and France, and that the once-flourishing Mechanics' Institutes failed to strike deep roots because of the paucity of elementary education, are among the established facts of nineteenth-century cultural history. What is less clear is the extent to which educational shortcomings, which Britain in the 1870's began slowly to repair, actually influenced later events. There were other reasons for the successful rivalry of Germany besides her technical institutes, which had their origin at least in the need to find a substitute for the workshop training more readily available in Britain and to meet the challenge offered by the often zealously guarded trade secrets of the older industrial power. There were also other reasons for the British lack of continued success which were an inescapable legacy from her past: the huge capital locked up in obsolescent plant; the high proportion of old family businesses, where the pioneering spirit had often flagged with the passage of the generations; and the extra cost and intractability of labour in the country where trade unions had had most time and opportunity to grow up. By 1900 the decline of Britain's former 'local advantages' was clearly accompanied by a decline in the comparative rate of adoption of new techniques that has had fateful consequences from the standpoint of general history. The causes, however, must be pronounced at present to be uncertain.

The conclusions to be drawn from a study of technological history must, then, be regarded for the time being as purely provisional; nevertheless, it can be seen to have at least a threefold bearing upon general history. The fortunes of mankind have been closely affected by the growth of technology; the same influence has helped to shape the relations of nations and classes; and in the life of the individual, technology plays an alternate role as servant or master of man's activities. As soon as mankind ceased to be a numerically insignificant species of food-gatherers and predators, technological factors began to exercise a determining influence upon his distribution over the earth's surface. It was as a farmer that civilized man emerged, for instance, in the Fertile Crescent, whence spread a culture and techniques that slowly, but none the less surely, influenced the western lands and made them the home of a numerous and settled population. The techniques of transportation were, of course, the second determinant of man's fortunes in that distant past; for even in the nineteenth century A.D. the prairie-schooner and the ox-wagon were the means of opening-up almost uninhabited regions, and still more recently the passage of the Pacific on a balsa-wood raft has reminded us of the primitive forms of water transport that carried men across unexplored oceans. But in prehistoric as in modern times transport, trade, and industry reacted upon each other: the existence of amber, for example, created as if by magic the facilities for a long-distance barter traffic, which carried it from the grey shores of the Baltic to glow in the sunshine of Aegean palaces. With the growth of transportation, settlement became more specialized; in place of a uniformly agricultural society, spread by the movement of peoples or techniques, there came to be some regions which exported a food surplus, others which exported raw materials from forest, quarry, or mine, and others again which exported their manufactures. The terms of trade have nearly always favoured the third category, a fact which has been a constant stimulus to the multiplication and improvement of industrial techniques, enabling those regions where they are most efficiently practised to hold in fee the producers of food and raw materials. From the days of the Pharaohs onwards all empires have borne something of this character, though it was the development of the railway and the steam-ship in the nineteenth century A.D. that brought these tendencies to a climax.

In the nineteenth century, too, technology made large areas of the earth's surface not merely more accessible than ever before but for the first time capable of supporting a considerable population. New devices for preserving food and maintaining warmth enabled civilized man to take his first tentative steps even towards the occupation of the Polar wastes. Of more immediate importance, the adaptation and transplantation of crops, the discovery of new mineral resources, and the beginning of the conquest of tropical diseases enabled much of the tropical, as well as hitherto backward regions in the temperate, zones to become fully a part of the general heritage of mankind.

When we study the fortunes, not of mankind as a whole but of particular groups of men, we find that the history of technology sheds much light upon the unending struggle for power which grew from intertribal into international politics. The Stone Age, the Bronze Age, and the Iron Age each produced its distinctive weapons, and from the time when the first 'civil engineer' designed the first earthwork for protection against human as well as animal marauders, every generation has left the earth's surface scarred with the evidence of power gained but not retained. Technology has always determined what are the effective geographical barriers to conquest: the desert before the domestication of the camel, the steppes before men tamed the horse, the seas until sails were hoisted, and the oceans—with few exceptions—down to the days of compass and carrack. As for the part technology plays in the service of the conqueror, offensive and defensive weapons are often said to have gained the upper hand in alternate ages, though a better explanation may lie in the circumstance that technological success in general encourages concentration upon defence in those who have, and a passion for the offensive in those who have not. Be that as it may, almost every new material of man's devising, from the bronze of his earliest swords to the alloy-steels of Krupp's guns and the new explosives for which they were designed, and every new source of power, from the bow-string to the turbine-engine, has been adapted—sooner rather than later, but with very varying degrees of imagination and insight—to purposes of war.

Two and a half millennia separate the military triumphs of the Assyrians, first users of iron, from those of the Federal forces in the American Civil War. During that long period technical efficiency, as well as various imponderable qualities, was generally on the side of the conqueror. But it was left for the Swedish inventor, John Ericsson, on the morrow of McClellan's failure to wrest Richmond from the Confederacy, to give Lincoln the assurance, which history has since endorsed, that technology had become the final arbiter in the quarrels of the nations. His words deserve quotation:

The time has come, Mr. President, when our cause will have to be sustained not by numbers, but by superior weapons. . . . Such is the inferiority of the Southern States in a mechanical point of view, that it is susceptible of demonstration that, if you apply our mechanical resources to the fullest extent you can destroy the enemy without enlisting another man.

Before the end of the century the relatively bloodless conquest of

Africa by the imperialist powers and such forgotten episodes as the naval encounters of the Spanish-American War had carried the argument to its logical conclusion: technical superiority could make military success not only certain but cheap.

In many different ages technological novelties have helped to consolidate the results of conquest. The stone road by which the Roman legion marched across Britain to crush Boadicea has its counterpart in the 4,000 miles of newly laid telegraph that facilitated the organization of resistance in the first desperate weeks of the Indian Mutiny in 1857. Trade has always followed the flag, using easily produced wares, from Minoan pottery and Greek wine to Manchester calico and cheap 'trade-guns', to reconcile at least an influential element among the conquered. In course of time this might lead, as did the toga and the forum, which Agricola encouraged in Britain, to a more general adoption of the way of life of the conqueror. But modern technology in this respect has decisive advantages. Whereas the ancient empires might hope to overawe conquered peoples by the magnitude of their constructional works, it was printing that first made mass propaganda possible. For at least 400 years control of the presses was one of the most powerful instruments in the hands of authority, moulding the fate of nations, and when direct censorship and even overt influence, such as was practised by Bismarck, became outmoded, the cinematograph film, and then the wireless broadcast, were to make available a more seductive and insidious means than the book or even the newspaper for controlling the minds of the masses.

What has just been said is clearly applicable, not only in the international field, but to the struggle of classes—social units that technology helped to form. The legends of Hephaestus, and even of Prometheus the forethinker, attest the veneration with which the Greeks from the time of Homer onwards regarded the craft of the smith; and more generally the 'cunning workman' whose labours gave an aesthetic value to his material, whether a precious metal or merely 'a tree that will not rot' (Isaiah xl. 20), had a special place in early society. In spite of the long-continued employment of slaves— involving a further stratification, from the hapless labour-gangs living in the underground barracks of a Roman magnate to the kind of slave that might be entrusted with the management of a large workshop or household and perhaps in due course be emancipated— it is possible to trace from ancient to modern times the continuous existence in the main centres of urban life of a class to which skill in a craft gave definite privileges. It is true that, whenever economic opportunities expanded, there was a tendency for some type of capitalist entrepreneur to be interposed between the craftsman and his customer, especially if the customer was distant. But the gap between the entrepreneur or merchant and the skilled maker of the goods was matched by the gap between the latter and the mass of unskilled labourers, so easily forgotten, whose work underlay and supported the execution of almost every important industrial process. Down to the last two centuries, technological progress tended to preserve, and often to strengthen, the position of the artisan class, which normally enjoyed a relatively secure livelihood at something above subsistence level. An important late example are the 'engineers', the far more numerous successors to the millwrights, who in the year of the Great Exhibition felt strong enough to launch their Amalgamated Society, restricted to fully trained workmen able to pay a substantial weekly subscription.

But the industrial revolution was by that time rapidly changing the stratification of the employed classes, both in Britain and elsewhere. The exploitation of elaborate and expensive new processes in almost every industry has favoured the formation of big units, with a huge resulting increase in the employment of managers, clerical staff, supervisors, and foremen. It also necessitated the growth of new professional categories—theoretically-trained engineers, chemists, draughtsmen, accountants, statisticians, and other highly qualified personnel. Thus the big modern factory or workshop interposed a very considerable new middle-class element between the owners of the capital and the men who actually produced the goods. But simultaneously what was once a much larger category, made up of skilled workers who had 'served their time to the trade', was steadily declining in relative importance. Not only were traditional handicrafts replaced by machine industries, but the increasing ingenuity of machines transformed machine-users into machine-minders. By 1900 apprenticeship had lost most of its industrial and social significance; the growing power of trade unions of semi-skilled and unskilled workers in the counsels of the Labour movement attested the decline of the artisan class, a victim of technological progress.

But at the close of the nineteenth century it was not only the artisan class which was threatened with ultimate extinction by the advance of the machine. Mass production, from its small beginnings in the days of Eli Whitney, had reached the stage at which the use of an assembly-line and conveyor-belt, with each worker performing a single operation, could readily be contemplated. The first modern mass-assembly plant, employing these devices, was designed for the Chicago mail-order firm of Sears, Roebuck in 1903, and this is said to have been carefully studied by Henry Ford before he introduced the system into the manufacture of his model-T motor-car a few years later. In any case, Ford's action heralded a new era, in which mass production and the mass appeal of new advertising techniques and hire-purchase facilities combined to sell standardized luxuries far beyond the limits of the luxury-proud middle class of the past. Today the clothing, transport, and amusement industries have gone far towards the creation of a classless society, a condition not necessarily favourable in the long run to the cultural advancement of mankind.

From the point of view of the individual—to whom we now turn in conclusion—the progress made in the first century and a half of the industrial revolution was prodigious. For technology exists to produce goods and services, and the western world had marvellously increased its productivity, measured in terms of human labour. The astonishing beauty and skilfulness of the *objets d'art* surviving from the earlier civilizations for our admiration, the greatness of their architectural monuments, and their achievements in the realm of ideas must not be allowed to obscure the fact that, in all the centuries before Malthus wrote in 1798, population did tend to press against the means of subsistence. This was not primarily due to man's fertility but to his inability to solve the problems of production and distribution. The normal lot of the labourer or poorer type of peasant cultivator, who in most forms of society made up the unprivileged majority, had been to work through all the daylight hours, eat meagrely, go poorly clothed and ill-housed, and to die young. It is therefore a fact of the utmost importance that by 1900, broadly speaking, the unskilled labourer in all the western countries was earning more and had a shorter working-day than the privileged class of skilled workers before the industrial revolution.

If technological progress may be defined as any increase in the efficiency with which man exploits his physical environment to meet his wants, then clearly the historian of technology must view the events of the nineteenth century as marking a tremendous advance. Productivity had increased more rapidly than a rapidly increasing population; machinery had already gone some way towards reducing the physical exhaustion as well as the duration of the average stint of labour; and there was as yet little fear that man's ingenuity might culminate in self-destruction. But to the more searching question, whether technological progress has on balance added to the happiness of the individual, we can at best offer no more than an affirmative answer hedged with qualifications, rejecting the temptation to pretend to weigh imponderables.

From this standpoint, the greatest indisputable benefits of modern technology are perhaps those conferred by branches which the present *Short History* has lacked space to emphasize as they deserve, namely, the revolutionary changes in the practice of medicine and surgery. Technological progress furthered the use of anaesthetics and new drugs, the growth of bacteriology, and the effectiveness of surgical operations undertaken not only with a vast range of new instruments and equipment but with wholly new precautions against infection, which has always been one of the deadliest scourges of mankind in both peace and war. We may link with this the improvements to the water-supply and drainage of large towns, which likewise much reduced the incidence of disease. In two generations (1841–1901) the annual death-rate in London fell from 25 to 20 per thousand; it never reached 20 again except in the year of the great influenza epidemic at the end of the First World War.

Health and happiness are closely related, and it would be difficult to deny that a more generous and more varied diet, better protection against cold and damp indoors and out, a higher standard of cleanliness, and other changes in living conditions that have been facilitated by modern technology, are directly conducive to happiness as well as to health. Moreover, invention has widened immeasurably the use that can be made of leisure: how would Bacon, who believed 'that reading maketh a full man', have regarded the potential benefits of that nineteenth-century revolution in illuminants which brought efficient artificial light for the long winter evenings into the homes of the masses?

But there is another side to the picture. The shorter working-day gained by the modern machine-operator was on the whole physically less exhausting than that of the craftsman, but it might also be psychologically less satisfying. The labours of a factory-hand—the term is significant—are very seldom in any sense creative: they are usually repetitive and monotonous; they may involve more strain than the repetitive monotony of craft-work, with its natural slow rhythm; and as for giving scope to individual initiative of any kind, the whole aim of the mass-production economy is to reduce active human intervention to a minimum. It is not surprising if the worker in such conditions may lack the sense of 'belonging' and of participation in a worth-while cycle of activity, which gave a kind of satisfaction to the humblest of field-labourers, and, because he feels himself during his employment to be no more than a cog in a vast machine, becomes robot-like also in the use of his rapidly increasing leisure. Additional leisure, including the leisure of the prematurely pensioned, may be associated with the growth of frustration rather than of happiness.

Finally, we must notice that by 1900 the most advanced societies were beginning to register a change in the aims, as distinct from the methods, of technology. For man was no longer pitting his wits against Nature merely for the easier satisfaction of long-felt wants. That struggle, indeed, had carried him far, as Sophocles well knew:

> The use of language, the wind-swift motion of brain
> He learnt; found out the laws of living together
> In cities, building him shelter against the rain
> And wintry weather.[1]

But with the entry upon a new period, in which necessity ceases to be the mother of invention and the inventor, as Ludwig Mond foresaw in 1889, 'may even create new wants . . . a distinct step in the development of human culture', the progress which the historian of technology records requires more than ever to be evaluated in relation to the general history of civilization.

[1] *Antigone* 22. 354–9 (E. F. Watling's translation).

TABLES

THESE Tables are designed for use in conjunction with the text of the book. They show the time-relations of selected events in technological history both to each other and to named events in general history. In the earlier Tables the dating is often only approximate; in the last three, where exact information is usually available, the date and place attributed to a process are—unless otherwise stated—those of its first invention.

B.C.	STAGE OR PERIOD	EVENTS
	PALAEOLITHIC	Intermittent periods of comparative warmth, enabli precursors of man and man himself in very small num bers to move into Europe from the south and sou east.
c. 20000	UPPER OR LATE PALAEOLITHIC	Retreat of Scandinavian and Alpine ice-sheets, uncoveri large areas of cold grass-land and swamp, where m flourished as a hunter.
c. 9000	MESOLITHIC	Further retreat of ice-sheets, with changes in sea-level, average temperature, and in rainfall, resulting in t spread of thick forest and restriction of man's habi to shores, hilltops, and forest edges, while he for the fi time colonized the arctic north: in some respects (e pictorial art) a period of retrogression and impoveris ment.
c. 3200	NEOLITHIC	Spread of stock-keeping and agriculture overland fro south-east; sea-borne movement north from Medite ranean associated with megalithic structures; opening- of communications by traders characterized by superi pottery.
c. 2000	BRONZE	The use of copper, followed by that of bronze, introduc from east Mediterranean lands by sea traders in sear of metal ores or forest products; overland trade a important between the middle Danubian and the Bal region.
c. 1000	EARLY IRON	Knowledge of iron-working brought from Greece Italy to the Hallstatt area of Austria, and spread partic larly by the Celts, pressing southward in a period worsened climate, and by the Iranian (Scythian) i vaders of south-eastern Europe.

CHARACTERISTIC ECONOMIC ACTIVITIES *xisting side by side with the more primitive*)	CHARACTERISTIC TOOLS OR WEAPONS (*slowly superseding the more primitive*)
ɔd-gathering, with some use of fire but no ɛttled abodes; some practice of hunting ɔy cave-dwellers.	Flaked hand-axes and other implements of flint and stone, supplementing those of wood, horn, ivory, or bone; wooden spears; heavy stone missiles.
ɪnting of mammoth, bison, wild horse, deer, ɛtc.; preparation of skins for clothing; cook-ɪng; inhabitation of caves, often embel-ished with hunting scenes, and of more ɛmporary tented dwellings.	Improved flint knife-blades, awls, and gravers; barbs, bone needles, harpoons; composite tools; flint-tipped javelins and bone spear-throwers; bows and arrows.
ɔd-gathering, small-scale hunting (prob-ɪbly helped by domestication of the dog), ɪnd increased reliance on fishing, including ɛa-fishing from boats.	Microliths, used in composite tools of wood or bone; elaboration of fishing-tackle (net, hook and line, fish-spear, trap); stone adzes and chisels.
ɪck-keeping and cultivation of wheat and ɔarley; wood-working; making of baskets, ɪimple textiles, and pottery. Flint-mining ɪnd growth of trade; common use of sledges ɪnd, in far north, skis; villages of mainly ʻectangular hut dwellings; some reduction ɪf forest area by burning and felling of trees.	Ground, polished, and occasionally drilled implements of flint and other hard stone, the design sometimes influenced by metal prototypes; hoes and sickles; spindles and looms; flint daggers; the wheel used for transport.
ʼread of west Asiatic types of sheep and ɪattle; use of woollen textiles; construction ɪf clinker-built boats. Trade in manufac-ʻured metal goods, ceramics, amber; grow-ɪng importance of luxury goods.	Small ploughs (*unci*); hammered axes, etc., of copper and bronze; superior implements of cast bronze; smiths' and carpenters' tools; copper and bronze spears; bronze sword evolved from dagger.
ːrease of arable area, with oats and rye in ɪorth; timber frame-houses and earthworks ɪonstructed with timber and stone; larger ɔlank-boats, some carvel-built; horse-rid-ɪng (with horse-shoes) and use of wheeled ʻvehicles became common, culminating in ɪhe Celtic war-chariot.	Large ploughs with share, etc., of iron; scythes; improved saws, chisels, and files for carpentry; wood-turning; the potter's wheel in common use; the first strong swords.

B.C.	MESOPOTAMIA (AND PERSIA)	EGYPT	PALESTINE, SYRIA, AND ASIA MINOR
3500	Sumerian city states in existence; copper used and alloyed First evidence of wheeled vehicle First records (cuneiform)	Copper tools in use	Walled town at Jericho
3250			
3000	Pottery made on the wheel	Beginning of hieroglyphics	
2750		365-day calendar *Zoser*: First (Step) Pyramid	
2500	Royal tombs of Ur	*Cheops*: Great Pyramid Sea-going sailing ships	
2250	*Sargon I—Akkadian Empire (Semitic language)*	Oldest surviving irrigation dam *Middle Kingdom*	
2000	Ziggurats	Bronze came into use Horse-drawn chariots	*Hittites invade Asia Min* Hittite capital at Hattusha (Bogazköy) with fir known Processional Wa

...ASTERN MEDITERRANEAN	WESTERN MEDITERRANEAN	CENTRAL AND NORTHERN EUROPE
...noan' palaces built at ...nossos and Phaestos		*Bronze Age*

B.C.	MESOPOTAMIA (AND PERSIA)	EGYPT	PALESTINE, SYRIA, AND ASIA MINOR
1750	*Hammurabi—Babylonian (Amoritic) Empire*	*Hyksos kings*	
		The New Empire	
	Kassite rule begins		
1500			
		Shadow-clock Great Hall of Karnak *Egyptian empire at its zenith*	
			Cementation steel made by Chalybes
	First rise of Assyrians		
		Tutankhamen Glass vessels in common use	
			Alphabet used at Ugarit
1250			
			Rise of Phoenician kingdom *Collapse of Hittite power* *Siege of Troy*
			Reigns of David and Solomon *Hiram, king of Tyre*
1000	*Assyrian revival* Iron equipment		Iron ploughshare
750	*Sargon II—Assyrian Empire*		*Ten tribes of Israel deported by the Assyrians*
	Sennacherib's stone canal and aqueduct	*Egypt under Assyrian rule*	*Decline of Phoenician power* Coinage introduced (Lydia) *Lydians dominant in Asia Minor*
	Nineveh destroyed by Medes and Chaldeans *Nebuchadnezzar: Neo-Babylonian (Chaldean) Empire* Euphrates bridge and Ishtar gate, Babylon		*586 Babylonian captivity: Jews* *Persian conquest*
	538 Babylon included in Persian Empire by Cyrus	*Persian conquest*	

...STERN MEDITERRANEAN	WESTERN MEDITERRANEAN	CENTRAL AND NORTHERN EUROPE
...sos at its zenith		Stonehenge erected
...ar writing of Greek ...ssos destroyed (acc. to ...vans)		
...cenean palaces ...aeans in Greece		
...ians in Greece		Iron industry in Austria (Hallstatt)
	Etruscans in Italy Carthage founded	
...ek colonial expansion		
...er mined at Laurion		
	Republic established at Rome	

B.C.	MESOPOTAMIA (AND PERSIA)	EGYPT	PALESTINE, SYRIA, AND ASIA MINOR
500	Darius's inscription at Behistun		
	Alexander destroys Persian Empire	*Conquest by Alexander*	
		Red Sea canal renewed by Ptolemy Philadelphus	
		Great Age of Alexandria	
		Lighthouse at Alexandria (Pharos)	Colossus of Rhodes
250			Parchment made at Perg: mum
		Eratosthenes' world map	
	Rise of the Parthians		
	Victory of Parthians over Romans (Carrhae)		
		Egypt a Roman province; deaths of Mark Antony and Cleopatra	Glass-blowing began Syria

Eastern Mediterranean	Western Mediterranean	Central and Northern Europe
ueduct of Samos ne Athenian pottery the in common use for wood-turning *eeks defeat Persians* ppodamus laid out Piraeus rthenon completed *ath of Pericles*		
	405–367 *Dionysius, ruler of* *Syracuse*	*Celtic expansion in western and* *central Europe* *Iron Age in Britain*
6–323 *Alexander, king of* *Macedon* *ath of Aristotle*		
	Romans supreme in Italy *Death of Archimedes* Catalan furnace in Spain	
mans destroy Corinth	Romans destroy Carthage	
	Julian Calendar *Augustus establishes Empire*	*Caesar's conquest of Gaul*

A.D.	THE EAST	EASTERN MEDITERRANEAN AND CONSTANTINOPLE	ITALY (WITH SPAIN AN PORTUGAL)
14			Use of brass
			Death of Augustus
			Drainage of Lake Fucinu
			Great Fire of Rome
			69–79 *Vespasian*
			Corn ground by water-m
		Heron's *Mechanics*	*Pompeii destroyed*
			81–96 *Domitian*
100			Pantheon built
			138–92 *Antonine empero (Pius, Marcus Aureliu Commodus)*
		Ptolemy's *Almagest* and *Geography*	Baths of Caracalla
200	*Sassanian Persian empire established*		Use of shafts for wagons
300			284–305 *Diocletian reorg izes empire*
			Large Vitruvian water-m
			312–37 *Constantine*
		330 *Constantinople founded*	
400			
		Death of St. Jerome	
	Huns advance into western Europe		
			Odoacer ends Roman Emp in West
			493–526 *Rule of Theodo in Italy*
500	*Avars introduce metal stir-rups*	527–65 *Justinian*	*Benedictine Order founded*
		Production of raw silk at- tempted	
		St. Sophia built	*Siege of Rome by the Ost goths; Byzantine r established in Italy*
			Mausoleum of Theodoric Ravenna
			Lombards enter Italy
			Emergence of Venice

CENTRAL AND NORTHERN EUROPE	FRANCE AND THE LOW COUNTRIES	BRITAIN/ENGLAND
		Roman conquest
Trajan extends empire north of lower Danube		Hadrian's wall
	458–81 *Childeric, king of (Salian) Franks*	
	Merovingian rule in France	
		Conversion of England begun

A.D.	THE EAST	EASTERN MEDITERRANEAN AND CONSTANTINOPLE	ITALY (WITH SPAIN AND PORTUGAL)
600	Windmill in Persia 622 *Birth of Islam*	*Persians and Avars besiege Constantinople* 'Greek fire'	
700	Alchemical works of Jabir Chinese paper-makers captured at Samarkand *Baghdad founded*		*Moorish conquest of Spain* *Charles Martel's victory over Moors*
800	Arabic translation of Ptolemy Chinese porcelain received and imitated in western Asia	Lateen sail	800 *Charlemagne crowned Roman emperor*
900	*Rise of Bokhara*		Cotton and silk established by Moors in Spain *Cordova at its zenith*
1000	Alhazen's writings on optics, etc. Baghdad potters migrate to Cairo	*Seljuk Turks occupy Asia Minor*	First use of magnetic compass Rebuilding of St. Mark's Venice First translations from Arabic science

...ENTRAL AND NORTHERN EUROPE	FRANCE AND THE LOW COUNTRIES	BRITAIN/ENGLAND
	Fair of St Denis in existence	
		Sutton Hoo ship-burial *Death of St Cuthbert*
	Church organs introduced from Constantinople	
...neland stoneware ...hen cathedral ...stad ship ...ing expansion*		
		871–99 *Alfred, king of Wessex*
...gyar incursions*		
...–73 *Otto the Great, emperor* ...ing in Harz mountains *...tward expansion of Germany*		960–88 *Dunstan, archbishop of Canterbury*
...4–39 *Conrad II, emperor*	Norman abbeys	1042–66 *Edward the Confessor* Westminster Abbey
	Fulling mills	1066–87 *William the Conqueror Domesday Book*

A.D.	THE EAST	EASTERN MEDITERRANEAN AND CONSTANTINOPLE	ITALY (WITH SPAIN A PORTUGAL)
1100	1096–9 1st Crusade Venetian traders in Levant		Paper-making by Moo
1150		Last great age of Byzantium	Stamp-mill used in pa making
	Saladin captures Jerusalem 3rd Crusade		
1200		4th Crusade captures Constantinople Hinged rudder	Venetian glass-making Italian silk-throwing m
	Mongols invade eastern Europe Mongol invasion of Mesopotamia, etc.		
1250	Travels of Marco Polo		Florin coined (gold) Naviglio Grande (G Canal of Lombardy)
			Plate armour (Milan)
1300	Ottoman Turks first enter Byzantine territory in Asia Minor		Spectacle-making (Venic Genoese ships enter Eng Channel Catalan Atlas Majolica ware

ᴇɴᴛʀᴀʟ ᴀɴᴅ Nᴏʀᴛʜᴇʀɴ Eᴜʀᴏᴘᴇ	Fʀᴀɴᴄᴇ ᴀɴᴅ ᴛʜᴇ Lᴏᴡ Cᴏᴜɴᴛʀɪᴇs	Eɴɢʟᴀɴᴅ
ᴜld-board added to plough	*Champagne fairs at their zenith* *Growth of the Cistercian Order*	Gloucester candlestick (*cire perdue*)
	Abbey church of St. Denis, Paris (gothic)	
German expansion east of ᴵbe		
2–90 Frederick Barba-ᴏssa, emperor		
	Foundation of University of Paris Bridge of Avignon Windmills	Old London Bridge
ᴄs built for northern trade	Fulling mills in wide use	1216–72 *Henry III* Westminster Abbey rebuilt: Portland stone Roger Bacon's experiments
ᴬGotthard Pass open to ᴀffic *of Hanse towns and League*	Beauvais choir built	
	Great age of stained glass *Zuider Zee at its maximum extent*	Salisbury Cathedral
		1272–1307 *Edward I* *Conquest of Wales completed* *Death of Eleanor of Castile*
ᴇ of open-sea route round ᴋaw	Flax-breaker	Units of length and area standardized Navigation weir on Thames
ᴇ-glazing of pottery	*Crecy*	1337–1453 *Hundred Years War*

A.D.	THE EAST	EASTERN MEDITERRANEAN AND CONSTANTINOPLE	ITALY (WITH SPAIN AN PORTUGAL)
1350		*Power of Ottoman Turks expands from Asia Minor into Europe*	*Italian renaissance begins*
1400			*Portuguese voyages organ by Prince Henry the N gator* Caravels Duomo, Florence

CENTRAL AND NORTHERN EUROPE	FRANCE AND THE LOW COUNTRIES	ENGLAND
8 *Black Death*	1348 *Black Death*	1348 *Black Death*
ndenburg an Electorate		
	Windmill-driven scoop-wheel	
	Canals with sluices	1377–99 *Richard II*
st summit-level canal, Germany		Salisbury cathedral clock
t-iron cannon, Germany		
	Modern lock (Damme)	
	Dutch drift-nets	
	Hollow-post mills in Holland	Tattershall castle (brick)
		King's College Chapel, Cambridge, begun

A.D.	WORLD RELATIONSHIPS OF EUROPE	ITALY, SPAIN, AND PORTUGAL	CENTRAL AND NORTHERN EUROPE
1450	1453 *Ottoman Turks capture Constantinople*		Gutenberg's printing-press (Mainz) Intensive silver-mining Blast-furnace introduced *Jakob Fugger II, 'the Rich*
		1471–84 *Pope Sixtus IV* Patents introduced at Venice Vitruvius's *De architectura* printed *Christian reconquest of Spain completed* 1494–1559 *Italian wars of France and Spain*	Instrument-making at Nuremberg (Regiomontanus)
	Diaz reaches Cape of Good Hope *Columbus's first voyage* *Papal line of demarcation* *da Gama reaches India* *Cabot's first voyage to Newfoundland*		
1500	*Aztecs of Mexico and Incas of Peru conquered by Spain* 1522 *First circumnavigation of the world (begun by Magellan)*	Mitre-gate pound-locks Wheel-lock invented in Italy	1519–56 *Charles V, emperor*
			Tinplate Iatrochemistry (Paracelsus) *Death of Erasmus*
		Dome of St Peter's designed by Michelangelo	Rail-way used in mining
1550			*De Re Metallica* (Agricola)
	Frobisher seeks North-West Passage	Potato introduced into Europe 1572–85 *Pope Gregory XIII* *Portugal annexed to Spain* Gregorian calendar Galileo's discovery of the principle of the pendulum 1585–90 *Pope Sixtus V*	

THE LOW COUNTRIES	FRANCE	ENGLAND
	Earliest surviving illustration of a carrack	1455–85 *Wars of the Roses*
...ying-dry' of drowned ...ands		
	1515–47 *Francis I*	1509–47 *Henry VIII*
		Dissolution of monasteries
		Casting of iron cannon
...ssels canal completed		1558–1603 *Elizabeth I* Recoinage
		Increased use of coal
...rcator's map of the world		Brass manufacture established
...2–1609 *Revolt of the* *...etherlands*		by Mineral and Battery Works *Royal Exchange founded* *Spanish Armada defeated* Lee's stocking-frame
...ndmill-driven saw	1589–1610 *Henry IV*	Log and back-staff
...-boat	*Edict of Nantes granting*	*Steelyard finally closed*
...ft ware	*toleration to Huguenots*	Rails first mentioned in colliery

A.D.	WORLD RELATIONSHIPS OF EUROPE	ITALY, SPAIN, AND PORTUGAL	CENTRAL AND NORTHER EUROPE
1600	*Foundation of East India Companies, England and Holland*	Accademia dei Lincei Galileo's telescope	Ribbon-loom (Danzig)
			1618–48 Thirty Years W Sulphuric acid made Nordhausen
			Gustavus Adolphus in venes in Germany Siege of Magdeburg
1650			*1640–88 Frederick Will Elector of Brandenburg*
		Piazza of St Peter's, Rome, completed	Oder–Spree canal
1700			*Peter of Russia's first to western Europe*
			Polhem's cast-iron ro process
			Porcelain (Meissen)
		1740–58 Pope Benedict XIV	*1740–86 Frederick II, of Prussia; attack Silesia*

THE LOW COUNTRIES	FRANCE	ENGLAND
	Dangon's improved draw-loom	1603–25 *James I* (*Union of Crowns*)
e Years Truce		Coal used in glass-making
known shipment of tea Europe		Inigo Jones's buildings
es–Dunkirk canal		*Statute of Monopolies*
		1625–49 *Charles I*
		Vermuyden's fenland drainage
	Briare canal completed	*Civil War begun*
	Flint-lock perfected	
otint		*First Dutch War*
		Pepys's diary
	1661–1715 *Personal rule of Louis XIV*	1660 Royal Society founded
	Rise of Colbert	Boyle's *Sceptical Chymist*
	Elaboration of furniture	*Fire of London*
	Cast plate glass	
		Flint glass
		Greenwich Observatory founded
	Languedoc canal opened	
	Vauban's fortifications	
	Versailles completed	
	1685 *Edict of Nantes revoked; flight of Huguenots from France*	Dome of St Paul's Cathedral begun
	Pont Royal built	*The Revolution*
	Papin's steam-engine	Savery's 'fire-engine'
h press introduced by ieuw		*Campaigns of Marlborough*
		Tull's seed-drill
		Act of Union with Scotland
		Coke-smelting of iron by Darby
	Treaty of Utrecht	Newcomen engine
		Lombe's silk-throwing mill
	Iron-making processes analysed by Réaumur	Zinc-smelting at Swansea
		Hadley's octant
		Kay's flying-shuttle
schenbroek's 'Leyden jar'	Mapping of France by triangulation begun	*Jacobite rebellion*
	École des Ponts et Chaussées	Carding-machine for wool
		Roebuck's lead-chamber process for sulphuric acid

A.D.	BRITAIN		CONTIN
1750		50 Westminster bridge completed	
		51 Crucible steel commercially established	51 *The Encyclopaedia mences publication*
	54 *Royal Society of Arts founded*		
	56 *Outbreak of Seven Years War*		56–63 *Seven Years War*
	57 *Clive's conquest of Bengal*	57 Sankey Navigation	
		58 Strutt's ribbed hosiery	
1760	60 *Accession of George III*	60 Smeaton's Eddystone lighthouse completed	
		60 Carron Iron Works	
		61 Worsley–Manchester canal opened	
		62 Harrison's chronometer No. 4 tested	
	63 *Peace of Paris*	62 Wedgwood's 'Queen's ware'	62–96 *Catherine II, em of Russia*
		64 Hargraves's jenny invented	65–90 *Joseph II, Habsb emperor*
		67 Rails cast at Coalbrookdale	
	68 *Cook's first voyage to the Pacific*		
		69 Arkwright's spinning-machine patented	
		69 Wedgwood established at Etruria	
1770	71 *Smeatonian Club founded*	70 Ramsden's screw-cutting lathe	
	74 *Excise on calico halved*	74 Wilkinson's boring-mill	74–92 *Louis XVI, king France*
	75–83 *War of American Independence*		
	76 *Adam Smith's* Wealth of Nations	76 Watt's steam-engine in use	
	78–83 *War with France (the Maritime War)*	78 Bramah's water-closet	
		79 Iron bridge at Coalbrookdale	
		79 Crompton's mule perfected	

EUROPE	AMERICA
Thiout's lathe	
	52 Franklin's lightning conductor
Rhine bridge at Schaffhausen	
	59 *British capture Quebec*
Trésaguet's method of road-making	
Cugnot's steam road-carriage	
	75–83 *War of Independence*
	76 *Declaration of Independence*

A.D.	BRITAIN		CONTINE
1780			80 *Intervention of Holland* *Maritime War*
	83 *Peace of Versailles*		
		84 Meikle's threshing-machine	
		84 Cort's introduction of puddling	
		85 Steam introduced in cotton industry	
	86 *Anglo-French commercial treaty*		86 *Death of Frederick II Prussia*
		87 Cartwright's power-loom in factory	
	88 *Colonization of Australia begun*		89 *French Declaration of Rights of Man*
1790	91 *Ordnance Survey established*		91 *Patent law in France*
	93–1815 *French Wars*	93 S. Bentham's patent for wood-working machinery	93 *Reign of Terror*
	93 *Board of Agriculture established*		
			94 *Lavoisier executed*
			94 *French conquest of B gium*
			95 *École Polytechnique est blished*
	99 *Royal Institution founded*		
	99 *Trade unions made illegal*		

EUROPE	AMERICA
Steam-boat *Pyroscaphe* on r. Sâone First balloon ascents (France) Christian VII of Denmark's Eider canal	83 *British settlement of Upper Canada*
Berthollet's use of chlorine in bleaching	85 *Jefferson, U.S. minister in Paris* 86 'Sea-island' cotton planted
Leblanc's soda-making process	89–97 *Washington, President*
	90 *First patent law*
Metre defined by French Academy of Sciences Chappe's semaphore	93 Whitney's cotton-gin
Balloon used for observation at battle of Fleurus	
Senefelder's invention of lithography Guinand's glass-stirrer Robert's paper-making machine Lebon's coal-gas patent	

A.D.	Britain		Contin
1800		oo Stanhope's iron print-ing-press	oo *Napoleon Bonaparte power*
		oo Trevithick's high-pres-sure steam-engine	oo *Treaty of San Ildefo*
		or Trevithick's steam road-carriage	
	o2 *Peace of Amiens*	o2 Mechanized manufac-ture of pulley-blocks for navy	
		o2 Steam tug-boat *Char-lotte Dundas*	
		o2 West India docks con-structed	
		o4 Telford's Caledonian canal begun	
		o4 Trevithick's railway locomotive	
		o5 Surrey Iron Railway opened	
	o6 *Orders in Council (trade blockade)*	o6 Gas-lighting of cotton-mills begun	o6 *Continental System (tr blockade)*
		o7 Maudslay's table-engine	o7 *Serfdom abolished in P. sia*
			o7 *French invade Portuga*
		o8 Dalton's atomic theory	o8–14 *Peninsular War*
		o9 Heathcoat's lace-mak-ing machine	
1810	11–20 *Regency period*	11 Bell Rock lighthouse	10 *French frontiers exten*
	11–16 *Luddite riots*	11 Standedge canal tunnel	*to Rome and Lübeck*
	12–15 *American War*	12 Steamship *Comet*	
	13 *Sunderland Society for preventing accidents in coal mines founded*	14 Steam cylinder-press printing of *The Times*	14 *First overthrow of Na leon*
		14 Stephenson's *Blucher*	
	15 *Battle of Waterloo; Corn Law*		15 *Second overthrow Napoleon*
			15–48 *The Age of Metterr in Central Europe a Italy*
	16 *Bombardment of Algiers*	16 Davy lamp	
	18 *Institution of Civil En-gineers founded*		18 *Beginning of Prussi customs union (Zollv rein)*
	19 *Gold standard established*	19 McAdam's *Practical Es-say on Roads*	

EUROPE	AMERICA
Voltaic pile	00 Whitney makes muskets with interchangeable parts
Jacquard loom Achard's sugar-beet factory	01 Finley's patent chain-bridge, Pennsyvania
	04 Evans's high-pressure steam-engine
	07 Steamship *Clermont* on r. Hudson
Appert's meat preservation St Quentin canal opened	11 Steamship *Orleans* on r. Ohio
	12 *War against Britain* 12 *Invasion of Canada*
Edward's compound steam-engine patented in France	
'Draisine' (patented dandy-horse)	18 Blanchard's copying-lathe for gunstocks

A.D.	BRITAIN		CONTIN[E]
1820	20 *Accession of George IV*	20 Hancock's rubber masticator	
		22 Roberts's power-loom	
	23 *Salt excise abolished*		
	24 *Trade unions legalized*	24 Aspdin's Portland cement	
		24 Manufacture of 'mackintoshes'	
	25 *Emigration of artisans legalized*	25 Stockton–Darlington railway opened	
		26 Paris's thaumatrope	
		26 Telford's Menai bridge	
		27 First friction matches	
		29 Neilson's hot-blast	
		29 Stephenson's *Rocket*	
1830		30 Roberts's self-acting mule perfected	30–48 *Orleans monarchy* [*in*] *France*
		30 Liverpool–Manchester railway opened	30 *Independence of Belgiu[m]*
	31 *British Association founded*	31 Gurney's steam-carriage	30 *Cholera epidemic in Rus[sia]*
		31 Faraday demonstrates electromagnetic induction	
		31 Bickford's safety fuse	
		31 Phillips's contact process for sulphuric acid patented	
	32 *Cholera epidemic reaches London*		
	33 *Emancipation of slaves in British Empire*	33 Pattinson's process for silver-extraction	
	33 *First successful Factory Act*		
	33 *China trade thrown open*		
			34 Zollverein *became wide[ly] established*
	37 *Accession of Queen Victoria*		
	38 *Royal Agricultural Society founded*	38 S.S. *Great Western* initiates regular Atlantic crossings	
	38 *Typhus epidemic in London*	38 Screw propeller	
	38 *Chartist movement begins*	38 London–Birmingham railway opened	
		38 Telegraph installed on railway	
		39 Nasmyth's steam-hammer	

EUROPE	AMERICA
	20 Ithiel Town's truss-bridge patented
Iron paddle-steamer *Aaron Manby* on r. Seine	
	24 Erie canal completed
Seguin's wire-suspension road-bridge	
Nicéphore Niepce's first photograph	
Fourneyron's water-turbine	
Ghent ship canal	
Seguin's multi-tubular boiler patented	28 Danforth's throstle and Thorp's ring-spinning frame invented
	30 Stevens's inverted-T rail
	31 Morris canal completed
de Girard's flax-heckling machine	32 First horse-tramway in New York
Gotha canal completed in Sweden	
	33 Iron-smelting with anthracite patented
Brussels–Malines railway	35 Colt revolver patented
Sorel's galvanized iron	36 *Patent Office established*
Paixhans's shell-gun adopted in France	
	38 Bruce's type-casting machine
Daguerreotype	
Tunnel-kiln (Denmark)	

741

A.D.	BRITAIN		CONTINE
1840	40 *Penny post instituted* 40 *Colonization of New Zealand* 40 *Bombardment of Acre* 42 *Shaftesbury's Coal Mines Act* 43 *Export of machinery legalized* 44 *Bank Charter Act* 45 *Royal College of Chemistry founded* 45 *Excise duties on glass repealed* 46 *Corn Laws repealed* 46 *Standard railway-gauge introduced* 48 *Mill's* Political Economy 49 *Navigation Acts repealed*	40 Elkington's electro-plating 41 Fox Talbot's calotype 43 Brunel's Thames tunnel opened 43 Lawes's superphosphate factory 45 McNaught's compound steam-engine	40 *Liebig's* Chemistry in F lation to Agricultur 42 Zollverein *patent conve tion*

EUROPE	AMERICA	
Roller-milling of grain begun in Hungary		
Dreyse's needle-gun		41 Goodyear invents vulcanization
Zola arched dam		
Schönbein's discovery of gun-cotton		45 Bigelow's Brussels power-loom
Rifled breech-loading artillery, Piedmont		
Heilmann's comb	45–49 *Presidency of Polk*	
	46 *Mexican War*	46 Deare's steel mould-boards
		46 Hoe's rotary press, Philadelphia
		46 Ether established as anaesthetic in operation
		47 St Lawrence improvements completed, Lake Ontario-Montreal
	48 *California gold-rush*	48 McCormick reaper factory-produced, Chicago
Krupp's steel gun tested		
Minié bullet		
Monier's reinforced con-concrete		

A.D.	BRITAIN		CONTIN...
1850	50 *Public Libraries Act*	50 R. Stephenson's Britannia bridge	
	51 *Great Exhibition (Crystal Palace)*	51 Dover–Calais cable sucfully established	
	51 *Discovery of gold in Australia*	51 Lister-Donisthorpe machine-comb	
			52 *Napoleon III, empero the French*
	53 *Gladstone's first Free Trade Budget*		
	54–55 *Siege of Sebastopol*		
	54–56 *Crimean War*		
	55 *Newspaper stamp duty repealed*		
	55 *Metropolitan Board of Works established*		
		56 Bessemer steel	
		56 Perkin's discovery of mauve	
	57 *Indian Mutiny*		
		58 Arc light, S. Foreland lighthouse	
		59 *Great Eastern* completed	59 *Franco-Austrian war Italy*
1860	60 *Anglo-French Commercial Treaty*		
			60 *Italy united (except V tia and Rome)*
	61 *Paper Duties repealed*	61 First all-iron warship, *Warrior*	61 *Emancipation of serf Russia*
	62 *International Exhibition*	62 Steel rails	
			62–90 *Bismarck in powe Prussia and (71- Germany*
	63 *Alkali Act*		
			64 *German war against L mark*
	65 *'Red Flag' Act*	65 Electrolytic refining of copper	
	65 *Last severe epidemic of cholera*		
	66 *Cattle Diseases Prevention Act*	56 Atlantic cable finally successful	66 *Austro-Prussian war*
			67 *Paris Exhibition*

EUROPE	AMERICA	
		51 Bogardus's cast-iron frame-buildings
		51 Kelly's steel-making converter
		51 Singer's sewing-machine
Vienna–Trieste railway through Alps		53 Colt's armoury (interchangeable system)
	54 *First trade treaty with Japan*	54 Gesner manufactures kerosene (paraffin oil)
Deville's aluminium	55 *Maury's* Physical Geography of the Sea	55 Turret lathe
Bunsen burner		55 Roebling's wire-cable bridge, Niagara
Köller's tungsten steel (Austria)		
Three-high steel mill, Motala		
		57 Otis's safety elevators installed
Bessemer steel perfected by Göransson		
French ironclad, *La Gloire*		59 Drake's oil-well, Pennsylvania
Steam-roller invented in France		
Exploitation of Stassfurt potassium deposits	61–65 *Lincoln, President*	
Solvay's soda-making process patented in Belgium	61–65 *Civil War*	
	62 *Land-grant colleges*	62 Brown's universal milling-machine
	62 Monitor *in action*	62 Gatling gun patented
Whitehead's torpedo designed in Austria	65 *Massachusetts Institute of Technology*	
	65 *Abolition of slavery completed by 13th Amendment*	
Chassepot rifle introduced in France		65 Atlantic cable finally successful
Furens arch dam completed		
Nobel invents dynamite		
Siemens-Martin open-hearth steel		
Michaux manufactured velocipedes	67 *Dominion constitution of Canada established*	68 Armour's meat-packing, Chicago
		68 Westinghouse brake
Suez Canal opened		69 First trans-continental railway
Alizarin synthesized, Germany		

745

A.D.	BRITAIN		CONTIN
1870	70 *Education Act*	70 Weldon's process for bleaching powder	70 *Franco-Prussian war*
			71 *German Empire established*
		72–76 World oceanographic survey by *The Challenger*	
	74–80 *Disraeli's second government: imperial expansion*		
	75 *Explosives Act*	75 London main drainage system completed	
		76 Contact process for sulphuric acid brought into use at Silvertown	77 *Full protection for pate in Germany*
		77 Rubber plants successfully established in Ceylon	
		78 Swan's carbon-filament lamp	
	79 *Board of Trade authorizes steel in bridges*	79 Gilchrist-Thomas basic steel	79 *Bismarck's first tariff creases*
1880			
		82 Kynoch's brass cartridge-case	82 *The Triple Alliance Germany, Austr Hungary, and Italy*
			83 *International patents convention*
		84 Maxim gun	84 *Charlottenburg Techni High School completed, Berlin*
		84 Parsons' steam-turbine	
		85 Rover 'safety' bicycle	
	86 *Nobel Dynamite Trust*	86 Severn tunnel opened	86 *Optical glass made at Ze works, Jena*
	87 *Golden Jubilee*	87 Cyanide process for gold and silver	
		88 Dunlop's pneumatic tyre	
		89 Ferranti's Deptford power station	

EUROPE	AMERICA	
Gramme's ring dynamo		
Mont Cenis tunnel opened	71 *Chicago fire*	
Baku oil industry		73 Remington Company's typewriter
		73 Brayton's oil-engine
		74 Eads's St Louis bridge
Otto gas-engine	76 *Centennial Exhibition, Philadelphia*	76 Bell's telephone
		76 Edison's phonograph
Reinforced concrete beams patented by Monier		
Frozen mutton shipped (Argentine–Le Havre)		
Laval's cream-separator		
Electric railway exhibited, Berlin	79 *War of the Pacific (Chile v. Bolivia and Peru)*	79 Edison's carbon-filament lamp
		80 Half-tone block used in *New York Daily Graphic*
		80 Carnegie's first big steel furnace
St Gotthard tunnel completed		82 Edison's Pearl Street generating station
		83 Completion of Brooklyn bridge
Magazine rifle adopted in Germany		84 Koller uses cocaine as anaesthetic
Electric trams in Germany		
Mannesmann's seamless steel tubes patented		85 Stephenson's rail-gauge standardized
Welsbach's gas-mantle		
Daimler's first petrol-engine		
Benz's first motor-car		
Vieille's *Poudre B*		86 Linotype first used by *New York Tribune*
		86 Niagara Falls hydroelectric installation begun
Aluminium produced electrolytically, Schaffhausen		
Steam-tricycle, France		
Laval's turbine		
Marey's *chambre chronophotographique*		88 Tesla's A.C. electric-motor
Eiffel Tower		88 Eastman's Kodak camera

A.D.	BRITAIN		CONTIN
1890		90 First 'tube' railway 90 *Daily Graphic*, fully illustrated 90 Forth bridge completed	
			92 *Witte Finance Ministe Russia* 92 *Méline tariff in Fran*
		94 Castner's electrolytic process for caustic soda	
	96 *Repeal of 'Red Flag' Act*		
	97 *Diamond Jubilee*	97 Parsons' *Turbinia*	
	98 *Battle of Omdurman*		
	99–1902 *South African War*		
1900	01 *Death of Victoria*		

EUROPE	AMERICA	
	90 *McKinley tariff*	90 First completely steel-framed building, Chicago
Trans-Siberian railway begun		
Benz's four-wheeled car	93 *World Exhibition, Chicago*	93 New Croton aqueduct tunnel completed, New York
Kiel canal		94 Edison's Kinetoscope Parlor, New York
Cinema set up by the Lumières, Paris		95 Northrop's automatic loom
		95 First main-line railway electrified
	96 *Bimetallist election campaign*	96 Ford's first automobile
Synthetic indigo made by Badische Fabrik		97 Monotype printing established
Diesel engine successfully manufactured in Germany		
French '75' quick-firing gun	98 *Spanish-American War (in Cuba, etc.)*	98 Owens's automatic bottle-making machine
Dortmund-Ems Canal		
First Zeppelin launched		
Marconi begins transatlantic wireless telegraphy		
		03 Orville Wright achieves heavier-than-air, powered flight

SELECT BIBLIOGRAPHY

THE following is a list of books available in English which amplify, and shed further light on, the histories of the various technologies discussed in the text. Preference has been given to recent work and to short surveys, where these are of sufficient authority. The objective has been to provide an adequate selection for each chapter, but achieving this has been made difficult by the fact that the literature of the subject is at present very unevenly divided among its branches. The lists for Chapters 1 and 10, the general historical surveys, draw attention chiefly to appropriate studies of economic and social history, as the political side is fully covered in several well-known and readily accessible series, including the Cambridge Ancient, Medieval, and Modern Histories, the Oxford History of England, and their American counterparts. For the political background to the technological development of the United States the British reader should consult any of the later editions of Morison and Commager's *Growth of the American Republic*.

General works on the history of technology are grouped together at the beginning; each of them provides much bibliographical information. This can be kept up to date by consulting the index of books and articles, including important foreign-language publications, in the annual *Transactions of the Newcomen Society*, London, and from the bibliographical references featured in *Technology and Culture*, the International Quarterly of the Society for the History of Technology (Wayne State University Press, Detroit).

GENERAL

SINGER, CHARLES, HOLMYARD, E. J., HALL, A. R., and WILLIAMS, TREVOR I. *A History of Technology* (5 vols.). Clarendon Press, Oxford, 1954–8.

USHER, A. P. *A History of Mechanical Inventions* (2nd ed.). Harvard University Press, Cambridge, Mass., 1954.

KIRBY, R. S., WITHINGTON, S., DARLING, A. B., and KILGOUR, F. G. *Engineering in History*. McGraw-Hill, New York, 1956.

MUMFORD, L. *Technics and Civilization*. Harcourt, New York, 1934.

LILLEY, S. *Men, Machines and History*. Cobbett, London, 1948.

FORBES, R. J. *Man the Maker*. Constable, London, 1958.

OLIVER, J. W. *History of American Technology*. Ronald Press, New York, 1956.

KLEMM, F. *A History of Western Technology* (Eng. trans. by D. W. Singer). Allen & Unwin, London, 1959.

NEEDHAM, J. *Science and Civilization in China* (Vols. 1–3). Cambridge University Press, 1954–9.

FORBES, R. J. *Studies in Ancient Technology* (Vols. I–VI). Brill, Leiden, 1955–8.

WOLF, F. *History of Science, Technology, and Philosophy in the Sixteenth and Seventeenth Centuries* (2nd ed.). Allen & Unwin, London, 1950.

—— *History of Science, Technology, and Philosophy in the Eighteenth Century* (2nd ed.). Allen & Unwin, London, 1952.

GILLISPIE, C. C. (ed.). *A Diderot Pictorial Encyclopaedia of Trade and Industry*. Dover Publications Inc., New York, 1959.

GIEDION, S. *Mechanization Takes Command*. Oxford University Press, New York, 1948.

Transactions of the Newcomen Society. London, Vols. 1–, 1922–.

The Encyclopaedia of the Social Sciences (15 vols.). Macmillan, New York, 1930–5.

CHAPTER 1. GENERAL HISTORICAL SURVEY

BREASTED, J. H. *Ancient Times* (2nd ed.). Ginn, London, 1928.

ROSTOVTZEFF, M. *A History of the Ancient World* (2 vols.). Clarendon Press, Oxford, 1926, 1928.

CLARK, J. G. D. *Prehistoric Europe*. Methuen, London, 1952.

TOUTAIN, J. *The Economic Life of the Ancient World*. Routledge & Sons, London, 1930.

FRANK, TENNEY. *Economic History of Rome* (2nd ed.). Cape, London, 1927.

CLAPHAM, J. and POWER, E. (ed.). *The Cambridge Economic History of Europe*, Vol. I. The Agrarian Life of the Middle Ages. Cambridge University Press, 1941.

POSTAN, M. and RICH, E. E. (ed.). *Ibid*., Vol. II. Trade and Industry in the Middle Ages. Cambridge University Press, 1952.

BOISSONNADE, P. *Life and Work in Medieval Europe*. Routledge & Sons, London, 1927.

THOMPSON, J. F. *Economic and Social History of the Middle Ages* (2 vols.). Constable, London, 1928.

HEATON, H. *Economic History of Europe* (rev. ed.). Hayes & Bros., New York, 1948.

TREVELYAN, G. M. *English Social History*. Longmans, London, 1944.

LIPSON, E. *Economic History of England* (Vols. 2 and 3, 6th ed.). Black, London, 1956.

CLOUGH, S. B. and COLE, C. W. *Economic History of Europe*. Heath, Boston, 1941.

CHAPTER 2. THE PRODUCTION OF FOOD

PROTHERO, R. E. (LORD ERNLE). *English Farming Past and Present* (4th ed.). Longmans, London, 1932.

ORWIN, C. S. *A History of English Farming*. Nelson, London, 1949.

FUSSELL, G. E. *The Farmer's Tools, 1500–1900*. Melrose, London, 1952.

FRANCIS, C. *A History of Food and its Preservation*. Princeton University Press, 1937.

SALAMAN, R. N. *The History and Social Influence of the Potato*. Cambridge University Press, 1949.

DEERR, NOEL. *The History of Sugar* (2 vols.). Chapman & Hall, London, 1949, 1950.

CHAPTER 3. PRODUCTION FOR DOMESTIC NEEDS

LANE, A. *Greek Pottery*. Faber, London, 1948.

CHARLESTON, R. J. *Roman Pottery*. Faber, London, 1955.

SAVAGE, G. *Porcelain*. Penguin Books, Harmondsworth, 1954.
ANGUS-BUTTERWORTH, L. M. *The Manufacture of Glass*. Pitman, London, 1948.
LIPSON, E. *The History of the Woollen and Worsted Industries* (3rd ed.). Black, London, 1950.
HEATON, H. *The Yorkshire Woollen and Worsted Industries from the Earliest Times up to the Industrial Revolution*. Clarendon Press, Oxford, 1920.
SALZMAN, L. F. *English Industries of the Middle Ages*. Clarendon Press, Oxford, 1923.
WATERER, J. W. *Leather and Craftsmanship*. Faber, London, 1950.
GLOAG, J. *A Short Dictionary of Furniture*. Allen & Unwin, London, 1952.

CHAPTER 4. THE EXTRACTION AND WORKING OF METALS

RICKARD, THOMAS A. *Man and Metals* (2 vols.). McGraw-Hill, New York, 1932.
AITCHISON, L. *A History of Metals* (2 vols.). Macdonald & Evans, London, 1960.
HOOVER, H. C. and L. H. Eng. trans. of Agricola's *De re metallica*. Mining Magazine, London, 1922.
SISCO, A. and SMITH, C. S. Eng. trans. of Réaumur's *Memoirs on Steel and Iron*. University of Chicago Press, 1956.
SCHUBERT, H. R. *History of the British Iron and Steel Industry*, c. *450 B.C.–A.D. 1775*. Routledge & Kegan Paul, London, 1957.
OMAN, SIR CHARLES W. C. *A History of the Art of War in the Middle Ages* (2 vols., 2nd ed.). Methuen, London, 1924.
NEF, J. U. *The Rise of the British Coal Industry* (2 vols.). Routledge & Sons, London, 1932.
COURT, W. H. B. *The Rise of the Midland Industries, 1600–1838*. Oxford University Press, 1938.
HAMILTON, H. *The English Copper and Brass Industries to 1800*. Longmans, London, 1926.
ASHTON, T. S. *Iron and Steel in the Industrial Revolution* (2nd ed.). Manchester University Press, 1951.
CARMAN, W. Y. *A History of Firearms*. Routledge & Kegan Paul, London, 1955.

CHAPTER 5. BUILDING CONSTRUCTION

STRAUB, H. *A History of Civil Engineering*. (Eng. trans. by E. Rockwell). Hill, London, 1952.
EDWARDS, I. E. S. *The Pyramids of Egypt*. Penguin Books, Harmondsworth, 1950.
TOY, S. *A History of Fortification from 3000 B.C. to A.D. 1700*. Heinemann, London, 1955.
HIBBERT, A. *Old European Cities*. Thames & Hudson, London, 1955.
MARGARY, I. D. *Roman Roads in Britain* (2 vols.). Phoenix House Ltd., London, 1955, 1957.
ASHBY, T. *The Aqueducts of Ancient Rome*, I. A. Richmond (ed.). Clarendon Press, Oxford, 1935.
ROBINS, F. W. *The Story of Water Supply*. Oxford University Press, London, 1946.

BRIGGS, M. S. *A Short History of the Building Crafts.* Clarendon Press, Oxford, 1925.

LLOYD, N. *A History of English Brickwork* (abr. ed.). Montgomery, London, 1935.

KNOOP, D. and JONES, G. P. *The Medieval Mason.* Manchester University Press, 1933.

SALZMAN, L. F. *Building in England down to 1540.* Clarendon Press, Oxford, 1952.

PARSONS, W. B. *Engineers and Engineering in the Renaissance.* Williams & Wilkins, Baltimore, 1939.

CHAPTER 6. TRANSPORT

FAYLE, C. E. *Short History of the World's Shipping Industry.* Allen & Unwin, London, 1933.

CLOWES, G. S. L. *Sailing Ships, their History and Development. Part I—Historical Notes* (5th ed.). Science Museum Handbooks, H.M.S.O., London, 1958.

BRÓGGER, A. W. and SHETELIG, H. *The Viking Ships, their Ancestry and Evolution.* (Eng. abr. and rev. trans. by Katherine John). Dreyer, Oslo, 1953.

BARBOUR, VIOLET. 'Dutch and English Merchant Shipping in the Seventeenth Century.' From *Essays in Economic History,* reprinted from the *Economic History Review,* E. M. Carus-Wilson (ed.). Arnold, London, 1954.

ABELL, SIR WESTCOTT. *The Shipwright's Trade.* Cambridge University Press, 1948.

TAYLOR, EVA G. R. *The Haven-Finding Art.* Hollis & Carter, London, 1956.

STURT, G. *The Wheelwright's Shop.* Cambridge University Press, 1934.

CHAPTER 7. COMMUNICATION AND RECORD

PARKER, R. A. *The Calendars of Ancient Egypt.* Chicago University Press, 1950.

WARD, F. A. B. *Collections Illustrating Time Measurement. Part I. Historical Review* (4th ed.). Science Museum Handbooks, H.M.S.O., London, 1958.

GORDON, G. F. C. *Clockmaking Past and Present* (rev. ed.). The Technical Press, London, 1949.

SYMONDS, R. W. *A Book of English Clocks.* Penguin Books, Harmondsworth, 1947.

GOULD, R. T. *The Marine Chronometer: its History and Development.* Potter, London, 1923.

DIRINGER, D. *The Alphabet* (2nd ed.). Hutchinson, London, 1948.

HUNTER, D. *Papermaking. The History and Technique of an Ancient Craft* (2nd ed.). Cresset Press, London, 1957.

BUTLER, P. *The Origin of Printing in Europe.* Chicago University Press, 1940.

ALDIS, H. G. *The Printed Book* (2nd ed.). Cambridge University Press, 1941.

BROWN, L. A. *The Story of Maps.* Cresset Press, London, 1951.

CHAPTER 8. EARLY SOURCES OF POWER

VOWLES, H. P. and M. W. *The Quest for Power.* Chapman, London, 1931.

PAYNE-GALLWEY, SIR RALPH W. F. *A Summary of the History, Construction and Effects in Warfare of the Projectile-Throwing Engines of the Ancients.* Longmans, London, 1907.

WAILES, R. *The English Windmill*. Routledge & Kegan Paul, London, 1954.
SKILTON, C. P. *British Windmills and Watermills*. Collins, London, 1947.

CHAPTER 9. THE BEGINNINGS OF THE CHEMICAL INDUSTRY

SARTON, G. *Introduction to the History of Science* (3 vols.). Carnegie Institute of Washington, Baltimore, 1927–48.
LEGGATT, W. F. *Ancient and Medieval Dyes*. Chemical Publishing Co., New York, 1944.
HOLMYARD, E. J. *Alchemy*. Penguin Books, Harmondsworth, 1957.
REED, J. *Through Alchemy to Chemistry*. Bell, London, 1957.
SINGER, C. *The Earliest Chemical Industry*. Folio Society, London, 1948.
TAYLOR, F. S. *A History of Industrial Chemistry*. Heinemann, London, 1957.
PARTINGTON, J. R. *A History of Greek Fire and Gunpowder*. Heffer, Cambridge, 1960.

CHAPTER 10. GENERAL HISTORICAL SURVEY
1750–1900 (*see also* Ch. 1)

MANTOUX, P. *The Industrial Revolution in the Eighteenth Century* (rev. ed.). Cape, London, 1928.
HAMMOND, J. L. and B. *The Rise of Modern Industry* (5th ed.). Longmans, London, 1937.
CLAPHAM, J. H. *An Economic History of Modern Britain* (3 vols.). Cambridge University Press, 1926–38.
HENDERSON, W. O. *Britain and Industrial Europe, 1750–1870*. Liverpool University Press, 1954.
Great Exhibition, 1851. Official Description and Illustrated Catalogue (3 vols. and supplement). London, 1851.
CLAPHAM, J. H. *The Economic Development of France and Germany, 1815–1914* (4th ed.). Cambridge University Press, 1936.
KNOWLES, L. C. A. *Economic Development in the Nineteenth Century. France, Germany, Russia, and the United States*. Routledge & Sons, London, 1932.
DUNHAM, A. L. *The Industrial Revolution in France, 1815–48*. Exposition Press, New York, 1955.
DAWSON, W. H. *The Evolution of Modern Germany*. Unwin, London, 1908.
FAULKNER, H. U. *American Economic History* (7th ed.). Harper & Bros., New York, 1954.

CHAPTER 11. THE STEAM-ENGINE (*see also* Ch. 8)

FAREY, J. *A Treatise on the Steam Engine, historical, practical, and descriptive*. London, 1827.
DICKINSON, H. W. *A Short History of the Steam-Engine*. Cambridge University Press, 1939.
—— *James Watt, Craftsman and Engineer*. Cambridge University Press, 1936.
—— and TITLEY, A. *Richard Trevithick, the Engineer and the Man*. Cambridge University Press, 1934.

SENNETT, R. and ORAM, H. J. *The Marine Steam Engine*. Longmans, London, 1917.

AHRONS, E. L. *The British Steam Railway Locomotive, 1825–1925*. Locomotive Publishing Co., London, 1927.

PARSONS, R. H. *The Development of the Parsons Steam Turbine*. Constable, London, 1936.

CHAPTER 12. MACHINE-TOOLS AND THEIR PRODUCTS

ROE, J. W. *English and American Tool Builders*. Yale University Press, New Haven, 1916.

BATHE, G. and D. *Oliver Evans, A Chronicle of Early American Engineering*. Historical Society of Pennsylvania, Philadelphia, 1935.

NASMYTH, J. *An Autobiography*. S. Smiles (ed.). London, 1883.

CHAPTER 13. MODERN TRANSPORT (*see also* Ch. 6)

ANDERSON, ROMOLA and R. C. *The Sailing Ship*. Harrap, London, 1926.

UNDERHILL, H. A. *Sailing Ship Rigs and Rigging*. Brown, Son, & Ferguson, Glasgow, 1938.

MACGREGOR, D. R. *The Tea Clippers*. Percival Marshall, London, 1952.

SMITH, E. C. *Short History of Naval and Marine Engineering*. Cambridge University Press, 1938.

SHERRINGTON, C. E. R. *A Hundred Years of Inland Transportation, 1830–1933*. Duckworth, London, 1934.

McCAUSLAND, H. *The English Carriage*. Batchworth Press, London, 1948.

FORWARD, E. A. *Railway Locomotives and Rolling Stock*. Science Museum Handbooks, H.M.S.O., London, 1931.

ELLIS, H. *British Railway History* (2 vols.). Allen & Unwin, London, 1954, 1959.

DUNCAN, H. O. *The World on Wheels*. Published by the author, Paris, 1926.

HARMSWORTH, H. C. (ed.). *Motors and Motor Driving*. Longmans, London, 1902.

GIBBS-SMITH, C. H. *A History of Flying*. Batsford, London, 1953.

CHAPTER 14. BUILDING CONSTRUCTION: REQUIREMENTS OF URBAN COMMUNITIES (*see also* Ch. 5)

KIRBY, R. S. and LAWSON, P. G. *The Early Years of Modern Civil Engineering*. Yale University Press, New Haven, 1932.

NORRIE, C. M. *Bridging the Years: a Short History of British Civil Engineering*. Arnold, London, 1956.

SMILES, S. *The Lives of the Engineers* (2 vols.). Murray, London, 1861.

HITCHCOCK, H. R. *Early Victorian Architecture in Britain* (2 vols). Architectural Press, London, 1954.

GIEDION, S. *Space, Time and Architecture*. Harvard University Press, Cambridge, Mass., 1943.

CHAPTER 15. BUILDING CONSTRUCTION: REQUIREMENTS OF TRANSPORT (*see also* Ch. 5)

GREGORY, J. W. *The Story of the Road, from the Beginning down to the Present Day* (2nd ed.). Black, London, 1938.

JACKMAN, W. T. *The Development of Transportation in Modern England* (2 vols). Cambridge University Press, 1916.

HADFIELD, C. *British Canals: an Illustrated History*. Phoenix House, London, 1950.

ROLT, L. T. C. *The Inland Waterways of England*. Allen & Unwin, London, 1950.

BOWEN, J. P. *British Lighthouses*. Longmans, London, 1947.

SHIRLEY SMITH, H. *The World's Great Bridges*. Phoenix House, London, 1953.

CHAPTER 16. COAL AND THE METALS (*see also* Ch. 4)

ASHTON, T. S. and SYKES, J. *The Coal Industry of the Eighteenth Century*. Manchester University Press, 1929.

BURN, D. L. *The Economic History of Steel-making, 1867-1939*. Cambridge University Press, 1939.

DAVIES, M. E. *The Story of Steel*. Burke Publishing Co., London, 1950.

BROWN, N. and TURNHILL, C. *A Century of Copper* (2 vols.). Wilson, London, 1899, 1900.

SMITH, J. B. *A Treatise upon Wire, its Manufacture and Uses*. Engineering, London, 1891.

CHAPTER 17. NEW MATERIALS: COAL-GAS, PETROLEUM, AND RUBBER

CHANDLER, D. and LACY, A. D. *The Rise of the Gas Industry in Britain*. British Gas Council, London, 1949.

ROBINS, F. W. *The Story of the Lamp and the Candle*. Oxford University Press, London, 1939.

O'DEA, W. T. *The Social History of Lighting*. Routledge & Kegan Paul, London, 1958.

GIDDENS, P. H. *The Birth of the Oil Industry*. Macmillan, New York, 1938.

WILLIAMSON, H. F. and DAUM, A. R. *The American Petroleum Industry 1859-1899*. Northwestern University Press, Evanston, Illinois, 1959.

PORRITT, B. D. *The Early History of the Rubber Industry*. McLaren, London, 1926.

SCHIDROWITZ, P. and DAWSON, T. R. *History of the Rubber Industry*. Heffer, Cambridge, 1952.

CHAPTER 18. THE RISE OF THE MODERN CHEMICAL INDUSTRY (*see also* Ch. 9)

HABER, L. F. *The Chemical Industry during the Nineteenth Century*. Oxford University Press, London, 1958.

ALLEN, J. F. *Some Founders of the Chemical Industry*. Sherratt & Hughes, London, 1906.

CLOW, A. and NAN L. *The Chemical Revolution: A Contribution to Social Technology*. Batchworth Press, London, 1952.

WILLIAMS, T. I. *The Chemical Industry Past and Present*. Penguin Books, Harmondsworth, 1953.

MIALL, S. *History of the British Chemical Industry*. Benn, London, 1931.

HARDIE, D. W. F. *A History of the Chemical Industry in Widnes*. Imperial Chemical Industries Limited, London, 1950.

HAYNES, W. *The American Chemical Industry, Vol. I, 1609–1911*. Van Nostrand, New York, 1957.

MACDONALD, G. W. *Historical Papers on Modern Explosives*. Whittaker, London, 1912.

CHAPTER 19. TEXTILES (*see also* Ch. 3)

WADSWORTH, A. P. and MANN, JULIA DE L. *The Cotton Trade and Industrial Lancashire, 1600–1780*. Manchester University Press, 1931.

DANIELS, G. W. *The Early English Cotton Industry*. Manchester University Press, 1920.

MURPHY, W. S. (ed.). *The Textile Industries* (3 vols.). Gresham, London, 1910.

BRADBURY, F. *Carpet Manufacture*. Lord & Nagle, Boston, Mass., 1904.

LYONS, L., ALLEN, T. W., and VINCENT, W. D. F. *The Sewing Machine*. Williamson, London, 1924.

CHAPTER 20. POTTERY AND GLASS (*see also* Ch. 3)

HONEY, W. B. *European Ceramic Art from the end of the Middle Ages to about 1815* (2 vols.). Faber, London, 1949.

POWELL, H. J. *Glass-making in England*. Cambridge University Press, 1923.

SCOVILLE, W. C. *Revolution in Glass Making*. Harvard University Press, Cambridge, Mass., 1948.

KING, H. C. *The History of the Telescope*. Griffin, London, 1955.

CHAPTER 21. THE INTERNAL COMBUSTION ENGINE

BEAUMONT, W. W. *Motor Vehicles and Motors* (2 vols.). Constable, London, 1900, 1906.

JENKINS, R. *Motor Cars and the Application of Mechanical Power to Road Vehicles*. Fisher & Unwin, London, 1902.

CHAPTER 22. THE ELECTRICAL INDUSTRY

APPLEYARD, R. *Pioneers of Electrical Communication*. Macmillan, London, 1930.

MACLAREN, M. *The Rise of the Electrical Industry during the Nineteenth Century*. Princeton University Press, 1943.

PARSONS, R. H. *The Early Days of the Power-Station Industry*. Cambridge University Press, 1940.

PASSER, H. C. *The Electrical Manufacturers, 1875–1900*. Harvard University Press, Cambridge, Mass., 1953.

GELATT, R. *The Fabulous Phonograph*. Cassell, London, 1956.

CHAPTER 23.
PRINTING, PHOTOGRAPHY, AND THE CINEMA (*see also* Ch. 7)

PLANT, MARJORIE. *The English Book Trade: an Economic History of the Making and Sale of Books*. Allen & Unwin, London, 1939.

BLAND, D. *The Illustration of Books*. Faber, London, 1951.

DARLEY, L. S. *Bookbinding Then and Now*. Faber, London, 1959.

GERNSHEIM, H. and A. *The History of Photography*. Oxford University Press, London, 1955.

QUIGLEY, M. *Magic Shadows: The Story of the Origin of Motion Pictures*. Georgetown University Press, Washington, 1948.

SOUTHWARD, J. *Progress in Printing and the Graphic Arts during the Victorian Era*. Simpkin, London, 1897.

CHAPTER 24. AGRICULTURE AND FOOD (*see also* Ch. 2)

GRAS, N. S. B. *A History of Agriculture in Europe and America* (2nd. ed.). Crofts, New York, 1940.

SEEBOHM, M. E. *The Evolution of the English Farm*. Allen & Unwin, London, 1952.

INNIS, H. A. *The Cod Fisheries*. Yale University Press, New Haven, 1940.

JENKINS, J. T. *The Herring and the Herring Fisheries*. King, London, 1927.

MATHIAS, P. *The Brewing Industry in England, 1700–1830*. Cambridge University Press, 1959.

BITTING, A. W. *Appertizing: or, the Art of Canning; its History and Development*. Trade Pressroom, San Francisco, 1937.

CRITCHELL, J. T. and RAYMOND, J. *A History of the Frozen Meat Trade*. Constable, London, 1912.

THE reprinting of this work in a paperback edition provides an opportunity of supplementing the above references. In the list that follows some titles are provided with numbers in brackets: these numbers indicate chapters to which the works are particularly relevant.

ARMYTAGE, W. H. G. *A Social History of Engineering*. Faber & Faber, London, 1961.

BLACKMORE, H. C. *Guns and Rifles of the World*. Batsford, London, 1965. [16]

BRUMBAUGH, R. S. *Ancient Greek Gadgets and Machines*. Thomas Y. Crowell, New York, 1966.

BURSTALL, A. F. *A History of Mechanical Engineering*. Faber & Faber, London, 1963.

CALVERT, M. A. *The Mechanical Engineer in America, 1830–1910; Professional Cultures in Conflict*. Johns Hopkins Press, Baltimore, 1967.

CARR, J. C. and TAPLIN, W. *A History of the British Steel Industry*. Harvard University Press, Cambridge, Mass., 1962. [16]

CIPOLLA, C. M. *Guns and Sails in Empires; the Early Phase of European Expansion, 1400–1700*. Pantheon Books, New York, 1965; Collins, London, 1965. [1]

CONDIT, C. W. *American Building: Materials and Techniques from the First Colonial Settlements to the Present*. University of Chicago Press, 1968. [14, 15]

DAUMAS, M. (ed.). *Histoire générale des techniques* (4 vols.). Presses Universitaires de France, Paris, 1962–

DAVEY, N. *A History of Building Materials*. Phoenix House, London, 1961. [5, 14, 15]

FINSBERG, H. P. R. (ed.). *The Agrarian History of England and Wales* (to be completed in 7 vols.). Cambridge University Press, 1967– .

GOODMAN, W. L. *The History of Woodcutting Tools.* G. Bell & Sons, London, 1964. [12]

HABAKKUK, H. J. *American and British Technology in the Nineteenth Century; the Search for Labour-Saving Inventions.* Cambridge University Press, 1962.

Journal of Industrial Archaeology. Lambarde Press, for Newcomen Society, Sidcup, England, 1964–

KRANZBERG, M. and PURSELL, C. W., jr. (ed.). *Technology in Western Civilization*, Vol. I. Oxford University Press, New York, 1967.

MERDINGER, C. J. *Civil Engineering through the Ages.* Society of American Military Engineers, 1963. [14, 15]

MUMFORD, L. *The Myth of the Machine.* Secker & Warburg, London, 1967.

MUSSON, A. E. and ROBINSON, ERIC. *Science and Technology in the Industrial Revolution.* Manchester University Press, Manchester, 1969.

PARNELL, J. P. M. *An Illustrated History of Civil Engineering.* Thames & Hudson, London, 1964. [14, 15]

POSTAN, M. and HABAKKUK, H. J. (ed.), *The Cambridge Economic History of Europe.* Vol. I (rev. ed. 1960); Vol. II (1952); Vol. III (1963); Vol. IV (1967); and Vol. VI (2 pts, 1965). Cambridge University Press.

RIDER, K. J. *The History of Science and Technology: a Select Bibliography for Students.* Library Association, London, 1967.

ROLT, L. T. C. *Tools for the Job.* Batsford, London, 1965. (Published in the U.S.A. as *A Short History of Machine Tools.* M.I.T. Press, Cambridge, Mass., 1965.) [12]

SCHMOOKLER, J. *Invention and Economic Growth.* Harvard University Press, Mass., 1966.

SMITH, C. S. (ed.). *The Sorby Centennial Symposium on the History of Metallurgy.* Gordon and Breach Science Publications, New York, 1965. [16]

—— *Sources for the History of the Science of Steel.* Society for the History of Technology, Chicago and the M.I.T. Press, Cambridge, Mass., 1968. [16]

STEEDS, W. *A History of Machine Tools, 1700–1910.* Clarendon Press, Oxford, 1969. [12]

WERTIME, T. A. *The Coming of the Age of Steel.* University of Chicago Press, 1962. [16]

WHITE, J. H., jr. *American Locomotives: An Engineering History, 1830–1880.* Johns Hopkins Press, Baltimore, 1968. [11]

WHITE, K. D. *Agricultural Implements of the Roman World.* Cambridge University Press, 1967. [2]

WHITE, L., jr. *Medieval Technology and Social Change.* Clarendon Press, Oxford, 1962.

WOODBURY, R. S. *History of the Lathe to 1850.* Society for the History of Technology, Chicago, 1961. [12]

WOODRUFF, W. *Impact of Western Man: A Study of Europe's Role in the World Economy 1750–1960.* Macmillan, London, 1966. [10]

INDEX OF SUBJECTS

THE Index is in two parts: a general index of subjects, and a list of persons (with dates of birth and death, when available) and places mentioned in any technological context. Bold type is used to indicate pages carrying important illustrations, and semicolons separate the entries for the two Parts, the division being at A.D. 1750.

INDEX OF PERSONS AND PLACE-NAMES